Raising Scores & Hands

- Emphasizes fundamentals first
- Provides solid time on task to develop, practice and maintain skills
- Makes real-life connections
- Assesses what matters
- Manages time, students, and materials

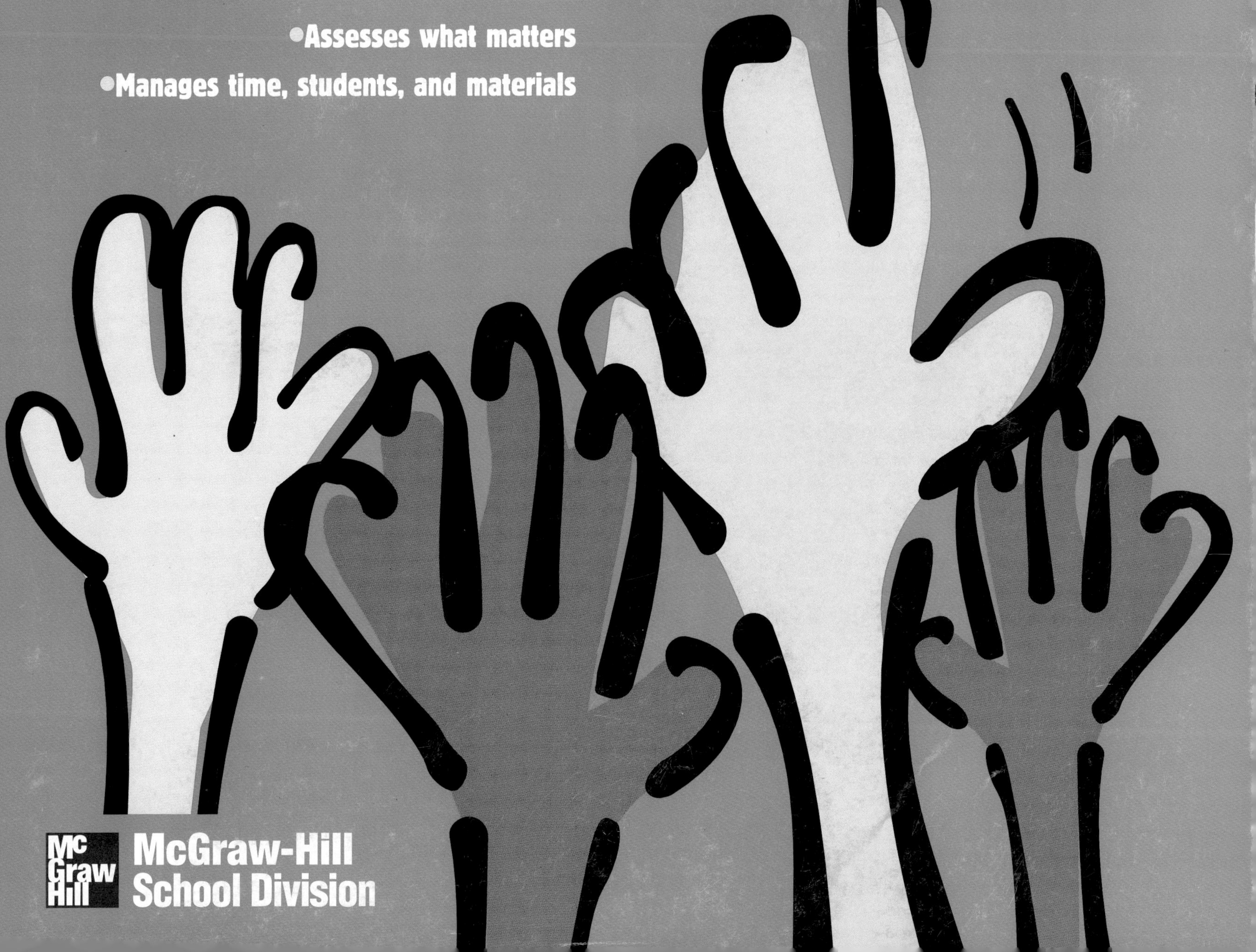

Mc Graw Hill
McGraw-Hill School Division

Connections That Bring Math To Life and Bring Life to Math

Connect to a child's experiences

Problem-solving activities utilize situations and challenges students face in their own lives, so the purpose and importance of math concepts are really brought home.

Bring life to math and wake up your students, too

Math in My World makes math interesting, with appropriate activities for every student in every class. Puppets, Big Books, and sing-alongs captivate primary students, while software, internet links, and real-life situations fascinate older children.

Make math meaningful

Math in My World builds on students' own ideas and strategies, for in–depth learning. Students consistently apply and review what they learn — in career features, science and technology connections, and more.

Teach effectively with solid time on task

A carefully designed instructional cycle makes the most of your time. Lesson plans develop concepts fully, and integrate practice with ongoing review and skills maintenance.

Solve problems in real life contexts

Students learn problem-solving strategies and skills, and every lesson includes features that help them apply those skills. Problems in real-life contexts make the importance of math clear to every learner.

Integrate technology every day

Technology in *Math in My World* is fully integrated with instruction. Every chapter in the Teacher's Edition provides an overview of technology resources, including internet links, for every topic. Math Van, new software developed step-by-step with *Math in My World*, enriches the curriculum with lots of additional child-friendly skills support.

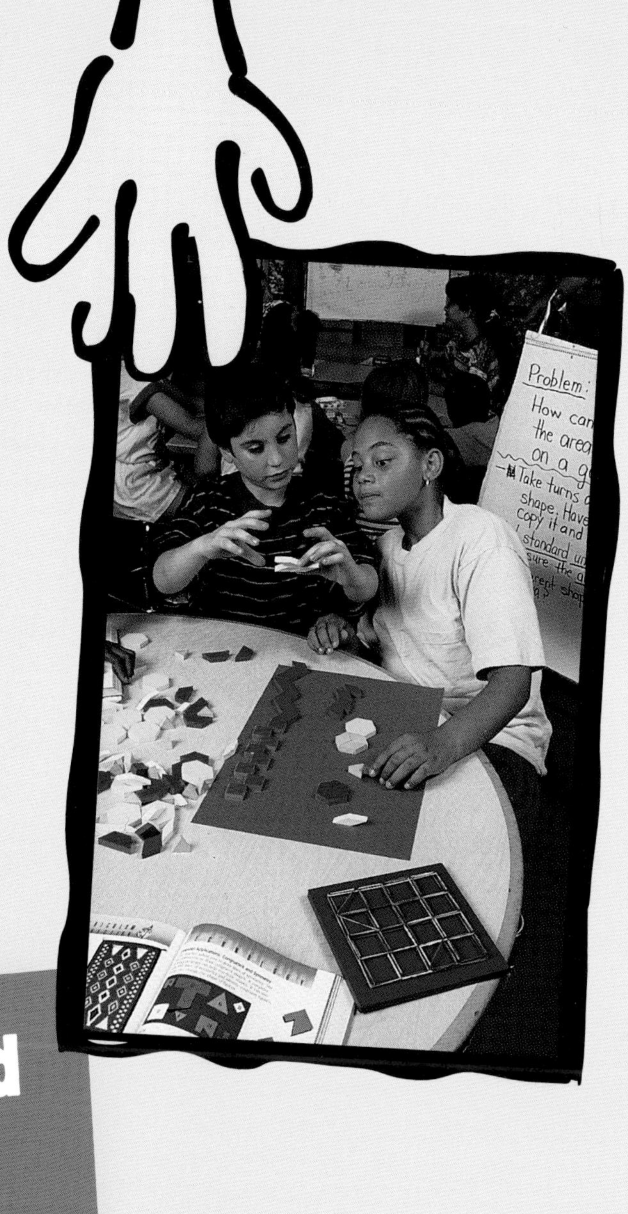

Fundamentals First and Last – with Lots of Practice in Between

McGraw Hill

Program Authors

Math in My World was developed by an experienced team of authors and consulting experts. The authors who collaborated to create the program represent McGraw-Hill's commitment to the most current thinking in mathematics education, and our deep sensitivity to the real-life challenges of today's classrooms.

DR. DOUGLAS H. CLEMENTS

Professor of Mathematics Education
State University of New York at Buffalo

Douglas H. Clements conducts research on computer applications in education, early development of mathematical ideas, and the learning and teaching of geometry. Dr. Clements taught kindergarten for five years and contributed to NCTM's Addenda series.

LOIS GORDON MOSELEY

Coordinator
General Education Department
Region IV Educational Service Center
Houston, Texas

In addition to fulfilling her pivotal responsibilities with the Region IV Education Service Center in Houston, Lois Gordon Moseley is the chairperson for the statewide Mathematics Texas Essential Knowledge and Skills writing team for grades PK - 12. She is also on the board of directors for the Association of African-American Mathematics Educators.

KENNETH W. JONES

Director OVEC - University of Louisville, Kentucky
Partnership for Professional Development

Ken Jones works closely with school districts in the Louisville region to develop ongoing professional development opportunities for teachers and administrators and to facilitate school improvement. He has been a middle school teacher and the director of several nationally-funded grant programs in mathematics. His special interests are performance assessment and portfolios.

DR. LINDA SCHULMAN

Professor of Mathematics and Mathematics Education
Lesley College
Cambridge, Massachusetts

Linda Schulman began her career as an elementary school teacher and is a leading author of innovative supplementary materials for the teaching of mathematics. Currently, her work focuses on the use of investigations and alternative assessment strategies in the elementary classroom.

Contributing Authors

DR. KATHY KELLY-BENJAMIN
Former Associate Professor - Mathematics Education Florida Institute of Technology, Melbourne, Florida

Dr. Kelly-Benjamin is an instructional design manager and educational consultant with expertise in instructional technology and assessment. Dr. Kelly-Benjamin has also been a middle school mathematics teacher, consultant and writer.

CHRISTINE A. FERNSLER
First Grade Teacher Sidwell Friends School Washington, D.C.

Christine Fernsler is a recognized authority on classroom practice in elementary math education. She has served as a school mathematics coordinator, presented workshops for NCTM, Virginia Council for Teachers of Mathematics (VCTM) and V-Quest. Ms. Fernsler has also taught courses at George Mason University and Catholic University.

DR. LIANA FOREST
Executive Director International Association for the Study of Cooperation in Education Felton, California

Dr. Forest has taught at levels from preschool to graduate school. For twenty years she has conducted research and written on learning and teaching in cooperative settings. She also facilitates professional development for teachers, professors and administrators with a focus on cooperative student groups, collaborative school teams and creating cooperative communities. Dr. Forest writes for and is Executive Editor of Cooperative Learning Publications for the International Association for the Study of Cooperation in Education (IASCE), where she also serves on the Executive Board.

MARIA R. MAROLDA
Mathematics Specialist Behavioral Neurology/Learning Disabilities Program Children's Hospital Boston, Massachusetts

Maria R. Marolda has extensive expertise and practical experience in mathematics learning profiles, alternative assessment techniques, and differentiated teaching approaches designed to address learning differences in mathematics.

DR. RICHARD H. MOYER
Professor of Science Education University of Michigan - Dearborn Dearborn, Michigan

Dr. Richard H. Moyer is a senior author of Macmillan/ McGraw-Hill Science as well as numerous other books and publications. Dr. Moyer, who has taught at all levels, is the recipient of many teaching awards and consults on the use of inquiry teaching methods both nationally and abroad.

DR. WALTER G. SECADA
Professor of Curriculum and Instruction University of Wisconsin - Madison Madison, Wisconsin

Dr. Walter Secada has written extensively about equity, the education of bilingual learners of mathematics, and the reform of school mathematics. In addition, he has conducted workshops involving authentic assessment, how children reason when they do mathematics, and multiculturalism in the mathematics curriculum. Dr. Secada is editor of an NCTM series of professional books, *Changing the Faces of Mathematics*, which helps teachers address the diversity of today's classrooms.

Managing time, students, and materials for greater learning, higher scores.

Help teachers meet accountability goals

Flexible organization, color-coded core and non-core lessons, and comprehensive planning guidance put teachers in control. Real manageability means that teachers know they can provide what children need, what parents look for, and what each individual school district expects.

Give every child the opportunity to learn

Every lesson integrates thorough, organized guidance for meeting the needs of every student. Help is where you need it for handling different learning styles, gifted and talented children, early finishers, and students in need of extra support. No child gets lost in the shuffle.

Enrich learning with valuable teaching resources

Teacher's Editions provide comprehensive guidance for using assessment, practice, reteaching, extension, home/school connections, literature, activities, manipulatives, and technology. McGraw-Hill gives you meaningful resources that truly enrich your teaching.

Assessment that aligns with instruction

Assessment in *Math in My World* follows the curriculum. That means test results tell teachers what they really need to know for class planning.

Meet the diverse needs of children

You'll always have a snapshot of your students' needs with assessment resources that give you the simplest, most useful picture of progress.

Choose the assessment you need – and the assessment you want

Math in My World supports all kinds of assessment. From traditional to alternative strategies, every option is integrated in teaching materials. Portfolios and journals help teachers organize the full range of assessment tools.

All kinds of assessment, from Andrew to Zoey

Program Components

Math in my World

	K	1	2	3	4	5	6
Teacher's Edition Volume 1	■	■	■	■	■	■	■
Teacher's Edition Volume 2		■	■	■	■	■	■
Pupil Edition, Consumable	■	■	■				
Pupil Edition, Non-Consumable				■	■	■	■
Testing Program Blackline Masters		■	■	■	■	■	■
Teacher's Assessment Resources	■	■	■	■	■	■	■
Practice Workbook	■	■	■	■	■	■	■
Reteach Workbook		■	■	■	■	■	■
Extend Workbook	■	■	■	■	■	■	■
Quick Review Blackline Masters				■	■	■	■
Home/School Connection				■	■	■	■
Read Aloud Anthology	■	■	■	■	■	■	■
Math Center Activity Pad	■	■	■	■	■	■	■
Problem of the Day Flip Chart	■	■	■	■	■	■	■
Teacher's Aids Blackline Masters	■	■	■	■	■	■	■
Panda Puppet	■						
Panda Rubber Stamp and Pad	■						
Panda Manipulative Counters	■						
Rhino Puppet		■					
Rhino Rubber Stamp and Pad		■					
Rhino Manipulative Counters		■					
Toucan Puppet			■				
Toucan Rubber Stamp and Pad			■				
Professional Handbook (one for K-6)	■	■	■	■	■	■	■
Jumbo Book and Stickers	■	■	■				
Literature Big Books (six titles per grade)	■	■	■				
Floor Mats		■	■				
Student Workmats		■	■				
Math Songs Audio Cassette (one for K-2)	■	■	■				
Grade Level Manipulative Kits	■	■	■	■	■	■	■
MathVan Software	■	■	■	■	■	■	■
Computer Test Generator Software				■	■	■	■
Internet Project Handbook				■	■	■	■
Math for You and Me		■	■				

McGraw-Hill School Division
A Division of The McGraw-Hill Companies

TEACHER'S EDITION
McGRAW-HILL MATHEMATICS

Math in my World

Douglas H. Clements

Kenneth W. Jones

Lois Gordon Moseley

Linda Schulman

McGraw-Hill School Division
New York Farmington

Contributors

Author Team

Program Authors

Dr. Douglas H. Clements

Kenneth W. Jones

Lois Gordon Moseley

Dr. Linda Schulman

Contributing Authors

Christine A. Fernsler

Dr. Liana Forest

Dr. Kathleen Kelly-Benjamin

Maria R. Marolda

Dr. Richard H. Moyer

Dr. Walter G. Secada

Multicultural and Educational Consultants

Rim An
Teacher
UN International School
New York, New York

Sue Cantrell
Superintendent of Schools
Madison County Schools
Marshall, North Carolina

Mordessa Corbin
Instructional Specialist
Mathematics Pre K - 12
Gilbert, Louisiana

Dr. Carlos Diaz
Project Director
Cultural Foundations in Education
Florida Atlantic University
Boca Raton, Florida

Carl Downing
Director of Native American
Language Development Institute
Oklahoma City, Oklahoma

Linda Ferreira
Teacher
Pinellas Park, Florida

Judythe M. Hazel
Elementary School Principal
Tempe, Arizona

Roger Larson
Mathematics Coordinator
Ramsey, Minnesota

Josie Robles
Mathematics Coordinator
Silver Springs, Maryland

Veronica Rogers
Director, Secondary Education
Mobile, Alabama

Telkia Rutherford
Mathematics Facilitator
Chicago, Illinois

Sharon Searcy
Teacher
Mandarin, Florida

Elizabeth Sinor
Teacher/Trainer
Mathematics and Assessment
Waddy, Kentucky

Michael Wallpe
Curriculum Development
Indianapolis, Indiana

Claudia Zaslavsky
Author, Africa Counts
New York, New York

Career Professionals

Jim Anderson
Stained Glass Artist

Robert Beard
Leather Carver

Bill Becoat
Inventor

Jack Bertagnolli
Rancher

Alex Bhattacharji
Reporter, Sports Illustrated

Dr. Sherrilyn Brannon
Veterinarian

Yvonne Campos
Marketing Executive

Theresa Cebuhar
Highway Maintenance Worker

Dave Chin
School Adjustment Counselor

Steve Crockett
Engineer

Susannah Druck
Program Coordinator,
Ecosphere Magazine

Larry Felix
Communications Officer

La Tondra Finley
Veterinarian's Receptionist

Charlotte Garcia
School Superintendent

Rich Garcia
American League Umpire

Alyssa Goodman
Astrophysicist

Marla Grossberg
Market Researcher

Clair Hain, Jr.
President of Great Coasters
International

Ruth Handler
Designer of Barbie and Ken Dolls

Kevin Hanson
Track Official

Kim Harrison
Marine Biologist

Beverly Harvard
Chief of Police

Maria Hayashida
Musher, Winner of 1996
Alaskan Iditarod Race

Colleen Heminger-Cordell
Business Owner

Patrick Hong
Automobile Road-Tester

David Juarez
Olympic Mountain Biker

Pat Kambesis
Speleologist

Frank Mazzotti
Wildlife Biologist

Mishelle Michaels
Meteorologist

Sterling Monroe
Statistician

Rusty Moore
Cordwainer

Sharon O'Connell
Founder of the Sadako/Paper
Crane Project

Sandy Pandiscio
Treasury Analyst

Martha Puente & Beatrice Gonzalez
Interior Decorators

Tom Rittenberry
Sales Representative,
Sun Microsystems

Raymond Rye
Museum Director

Susan Solomon
Ozone Researcher

Monty & Ann Stambler
Game Inventors

Donald Stull
Architect

Priscilla Warren
Rug Weaver

Tina Yao
Graphic Designer

Suzanne Yin
Marine Biologist

McGraw-Hill School Division
A Division of The McGraw-Hill Companies

McGraw-Hill School Division
1221 Avenue of the Americas
New York, New York 10020

Printed in the United States of America
ISBN 0-02-109500-0 / 1, Pt. 1
2 3 4 5 6 7 8 9 073 03 02 01 00 99 98 97

Contributors

Thanks to all of the teachers, students, and schools who contributed to this project.

Educators and Schools

Phyllis Adcock
West Lake Elementary School
Apex, North Carolina

Leigh Anne Akey
Pauline O'Rourke Elementary School
Mobile, Alabama

Linda Allen
Goshen Elementary School
Goshen, Kentucky

Harriet Anagnostopoulos
John J. Shaughnessy
Humanities School
Lowell, Massachusetts

Susan Ardissono
Shoreline, Washington

Catherine Battle
Snowden Elementary School
Memphis, Tennessee

Sylvia Bednarski
Centerfield Elementary School
Crestwood, Kentucky

Lorraine Bege
Luis Munoz Marin School
Bridgeport, Connecticut

Tricia Bender
Pauline O'Rourke Elementary School
Mobile, Alabama

G. Renee Black
Pauline O'Rourke Elementary School
Mobile, Alabama

Sandy Blagborne
McPherson Middle School
Howell, Michigan

Denise Blume
Slidell, Louisiana

Kaye Bybee
Southland Elementary School
Riverton, Utah

Betty Byrne
Snowden Elementary School
Memphis, Tennessee

Brent Caldwell
Madison Middle School
Marshall, North Carolina

Ellen Carlson
Northwest Elementary School
Howell, Michigan

Walter Carr
Mandarin Middle School
Jacksonville, Florida

Hope Carter
Pauline O'Rourke Elementary School
Mobile, Alabama

Cynthia Carter
Mandarin Oaks Elementary School
Jacksonville, Florida

Denise Clark
Crestwood Elementary School
Crestwood, Kentucky

Patsy Cohen
Louisville Collegiate School
Louisville, Kentucky

Linda Colburn
E.N. Rogers School
Lowell, Massachusetts

Tammy Cooper
Latson Road Elementary School
Howell, Michigan

Lynne Copeland
John Yeates Middle School
Suffolk, Virginia

Naomi Damron
Southland Elementary School
Riverton, Utah

Peg Darcy
Kammerer Middle School
Louisville, Kentucky

Talmdage Darden
John Yeates Middle School
Suffolk, Virginia

Mary Davis
Snowden Elementary School
Memphis, Tennessee

Winifred Deavens
St. Louis Public Schools
St. Louis, Missouri

Terri Dickson
Snowden Elementary School
Memphis, Tennessee

Kris Dillon
Elephant's Fork Elementary School
Suffolk, Virginia

Karen Doidge
West Lake Elementary School
Apex, North Carolina

Hope Donato
Piney Grove Elementary School
Charlotte, North Carolina

Jo Doty
Mandarin Oaks Elementary School
Jacksonville, Florida

Marna Draper
Hawthorne Elementary School
Indianapolis, Indiana

Renee Duckenfield
West Lake Elementary School
Apex, North Carolina

Susan Farrar
Hawthorne Elementary School
Indianapolis, Indiana

Mary Jo Farrell
John J. Shaughnessy
Humanities School
Lowell, Massachusetts

Katrina Fives
Pauline O'Rourke Elementary School
Mobile, Alabama

Katie Flaherty
East Cobb Middle School
Marietta, Georgia

Ellen Flamer
Piney Grove Elementary School
Charlotte, North Carolina

Winston Fouche
Webster Middle School
St. Louis, Missouri

Gil French
Baltimore, Maryland

Melissa Garrone
Snowden Elementary School
Memphis, Tennessee

Dana Geils
P.S. 144/District 28 Queens
Forest Hills, New York

Vera Greer
Snowden Elementary School
Memphis, Tennessee

Paul Groth
Highlander Way Middle School
Howell, Michigan

Marguerite Guthrie
Anchorage Public School
Anchorage, Kentucky

Terri Haarala
Pauline O'Rourke Elementary School
Mobile, Alabama

Carol Harris
Elephant's Fork Elementary School
Suffolk, Virginia

Beverly Hartz
Elephant's Fork Elementary School
Suffolk, Virginia

Lori Harvey
Snowden Elementary School
Memphis, Tennessee

Judy Haskell
Northwest Elementary School
Howell, Michigan

Mary Lynne Havey
McPherson Middle School
Howell, Michigan

Diane Hayes
Pauline O'Rourke Elementary School
Mobile, Alabama

Gayle Hendershot
Garland, Texas

Hector Hirigoyen
Miami, Florida

Janice Holland
Elephant's Fork Elementary School
Suffolk, Virginia

Daisy Irvin
Luis Munoz Marin School
Bridgeport, Connecticut

Barbara Jacobs
H.B. Slaughter School
Louisville, Kentucky

Lisa James
Carroll Middle School
Carrollton, Kentucky

Roberta Johnson
Anchorage Public School
Anchorage, Kentucky

Barbara Jones
Mandarin Oaks Elementary School
Jacksonville, Florida

Faye Jones
West Lake Elementary School
Apex, North Carolina

Lori Jones
Mandarin Middle School
Jacksonville, Florida

Steve June
West Lake Elementary School
Apex, North Carolina

Sydell Kane
P.S. 144/District 28 Queens
Forest Hills, New York

Alisha Kelly
Southwest Elementary School
Howell, Michigan

Kathy Kelly
Hawthorne Elementary School
Indianapolis, Indiana

Mona Kennedy
Southland Elementary School
Riverton, Utah

Larry Kiernan
Raymond Park Middle School
Indianapolis, Indiana

Dina Kruckenberg
Ira Ogden Elementary School
San Antonio, Texas

Cathy Kuhns
Coral Springs, Florida

Judy Lane
Hawthorne Elementary School
Indianapolis, Indiana

Carol Lehrman
P.S. 144/District 28 Queens
Forest Hills, New York

Eleanor Levinson
West Lake Elementary School
Apex, North Carolina

Contributors

Clarice Loggins
Snowden Elementary School
Memphis, Tennessee

Jim Long
Snowden Elementary School
Memphis, Tennessee

Melanee Lucado
Snowden Elementary School
Memphis, Tennessee

Diane Lucas
Pauline O'Rourke Elementary School
Mobile, Alabama

Debra Luke
Pauline O'Rourke Elementary School
Mobile, Alabama

Debbie Lytle
Piney Grove Elementary School
Charlotte, North Carolina

Jim Madsen
Southland Elementary School
Riverton, Utah

Maria Marquez
Ira Ogden Elementary School
San Antonio, Texas

Ofelia Martinez
Ira Ogden Elementary School
San Antonio, Texas

Lisa Martire
Luis Munoz Marin School
Bridgeport, Connecticut

Rae Ann Maurer
P.S. 144/District 28 Queens
Forest Hills, New York

Ellen McClain
Hawthorne Elementary School
Indianapolis, Indiana

Kelley McDaniel
South Oldham County Middle School
Crestwood, Kentucky

Debra McElreath
Mandarin Oaks Elementary School
Jacksonville, Florida

Nancy McLaughlin
DeSoto, Texas

Jim McMann
Lowell Public Schools
Lowell, Massachusetts

Debbie Miller
Hawthorne Elementary School
Indianapolis, Indiana

Milvern Miller
South Bend, Indiana

Melinda Monserrate
Gateway Middle School
St. Louis, Missouri

Phyllis Moore
Madison Middle School
Marshall, North Carolina

Joan Murphy
E.N. Rogers School
Lowell, Massachusetts

Vickey Myrick
West Lake Elementary School
Apex, North Carolina

Dennis Nelson
Tempe, Arizona

Martha O'Donnell
St. Francis School
Goshen, Kentucky

Tom O'Hare
E.N. Rogers School
Lowell, Massachusetts

Wanda Peele
Emma Elementary School
Asheville, North Carolina

Linda Perry-Clarke
Elephant's Fork Elementary School
Suffolk, Virginia

Taylor Phelps
John Yeates Middle School
Suffolk, Virginia

Alda Pill
Mandarin Oaks Elementary School
Jacksonville, Florida

Kay Pitts
Snowden Elementary School
Memphis, Tennessee

Barbara Rea
North Oldham County Middle School
Goshen, Kentucky

Susan Rhyne
Piney Grove Elementary School
Charlotte, North Carolina

Mary Riley
Madison, Wisconsin

Carolyn Rooks
Snowden Elementary School
Memphis, Tennessee

Nancy Rose
Luis Munoz Marin School
Bridgeport, Connecticut

Jeffrey Rosen
East Cobb Middle School
Marietta, Georgia

Charlene Ruble
Centerfield Elementary School
Crestwood, Kentucky

Patricia Sanford
Mandarin Oaks Elementary School
Jacksonville, Florida

Jim Santo
Luis Munoz Marin School
Bridgeport, Connecticut

Lee Sawyer
West Lake Elementary School
Apex, North Carolina

Virginia Schurke
Mandarin Oaks Elementary School
Jacksonville, Florida

Shadonica Scruggs
Snowden Elementary School
Memphis, Tennessee

Ellen Sears
Anchorage Public School
Anchorage, Kentucky

Tim Sears
Anchorage Public School
Anchorage, Kentucky

Mary Sevigney
John J. Shaughnessy
Humanities School
Lowell, Massachusetts

Ann Sievert
Highlander Way Middle School
Howell, Michigan

Laura Silverman
P.S. 144/District 28 Queens
Forest Hills, New York

Ada Simmons
East Cobb Middle School
Marietta, Georgia

Dot Singleton
Winston Salem, North Carolina

Jo Ann Sipkin
West Lake Elementary School
Apex, North Carolina

Hilda Skiles
South Oldham County Middle School
Crestwood, Kentucky

Sue Slesnick
Louisville Collegiate School
Louisville, Kentucky

Venus Smith
Snowden Elementary School
Memphis, Tennessee

Judy Smizik
Pittsburgh, Pennsylvania

Doug Soards
Mt. Washington Middle School
Mt. Washington, Kentucky

Kristen Sousa
Pauline O'Rourke Elementary School
Mobile, Alabama

Nancy Souza
North Oldham County Middle School
Goshen, Kentucky

Laura Stander
John J. Shaughnessy Humanities School
Lowell, Massachusetts

Trish Strain
Mandarin Oaks Elementary School
Jacksonville, Florida

Mary Sullivan
Pauline O'Rourke Elementary School
Mobile, Alabama

Jeff Swensson
Raymond Park Middle School
Indianapolis, Indiana

Rebecca True
Raymond Park Middle School
Indianapolis, Indiana

Charlie Waller
Pauline O'Rourke Elementary School
Mobile, Alabama

Judy Wayne
E.N. Rogers School
Lowell, Massachusetts

Vickie Wheatley
LaGrange Elementary School
LaGrange, Kentucky

Carol Wietholter
Hawthorne Elementary School
Indianapolis, Indiana

Christine Wilcox
Centerfield Elementary School
Crestwood, Kentucky

Kathryn Williams
Pauline O'Rourke Elementary School
Mobile, Alabama

Ronna Young
Hawthorne Elementary School
Indianapolis, Indiana

Karen Zinman
Rye Brook, New York

Field Test Schools

Alexander Middle School
Huntersville, North Carolina

Benjamin Franklin Elementary School
Yorktown Heights, New York

Bow Elementary School
Detroit, Michigan

Burrville Elementary School
Washington, DC

Candler Elementary School
Candler, North Carolina

Cattell Elementary School
Des Moines, Iowa

Crestwood Elementary School
Crestwood, Kentucky

David Cox Elementary School
Henderson, Nevada

Emma Elementary School
Asheville, North Carolina

JHS 263K
Brooklyn, New York

Longfellow Elementary School
Des Moines, Iowa

Onalaska Middle School
Onalaska, Wisconsin

Studebaker Elementary School
Des Moines, Iowa

W.C. Pryor Middle School
Fort Walton Beach, Florida

Contents

1 Rhino Country

2 Getting Around

3 Food for 10

4 Folktales and Rhymes

5 Number Fun

6 One Big Family

7 High-Flying Kites

8 Our Store

9 Fun and Games

10 Under the Water

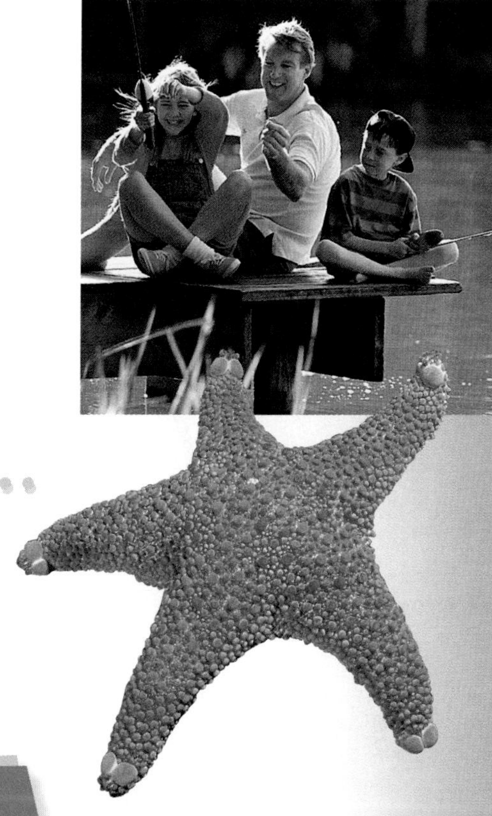

11 Dinosaurs and Me

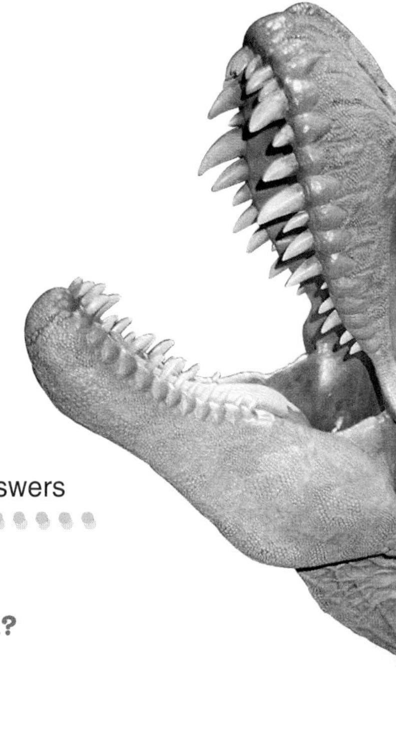

12 Music

Welcome to your new math book!

This year you will learn about many ways to use math in your world.

How many children in all?

How much does it cost?

How long is a foot?

Dear Family,

We are beginning the first chapter in our mathematics book. During the next few weeks we are going to learn about numbers and patterns and solving problems.

My class will also be talking about rhinos and other wild animals. Please help me complete this interview.

Your child,

____
Signature

Interview

Did you ever see a rhino? __________

Where did you see it? (Check as many as you want.)

❑ Zoo ❑ Safari park ❑ Television or movie

❑ Other __________

What do you remember most about the rhino?

❑ How big it was ❑ Its horns

❑ Other __________

____

AT A GLANCE

Family Activities

PURPOSE Give family members an opportunity to share in their child's mathematics learning.

Using the Preview

Page 2

Discuss the content of the page with children and have them sign the letter at the top. Be sure they understand how to conduct an interview with a family member, friend, or neighbor.

Explain to children that they may share what they learn during their next math lesson. You may wish to have children bring back the page.

CHAPTER 1 ORGANIZER

NUMBERS TO 10

Planning for Learning

Suggested Pacing: 13–15 days **Theme: Rhino Country**

Lesson Title/Description	Pages	Pacing	Real-life Connection	Chapter Objectives	Materials	Reteach/ Practice/Extend	Math Center Cards
Preview	2						
Introduction	3		going to the zoo				
What Do You Know? (J) (P)	4						
▶ 1. Numbers to 5	5–6	1-day lesson		1B	rhino counters	1	1
▶ 2. One, Two, Three, Four, Five (J)	7–10	2-day lesson		1A, 1B	counters, 5-frames (TA 4), numeral sheets (TA 6), dot cards (TA 2)	2–3	2
Extra Practice Activity: Where's the Rhino?	11–12						
▶ 3. Zero	13–14	1-day lesson	identifying wild animals	1A, 1B	counters, 0–5 spinners (TA 7)	4	3
Midchapter Review (J)	15				counters, 5-frames (TA 4)		
Extra Practice Game: Animal Walk	16				2-color counters, blank spinners (TA 7)		
Real-life Investigation: Applying Counting (P)	17–18		drawing a rhinoceros				
▶ 4. Numbers to 10	19–20	1-day lesson		1A, 1B	rhino counters, dot cards (TA 2–3), Workmat 2	5	4
▶ 5. Six, Seven, Eight, Nine, Ten	21–24	2-day lesson		1A, 1B	counters, Workmat 2, numeral sheets (TA 6), 10-frames, 5-frames (TA 4)	6–7	5
Extra Practice Game: Climb to the Top	25–26						
▶ 6. Problem-Solving Strategy: Use a Pattern	27–28	1-day lesson	making up an animal rhyme	1D	2-color counters, crayons, connecting cubes	8	6
▶ 7. Order Numbers Teaching with Technology (Math Van)	29–30	1-day lesson		1C		9	7
▶ 8. Count Pennies	31–32	1-day lesson	collecting and sorting coins	1B	pennies	10	8
▶ 9. Problem Solvers at Work	33–34	1-day lesson	counting and beating a rhythm	1D	2-color counters, connecting cubes	11	9
ASSESSMENT OPTIONS (J) (P) Chapter Review Chapter Test Performance Assessment	 35–36 37 38				2-color counters, 5-frames, 10-frames (TA 4)		
CONNECTIONS (P) MATH: Statistics SOCIAL STUDIES Home Connection	 39 40 41						

(J) = JOURNAL OPPORTUNITY (P) = PORTFOLIO OPPORTUNITY TA= TEACHER AID

Technology Links	NCTM Standards
Online Exploration, p. 4B Math Forum, p. 4B	4, 6
Math Van Aid, p. 6B Math Forum, p. 6B	6
Math Forum, p. 12B	6
	1, 2, 3, 4, 6
Math Van: Counters tool Math Forum, p. 18B	4, 6
Math Van: Counters tool Math Forum, p. 20B	6
Math Van: Counters tool Math Forum, p. 26B	1, 2, 3, 4, 13
Math Van: *Camel Roundup* Math Forum, p. 28B	4, 6
Math Van: Money Models Math Forum, p. 30D	4, 6
Math Van: Counters tool Math Forum, p. 32B	1, 2, 3, 4, 13
Math Van: Graph tool	1, 4, 6, 11

ASSESSMENT OPTIONS

INFORMAL

Ongoing Assessment

- Observation Checklist, pp. 13, 23, 27, 29, 31, 33
- Interview, pp. 5, 9, 19
- Anecdotal Report, pp. 7, 21

Portfolio Opportunities

- Chapter Project, p. 2F
- What Do You Know? p. 4
- Investigation, pp. 17–18
- Journal Writing, pp. 4, 10, 15, 35
- Performance Assessment, p. 38

FORMAL

Chapter Tests

Student Book

- Midchapter Review, p. 15
- Chapter Review, pp. 35–36
- Chapter Test, p. 37

Test Masters

- Free-Response Test: Form C
- Multiple-Choice Test: Forms A and B

Performance Assessment

- What Do You Know? p. 4
- Performance Assessment, p. 38
- Self-Assessment: What Do You Think? p. 35
- Holistic Scoring Guide, Teacher's Assessment Resources, pp. 29–32
- Follow-Up Interviews, p. 38

Teacher's Assessment Resources

- Portfolio Guidelines and Forms, pp. 6–9, 33–36
- Holistic Scoring Guide, pp. 29–32
- Samples of Student Work, pp. 37–61

Chapter Objectives		Standardized Test Correlations
1A	Read, write, and represent numbers, 0 to 10	MAT, CAT, SAT, ITBS, CTBS
1B	Identify the number of objects in a group, including pennies, to 10	MAT, CAT, SAT, ITBS, CTBS
1C	Order numbers, to 10	MAT, CAT, SAT, ITBS, CTBS
1D	Solve problems, including those that involve numbers to 10 and patterns	MAT, CAT, SAT, ITBS, CTBS

NCTM Standards Grades K–4

1 Problem Solving	8 Whole Number Computation
2 Communication	9 Geometry and Spatial Sense
3 Reasoning	10 Measurement
4 Connections	11 Statistics and Probability
5 Estimation	12 Fractions and Decimals
6 Number Sense and Numeration	13 Patterns and Relationships
7 Concepts of Whole Number Operations	

Meeting Individual Needs

LEARNING STYLES

- AUDITORY/LINGUISTIC
- LOGICAL/ANALYTICAL
- VISUAL/SPATIAL
- MUSICAL
- KINESTHETIC
- SOCIAL
- INDIVIDUAL

Children who are talented in art, language, and physical activity may better understand mathematical concepts when these concepts are connected to their areas of interest. Use the following activities to stimulate the different learning styles of some of your children.

Kinesthetic Learners

Have children make sand tables by spreading sand on the inside top covers of shoe boxes. Then clap a number and tell children to write that number in the sand with their fingers. Repeat the activity as children learn new numbers.

Visual/Spatial Learners

Distribute one set of number cards for 0 to 5 in random order. Call out the numbers in order starting with zero. Tell children to come to the front of the room as you call their numbers. Have the children line up in order and hold up their cards. Repeat the activity several times.

See Lesson Resources, pp. 4A, 6A, 12A, 18A, 20A, 26A, 28A, 30C, 32A.

GIFTED AND TALENTED

Some children can visualize groups of numbers quickly. Set aside ten minutes each day for one week for children to explain their counting or grouping strategies to the class. As children explain their strategies record what was said. Have other children listen and restate the strategies.

See also Meeting Individual Needs, p. 23.

EXTRA SUPPORT

Specific suggestions for ways to provide extra support to children appear in every lesson in this chapter.

See Meeting Individual Needs, pp. 5, 7, 13, 19, 21, 27, 29, 31, 33.

EARLY FINISHERS

Children who finish their class work early may make smaller, individual number banners, choosing their own numbers and using 8 × 10 paper and crayons. (See *Chapter Project*, p. 2F.)

See also Meeting Individual Needs, pp. 5, 7, 13, 19, 21, 27, 29, 31, 33.

STUDENTS ACQUIRING ENGLISH

Have a variety of picture books available, especially those that show animals, so that children can see and name the different kinds. Children can also look through magazines and cut out animal pictures. You may wish to have the class make an animal counting book. Include number symbols and number words in the book. Encourage children to name and count the animals.

See also Meeting Individual Needs, p. 9.

INCLUSION

- **For** inclusion **ideas, information, and suggestions, see pp. 23, T15.**
- **For** gender fairness **tips, see pp. T15.**

USING MANIPULATIVES

Building Understanding Both number cards and cards showing dots in a variety of configurations can help children make the connection between an amount and the number that represents it. Hold up a number card and have children find a dot card that matches the number shown. Discuss how different dot cards can show the same number. Have children use the cards for counting, matching, and number games.

Easy-to-Make Manipulatives Distribute small zip-lock bags, containing 10 buttons each, to children. Children take turns choosing a number card and counting out that number using the buttons.

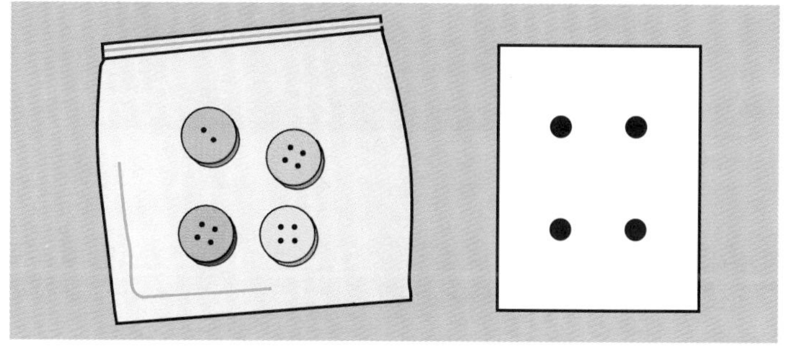

USING COOPERATIVE LEARNING

Community Circle This strategy helps unify the group by ensuring eye contact, and making children feel more comfortable within a group setting.

- **Children sit in a circle.**
- **Children take turns sharing ideas or answering a question around the circle.**
- **Allow children to pass if they wish.**

USING LITERATURE

Use the Big Book *Rhino Country* to introduce the chapter theme, Rhino Country.

Also available in the Read-Aloud Anthology is the selection *How the Rhinoceros Got His Skin,* page 1, as well as the poems "One, Two, Eat Fish Stew," page 21; "The Graceful Elephant," page 22; and "Counting Song," page 44.

RHINO COUNTRY

Linking Technology

This integrated package of programs and services allows students to explore, develop, and practice concepts; solve problems; build portfolios; and assess their own progress. Teachers can enhance instruction, provide remediation, and share ideas with other educational professionals.

MATH VAN ACTIVITY

In *Camel Roundup,* students use counters to find the number of camels in a caravan. Students can use the online notebook to write about how they count. To extend the activity, students use the Math Van tools to complete an open-ended problem related to the concept. *Available on CD-ROM.*

MATH VAN TOOLS

Students can use Math Van's counters to explore numbers to 10. The Tech Links on the Lesson Resources pages highlight opportunities for students to use this and other tools such as money models, graphs, online notes, and calculator to provide additional practice, reteaching, or extension. *Available on CD-ROM.*

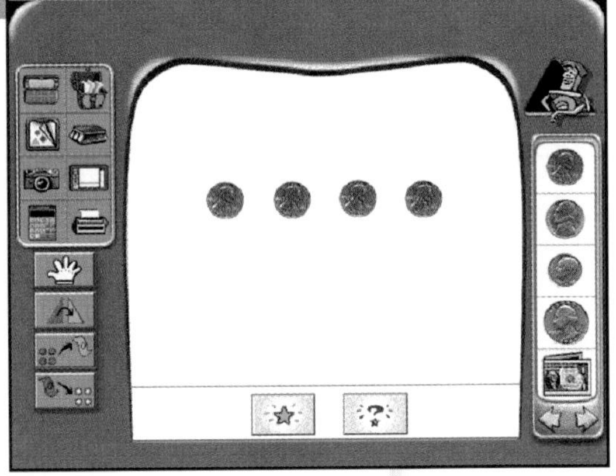

WEB SITE http://www.mhschool.com

Teachers can access the McGraw-Hill School Division World Wide Web site for additional curriculum support at http://www.mhschool.com. Click on our Resource Village for specially designed activities linking Web sites to reading, writing, and counting numbers to 10. Motivate children by inviting them to explore Web sites that develop the chapter theme of "Rhino Country." Exchange ideas on classroom management, cultural diversity, and other areas in the Math Forum.

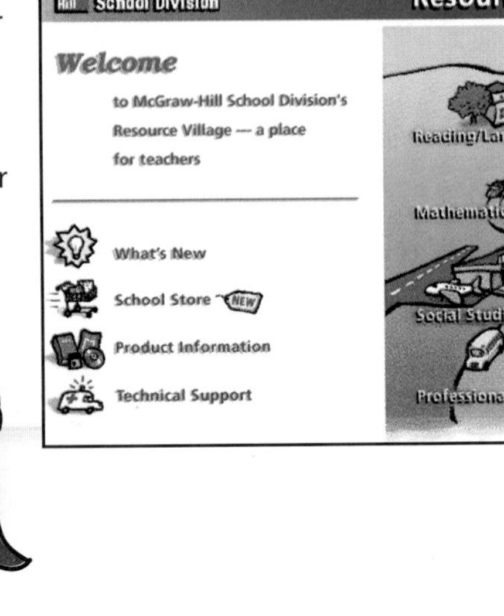

Chapter Project

Highlighting the Math

- write numbers, 0 to 10
- represent numbers with 10-frames

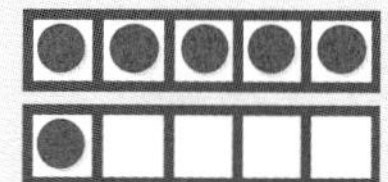

6

- draw or find pictures of sets of objects to show numbers

1 Starting the Project

Introduce the idea of making number banners. Have children discuss what the banners should include: a numeral, its number word, a 10-frame showing the number, and pictures of the appropriate number of objects.

Have two children at a time pick a number from 0 to 10, making sure that each number will be represented on at least one banner. Consider ways in which family and community members can participate.

2 Continuing the Project

- Each group of two enters on its banner the number, the number word, a picture of a 10-frame with that many counters, and pictures of objects.
- Children create the banners using materials such as brown craft paper, crayons, markers,10-frames (TA 4), and drawings or magazine cut-outs.

3 Finishing the Project

Allow time for the children to share their banners. Hang a clothesline in the room and fasten the banners to it.

Community Involvement

Have banners on display for Parents' Night. Invite other classes to view the clothesline banner display.

PORTFOLIO

BUILDING A PORTFOLIO

Have children draw pictures of themselves making the banner. If possible, take photos of children with the banners they made. Each child's portfolio should include the drawing, photos (if available), and any notes you made about the child's work.

To assess the work, refer to the Holistic Scoring Guide on page 27 in the Teacher's Assessment Resources.

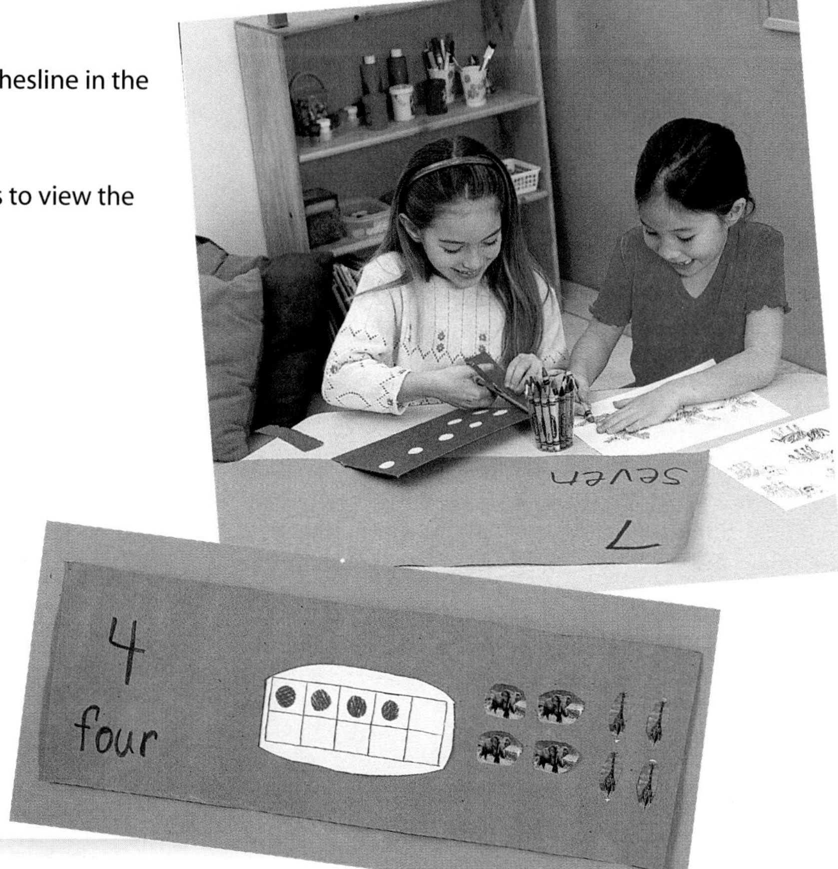

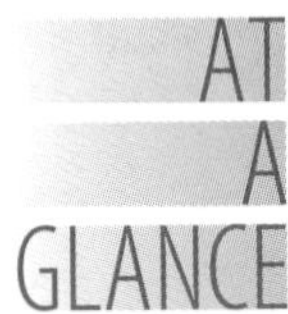

PURPOSE Introduce the theme of the chapter.

Resource Literature Big Book: *Rhino Country*

Using Literature

Page 3

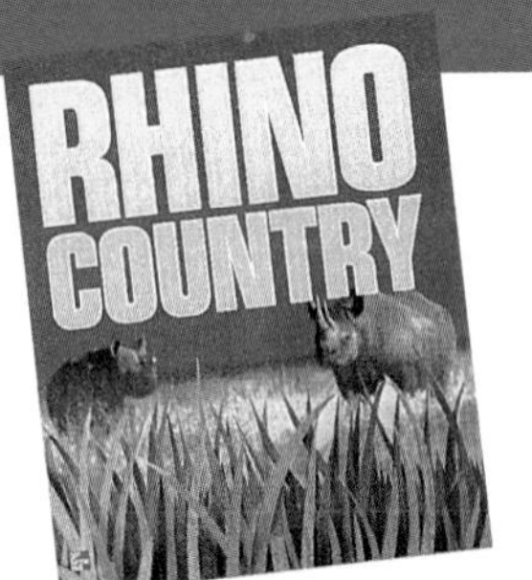

Synopsis of the Book

Rhino Country provides an overview of wildlife in Serengeti National Park. Not only rhinos, but also gazelles, lions, zebras, elephants, mongooses, baboons, wildebeest, and giraffes make their homes there. Bright photos provide a vehicle for children to practice their counting skills.

Talk about the different animals shown and discussed in the book—what they look like, what they eat, and if possible, how many are shown on the page.

Developing the Theme

The theme of this chapter is "Rhino Country." Explain that the word *rhino* comes from the longer word *rhinoceros.* Use the book illustrations to help children see that these rhinos live in places that are grassy and flat.

Create a class mural entitled "Rhino Country" after listening to and discussing the story.

The theme will be revisited throughout the chapter. (See pages 2, 5, 11, 17, 19.)

Making Cultural Connections

Locate the area where you live on a world map or globe. Ask children to describe animals they know live there. Show them Kenya and Tanzania in Africa. Explain that this is where the rhinos and other animals they read about in *Rhino Country* live.

Encourage children to tell about experiences they may have had at the zoo. Discuss zoos as places where animals from many parts of the world live. People enjoy going to zoos to see and learn about animals.

Rhino Country

Numbers to 10

CHAPTER 1

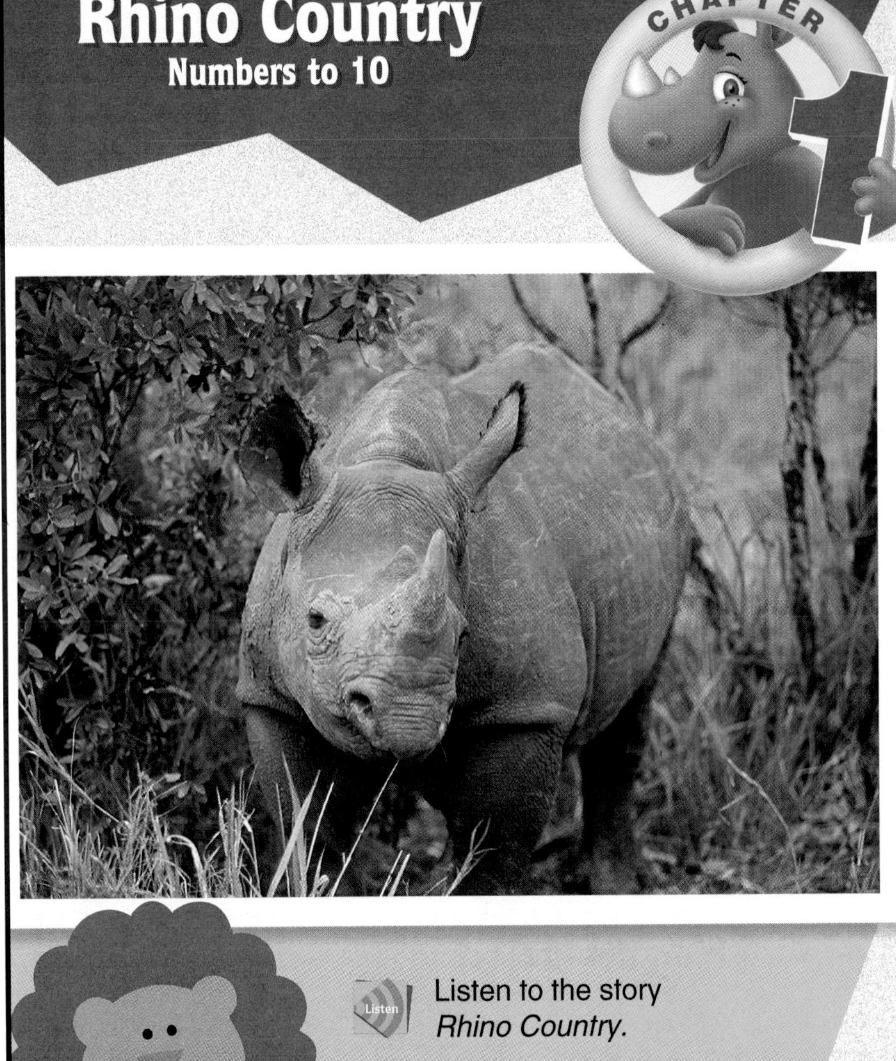

Listen Listen to the story *Rhino Country.*

Talk Tell what you know about rhinos.

CHAPTER BIBLIOGRAPHY

One Sun Rises: An African Wildlife Counting Book by Wendy Hartmann. New York: Dutton Children's Books, 1994. ISBN 0-525-45225-7.

Rainbow Rhino by Peter Sis. New York: Alfred A. Knopf Books for Young Readers, 1993. ISBN 0-679-85005-8.

Ten Black Dots by Donald Crews. New York: Greenwillow Books, 1986. ISBN 0-688-06067-6.

COMMUNITY INVOLVEMENT

Contact the local zoo and request information about their work with endangered species. Invite a worker to come to class to explain the role of zoos in preserving rare animals. Have them bring data about the species with which they are involved. Help children prepare questions ahead of time.

Name

What Do You Know?

Match.

How many [rhino] ? Children may count and tell that there are 4 rhinos and 3 birds.

How many [bird] ?

See Teacher's Edition.

VOCABULARY

These math words will be used in this chapter:

more (p. 5)	**zero, 0** (p. 13)	**after** (p. 29)
most (p. 5)	**fewer** (p. 19)	**before** (p. 29)
same (p. 5)	**fewest** (p. 19)	**order** (p. 29)
one, 1 (p. 7)	**eight, 8** (p. 21)	**penny** (p. 31)
three, 3 (p. 7)	**seven, 7** (p. 21)	**cent, ¢** (p. 31)
two, 2 (p. 7)	**six, 6** (p. 21)	**cents, ¢** (p. 31)
five, 5 (p. 9)	**nine, 9** (p. 23)	**heads** (p. 31)
four, 4 (p. 9)	**ten, 10** (p. 23)	**tails** (p. 31)
one more (p. 9)		

JOURNAL Children may record new words in their math journals. Encourage them to show examples and draw pictures to help tell what the words mean.

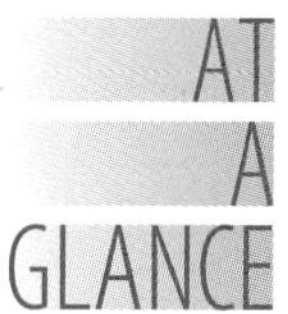

AT A GLANCE **PURPOSE** Assess children's ability to apply prior knowledge of one-to-one correspondence and counting.

Assessing Prior Knowledge

Ask children to describe situations where people count things. Make sure they include some examples from outside of math time.

Draw 5 large dots on the board. Ask a volunteer to come up to the board to show how to count the dots. Then ask at least one more volunteer to show another way to count the dots. Give positive feedback to children on what they already know about numbers and counting. Tell them that they will be learning more about numbers, counting, and solving problems.

Page 4

Have children point to the rhinos in the picture in the top left hand corner. Then ask them to point to the birds. Ask them to match the birds with the rhinos. Have them draw a solid line over the dashed lines. Ask whether there are more rhinos, more birds, or the same number of each. *[the same number]* Ask how they know. *[Possible answer: because there are no rhinos or birds left over after matching them up.]*

Ask children to draw lines to match the birds with the rhinos in the picture in the top right hand corner. Ask whether there are more rhinos, more birds, or the same number of each. *[more rhinos]* Ask how they know. *[Possible answers: because there is one rhino that is not matched up with a bird, because there are 4 rhinos and 3 birds]*

Prerequisite Skills

- *Can children count the number of objects in a group of objects?*
- *Can children show a one-to-one correspondence between the objects in one group and the objects in another group?*

After children have drawn lines to match the birds with the rhinos in the second picture, ask a volunteer to show how he or she drew the lines. Ask if anyone matched up the birds with the rhinos in a different way.

Building a Portfolio

Talk to children individually or in small groups about the picture at the bottom of the page. This piece provides an indicator of where children are in their understanding of counting and one-to-one correspondence. Make notes about what each child says on his or her copy of the Student Book page.

Ask children how many rhinos there are. Then ask them how many birds there are. Ask what else they can tell you about the picture. *[Possible answers: There are more rhinos than birds, one rhino has no bird on its back, there is one more rhino than there are birds.]*

A Portfolio Checklist for Students and a Checklist for Teachers are provided in Teacher's Assessment Resources, pp. 33–34.

LESSON 1.1

EXPLORE ACTIVITY

Numbers to 5

OBJECTIVE Explore the concept of number, 1 to 5.

Day 1 Explore Activity: Numbers to 5

RESOURCE REMINDER
Math Center Card 1
Practice 1, Reteach 1, Extend 1

SKILLS TRACE	
GRADE K	• Explore the concept of number, to 5. *(Chapter 4)*
GRADE 1	• Explore the concept of number, to 5.
GRADE 2	• Explore reading, writing, and representing tens and ones. *(Chapter 3)*

MANIPULATIVE WARM-UP

Cooperative Pairs — **Logical/Analytical**

OBJECTIVE Use one-to-one correspondence to show equal numbers.

Materials per pair: 5 blue and 5 yellow connecting cubes, egg carton

Prepare Cut the egg cartons so that each has 10 cups.

▶ One partner places some blue cubes on the table. The other partner tries to match the number of blue cubes with yellow cubes, and places them on the table.

▶ Each child places his or her cubes in the cups of one row of the egg carton, one cube per cup. Partners adjust, if necessary, the number of yellow cubes to match the number of blue cubes. Play continues, with children alternating who goes first. Each child should have three or more turns to go first.

CONNECTION ACTIVITY

Whole Class — **Visual/Spatial**

OBJECTIVE Connect finding countable objects with pictures.

Resource Literature Big Book: *Rhino Country*

Materials per child: 10 counters

▶ Display a page of the book, *Rhino Country*. Point out two countable parts of the picture. Have children try to arrange their counters in one-to-one correspondence with each picture. Ask a volunteer to tell whether the counters show the same number or different numbers.

▶ Continue, selecting other pictures so that children have an opportunity to show each of the numbers from 1 to 5.

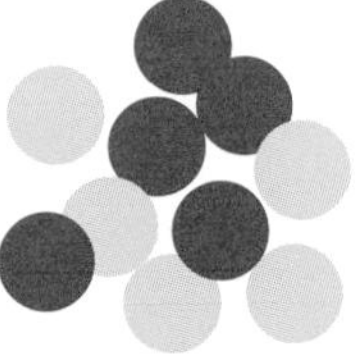

DAILY MATH

PREVIOUS DAY QUICK REVIEW

Which does not belong?

1. dog, tree, cat, tiger *[tree]*
2. circle, fish, square, triangle *[fish]*
3. penny, nickel, dime, boat *[boat]*

Problem of the Day • 1

Read aloud to children:

Ryan wears a glove on each hand.
He wears a hat on his head.
Does he wear more gloves or hats? *[more gloves]*

TECH LINK

ONLINE EXPLORATION

Use our Web-linked activities and lesson plans to connect your students to the real world of wild animals.

MATH FORUM

Idea I have children use the rows on inch graph paper (TA 1) when placing groups of counters in one-to-one correspondence. Each group is placed in one row, one counter per square.

Visit our Resource Village at http://www.mhschool.com to access the Online Exploration and the Math Forum.

MATH CENTER

Practice

OBJECTIVE Explore the concept of number, to 5.

Materials per child: blank spinner, (TA 8), Math Center Recording Sheet (TA 38 optional)

Prepare Draw 1 to 5 dots on each section of the spinner.

Child spins to get a set of dots, then draws the set. The child then draws a set with more dots. *[Check children's drawings to see if the second set has more than the first.]*

Problem Solving

OBJECTIVE Explore the concept of number, to 5.

Materials per child: crayon, Math Center Recording Sheet (TA 38 optional)

Children choose toys whose prices are indicated by symbols. They ring the item with more symbols. *[Answers may vary. Check to see that children ring the set with more.]*

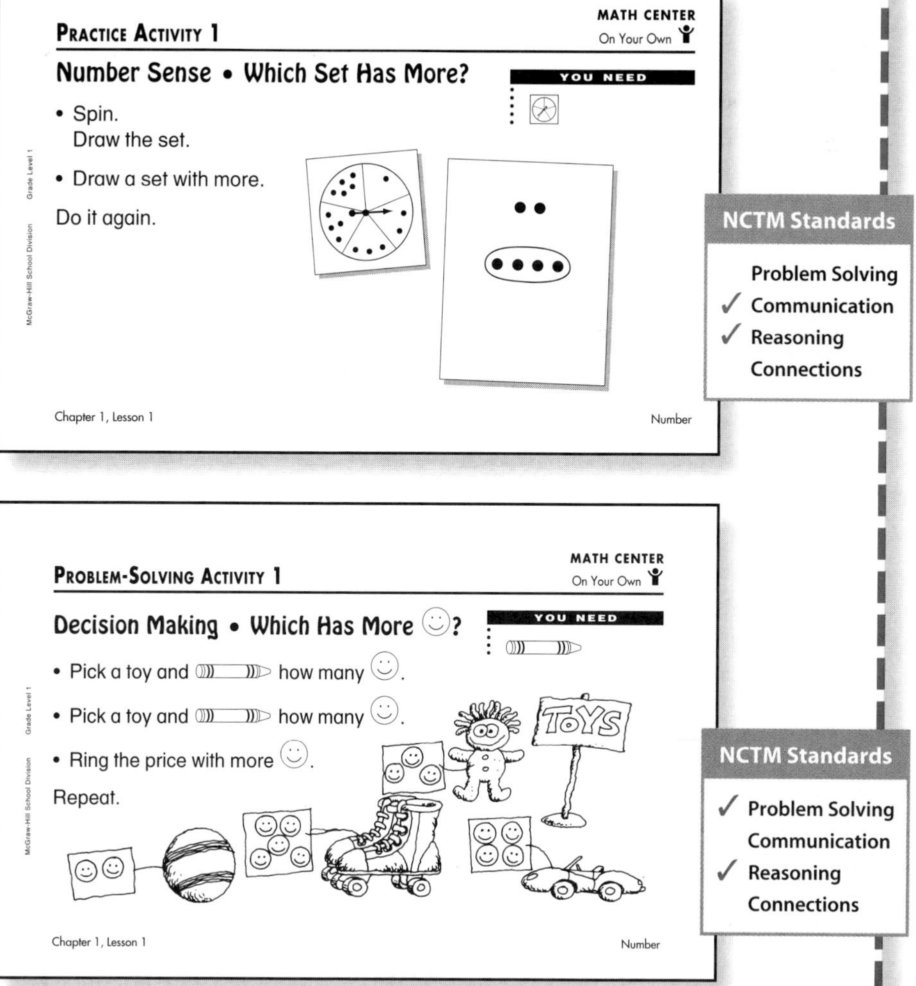

PRACTICE ACTIVITY 1 — MATH CENTER — On Your Own

Number Sense • Which Set Has More?

YOU NEED

- Spin.
  Draw the set.
- Draw a set with more.

Do it again.

Chapter 1, Lesson 1 — Number

NCTM Standards

- Problem Solving
- ✓ Communication
- ✓ Reasoning
- Connections

PROBLEM-SOLVING ACTIVITY 1 — MATH CENTER — On Your Own

Decision Making • Which Has More ☺?

YOU NEED

- Pick a toy and [crayon] how many ☺.
- Pick a toy and [crayon] how many ☺.
- Ring the price with more ☺.

Repeat.

Chapter 1, Lesson 1 — Number

NCTM Standards

- ✓ Problem Solving
- Communication
- ✓ Reasoning
- Connections

Lesson 1.1

DAY 1

EXPLORE ACTIVITY

Numbers to 5

OBJECTIVE Children explore the concept of number, to 5.

Materials per child: 6 rhino counters

1 Motivate — Whole Class

Resources Jumbo Activity Book, page 1; Stickers, sheet 1 (rhino counters)

Place 2 groups of 3 rhino stickers, a group of 4 rhino stickers, and a group of 5 rhino stickers on Jumbo Activity Book page 1. Point out that the groups of 3 stickers have the *same* number, the groups of 4 stickers and 5 stickers have *more* than the groups of 3 stickers, and the group of 5 stickers has the *most* stickers.

Point to a group with 3 rhino stickers. Ask:

- **Which groups have more rhinos than this?** *[the groups with 4 and 5 rhino stickers]*
- **What could we do so this group (the group with 4) has the same as this group (the group with 5)?** *[Add another sticker.]*
- **Which group has the most rhinos?** *[the group with 5 rhino stickers]*

Present additional examples as necessary.

2 Develop

Page 5

Working Together Assign each child a partner. Children place up to 5 counters on the workspace of their partner's page. First each child draws the number of counters their partner gave them, then each child draws a group with more. Children should show a different number of counters in each space. They can check each other's work by placing counters on each drawing.

Critical Thinking
After children have finished the first exercise, ask:

- **Which group has the most? Mark it.** *[Check children's answers.]*

Page 6

Try These Assign the practice exercises.

3 Close

Check for Understanding by drawing groups of 3, 3, and 5 circles on the chalkboard. Ask:

- **Which groups have the same number of circles?** *[the two groups of 3]*
- **Which group has the most circles?** *[the group with 5 circles]*

Name ______________________

Working Together

You need .

Make a group.

Put some here.

Draw your group.

Draw a group with more.

MEETING INDIVIDUAL NEEDS

EARLY FINISHERS

Have partners each draw a third, different group of counters for one of the exercises on page 6, exchange papers, and tell which group has the most counters.

EXTRA SUPPORT

Help children write and illustrate *same* and *more*. They can refer to these papers as needed.

ONGOING ASSESSMENT

Interview Determine if children understand the concept of *most* by directing their attention to page 5 and asking:

- **Which of the groups you drew has the most counters?** *[Answers may vary.]*

Follow Up Children having difficulty with page 6 can count and draw to match, and then draw more. Assign **Reteach 1**.

For children who understand the concept, assign **Extend 1**.

Try These!

Count. Draw a group with more.

Answers may vary. Possible answers are given.

At Home You may want to ask your child to tell about drawing groups with *more* objects.

Alternate Teaching Strategy

Materials per pair: 14 two-color counters; paper cup

Prepare For each student, fold a sheet of paper in half length-wise and write the headings *same* and *more* at the top of the columns.

Draw 5 circles on the chalkboard to show children the number of counters to place in the cup.

Have children work with a partner. One partner shakes the counters in the cup, turns them out on the table, and makes a group of the red counters. The other partner makes a corresponding group of yellow counters. Each child draws the groups in the "same" column on his or her paper.

The first partner adds 1, 2, or 3 red counters to the red group. Each child draws the new group in the "more" column. Partners repeat steps, with the second partner going first.

Partners mark on their papers the group with the most counters and compare answers. Continue until each child has had 3 chances to go first.

PRACTICE • 1

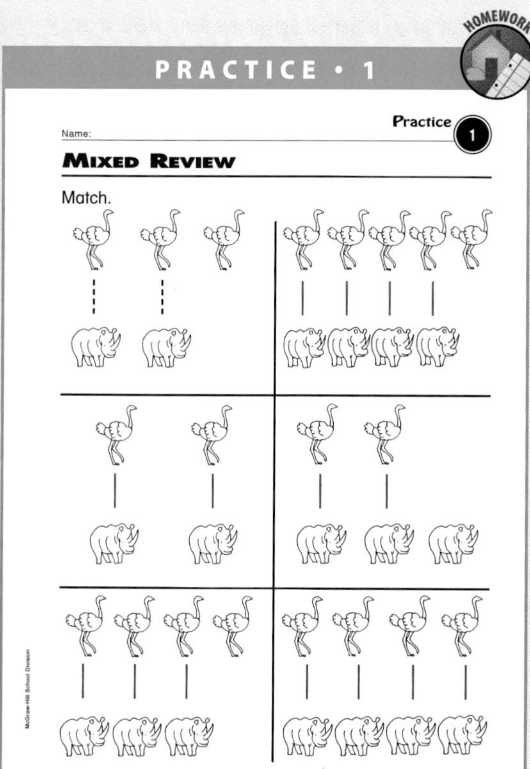

RETEACH • 1

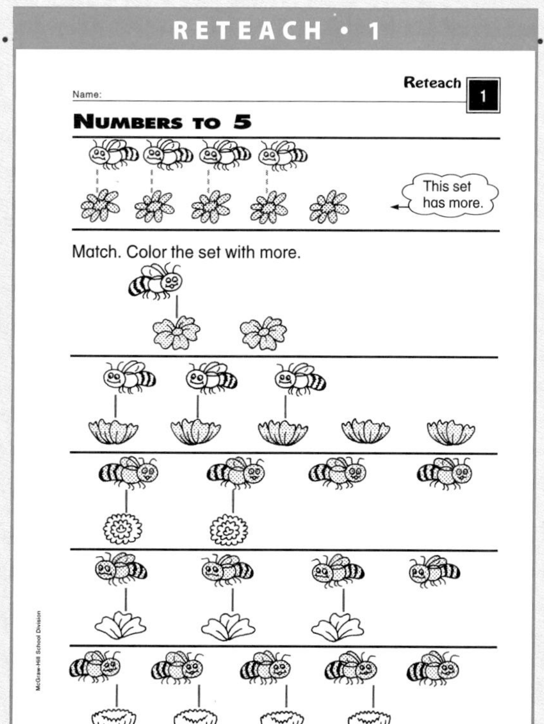

EXTEND • 1

LESSON 1.2

One, Two, Three, Four, Five

OBJECTIVES Read and write numerals, 1 to 5; identify the number of objects in a group, 1 to 5.

Day 1 One, Two, Three
Day 2 Four, Five

RESOURCE REMINDER
Math Center Cards 2
Practice 2–3, Reteach 2–3, Extend 2–3

SKILLS TRACE

GRADE K	• Read and represent numbers, 0 to 5. *(Chapter 4)* • Identify the number of objects in a group, 0 to 5 *(Chapter 4)*
GRADE 1	• Read and write numerals, 1 to 5. • Identify the number of objects in a group, 1 to 5.
GRADE 2	• Explore reading, writing, and representing tens and ones. *(Chapter 3)*

LESSON RESOURCES

MANIPULATIVE WARM-UP

Whole Class | **Individual**

OBJECTIVE Explore different ways to represent groups of 1 to 5.

Materials dot cards, two each of the numbers 1 to 5 (TA 2); per child: 6 rhino counters, 5-frame (TA 4)

▶ Teach children the Flash Five Game. Before beginning, make sure the dot cards are in random order. Flash a dot card. Have children use counters on a 5-frame to show the number represented on the card. Hold up the card again for children to check their answers.

▶ Repeat for each dot card. You may wish to play this game at various points in the chapter to reinforce the concepts and to build up speed.

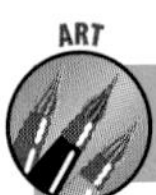

CONNECTION ACTIVITY

Whole Class | **Kinesthetic**

OBJECTIVE Connect creating numerals with a visual display.

Materials per child: construction paper; beans, seeds, stickers, or macaroni; paste

▶ Draw a large numeral from 1 to 5 on each sheet of paper. Ask children to trace with a finger the numeral on their papers. Explain that they are going to decorate the numeral by gluing beans, seeds, stickers, or macaroni onto it. Allow time for children to do this.

▶ Ask a child to hold up his or her finished picture, and invite other children with the same numeral to show their pictures.

▶ Continue until each numeral from 1 to 5 has been displayed.

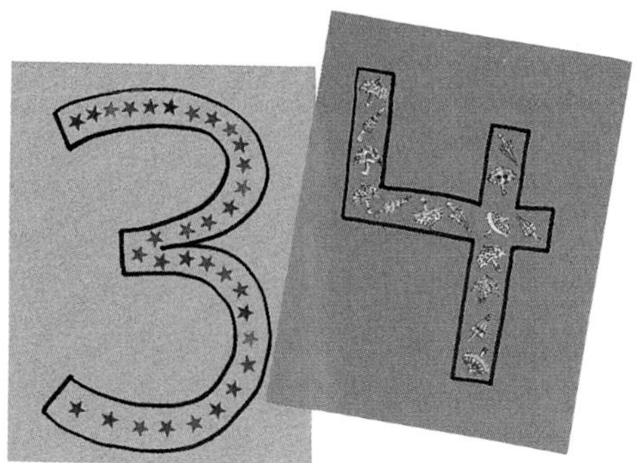

DAILY MATH

PREVIOUS DAY QUICK REVIEW

Draw a group with more. *[Check children's work.]*

1. ◯
2. ◯ ◯
3. ◯ ◯ ◯

Problem of the Day • 2

Read aloud to children:

I am round.
I am small.
I am copper.
I am used to buy things.
What am I? *[a penny]*

TECH LINK

MATH FORUM

Multi-Age Classes I pair older children with younger children to practice counting sets of classroom objects.

Visit our Resource Village at http://www.mhschool.com to see more of the Math Forum.

MATH CENTER

Practice

OBJECTIVE Count and identify the number of objects in a group.

Materials per pair: 4 sets of number cards 1 to 5 (TA 9), blank spinner (TA 7)

Prepare Draw 1 to 5 dots on each section of the spinner.

A child spins a number and finds the number on a card. The child keeps the card. Partners take turns. When all cards for a number are used up, play passes to the other partner.

Problem Solving

OBJECTIVE Identify and write the number of objects in a group.

Materials per child: crayon, Math Center Recording Sheet (TA 38 optional); have available: counters

Children copy a picture of a group of shapes and write the number of shapes they see. They repeat with a second group, and draw a ring around the group with more.

Some children may wish to use counters instead of drawing shapes. *[Check children's work.]*

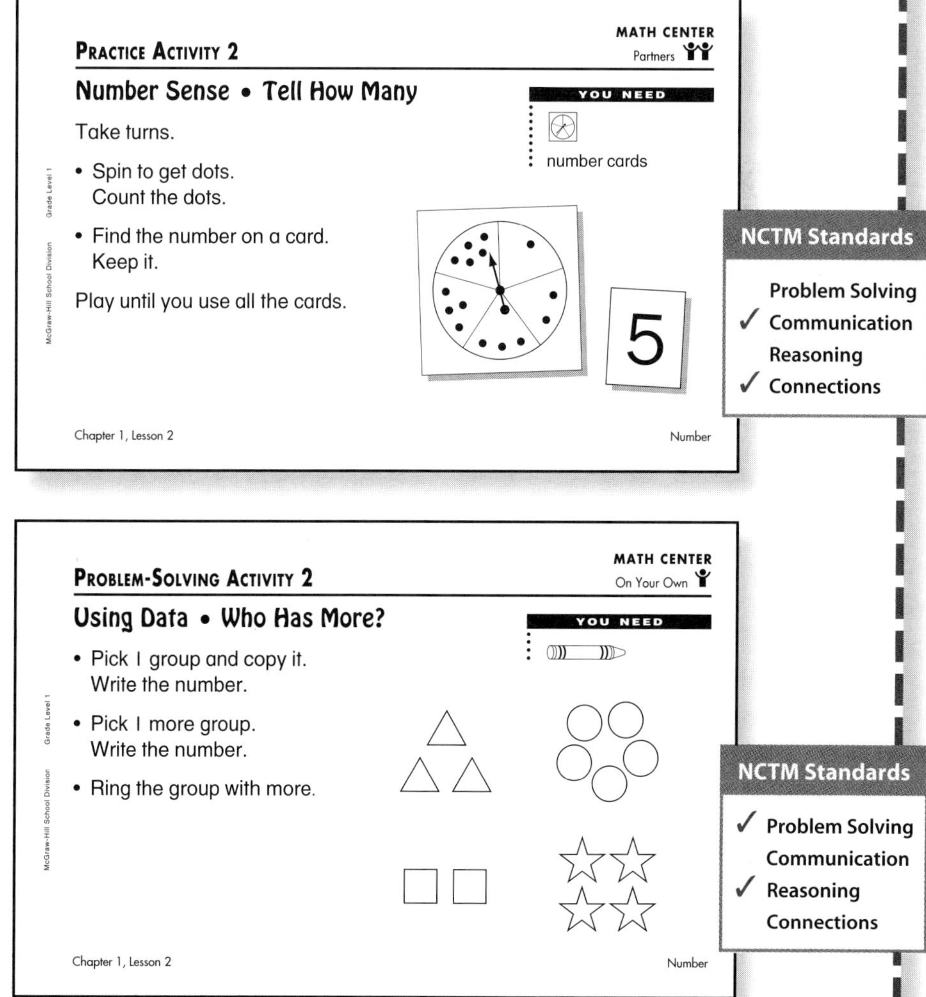

MATH CENTER
Partners

PRACTICE ACTIVITY 2

Number Sense • Tell How Many

YOU NEED
number cards

Take turns.

- Spin to get dots. Count the dots.
- Find the number on a card. Keep it.

Play until you use all the cards.

Grade Level 1 · McGraw-Hill School Division

Chapter 1, Lesson 2 · Number

NCTM Standards

- Problem Solving
- ✓ Communication
- Reasoning
- ✓ Connections

MATH CENTER
On Your Own

PROBLEM-SOLVING ACTIVITY 2

Using Data • Who Has More?

YOU NEED

- Pick 1 group and copy it. Write the number.
- Pick 1 more group. Write the number.
- Ring the group with more.

Grade Level 1 · McGraw-Hill School Division

Chapter 1, Lesson 2 · Number

NCTM Standards

- ✓ Problem Solving
- Communication
- ✓ Reasoning
- Connections

Lesson 1.2

One, Two, Three

OBJECTIVES Children read and write numerals, 1 to 3; children identify the number of objects in a group, 1 to 3.

Materials per child: 3 two-color counters

1 Motivate — Whole Class

Materials per child: 3 two-color counters, 5-frame (TA 4), Numeral Writing Sheet (TA 6)

Draw a 5-frame on the chalkboard or on chart paper to introduce the number words *one, two,* and *three.* Color the frame as shown.

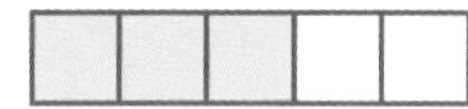

Ask children to tell how many parts are yellow. *[3]* Emphasize that two is *one more* than one, and three is *one more* than two.

Demonstrate how to write the numerals 1, 2, and 3 on the chalkboard. Have children imitate the motions, first with their fingers in the air, then with pencils on paper.

Have children show each number with counters on their 5-frames, and then write the numeral. Ask questions such as:

- **How do you show the number 2 with counters? How do you write it?** *[Children show two counters; 2.]*

2 Develop

Page 7

Identify both the number words and numerals in the picture at the top of the page. Have children place counters on top of the counters pictured before they draw the counters and write the numerals.

Critical Thinking
Point to the panel that shows 3. Ask:

- **What is another way to show 3 using counters?** *[Possible answers: 3 red; 3 yellow; 2 red and 1 yellow]*

Name

One, Two, Three

Show how many.	Draw. Drawings may vary.	Write.
horns		2
tails		1
toes		3
ears		2

CHAPTER 1 *Lesson 2* — seven • 7

MEETING INDIVIDUAL NEEDS

EARLY FINISHERS

Children can use two-color counters to copy and extend the pattern created by the counters on the left side of page 8. *[yellow, red, red, yellow, red, red]*

EXTRA SUPPORT

Provide pans of sand for children to practice writing the numerals 1 to 5 with their fingers.

ONGOING ASSESSMENT

Anecdotal Report Make notes on whether children successfully connect the number word, numeral, and representation for each number, 1 to 3.

Follow Up Children who can identify the numerals 1 to 3 can find examples of those numerals in the classroom. Assign **Extend 2**.

For children who are having difficulty, assign **Reteach 2**.

Try These!

Count. Draw. Write.

Count.	Draw.	Write.
3 counters	3 circles	3
1 counter	1 circle	1
2 counters	2 circles	2
3 counters	3 circles	3
1 counter	1 circle	1
2 counters	2 circles	2

Position of drawings may vary.

Talk **Talk about patterns you see.** Children may recognize the 3, 1, 2 pattern or the yellow, red pattern.

At Home: Ask your child to count things found at home.

Page 8

Try These Assign the practice exercises.

Do the first exercise together with the children.

3 Close

Check for Understanding by writing 1, 2, and 3 on the chalkboard, and asking children to say the name of each number and hold up that many fingers.

Tomorrow children will learn about the numbers 4 and 5.

PRACTICE • 2

HOMEWORK

Name:

Practice 2

One, Two, Three

Position of drawings may vary. Sample answers are given.

Count. Draw. Write.

2, 3, 1, 2, 3, 1

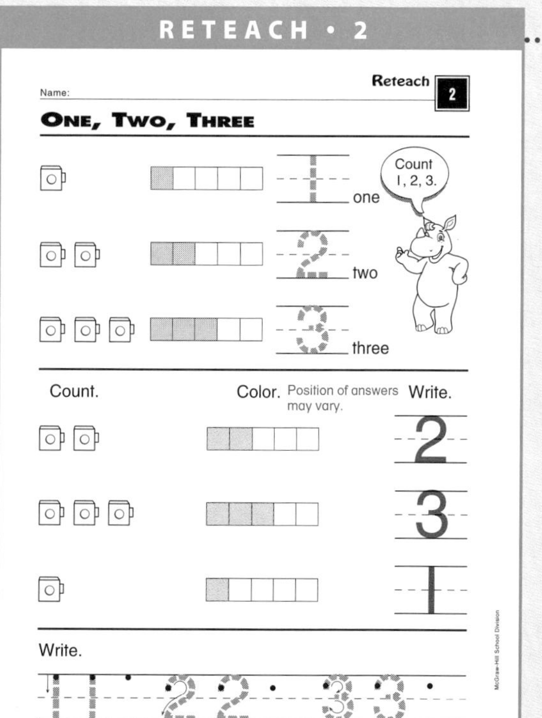
RETEACH • 2

Name:

Reteach 2

One, Two, Three

1 one

2 two

3 three

Count. Color. Position of answers may vary. Write.

2, 3, 1

Write.

EXTEND • 2

Name:

Extend 2

One, Two, Three

Deep Sea

Write how many.

2, 1, 2, 3, 3, 1

Lesson 1.2

DAY 2

Four, Five

OBJECTIVES Children read and write numerals, 4 and 5; children identify the number of objects in a group, 1 to 5.

Materials per child: 5 two-color counters

1 Motivate — Whole Class

Resources Jumbo Activity Book, page 2; Stickers, sheet 1 (red and yellow counters)

Materials dot cards, 1 to 5 (TA 2); per child: 5 two-color counters, 5-frame (TA 4), Numeral Writing Sheet (TA 6)

Use the Jumbo Activity Book 5-frame and stickers to introduce the number names *four* and *five*. Place stickers in the frame from left to right. Emphasize that each subsequent number is *one more* than the number just before. Have children show each number with counters on their 5-frames.

Show children how to write the numerals 4 and 5 and have them practice writing them, first in the air with their elbows, then on their papers with a pencil.

Play a variation of the Flash Five Game, described in the Manipulative Warm-Up on page 6A. Flash a dot card. Have children write the corresponding numeral. Show the card again, and have children say the number name.

2 Develop

Page 9

Identify both the number words and numerals in the picture at the top of the page. Remind children to use their counters to show the number before they write it.

CRITICAL THINKING

After children have completed the page, ask:

- **How many ways can you show 4 using counters?** *[5 ways: 4 red; 4 yellow; 3 red, 1 yellow; 2 red, 2 yellow; 1 red, 3 yellow]*

Page 10

Try These Assign the practice problems.

Encourage children to draw a group of objects representing their favorite number, in addition to writing the numeral. They may choose numbers greater than 5.

3 Close

Check for Understanding by writing the numeral 3 or the numeral 4 on the chalkboard and asking children to show you that number of counters, first in a group and then on a 5-frame. Then show 5 counters and ask:

- **How many counters would you need to show this number?** *[5]*

Name

Four and Five

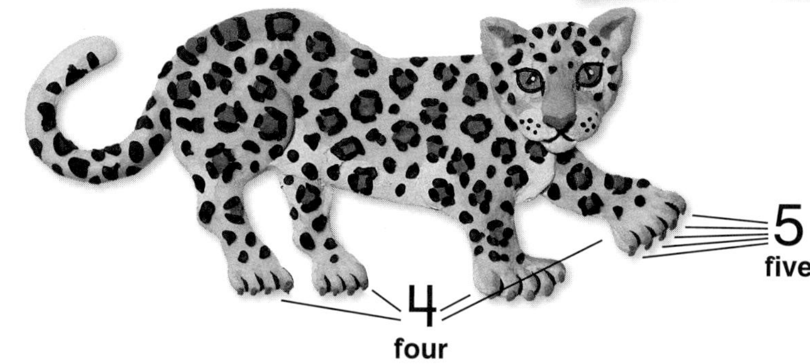

Show.	Draw. Drawings may vary.	Write.
5 counters	5 circles	5
4 counters	4 circles	4
4 counters	4 circles	4
5 counters	5 circles	5

MEETING INDIVIDUAL NEEDS

STUDENTS ACQUIRING ENGLISH

Many children can already count and write numerals in their language of origin. To provide practice in reciting the numbers in English, teach them a counting rhyme, such as "One Two, Buckle My Shoe."

COMMON ERROR

Some children make the numeral 5 like an *S*. Break down the action of writing the numeral into small, distinct steps. Have children practice the first step and add on other steps as they demonstrate mastery.

ONGOING ASSESSMENT

Interview Determine if children can identify 4 and 5 objects in a group on page 10.

- **Find a group of 4.**
- **Find a group of 5.**
- **Which group has more?** *[the group with 5]*

Follow Up Show a group of up to 5 counters and ask children to draw a group with one more. Assign **Reteach 3**.

For students who demonstrate understanding, assign **Extend 3**.

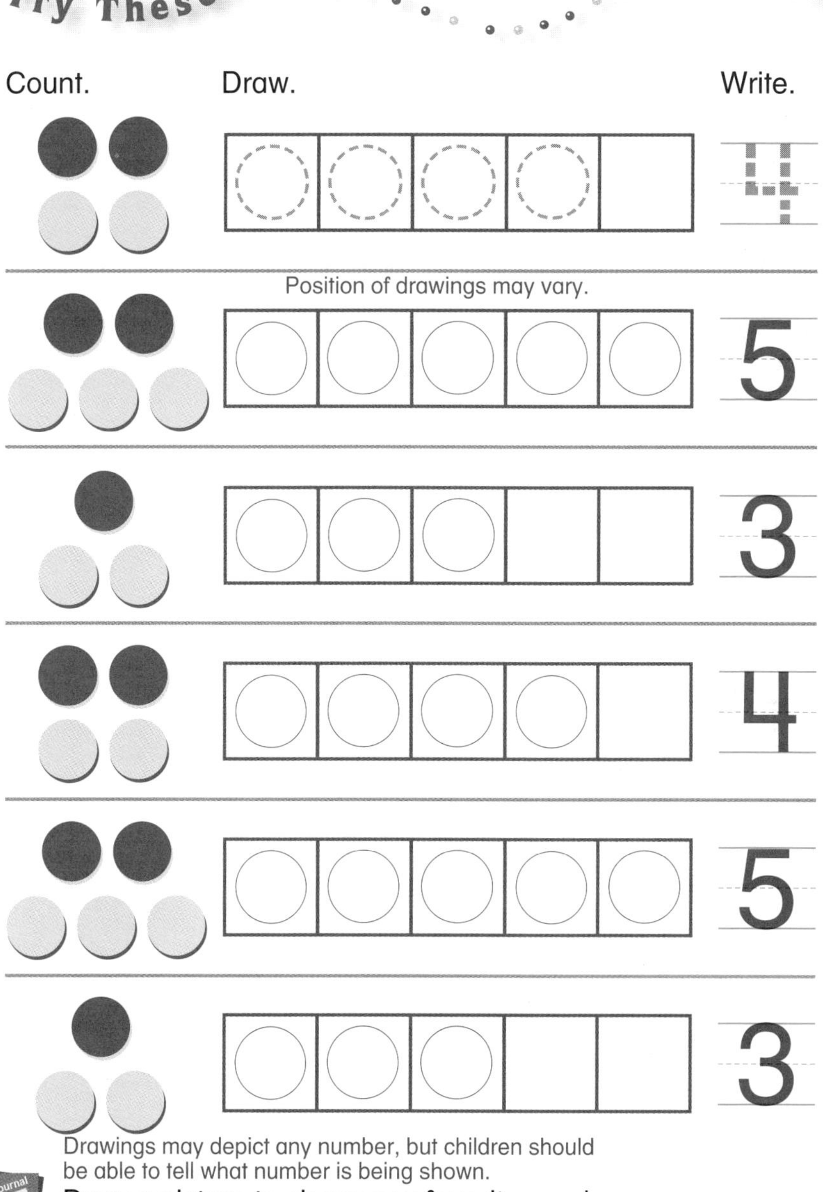

Drawings may depict any number, but children should be able to tell what number is being shown.

Journal Draw a picture to show your favorite number.

At Home Encourage your child to count objects and tell you how many.

Alternate Teaching Strategy

Materials per child: 5 rhino counters, 5-frame (TA 4), Numeral Writing Sheet (TA 6)

Draw a 5-frame on the board or on chart paper. Have children help you create number rhymes, such as:

One rhino has some fun.
Two rhinos go to the zoo.
Three rhinos climb a tree.
Four rhinos on the floor.
Five rhinos like to dive.

Display each amount on the 5-frame. Then have children show each number with rhino counters on their 5-frames.

Demonstrate how to write each numeral, 1 to 5. Have children practice the motions involved, first tracing in the air with fingers or elbows, and then writing on their papers.

Invite volunteers to create new verses, and have children write the corresponding numerals.

PRACTICE • 3

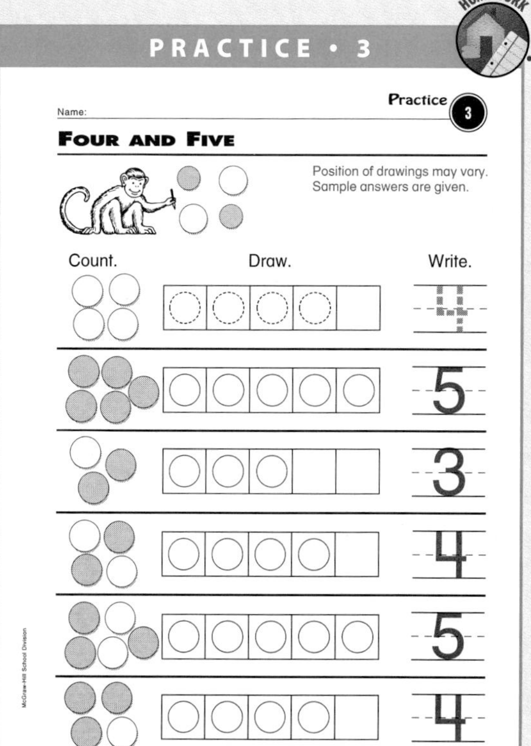

RETEACH • 3

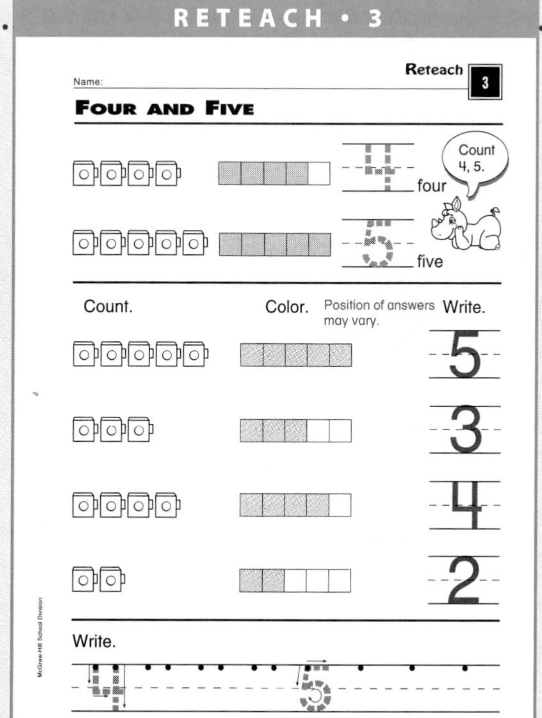

EXTEND • 3

EXTRA PRACTICE

PURPOSE Provide an opportunity for review and practice.

Materials per child: crayons (green, yellow, blue, orange, purple)

Using the Extra Practice

Page 11

Tell children there's a rhino hiding on the page and by coloring the page they'll find it. Discuss the key with children. Make sure they understand that if a shape has dots, they must count the dots to find out the number.

After children finish coloring, ask:

- **How did you find the rhino?** *[Possible answer: I colored the shapes with the numbers 1 to 5 around it. Then I could see it.]*
- **What other animal was hiding on the page? What shapes did you color to find it?** *[elephant; shapes with 2, 2 dots, 5, and 5 dots]*

Page 12

Have children practice writing numerals. Point out the direction of the writing arrows. Have children practice tracing the numerals in the air before they write them on the page. You may want to have children show each number with counters and 5-frames before writing it. After they finish, ask children to mark the number they think looks the best in each row.

Using the Additional Practice

The section below provides additional practice that you may want to write on the chalkboard or on a reproducible master.

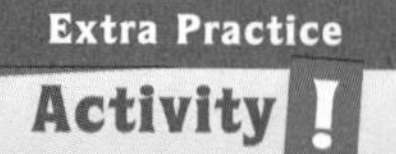

Name

Where's the Rhino?

Color.

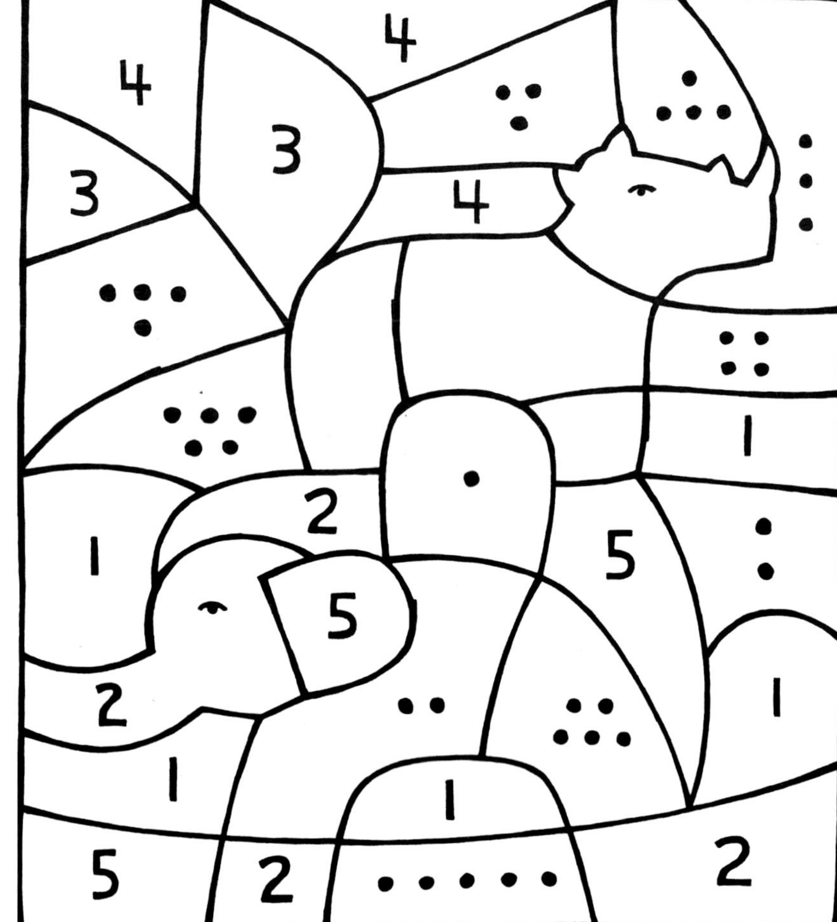

ADDITIONAL PRACTICE

Match.

1. 2, 3, 5, 1, 4 (matched to 5-frames showing 5, 3, 2, 4, 1)

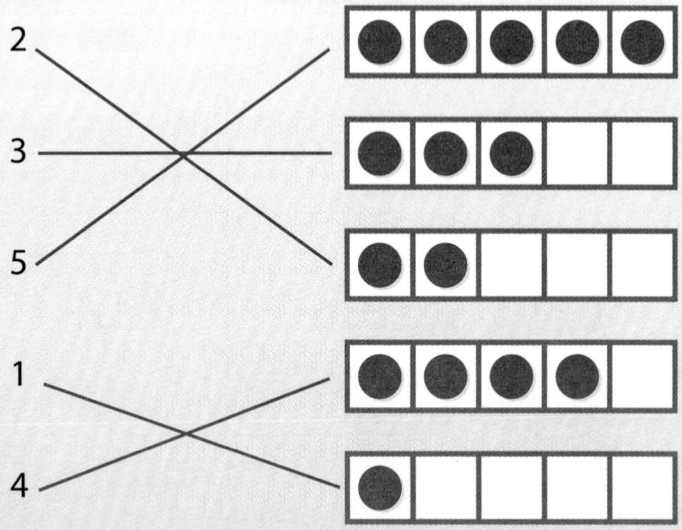

2.

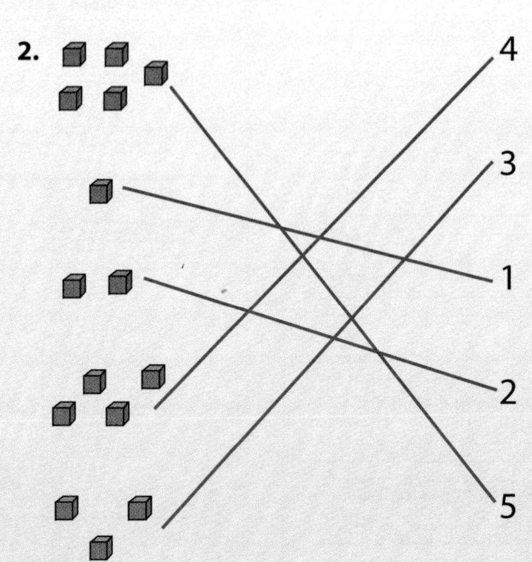

Write the numbers.

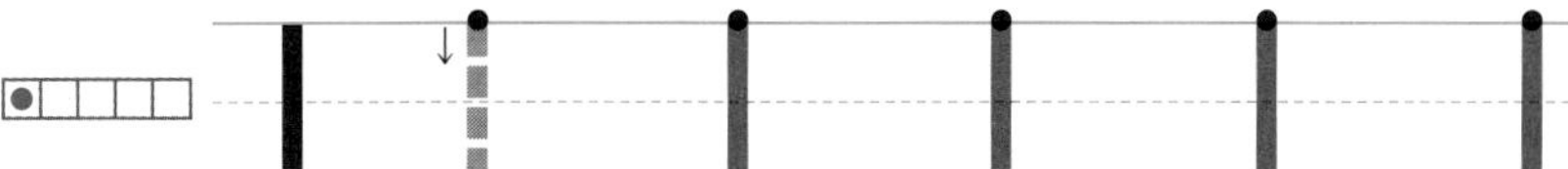

2 2 2 2 2 2

3 3 3 3 3 3

4 4 4 4 4 4

5 5 5 5 5 5

Write the numbers.

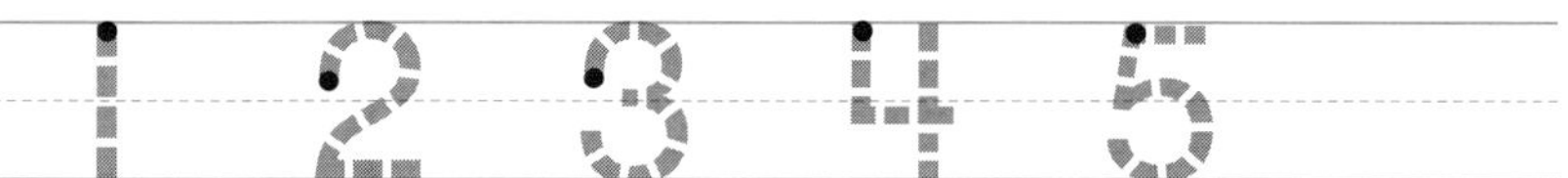

EXTRA PRACTICE Pages 11–12

DEVELOPING SPATIAL SENSE

This section provides another opportunity for children to practice spatial-sense concepts.

How many circles?

1. [2]

2. 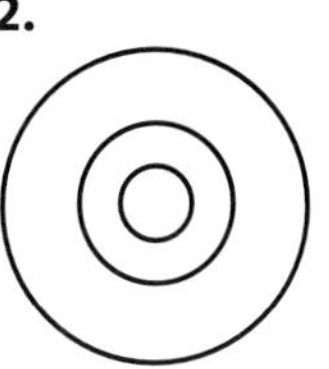

[3]

Write the number.

1. [2]

2. [5]

3. [1]

4. [3]

5. [4]

6. [4]

7. [1]

8. [3]

9. [5]

10. [2]

LESSON 1.3

Zero

OBJECTIVES Read and write the numeral 0; identify the number of objects in a group, 0 to 5.

Day 1 Zero

RESOURCE REMINDER
Math Center Cards 3
Practice 4, Reteach 4, Extend 4

SKILLS TRACE	
GRADE K	• Read and represent numbers, 0 to 5. *(Chapter 4)* • Identify the number of objects in a group, 0 to 5 *(Chapter 4)*
GRADE 1	• Read and write the numeral, 0. • Identify the number of objects in a group, 0 to 5.
GRADE 2	• Explore reading, writing, and representing tens and ones. *(Chapter 3)*

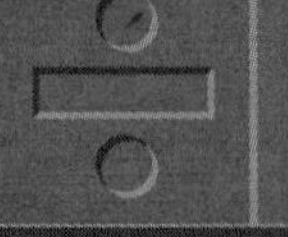

LESSON RESOURCES

MANIPULATIVE WARM-UP

Cooperative Pairs — **Auditory/Linguistic**

OBJECTIVE Explore the concept of zero.

Materials per pair: 6 two-color counters

▶ Have students play the Zero Game. One partner takes one counter and hides it in his or her hand. The other partner takes 5 counters. The first partner holds both hands, and the second partner chooses the one that he or she thinks is empty.

▶ If the second partner chooses the empty hand, he or she gives the first player a counter. The steps are repeated until the second partner has given away all 5 counters. Children switch roles and play again.

CONNECTION ACTIVITY

Whole Class — **Musical**

OBJECTIVE Connect the concept of *none* with music.

Resource Read-Aloud Anthology, page 47

Materials 5 index cards, each with a picture of a duck

▶ Teach children the song "Five Little Ducks," found in the Read-Aloud Anthology, or say it as a rhyme. Choose 5 volunteers to be little ducks and give each one a duck card. Choose a volunteer to be Mother Duck. Have them act out the song as other children sing it.

▶ In the first verse, one child leaves the group. In the second verse, another child leaves, and so on.

- **How many little ducks were left when one little duck went out, but didn't come back?** *[none]*

DAILY MATH

PREVIOUS DAY QUICK REVIEW

Write how many you have.

1. eyes *[2]*
2. nose *[1]*
3. fingers on one hand *[5]*
4. ears *[2]*

Problem of the Day • 3

Read aloud to children:

Five children are playing musical chairs. How many chairs are there? *[4]*

TECH LINK

MATH FORUM

Idea I reinforce how numerals are written by creating large numerals using masking tape on the floor. Children walk, hop, or skip along the lines in the same direction they would write the numbers.

Visit our Resource Village at http://www.mhschool.com to see more of the Math Forum.

MATH CENTER

Practice

OBJECTIVE Identify the number of objects in a group of zero to 5 and write the number.

Materials per child: blank cards, Math Center Recording Sheet (TA 38 optional)

One child shows from zero to 5 fingers by hiding any or all behind a card. The partner counts the fingers showing and writes the number. *[Activity is self-checking between partners.]*

PRACTICE ACTIVITY 3 — MATH CENTER — Partners

Number Sense • How Many Fingers?

YOU NEED: cards

Take turns.

- Hold up your hand.
- Hide some fingers.
- Your partner counts the fingers left.
- Your partner writes the number.

Repeat.

3

Chapter 1, Lesson 3 — Number

Grade Level 1 — McGraw-Hill School Division

NCTM Standards

Problem Solving
✓ Communication
Reasoning
✓ Connections

Problem Solving

OBJECTIVE Match the number of objects in a group of zero to 5 to a number.

Materials per child: 15 connecting cubes, chart with numbers 0 to 5

Prepare Divide a sheet of paper into six parts. Starting at the top left, write one number in a box. Use the numbers 0, 1, 2, 3, 4, and 5.

Children make cube trains to match given numbers.

Check to make sure that children match the cube trains with the correct box on the paper.

PROBLEM-SOLVING ACTIVITY 3 — MATH CENTER — On Your Own

Using Data • How Many Things?

YOU NEED: chart with 0–5; 15 cubes

- Make these five cube trains.

1 2 3 4 5

- Use the chart.

Put each cube train in the matching box.

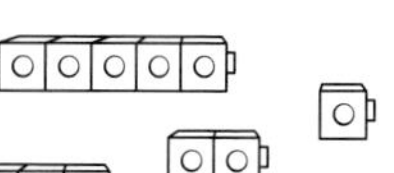

2	5	3
4	0	1

Chapter 1, Lesson 3 — Number

Grade Level 1 — McGraw-Hill School Division

NCTM Standards

✓ Problem Solving
✓ Communication
Reasoning
Connections

Lesson 1.3

DAY 1

Zero

OBJECTIVES Children read and write the numeral, 0; children identify the number of objects in a group, 0 to 5.

Materials 5 two-color counters

1 Motivate — Cooperative Pairs

Materials spinner blank (TA 8); per pair: 5 rhino counters, a sheet of blue paper, a sheet of green paper

Prepare Label a 6-part spinner from 0 to 5.

To introduce *zero,* begin with 5 counters. Count backward, removing one counter for each number. Demonstrate how to write the numeral. Have children practice with you.

Tell children that the blue paper is water and the green paper is land. Have partners place their 5 rhino counters in the "water." Explain that the rhinos will be going from the "water" to the "land." Then read this jingle aloud:

Black Rhino, Black Rhino,
Let (a number from 1 to 5) rhino(s) come over.

Spin the spinner. Have children say the number, use it in the jingle, and move that many rhinos out of the "water" onto the "land." Repeat, until all the rhinos are out of the "water." If you spin a number greater than the number of rhinos left, have children say, "Can't be done." When all the rhinos are out of the water, children can cheer, "Zero rhinos!"

2 Develop

Page 13

Make sure children understand that in the picture at the top of the page, the numbers stand for how many birds, and that they count the mother bird along with the babies. Explain that in the first row they count birds, and in the second row, bugs.

CRITICAL THINKING
Direct children's attention to the empty nest at the top of the page and ask:

- **What words can you use to tell how many birds are in the nest?** *[Possible answers: zero birds, no birds, none]*

Page 14

Try These Assign the practice exercises.

Help children identify the different animals shown. *[leopards, elephants, zebras, rhinos, antelope, giraffes, tick birds]*

3 Close

Check for Understanding by asking:

- **When does a classroom have zero children in it?** *[Possible answer: after everyone goes home]*

Name ________________

Zero

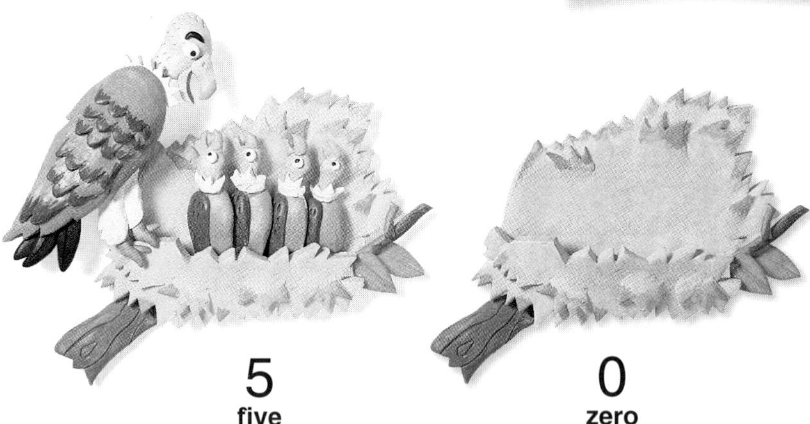

Write how many.

MEETING INDIVIDUAL NEEDS

EARLY FINISHERS

Have children write each numeral from 0 to 5, and beside each draw groups of objects that represent each number.

EXTRA SUPPORT

Use sentences with *none* or *nothing* to illustrate the meaning of the words. For example, ask questions such as "Who has nothing on their desk?"

ONGOING ASSESSMENT

Observation Checklist Determine if children understand how to read, write, and show numbers 0 to 5 by having them use counters to show each number, then write the numerals.

Follow Up Children having difficulty writing the numerals can evaluate the ones they've written, marking a 'best one' for each number. Then they should try to write each one again. Assign **Reteach 4**.

For students who demonstrate understanding, you may wish to assign **Extend 4**.

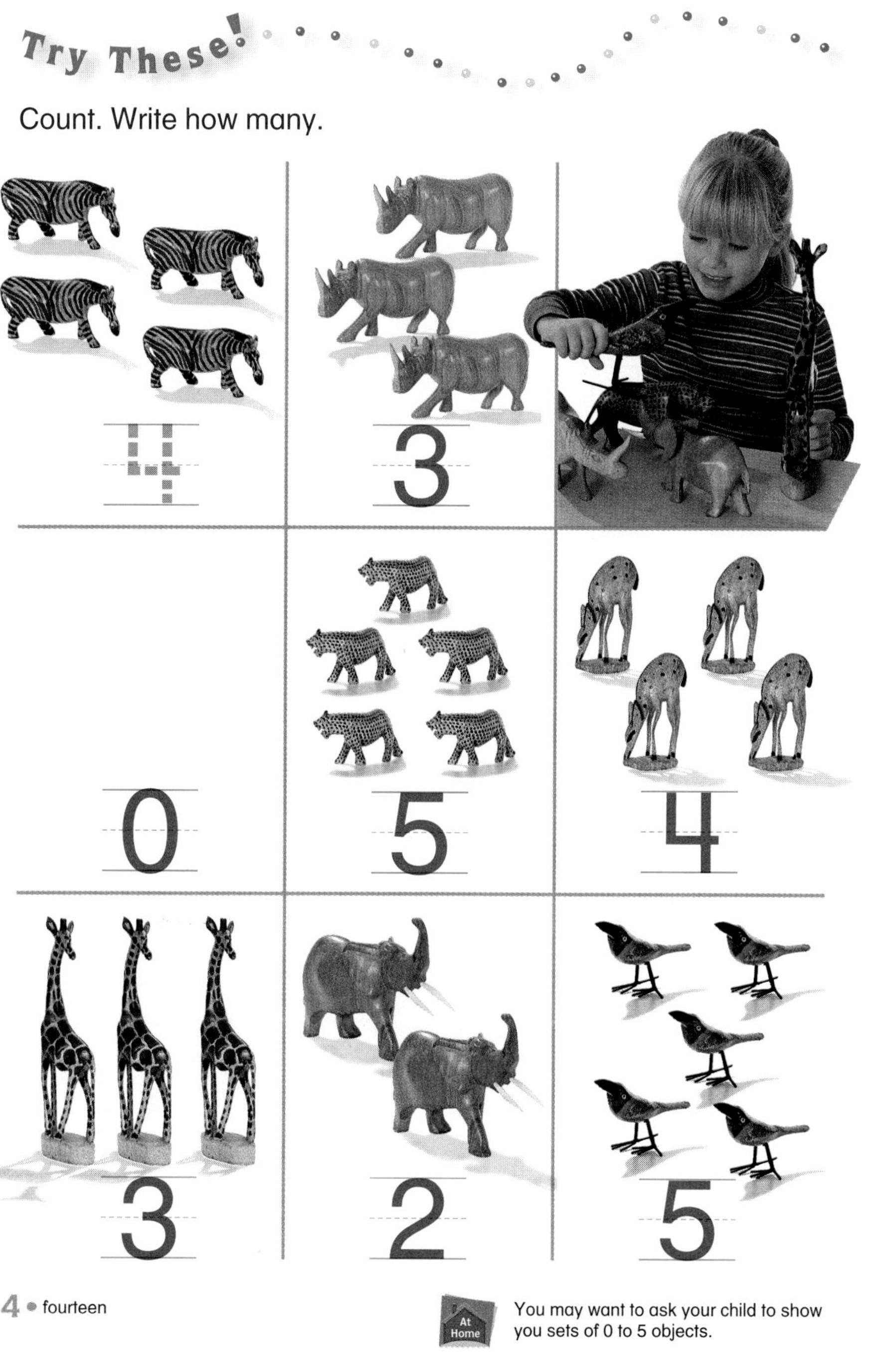
Try These!

Count. Write how many.

4	3	
0	5	4
3	2	5

14 • fourteen

At Home You may want to ask your child to show you sets of 0 to 5 objects.

Alternate Teaching Strategy

Materials 5 crayons; per pair: 2 Numeral Writing Sheets (TA 6), calculator

To introduce zero, display 5 crayons. Count backward, removing one crayon for each number. When you reach zero, ask:

- **How many crayons are left?** *[zero, none]*

Have children look at the calculator. Then have them find and press the keys for the numbers 0 to 5 so all six numerals appear in the display. Make sure children can identify each numeral.

Display other objects in groups of zero to 5 for children to count. For each group, one child in the pair presses the corresponding key on the calculator, and the other child writes the numeral. They compare answers and then clear their calculator displays. They switch roles after three rounds.

PRACTICE • 4

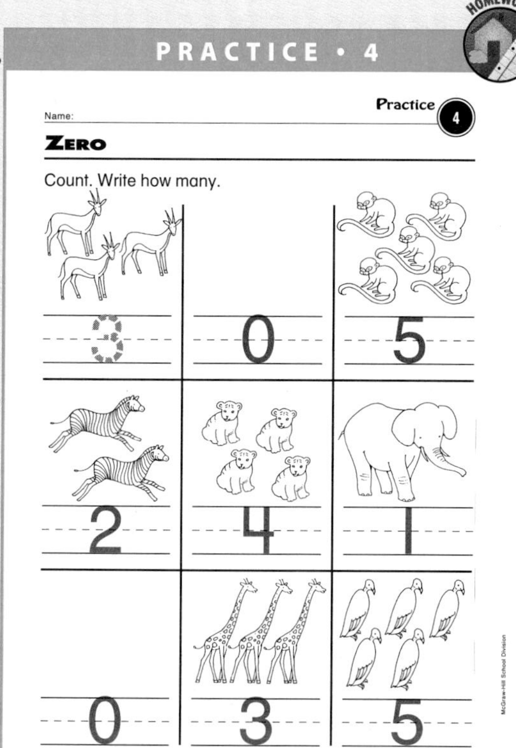
HOMEWORK

Name: Practice 4

ZERO

Count. Write how many.

3	0	5
2	4	1
0	3	5

RETEACH • 4

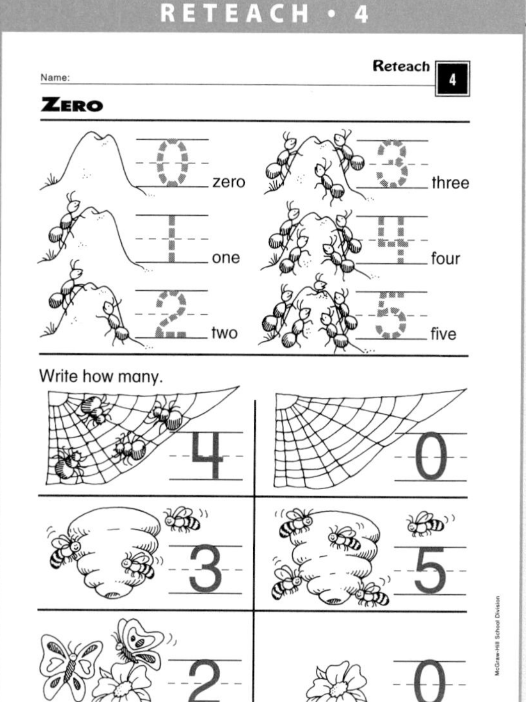
Name: Reteach 4

ZERO

0 zero
1 one
2 two
3 three
4 four
5 five

Write how many.

4	0
3	5
2	0

EXTEND • 4

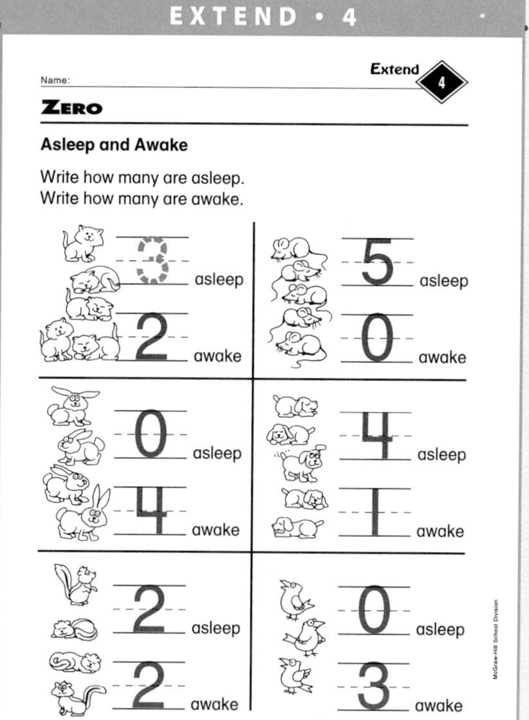
Name: Extend 4

ZERO

Asleep and Awake

Write how many are asleep.
Write how many are awake.

3 asleep, 2 awake	5 asleep, 0 awake
0 asleep, 4 awake	4 asleep, 1 awake
2 asleep, 2 awake	0 asleep, 3 awake

MIDCHAPTER REVIEW

PURPOSE Maintain and review the concepts, skills, and strategies that children have learned thus far in the chapter.

Materials have available: two-color counters, 5-frames (TA 4)

Using the Midchapter Review

Page 15

The **Midchapter Review** may be completed independently or by the class as a whole. Go over the directions on the page with children as necessary.

Children may represent 5 with the numeral, the word, and groups of objects. Encourage children to include each of these representations.

Vocabulary Review

Write the following words on the chalkboard:

five, 5	**one more**
four, 4	**same**
more	**three, 3**
most	**two, 2**
one, 1	**zero, 0**

Ask volunteers to explain, show, or act out the meanings of these words.

Name

Midchapter Review

Draw. Write.

Position of drawings may vary.

2 ◯◯ 2

5 ◯◯◯◯◯ 5

3 ◯◯◯ 3

4 ◯◯◯◯ 4

Do your best!

Write how many.

Show 5 in many different ways. Children may show the numeral, pictures of 5 objects, a 5-frame with counters, or other displays.

Reinforcement and Remediation

CHAPTER OBJECTIVES	MIDCHAPTER REVIEW ITEMS	STUDENT BOOK PAGES	TEACHER'S EDITION PAGES: Activities	TEACHER'S EDITION PAGES: Alternate Teaching Strategy	TEACHER RESOURCES: Reteach
*1A	1–4	7–14	6A, 12A	10, 14	1–4
*1B	5–10	7–14	6A, 12A	10, 14	1–4

*1A Read, write, and represent numbers, 0 to 10

*1B Identify the number of objects in a group, including pennies, to 10

Extra Practice **Game!**

Animal Walk

START

You need a [spinner] and a [counter].

Take turns.

- Spin and move.
- [rhino space] means **go ahead** 1 space.
- [leopard space] means **go back** 2 spaces.
- Play until you reach **End.**

AT A GLANCE

PURPOSE Provide an opportunity for review and practice.

Materials per pair: 2 rhino counters; blank spinner labeled 0, 0, 1, 1, 2, 2, 3, 3, 4, 5 (TA 7)

Using the Extra Practice

Page 16

Children play in pairs. Explain the rules of the game. Point out that Start is at the top of the page, so to go ahead they move down the page. To go back, they move up the page.

After children finish playing, ask:

- **What number did you want the spinner to point to? Why?** *[Possible answer: 5, because I get to move forward the most spaces.]*

Using the Additional Practice

The section below provides additional practice that you may want to write on the chalkboard or on a reproducible master.

ADDITIONAL PRACTICE

Count. Write how many.

1. ★ ★ ★ ★ *[4]*
2. (empty box) *[0]*
3. ★ *[1]*
4. ★ ★ ★ *[3]*
5. ❄ ❄ ❄ ❄ ❄ *[5]*
6. ❄ ❄ *[2]*
7. ❄ ❄ ❄ *[3]*
8. ❄ ❄ ❄ ❄ *[4]*

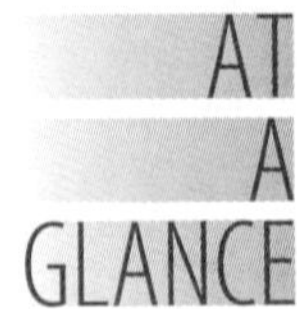

Applying Counting

OBJECTIVE Children use counting in a science setting.

Materials large sheet of poster board; per child: large sheet of drawing paper, crayons

1 Engage — Cooperative Pairs

Play the game, "I'm Thinking of an Animal." For example, say:

- **I'm thinking of an animal that has 2 eyes, zero legs, 1 tail fin, and 2 flippers. What animal could it be?** *[dolphin]*
- **I'm thinking of an animal that has 2 eyes, zero arms, 2 legs, and 1 wide mouth. What animal could it be?** *[frog]*
- **I'm thinking of an animal that has 6 legs and many dots on its back. What animal could it be?** *[ladybug]*

Let children take turns being "It."

2 Investigate

Page 17

Talk about the rhino in the picture. Encourage children to count as many body parts as possible. *[1 head, 1 mouth, 2 eyes, 1 nose, 2 horns, 1 tail, 4 legs]*

Distribute the crayons and drawing paper.

Working Together Have children work in pairs to find things on each other that show the numbers 0 to 5.

Discuss children's pictures. Talk about how children and the rhino have the same and different numbers of parts. *[Possible answer: Same—both have 1 head, 1 nose, 2 eyes, and 2 ears; different—rhino has 2 horns, 1 tail, zero arms, and 4 legs; children have zero horns, zero tails, 2 arms, and 2 legs.]*

3 Reflect and Share

Page 18

Using the Community Circle Strategy, have children sit in a circle. Children take turns around the circle sharing ideas about how to make a class display of the items and numbers in children's drawing. Allow a child to pass if they wish.

Children may suggest using words to make lists of things under titles such as "Sets of 2," drawing pictures of sets next to numbers, or a combination of pictures, words, and numbers.

Write a Report Discuss the class display. Ask questions such as:

- **Do you show more sets of 2 or more sets of 4?**
- **Which number is shown the most?**
- **How many different things did you find for zero?**

Name

Counting on Ourselves

Count the parts of a rhino. Children may count legs, ears, horns, eyes, and nose.

Working Together

- ▶ Find things that show 0, 1, 2, 3, 4, 5 on your partner.
- ▶ Draw what you find.
- ▶ Write the numbers.

Drawings may vary.

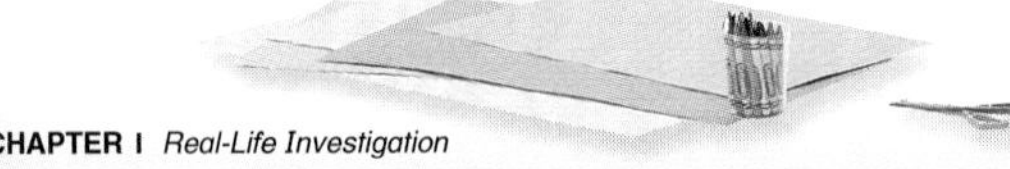

MORE TO INVESTIGATE

Predict Possible answers: clocks, chairs, books, tables.

Explore Children may find things that show numbers greater than 5, such as windows, tables, chairs, books, and crayons.

Find Sample responses: There would be more numbers, more words, or more pictures; the display would be much bigger.

Bibliography Children may enjoy reading the following books:

Count on Your Fingers African Style by Claudia Zaslavsky. New York: Writers & Readers Publishing, Inc., 1996. ISBN 0-86316-240-1.

I Spy Two Eyes by Lucy Micklethwait. New York: Greenwillow Books, 1993. ISBN 688-12642-1.

Decision Making Answers may vary. See Teacher's Edition for sample of children's work.

Talk

Make a class picture for 0, 1, 2, 3, 4, 5. Decide how to show what each group counted.

Write a report.

1. Tell about the class picture.
2. What can you tell about the numbers?

More to Investigate

See Teacher's Edition.

PREDICT What else can you count in your classroom?

EXPLORE Find things that show other numbers.

FIND How would your class picture change?

Children's Work

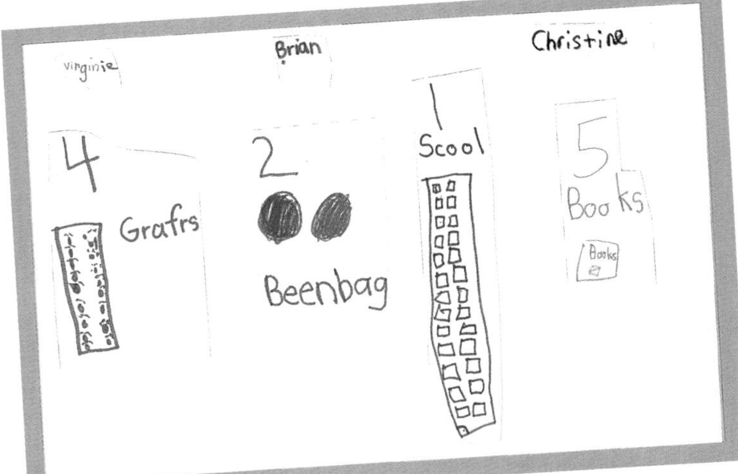

Lauren
We shode wut thar wur 0 1 4 5 uv in the clasroom.

BUILDING A PORTFOLIO

This assignment will provide insight into children's ability to organize their thinking about groups of objects and numbers and about the relationships among numbers.

Allow children to revise their work for the portfolio. Each child's portfolio piece should consist of her or his drawing, written report, and any notes you made about the child's work.

You may wish to use the Holistic Scoring Guide and the annotated Samples of Children's Work to assess this task. See page 27 in Teacher's Assessment Resources.

LESSON 1.4

EXPLORE ACTIVITY

Numbers to 10

OBJECTIVE Explore the concept of number, to 10.

Day 1 Explore Activity: Numbers to 10

RESOURCE REMINDER
Math Center Cards 4
Practice 5, Reteach 5, Extend 5

SKILLS TRACE	
GRADE K	• Explore the concept of number, to 10. *(Chapter 6)*
GRADE 1	• Explore the concept of number, to 10.
GRADE 2	• Explore reading, writing, and representing tens and ones. *(Chapter 3)*

LESSON RESOURCES

MANIPULATIVE WARM-UP

Cooperative Pairs — Visual/Spatial

OBJECTIVE Explore the comparative concept of fewer.

Materials per pair: 20 rhino counters, timer or stopwatch

▶ Have children do this activity with a partner. Partners say, "1, 2, 3, show!" On the word "show," each partner shows a number of fingers from 0 to 10 and says the number.

▶ Children compare numbers. The one showing fewer fingers takes a rhino counter. If the numbers are the same, both partners take a counter.

▶ Play lasts for 3 minutes. The partner with the most counters is the winner. Then partners play again. This time, the partner who has fewer counters at the end of 3 minutes is the winner.

CONNECTION ACTIVITY

Whole Class — Social

OBJECTIVE Connect comparison words with size or number.

Materials 6 index cards labeled *small, smaller, smallest; few, fewer, fewest*

▶ On the chalkboard, draw 3 different-sized stars. Point out the largest of the three. Ask children to identify a smaller star and then the smallest star, and place the appropriate label beneath each picture.

▶ Then draw apples in groups of 5, 3, and 4. Identify the group of 5 as "a few apples." Have the class label the group with fewer and fewest apples.

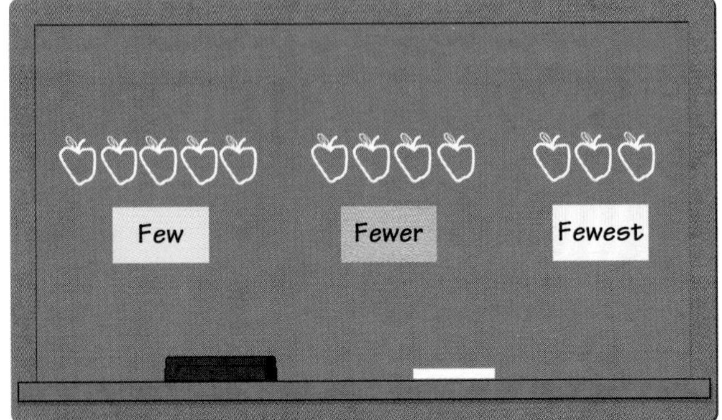

DAILY MATH

PREVIOUS DAY QUICK REVIEW

How many?

1. ●●●●● *[5]*
2. ☐☐☐☐☐ *[0]*
3. ●●●☐☐ *[3]*

Problem of the Day • 4

Read aloud to children:

Kara, Tim, and Van are standing in line.
Van is after Tim.
Van is before Kara.
Who is first in line? *[Tim]*

TECH LINK

MATH VAN

Tool You may wish to use the Counters tool with this lesson.

MATH FORUM

Management Tip I have children put their 10 counters in plastic bags to save me from having to count them out again each time.

Visit our Resource Village at http://www.mhschool.com to see more of the Math Forum.

MATH CENTER

Practice

OBJECTIVE Compare groups of 6 to 10 objects and determine which group has fewer.

Materials per pair: 20 index cards

Prepare Draw 6 triangles on four cards; draw 7, 8, 9, and 10 on four more. Stack cards facedown.

Children compare groups of 6 to 10 objects and determine which has fewer. The child with fewer triangles keeps the two cards. *[Activity is self-checking between partners.]*

PRACTICE ACTIVITY 4 — MATH CENTER, Partners

Game • Look for Fewer

YOU NEED: number cards

Take turns.

- Each player picks 1 card.
- Show your card.
- The player with fewer △ gets both cards.

Play until you have used all the cards.

Grade Level 1 — McGraw-Hill School Division

Chapter 1, Lesson 4 — Number

NCTM Standards

- Problem Solving
- ✓ Communication
- ✓ Reasoning
- Connections

Problem Solving

OBJECTIVE Compare sets of objects and determine which is fewer.

Materials per child: crayon, Math Center Recording Sheet (TA 38 optional)

Children choose two foods to "buy" and compare to see which requires fewer symbols. They repeat the activity. *[Check to see that students have circled the set with fewer smiling faces.]*

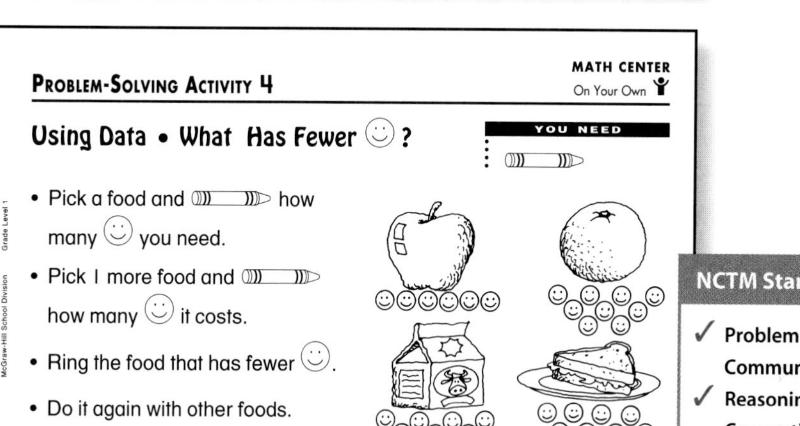

PROBLEM-SOLVING ACTIVITY 4 — MATH CENTER, On Your Own

Using Data • What Has Fewer ☺?

YOU NEED: crayon

- Pick a food and (crayon) how many ☺ you need.
- Pick 1 more food and (crayon) how many ☺ it costs.
- Ring the food that has fewer ☺.
- Do it again with other foods.

Grade Level 1 — McGraw-Hill School Division

Chapter 1, Lesson 4 — Number

NCTM Standards

- ✓ Problem Solving
- Communication
- ✓ Reasoning
- Connections

Lesson 1.4

DAY 1

EXPLORE ACTIVITY
Numbers to 10

OBJECTIVE Children explore the concept of number, to 10.

Materials per child: 10 rhino counters

1 Motivate — Cooperative Pairs

Materials dot cards for 6-10 (TA 3); per child: 10 rhino counters, Workmat 2 (10-frame)

Use dot cards to introduce the terms *fewer* and *fewest*. Place dot cards for 9 and 7 in the chalkboard ledge.

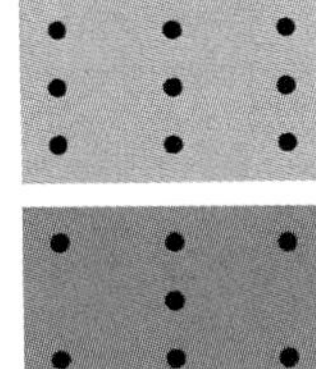

Have children tell how many dots there are in each group.

- **Which group has fewer dots?** *[the group of 7]*

Add a dot card for 6 to the display. Have children tell how many dots are in the group.

- **Which group has the fewest dots?** *[the group of 6]*

Play the Flash Ten Game. Flash a dot card. Have one child show the number with counters on Workmat 2. Flash a second card for the partner to show with counters. Have partners compare counters and tell who has fewer.

2 Develop

Page 19

Working Together Read aloud the instructions as two volunteers demonstrate the activity. Partners can check each other's work by placing counters on top of the ones they drew.

CRITICAL THINKING
After children complete the page, ask:

- **Which set has the fewest? Mark it.** *[Answers may vary depending on children's drawings.]*

Page 20

Try These Assign the practice exercises.

More to Explore Children are shown two sets of counters and are asked to determine by looking, not counting, which set has fewer counters.

3 Close

Check for Understanding by drawing 7 circles on the chalkboard and asking children to show you a set with fewer counters.

Name

Explore Activity
Numbers to 10

Working Together

You need 🦏.

Make a group.

Put some 🦏 here.

Draw your 🦏 group.

Draw a group with fewer.

MEETING INDIVIDUAL NEEDS

EARLY FINISHERS

Have children pick a number from 5 to 10 and find all the groups in the room with fewer than that many objects.

EXTRA SUPPORT

If children need extra support, have available other countable objects—fingers on a glove, buttons on a shirt, chairs in a row.

ONGOING ASSESSMENT

Interview Show 8 counters and 5 counters. Point to the 5 counters. Ask:

- **Which group has fewer?** *[the group with 5 counters]*

Follow Up If children have difficulty with the concept of *fewer*, assign **Reteach 5.**

Children who understand *fewer* can draw a set of objects less than 10, and then draw all the possible groups with fewer objects. Assign **Extend 5.**

Try These!

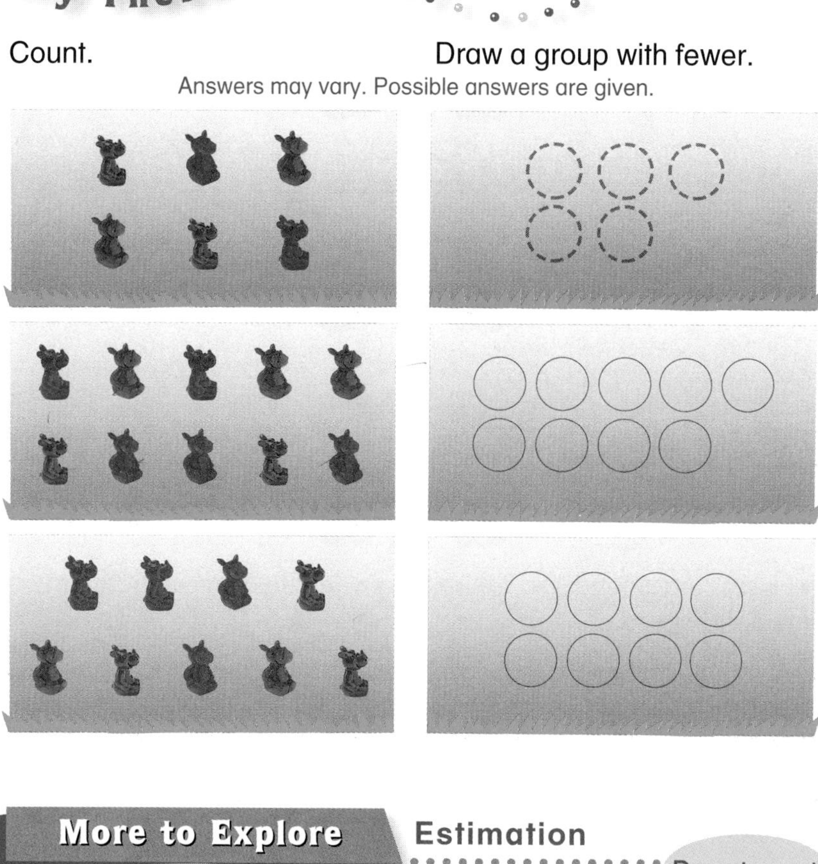

Count. Draw a group with fewer.

Answers may vary. Possible answers are given.

More to Explore Estimation

Look.
Ring the group with fewer.

Do not count.

At Home: You may want to ask your child to tell about drawing sets with *fewer* objects.

Alternate Teaching Strategy

Materials per child: 10 two-color counters, Workmat 2 (10-frame), paper cup

Have children play this game with a partner: each child puts the counters in his or her cup and turns them out onto the table. Then, he or she makes a group of yellow counters. Partners place their counters on 10-frames and compare them to determine which group has fewer.

The child who has fewer counters draws a star on his or her paper. If both groups show the same amount, neither child draws a star.

Children play five rounds. The child with the most stars is the winner.

PRACTICE • 5 (HOMEWORK)

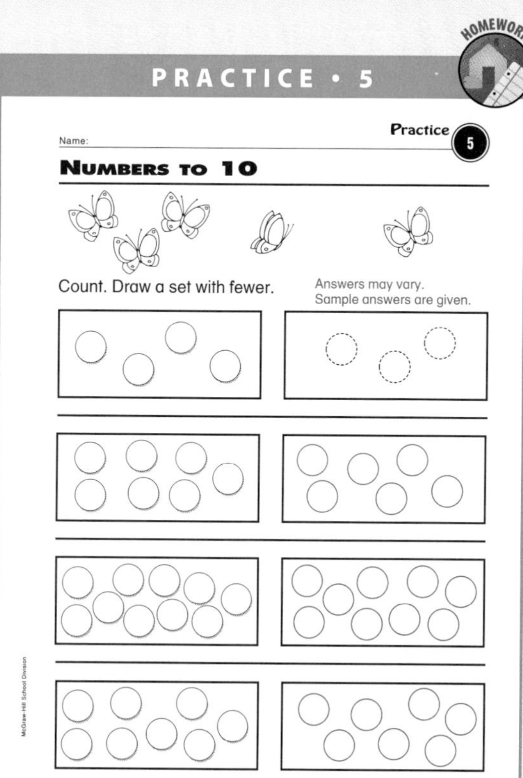

Name:

Practice 5

Numbers to 10

Count. Draw a set with fewer.

Answers may vary. Sample answers are given.

RETEACH • 5

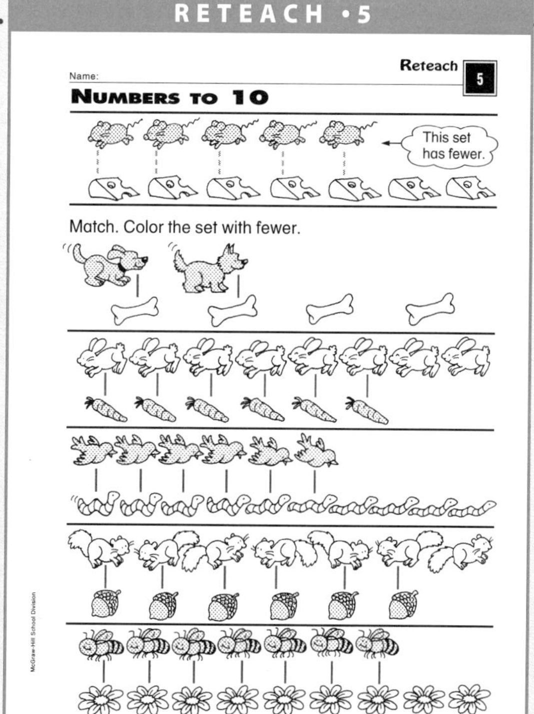

Name:

Reteach 5

Numbers to 10

This set has fewer.

Match. Color the set with fewer.

EXTEND • 5

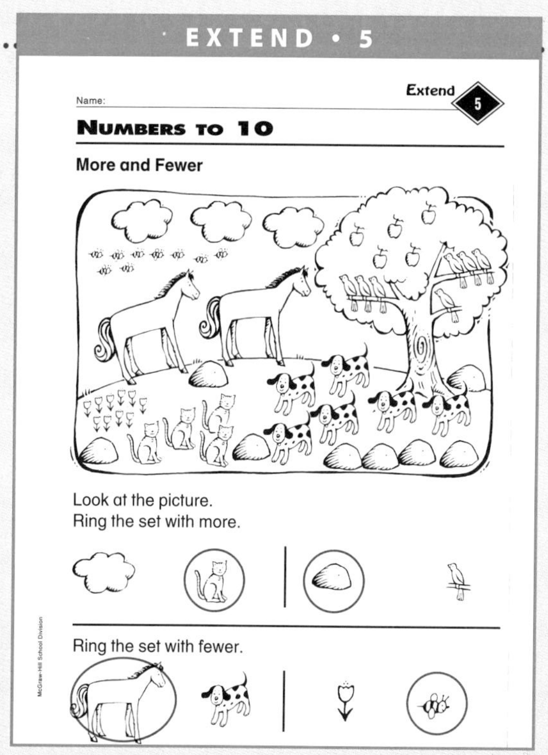

Name:

Extend 5

Numbers to 10

More and Fewer

Look at the picture.
Ring the set with more.

Ring the set with fewer.

LESSON 1.5

LESSON RESOURCES

Six, Seven, Eight, Nine, Ten

OBJECTIVES Read and write numerals, 6 to 10; identify the number of objects in a group, 6 to 10.

Day 1 Six, Seven, Eight
Day 2 Nine, Ten

RESOURCE REMINDER
Math Center Cards 5
Practice 6–7, Reteach 6–7, Extend 6–7

SKILLS TRACE	
GRADE K	• Read and represent numbers, 6 to 10. *(Chapter 6)* • Identify the number of objects in a group, 6 to 10. *(Chapter 6)*
GRADE 1	• Read and write numerals, 6 to 10. • Identify the number of objects in a group, 6 to 10.
GRADE 2	• Explore reading, writing, and representing tens and ones. *(Chapter 3)*

MANIPULATIVES

MANIPULATIVE WARM-UP

Whole Class **Kinesthetic**

OBJECTIVE Explore identification of numbers 6 to 10.

Materials dot cards, 2 each of numbers 1–10 (TA 2–3); per child: 10 two-color counters, Workmat 2 (10-frame)

▶ Play the Flash Ten Game. Before beginning, make sure the dot cards are in random order. Flash a dot card. Have children use counters on a 10-frame to show the number represented on the card. Hold up the card again for children to check their answers.

▶ Repeat for each card. Spend 3 to 5 minutes playing the game at frequent intervals. Encourage speed.

▶ You may vary the game by making several cards for each number, varying the position of the dots on the cards.

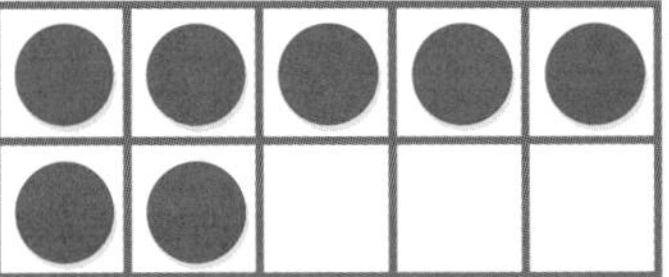

SCIENCE

CONNECTION ACTIVITY

Cooperative Pairs **Visual/Spatial**

OBJECTIVE Connect numbers with groups of objects, animals, or people.

Materials per pair: number cards 1–10 (TA 9), several picture books and magazines about science or nature

▶ Partners each take 5 number cards and a picture book or magazine.

▶ Each partner looks for a picture containing a number of items that matches the number on one of their cards. When a picture is found, they use the card to mark their place.

▶ Help students put their number card pictures in order from 1 to 10.

DAILY MATH

PREVIOUS DAY QUICK REVIEW

Say the number that is one less.

1. 4 *[3]*
2. 10 *[9]*
3. 7 *[6]*
4. 3 *[2]*

Problem of the Day • 5

Read aloud to children:

Elena has more than 3 stickers.
She has fewer than 5 stickers.
How many stickers does she have?
[4 stickers]

TECH LINK

MATH VAN

Tool You may wish to use the Counters tool with this lesson.

MATH FORUM

Cultural Diversity I encourage children who know counting songs from other cultures to share them with the class. Keep number cards available for them to use.

Visit our Resource Village at http://www.mhschool.com to see more of the Math Forum.

MATH CENTER

Practice

OBJECTIVE Read numerals 0–9 and practice them.

Materials per pair: blank 10-part spinner (TA 7), 2 two-color counters

Prepare Write the numbers 0–9 on each section of the spinner. Draw a game board as shown on card.

Children check their ability to read numbers as they play the game.

PRACTICE ACTIVITY 5 MATH CENTER Partners

Game • Race to the End

YOU NEED: game board, 2 counters

Take turns.

- Spin 1 number.
- Move your counter that many spaces.

Play until you get to the end.

Do you want the game to be longer? Go around the game board again.

START END

Grade Level 1 McGraw-Hill School Division

Chapter 1, Lesson 5 Number

NCTM Standards
- ✓ Problem Solving
- Communication
- Reasoning
- ✓ Connections

Problem Solving

OBJECTIVE Solve number riddles with *more than* and *less than.*

Materials per pair: 10 connecting cubes, Math Center Recording Sheet (TA 38 optional)

Partners take turns reading and solving the riddles. *[**1.** 6; **2.** 9.]*

PROBLEM-SOLVING ACTIVITY 5 MATH CENTER Partners

Logical Reasoning • What Number Am I?

YOU NEED

Solve.

1. I am more than 5 and less than 7.
   What number am I?
   Pick a number from these and write your answer.
2. I am less than 10 and more than 8.
   What number am I?
   Pick a number from these and write your answer.

5 ? 7 ? ? 9 ? 6 10 ? 8 ?

Grade Level 1 McGraw-Hill School Division

Chapter 1, Lesson 5 Number

NCTM Standards
- ✓ Problem Solving
- ✓ Communication
- ✓ Reasoning
- Connections

DAY 1

Six, Seven, Eight

OBJECTIVES Children read and write numerals, 6 to 8; children identify the number of objects in a group, to 8.

1 Motivate — Whole Class

Materials per child: 8 two-color counters, Workmat 2 (10-frame), Numeral Writing Sheet (TA 6)

Draw three 10-frames on the chalkboard and fill in the boxes to introduce the numbers *six, seven,* and *eight,* as follows:

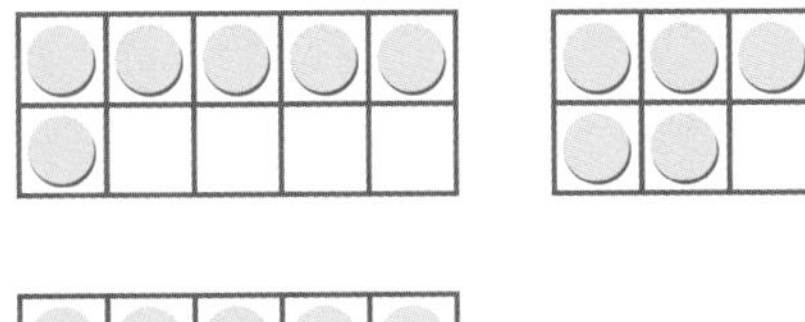

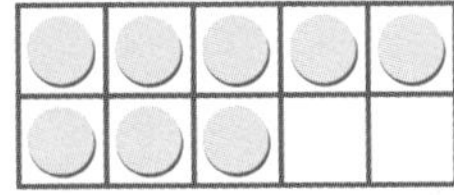

Have children verify that the filled top row on the 10-frame shows 5, like a 5-frame. Ask:

- **How many more boxes do I need to fill to show 6? 7? 8?** *[1, 2, 3]*

Help children see that each number is *one more* than the previous number.

Show children how to write the numerals 6, 7, and 8 and have them practice, first in the air, then with pencil on paper.

2 Develop

Page 21

Have children count each group of animals aloud and match them to the number words and numerals. Discuss the worked-out example and have children complete the page.

Critical Thinking
After children do the exercises, ask:

- **If you have 5 counters, how many more do you need to make 7?** *[2]*

Name

Six, Seven, Eight

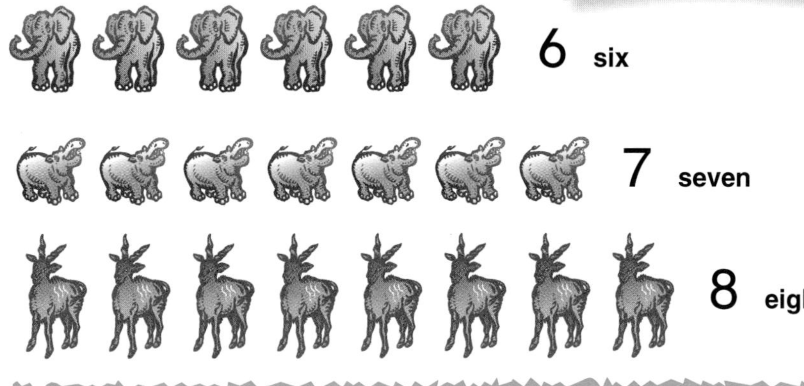

Count. Draw. Write.

Position of drawings may vary.

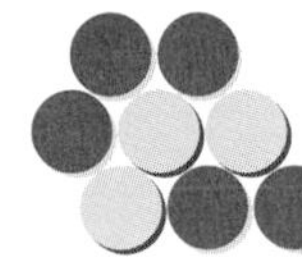

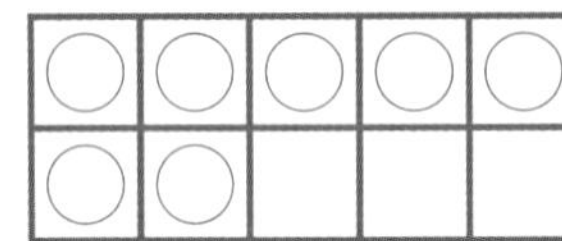

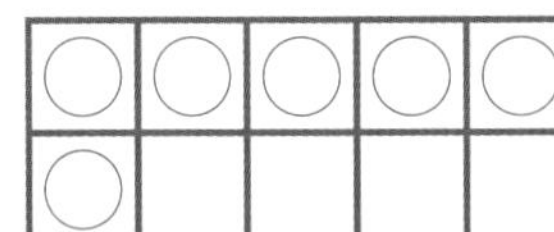

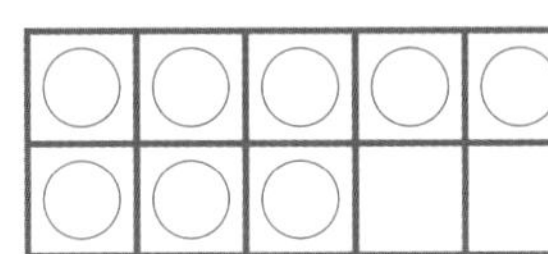

MEETING INDIVIDUAL NEEDS

EARLY FINISHERS

Have children use 7 two-color counters to show different ways to represent the number 7. They can draw to record their answers. *[There are 8 possible arrangements.]*

EXTRA SUPPORT

To help children keep track of the items they have counted in a group, have them draw a line through each item as they count.

ONGOING ASSESSMENT

Anecdotal Report Make notes on whether children identify numbers 6 to 8 on a 10-frame by beginning with the filled-in row of 5, or whether they begin counting from 1.

Follow Up Children having difficulty can place a counter in a 10-frame for each animal belonging to a group on page 22. Then they can count to find the number. Assign **Reteach 6.**

For children who demonstrate understanding, assign **Extend 6.**

Try These!

Write how many.

bird	3	sun	1
tree	2	hyena	8
giraffe	7	bird	6

At Home: Encourage your child to tell you a story about the picture.

Page 22

Try These Assign the practice exercises.

Have children identify the animals in the picture. Encourage them to mark each animal as they count.

3 Close

Check for Understanding by asking children to draw a group of 7 animals and write the number 7. Have children switch papers to check each other's work.

Tomorrow children will learn about the numbers 9 and 10.

PRACTICE • 6

RETEACH • 6

EXTEND • 6

DAY 2

Nine, Ten

OBJECTIVES Children read and write numerals, 9 and 10; children identify the number of objects in a group, to 10.

1 Motivate — Cooperative Pairs

Materials dot cards (TA 2–3); per pair: 10 counters, Workmat 2 (10-frame), 5-frame (TA 4), 2 copies of Numeral Writing Sheet (TA 6)

Draw a 10-frame and a 5-frame on the chalkboard, filled in as shown:

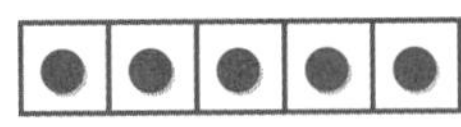

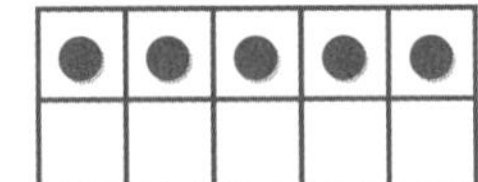

Have partners place counters in their own 10-frames to verify that the top row on the 10-frame shows 5. Continue filling in boxes one at a time as children count aloud with you to 10.

- **How can you use the 5-frame to help you count 10?** *[Two 5-frames means you have 10 altogether.]*

Demonstrate writing 9 and 10, and have children practice.

Play the Flash Ten Game. Show dot cards for 0 to 10 in random order. One child in each pair shows the numbers with counters on the 10-frame. The other child writes the numerals. Have partners compare answers.

2 Develop

Page 23

Identify, or have children identify, the animals shown (giraffes, gnu). Have children count them aloud. Ask volunteers to point out the numerals and their corresponding number words.

Critical Thinking
After children complete the page, ask:

- **If you have 5 counters, how many more do you need to make 9?** *[4]*

Page 24

Try These Assign the practice exercises.

Help children identify the animals and trees. As on page 22, children may want to mark each animal as they count it.

3 Close

Check for Understanding by drawing 9 circles on the chalkboard and asking:

- **How many are there? What number is one more than this?** *[9; 10]*

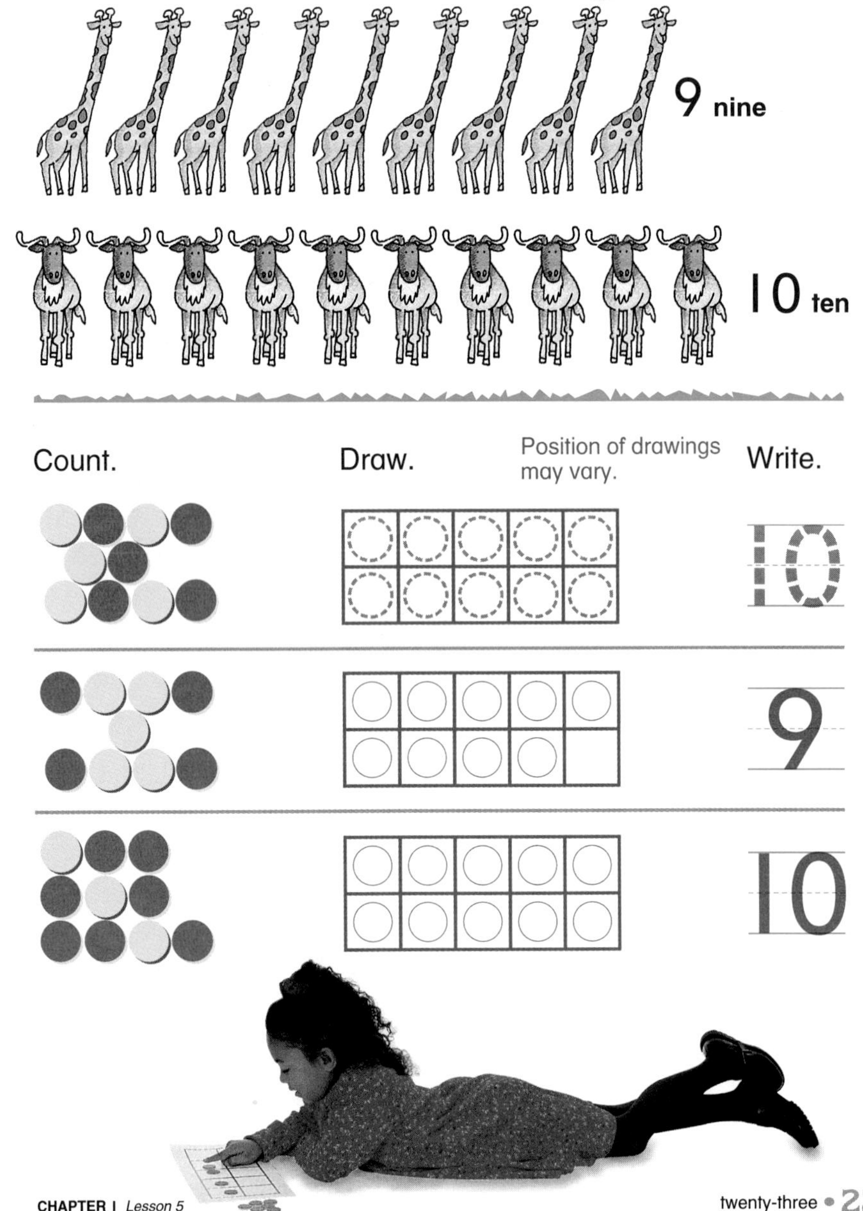

MEETING INDIVIDUAL NEEDS

INCLUSION

If any children are visually impaired, make 10-frames from egg cartons by cutting two cups off. Children will enjoy the variety, and individuals who need the accommodation will not feel conspicuous.

GIFTED AND TALENTED

Children who can write and identify the number of objects in a group to 10, can create their own number book, one number to a page, dictating a story involving each number.

ONGOING ASSESSMENT

Observation Checklist Determine if children can read, write, and represent numbers 0 to 10 by observing how smoothly they make the transition from 1-digit to 2-digit numbers.

Follow Up Children having difficulty can use counters and a 10-frame to show each number on page 23 before they draw and write it. Then assign **Reteach 7.**

If children demonstate understanding, assign **Extend 7.**

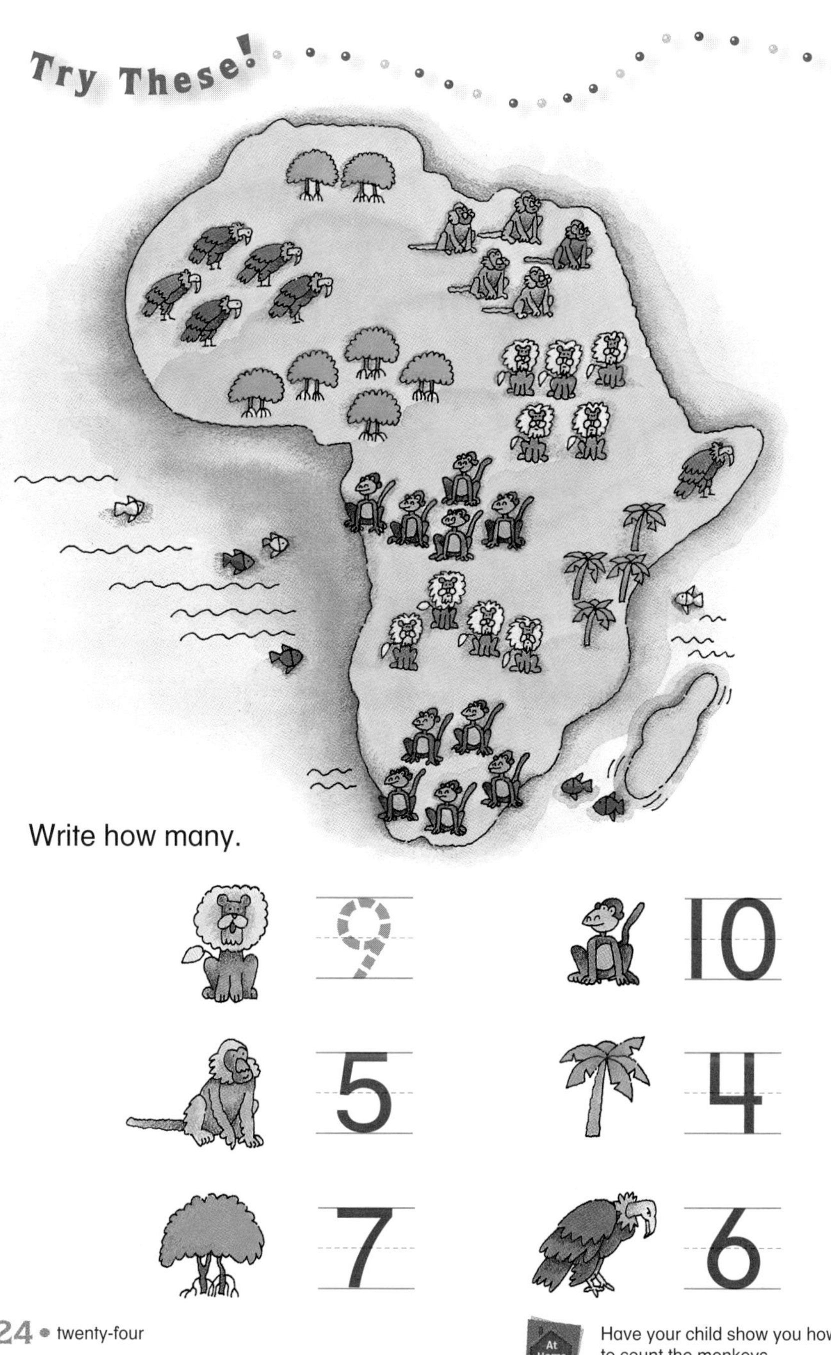

Try These!

Write how many.

9 (lions) 10 (monkeys)

5 (apes) 4 (palm trees)

7 (trees) 6 (vultures)

24 • twenty-four

At Home: Have your child show you how to count the monkeys.

Alternate Teaching Strategy

Materials large number cards, 0–10; per child: Numeral Writing Sheet (TA 6)

Prepare Write numbers 0 through 10 on large sheets of paper.

Play a game of Simon Says. Give directions such as:

- **Simon says hop 6 times.**
- **Simon says clap your hands 7 times and 1 more time.**
- **Simon says nod your head 10 times.**
- **Simon says wave your hand 5 times and 3 more times.**

After a period of play, display the number cards to show how many times to do an action.

Demonstrate how to write the numerals and have children practice, first by tracing the numerals in the air, then by writing on paper.

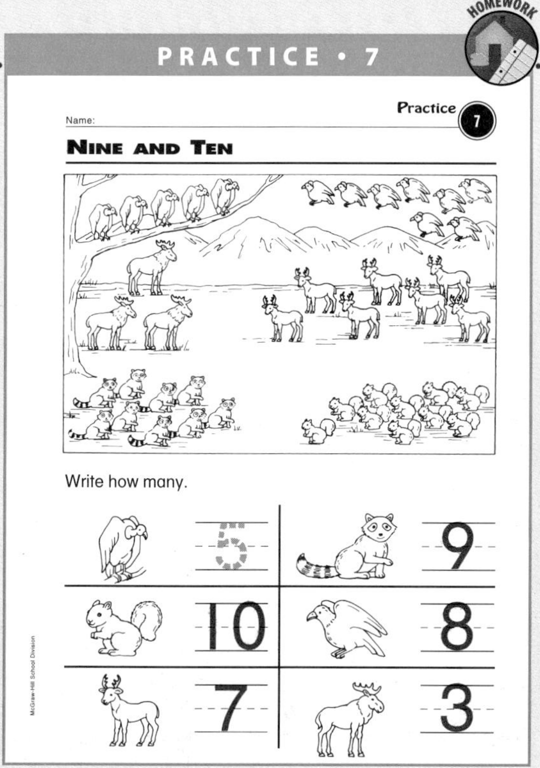

PRACTICE • 7

HOMEWORK

Name: Practice 7

Nine and Ten

Write how many.

(vulture)	5	(raccoon)	9
(squirrel)	10	(bird)	8
(deer)	7	(moose)	3

McGraw-Hill School Division

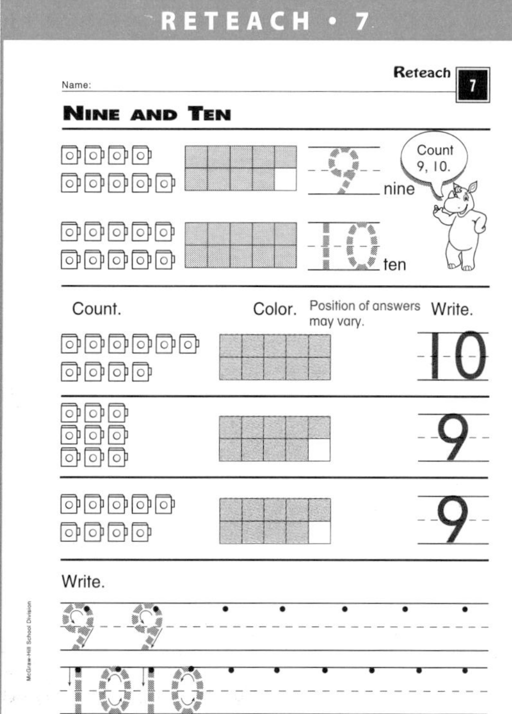

RETEACH • 7

Name: Reteach 7

Nine and Ten

9 nine

10 ten

Count. Color. Position of answers may vary. Write.

10

9

9

Write.

9 9

10 10

McGraw-Hill School Division

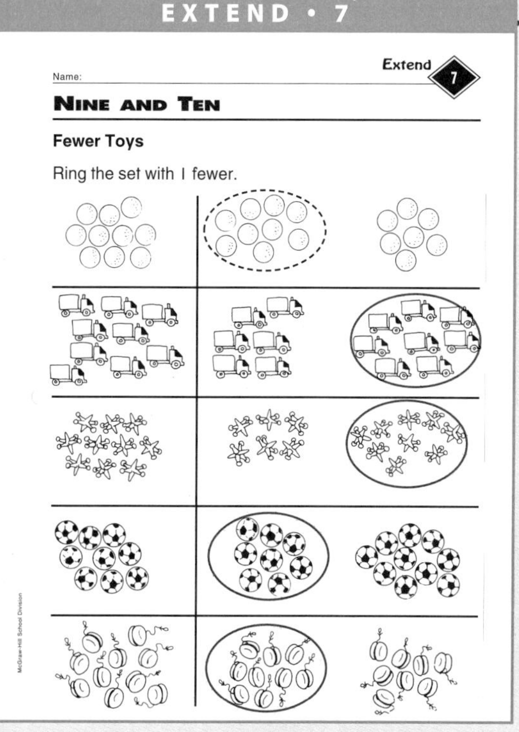

EXTEND • 7

Name: Extend 7

Nine and Ten

Fewer Toys

Ring the set with 1 fewer.

McGraw-Hill School Division

AT A GLANCE

PURPOSE Provide an opportunity for review and practice.

Materials per pair or group: blank spinner labeled 1–10 (TA 7); per child: 10 two-color counters, 10-frame (TA 4)

Using the Extra Practice

Page 25

Explain to children that they are going to play a mountain-climbing game and discuss the rules. Children play in pairs, each on his or her own page. Make sure they understand that they use one counter to cover each group of stones. If they spin a number they have already covered, play passes to the next player.

After children finish playing, ask:

- **Was it better to spin a 9 than a 3? Explain.** *[Possible answer: Only if the 9 on your game board was not covered and the 3 was.]*

Page 26

Have children complete the exercises independently or in pairs. Point out the starting point and the writing arrows. Have children practice tracing the numerals before they write them. You may want to have them show each number with counters and 10-frames before writing it. After they finish, ask them to mark the number they think looks the best in each row.

Using the Additional Practice

The section below provides additional practice that you may wish to write on the chalkboard or on a reproducible master.

Name ____________________

Extra Practice
Game!

Climb to the Top

You need 10 counters and a spinner.

Take turns.

- ▶ Spin.
- ▶ Put a counter on the dots for the number.
- ▶ Play until you cover all the spaces.

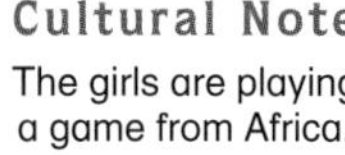

Cultural Note
The girls are playing a game from Africa.

ADDITIONAL PRACTICE

Count. Write the number.

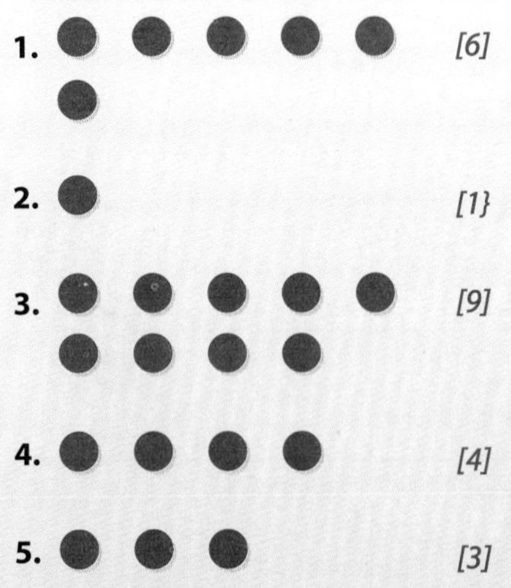

1. *[6]*
2. *[1]*
3. *[9]*
4. *[4]*
5. *[3]*
6. *[10]*
7. *[8]*
8. *[5]*
9. *[7]*
10. *[2]*

Write.

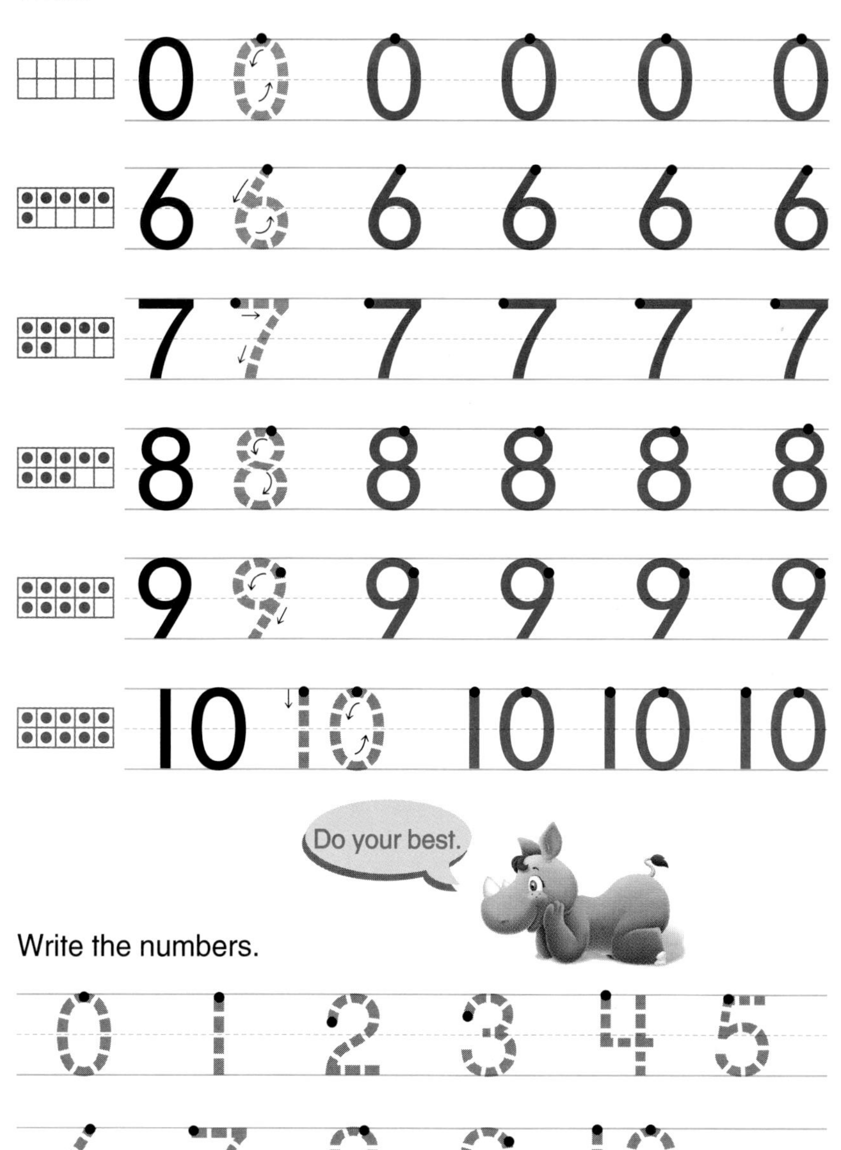

Write the numbers.

EXTRA PRACTICE — Pages 25–26

Developing Number Sense

This section provides another opportunity for students to reinforce number-sense concepts. You may want to write it on the chalkboard or on a reproducible master.

Use counters and a 10-frame. Write how many are missing.

1. 8 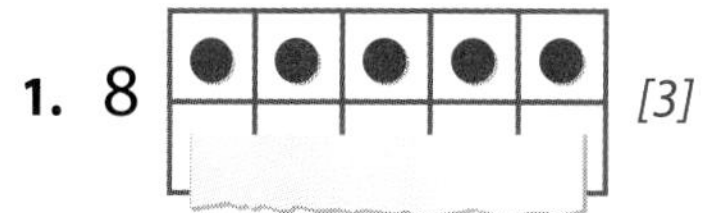 *[3]*

2. 7 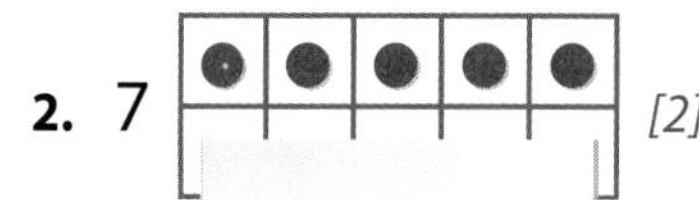 *[2]*

3. 9 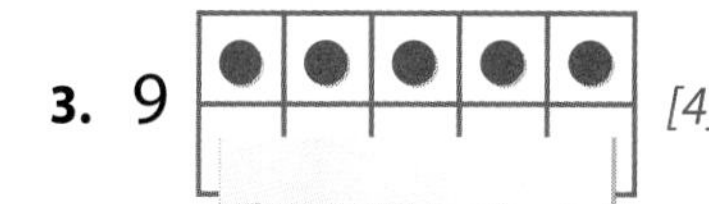 *[4]*

Draw counters. Show the number.

1. 8

2. 2 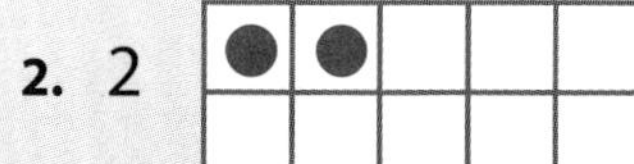

3. 7 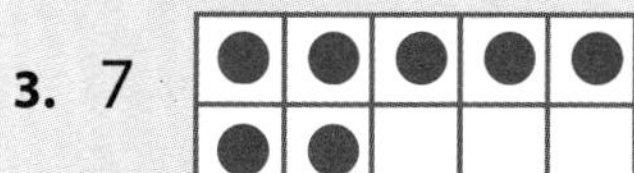

4. 10

5. 1 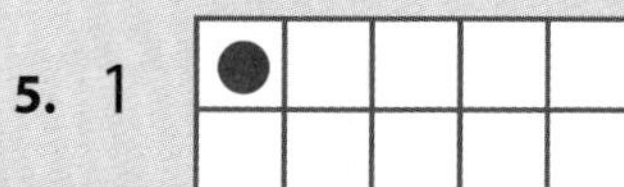

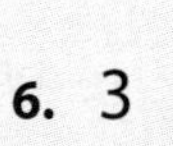 6. 3 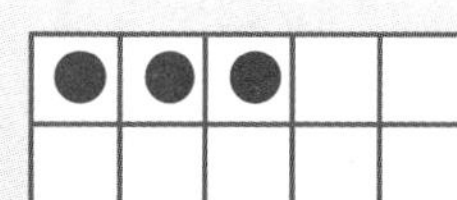

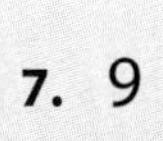 7. 9 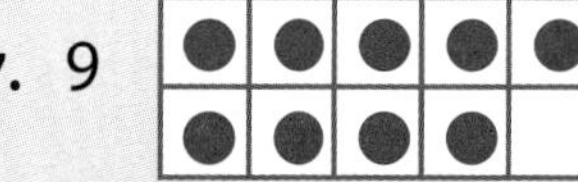

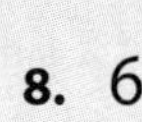 8. 6 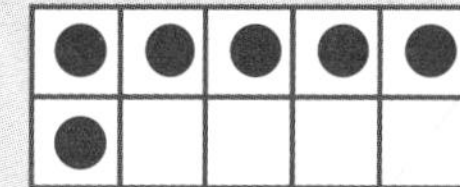

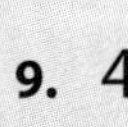 9. 4 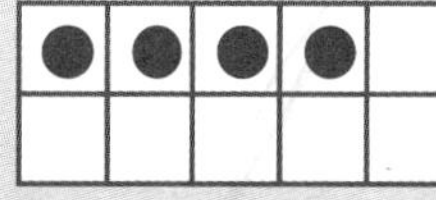

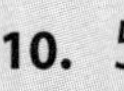 10. 5 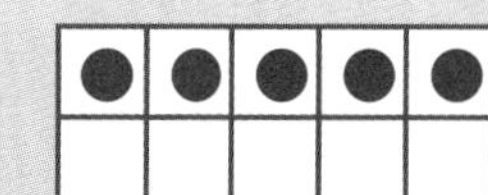

LESSON 1.6

Problem-Solving Strategy: Use a Pattern

OBJECTIVES Copy a pictorial pattern to solve a problem; find and correct errors in pictorial patterns.

Day 1 Problem-Solving Strategy: Use a Pattern

RESOURCE REMINDER
Math Center Cards 6
Practice 8, Reteach 8, Extend 8

SKILLS TRACE

GRADE K	• Explore using a pattern to solve problems. *(Chapter 6)*
GRADE 1	• Copy a pictorial pattern to solve problems. • Find and correct errors in pictorial patterns.
GRADE 2	• Solve problems by finding and using a pattern. *(Chapter 9)*

LESSON RESOURCES

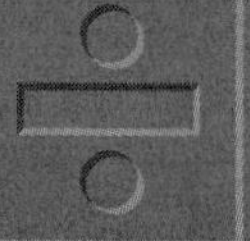

MANIPULATIVE WARM-UP

Cooperative Pairs — **Logical/Analytical**

OBJECTIVE Classify objects by color and shape.

Resources Jumbo Activity Book, page 4; Stickers, sheets 1 (round counters) and 3 (square counters)

Materials per pair: 10 two-color counters, 15 connecting cubes (5 red, 5 blue, 5 yellow), Workmat 3 (part-part-whole mat)

▶ Place a mixed group of counter and cube stickers on the bottom panel of Jumbo Activity Book page 4. Ask children to make comparisons.

▶ Have partners copy the stickers onto their workmats, using actual counters and cubes, and sort them into separate groups.

CONNECTION ACTIVITY

Whole Class — **Auditory/Linguistic**

OBJECTIVE Connect finding patterns with rhythms in poetry.

▶ Recite the rhyme, "One, Two, Buckle My Shoe," and ask children to say it with you. As you recite, clap out the rhythm. Help children see that the rhythm, or pattern, is two slow claps followed by three syncopated claps.

▶ Recite the rhyme again, stressing the rhyming words—*two* and *shoe, four* and *door,* and so on.

- **What other rhyming words do you hear?** *[Possible answer: There are words that sound the same, like two and shoe.]*
- **Which number words have rhyming words?** *[two, four, six, eight, ten]*
- **What are they?** *[shoe, door, sticks, straight, hen]*

▶ Recite the rhyme again with children. Ask them to clap when they say a number word and again when they say its rhyming word.

DAILY MATH

PREVIOUS DAY QUICK REVIEW

Write how many.

1. [3]

2. [8]

Problem of the Day • 6

Read aloud to children:

Miri has 9 blue beads and 7 red ones. Jamie has 10 blue beads and 6 red ones. Who has fewer red beads? *[Jamie]*

TECH LINK

MATH VAN

Tool You may wish to use the Counters tool with this lesson.

MATH FORUM

Idea I create a bulletin board display of color, number, and shape patterns. Then I encourage children to find examples to add to the display.

Visit our Resource Village at http://www.mhschool.com to see more of the Math Forum.

MATH CENTER

Practice

OBJECTIVE Make a pictorial pattern to solve a problem.

Materials per child: blank number cube, crayons, Math Center Recording Sheet (TA 38 optional)

Prepare Number the faces of a blank number cube 1, 1, 2, 2, 3, and 3.

Children roll two numbers and draw that many triangles and circles. Then children make a set of beads showing a pattern of triangles and circles.

PRACTICE ACTIVITY 6 — MATH CENTER, On Your Own

Patterning • Use a Pattern

YOU NEED

- Roll the [number cube].
- [crayon] that many △.
- Roll the [number cube] again.
- [crayon] that many ○.
- Copy the pattern.
- Use the pattern to [crayon] a set of beads.

Grade Level 1

McGraw-Hill School Division

Chapter 1, Lesson 6 — Number

NCTM Standards

- ✓ Problem Solving
- Communication
- ✓ Reasoning
- ✓ Connections

Problem Solving

OBJECTIVE Find and correct errors in pictorial patterns.

Materials per child: 24 shapes—8 circles, 8 squares, 8 triangles; 2 different colored crayons, Math Center Recording Sheet (TA 38 optional)

Prepare Cut out shapes from construction paper.

Children analyze geometric shape patterns and locate the error in each one. *[**1.** 3rd repeat: circle, triangle, triangle. **2.** 4th repeat: square, square, circle. **3.** 3rd repeat: triangle, square, triangle.]*

PROBLEM-SOLVING ACTIVITY 6 — MATH CENTER, On Your Own

Patterning • Find the Mistake

YOU NEED: [crayon], shapes

- Look at Pattern A. Find the mistake.
- Use ○ and △ to help.
- Draw the right pattern on your paper and [crayon] it. Ring the part you fixed.
- Do the same with Patterns B and C.

A ○△△○△△○△△△△△

B □□○□□○□□○□○○

C △□△△□△△□△△□□

Grade Level 1

McGraw-Hill School Division

Chapter 1, Lesson 6 — Number

NCTM Standards

- ✓ Problem Solving
- ✓ Communication
- ✓ Reasoning
- Connections

Problem-Solving Strategy: Use a Pattern

OBJECTIVES Children copy a pictorial pattern to solve a problem; children find and correct errors in pictorial patterns.

Materials per child: 10 two-color counters, crayons

1 Motivate — Cooperative Pairs

Materials per pair: 8 blue and 8 red connecting cubes

Use the blue and red cubes to make an AB pattern, such as blue, red, blue, red, blue, red. Ask children to describe the pattern.

- **What is the pattern?** *[blue, red]*
- **What color cube would be next?** *[blue]*

Have partners work together to copy the pattern, check it, and extend it.

Continue the activity, creating other patterns for children to identify, copy, and extend.

Then tell each partner to create a pattern cube train. Have partners switch trains and continue the patterns.

2 Develop

Page 27

Discuss the picture of the boy making a necklace. Explain to children that they will need to listen as you read each problem aloud, found on the reduced Student Book page. They will first copy the pattern with their counters, then copy it again by coloring the beads on the page.

CRITICAL THINKING
After children complete the page, ask:

- **How can you tell about each pattern using numbers?** *[Dembe's pattern: 1 red, 1 yellow; Cora's pattern: 2 red, 1 yellow; Grandma's pattern: 1 red, 2 yellow]*

Page 28

Try These Read the practice problems aloud.

In the last two problems, children create a pattern of their own and copy a partner's pattern.

3 Close

Check for Understanding by drawing the following pattern on the chalkboard and having children copy and extend it.

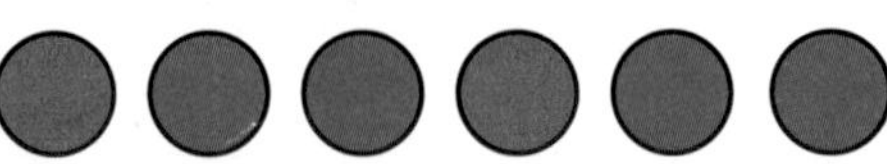

Name

Use a Pattern

You need 10 .

Listen to the problem.

Use counters to copy the pattern.
Color.

Dembe's beads

"Dembe made this pattern with red and yellow beads. How many red beads did he use? How many yellow beads did he use?" 5 red 5 yellow

Cora's beads

"Cora made this pattern. How many red beads did she use? How many yellow beads?" 6  3

Grandma's beads

"Grandma made this pattern. How many yellow beads did she use? How many red beads?" 6  4

MEETING INDIVIDUAL NEEDS

EARLY FINISHERS

Have children use counters to show what Jan's beads on page 28 would look like without the mistake. They can record their answers by drawing.

EXTRA SUPPORT

Use pattern blocks to create shape patterns for children who have difficulty distinguishing colors. Ask them to copy and extend AB patterns such as triangle, square, triangle, square, triangle, square.

ONGOING ASSESSMENT

Observation Checklist
Observe children at work to determine if they are able to solve problems and identify and describe number and color patterns.

Follow Up For children having difficulty identifying patterns, assign **Reteach 8.**

Children who are adept at identifying 2-color patterns may copy and extend 3-color patterns or patterns created with shapes and color.

Try These!

Listen to the problem.

Kim's beads

"Kim started this pattern.
Color to show which beads come next."

Len's beads

"Len started this pattern.
Color to show which beads come next."

Jan's beads

"Jan made this pattern. Draw a line to show where she made a mistake. What color bead is missing?"

Your beads

Patterns may vary.

Your partner's beads

Patterns may vary.

Have your child make a pattern and then tell about it.

Alternate Teaching Strategy

Materials blank 5-part spinner (TA 7); per pair: 20 blue and 20 yellow connecting cubes

Prepare: Label the sections on a blank 5-part spinner 1, 2, 1, 2, 1.

Spin two numbers and write them on the chalkboard. Show the first number with blue connecting cubes and the second number with yellow connecting cubes. For example, if you spin 2 and 1, show 2 blue cubes and 1 yellow cube. Then show how to continue the pattern with two more sets of 2 blue cubes and 1 yellow cube.

Have children copy the pattern, then extend it with another set of cubes.

- **How many blue cubes are there? How many yellow cubes?** *[8 blue; 4 yellow]*

Continue the activity, spinning first two and then three numbers. Have each child show the pattern with cubes. Pass the cube train around the group with each child adding a cube to extend the pattern.

For each pattern, make a train of your own, sometimes doing it incorrectly. Have children compare their trains with yours and identify the errors.

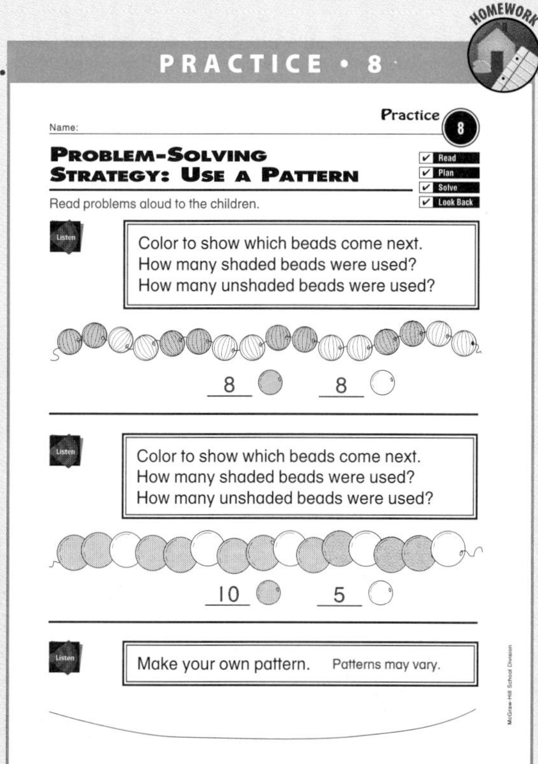

PRACTICE • 8

HOMEWORK

Name:

Practice 8

PROBLEM-SOLVING STRATEGY: USE A PATTERN

Read · Plan · Solve · Look Back

Read problems aloud to the children.

Color to show which beads come next.
How many shaded beads were used?
How many unshaded beads were used?

8 (shaded) 8 (unshaded)

Color to show which beads come next.
How many shaded beads were used?
How many unshaded beads were used?

10 (shaded) 5 (unshaded)

Make your own pattern. Patterns may vary.

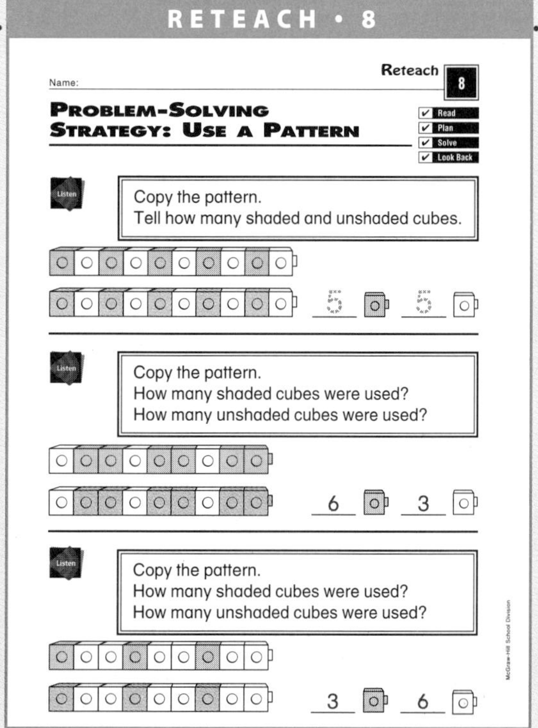

RETEACH • 8

Name:

Reteach 8

PROBLEM-SOLVING STRATEGY: USE A PATTERN

Read · Plan · Solve · Look Back

Copy the pattern.
Tell how many shaded and unshaded cubes.

5 (shaded) 5 (unshaded)

Copy the pattern.
How many shaded cubes were used?
How many unshaded cubes were used?

6 (shaded) 3 (unshaded)

Copy the pattern.
How many shaded cubes were used?
How many unshaded cubes were used?

3 (shaded) 6 (unshaded)

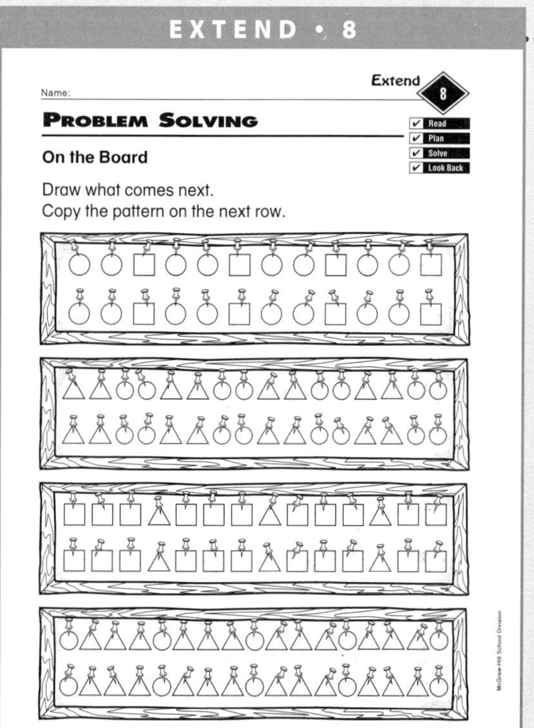

EXTEND • 8

Name:

Extend 8

PROBLEM SOLVING

Read · Plan · Solve · Look Back

On the Board

Draw what comes next.
Copy the pattern on the next row.

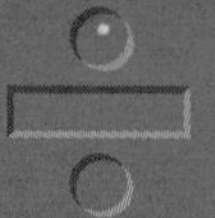

LESSON RESOURCES

LESSON 1.7

Order Numbers

OBJECTIVE Order numbers, to 10.

Day 1 Order Numbers

Teaching with Technology
See alternate computer lesson, pp. 30A–30B.

RESOURCE REMINDER
Math Center Cards 7
Practice 9, Reteach 9, Extend 9

SKILLS TRACE	
GRADE K	• Explore ordering numbers, to 10. *(Chapter 6)*
GRADE 1	• Order numbers, to 10.
GRADE 2	• Order numbers, to 100. *(Chapter 3)*

WARM-UP

Whole Class — **Visual/Spatial**

OBJECTIVE Explore how numbers are ordered.

Materials analog clock; computer keyboard or telephone; classroom items with numbers, such as calculators, rulers

▶ Ask children to count from 0 to 10 and, as they count, write the numerals in order on the chalkboard. Point to an analog clock and show how the numbers are read in a clockwise direction.

- **Are these numbers in the same order as the ones you counted?** *[Yes.]*

▶ Display a telephone or a computer keyboard, and ask whether the order of the numbers is the same or different from the counting order.

- **How does knowing the order of the numbers help you to use this?** *[You know where to find the numbers, so you can find them faster.]*

▶ Have children in groups examine other classroom items to determine whether the order of the numbers is the same as the counting order.

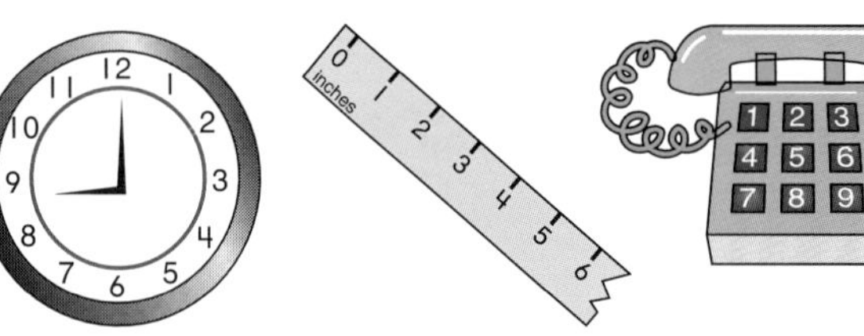

CONNECTION ACTIVITY

Whole Class — **Kinesthetic**

OBJECTIVE Connect a launch countdown with reverse number order.

▶ Invite children who have seen a space shuttle liftoff in real life or on television to describe their experiences. Do the countdown as a group: *ten, nine, eight, seven, six, five, four, three, two, one, liftoff!*

- **How is that different from the way you usually count?** *[It's backward.]*

▶ Group two or three children in a clear area of the room. Have the rest of the class do the counting. The group acts out a space shuttle liftoff by crouching down, then jumping up when they hear "liftoff!"

▶ Repeat with different groups until each child who wants to has had a chance to act it out.

DAILY MATH

PREVIOUS DAY QUICK REVIEW

Draw dots to show how many.

1. eight *[8 dots]*
2. seven *[7 dots]*
3. ten *[10 dots]*
4. nine *[9 dots]*

Problem of the Day • 7

Read aloud to children:

Five children are standing in line.
Jan is behind Bill and Allie.
Sara is in front of Bill, and Tom is behind Jan.
Who is first in line? *[Sara]*

TECH LINK

MATH VAN

Activity You may wish to use the *Camel Roundup* activity to teach this lesson.

MATH FORUM

Idea I keep on hand simple connect-the-dots puzzles to reinforce the idea of numbers in order.

Visit our Resource Village at http://www.mhschool.com to see more of the Math Forum.

MATH CENTER

Practice

OBJECTIVE Order numbers 0–10.

Materials per pair: number line (TA 11), 2 two-color counters

One child closes his or her eyes while the other hides a number with a counter. The first child identifies the hidden number. They repeat, hiding two numbers. *[Activity is self-checking when counter is removed from number line.]*

Problem Solving

OBJECTIVE Count backward, numbers 0–10.

Materials per child: number cards 0–10 (TA 9), 11 counters, sheet with numbered boxes

Prepare Create a sheet with 11 boxes numbered backwards from 10 to 0. Write numbers so they can be hidden by a counter.

Children can check each other by removing the counter and checking that the number and card match.

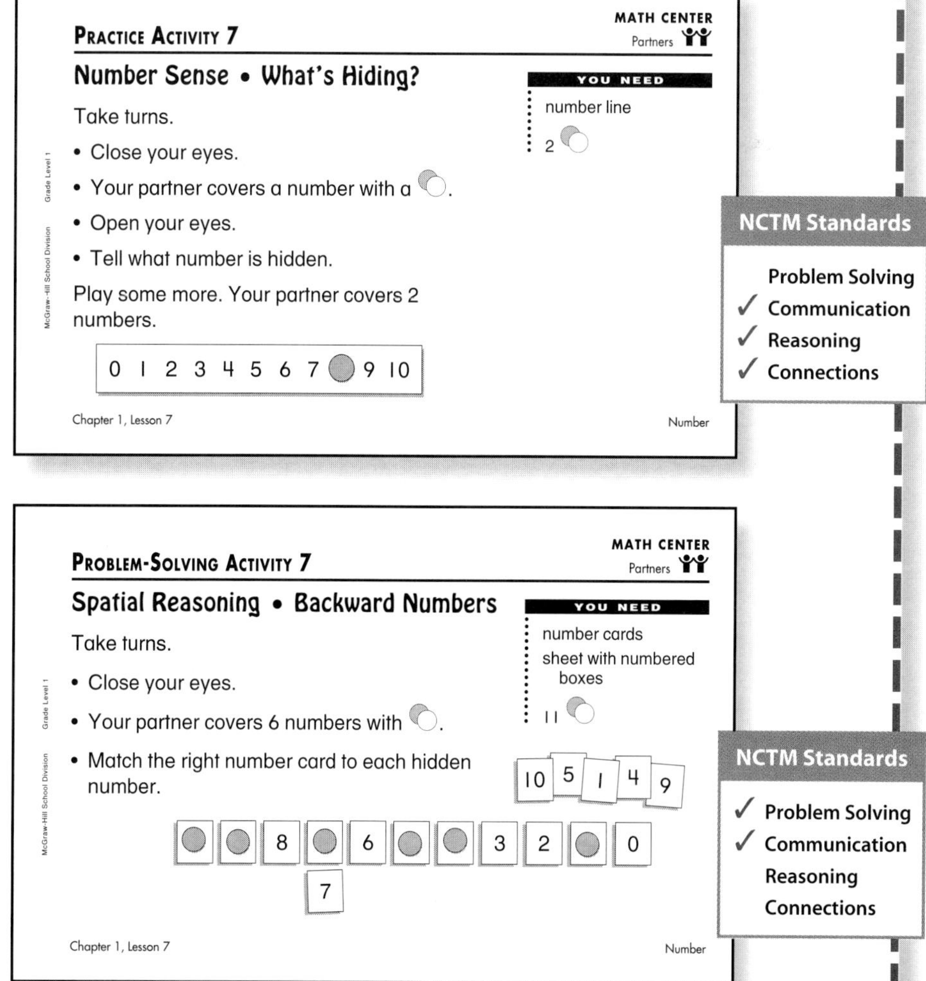

PRACTICE ACTIVITY 7 — MATH CENTER, Partners

Number Sense • What's Hiding?

YOU NEED: number line, 2 counters

Take turns.

- Close your eyes.
- Your partner covers a number with a counter.
- Open your eyes.
- Tell what number is hidden.

Play some more. Your partner covers 2 numbers.

0 1 2 3 4 5 6 7 ● 9 10

Chapter 1, Lesson 7 — Number

NCTM Standards
- Problem Solving
- ✓ Communication
- ✓ Reasoning
- ✓ Connections

PROBLEM-SOLVING ACTIVITY 7 — MATH CENTER, Partners

Spatial Reasoning • Backward Numbers

YOU NEED: number cards, sheet with numbered boxes, 11 counters

Take turns.

- Close your eyes.
- Your partner covers 6 numbers with counters.
- Match the right number card to each hidden number.

10 5 1 4 9

● ● 8 ● 6 ● ● 3 2 ● 0

7

Chapter 1, Lesson 7 — Number

NCTM Standards
- ✓ Problem Solving
- ✓ Communication
- Reasoning
- Connections

Lesson 1.7

DAY 1

Order Numbers

OBJECTIVE Children order numbers, to 10.

1 Motivate — Whole Class

Draw a line and 11 tic marks for a number line 0–10 on the chalkboard. Ask children to count from 0 to 10. As they count, write the numbers on the number line.

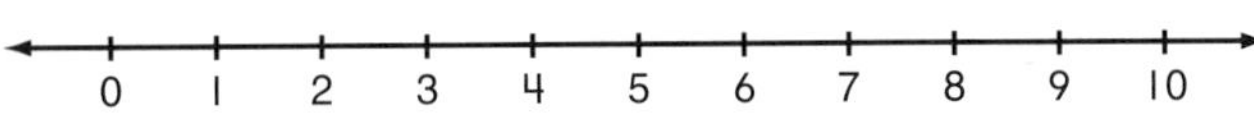

Have children take turns covering a number on the number line while others name the missing number.

Use the number line to introduce *before, after,* and *between*. Call on volunteers to demonstrate at the chalkboard.

- **Point to 6 on your number line. What number is after 6?** *[7]* **Before 6?** *[5]*
- **Put one finger on 7 and another finger on 9. What number is between 7 and 9?** *[8]*

2 Develop

Page 29

Explain that the 5- and 10-frames on this page are towers. If need be, have children turn their papers so they can see the frames in the familiar position. Have children count forward and backward as they point to the numbers on the line at the top of the page.

CRITICAL THINKING

After children complete the page, ask:

- **How old are you? How old will you be next year? How old were you last year?** *[Possible answers: 6; 7; 5]*

Page 30

Try These Assign the practice exercises.

Read the directions aloud for each set of exercises.

3 Close

Check for Understanding by writing the numerals 1, 4, 3, 0, 5, 2 on the chalkboard and asking children to write them in order.

Mixed Review Children read the number words and write the numerals.

Name ____________ **Order Numbers**

0 1 2 3 4 5 6 7 8 9 10

Write the missing number.

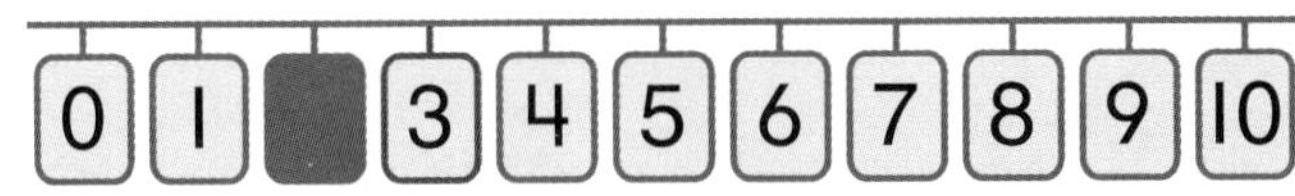

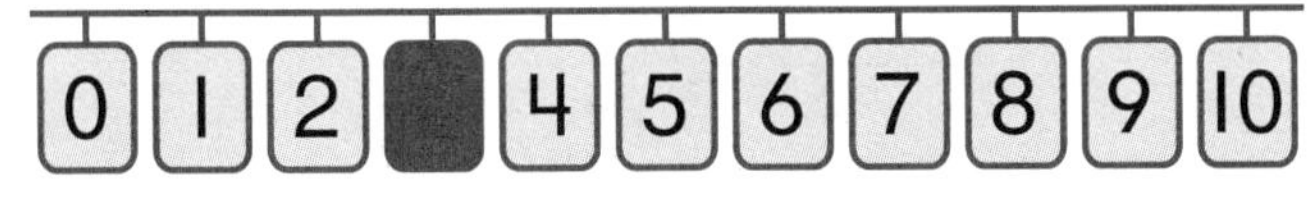

MEETING INDIVIDUAL NEEDS

EARLY FINISHERS

Help pairs of children make a number line on construction paper showing numerals and number words for 0 to 10.

EXTRA SUPPORT

Have children make cube trains for each number 1 to 10, and place the trains in size order on paper. Children can count the cubes in each train and write the number below the train.

ONGOING ASSESSMENT

Observation Checklist Observe children at work to determine if they can order numbers 0 to 10.

Follow Up Children having difficulty writing numbers in reverse order can use a 10-frame and counters to show 10, and then remove counters one at a time, writing each number represented. You may also assign **Reteach 9.**

For children who understand the concept of the order of numbers, assign **Extend 9.**

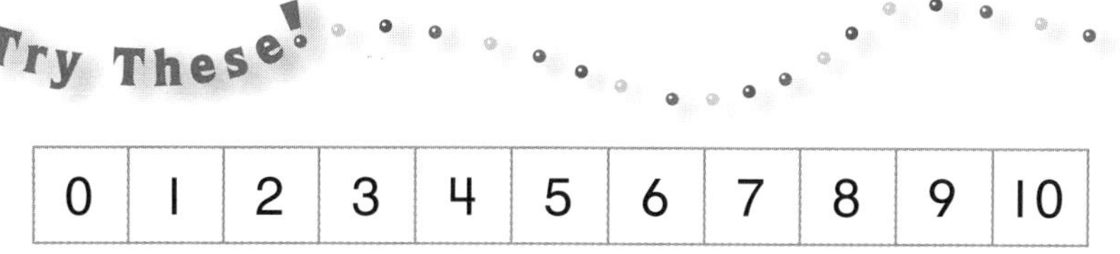

Write the numbers in order.

0 1 2 3 4 5

6 7 8 9 10

Count backward and write the numbers.

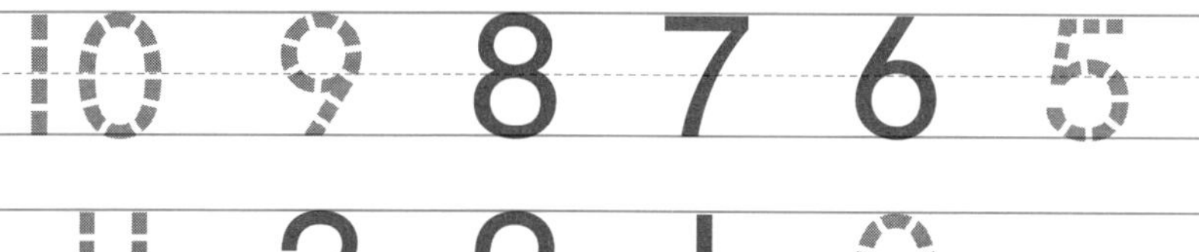

10 9 8 7 6 5

4 3 2 1 0

Mixed Review

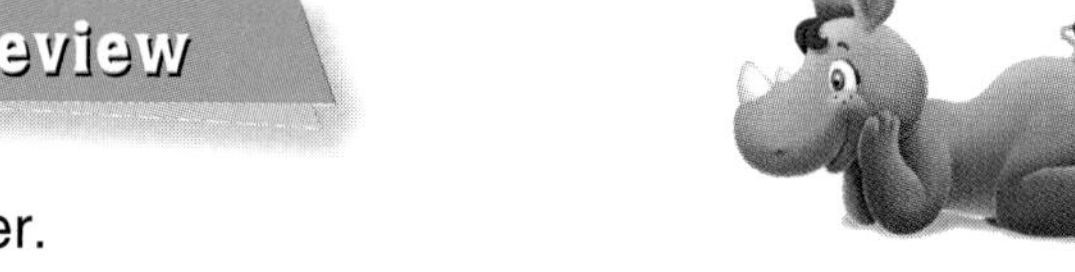

Write the number.

zero	one	two	three	four	five
0	1	2	3	4	5

six	seven	eight	nine	ten
6	7	8	9	10

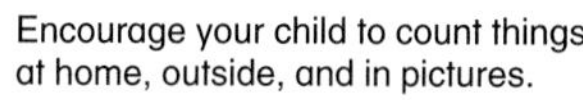

At Home: Encourage your child to count things at home, outside, and in pictures.

Alternate Teaching Strategy

Materials 11 sheets of drawing paper

Prepare Make a set of number cards for 0 to 10. On each card, write the numeral and draw the matching 10-frame.

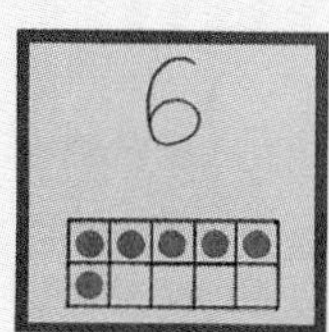

Write the numbers 0 to 10 in order on the chalkboard. Review the position words *after, before,* and *between.*

Ask eleven children to stand in a line. Mix up the number cards and give one to each child. Ask children at their seats to give directions on how the children should move so that the numbers will be in the right order. Encourage them to use *after, before,* and *between* in their directions.

Allow children time to evaluate periodically whether the cards are in order. At those points, have children standing in line "count off" to check.

Ask other volunteers to hold the cards and repeat the activity.

PRACTICE • 9

RETEACH • 9

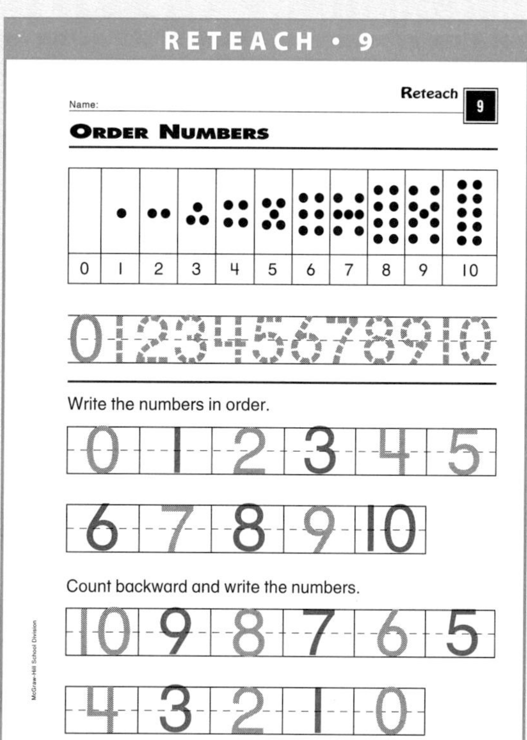

EXTEND • 9

Teaching With Technology

Order Numbers

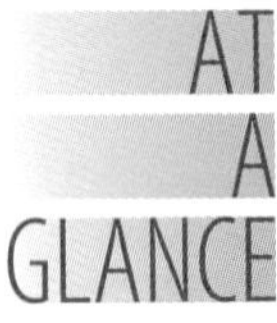

AT A GLANCE

OBJECTIVE Children use counters to count, read, write, and order numbers up to 10.

Resource Math Van Activity: *Camel Roundup*

SET UP

Launch the ***Math Van*** program. Click the right arrow to locate Activity 1, *Camel Roundup*. After listening to the activity's description, click *Start*.

Using the Math Van Activity

1 Getting Started Allow children to practice stamping, and moving the counters on the Open Mat within the Counters tool.

2 Practice and Apply Children apply their knowledge of *one more* to stamp 6 camels, then 7, 8, 9, and finally 10 camels. They count the camels and type the number in the student input box.

3 Close Have children use the pictures from their Math Journal to practice counting in order. Have them discuss their work with you, each other, or the class.

Extend Children can do the activity with *one less*. Have children work with partners and take turns. The first child stamps a set of objects on the screen. The second child erases one object and then types the number of objects in the Student Input box.

TIPS FOR TOOLS

Reassure any children who appear nervous about making mistakes at the computer. Show them how they can use the Eraser tool to correct mistakes.

SCREEN 1

Children listen to a description of the *Camel Roundup* activity.

SCREEN 2

The activity opens with a set of 5 camels on the Open Mat.

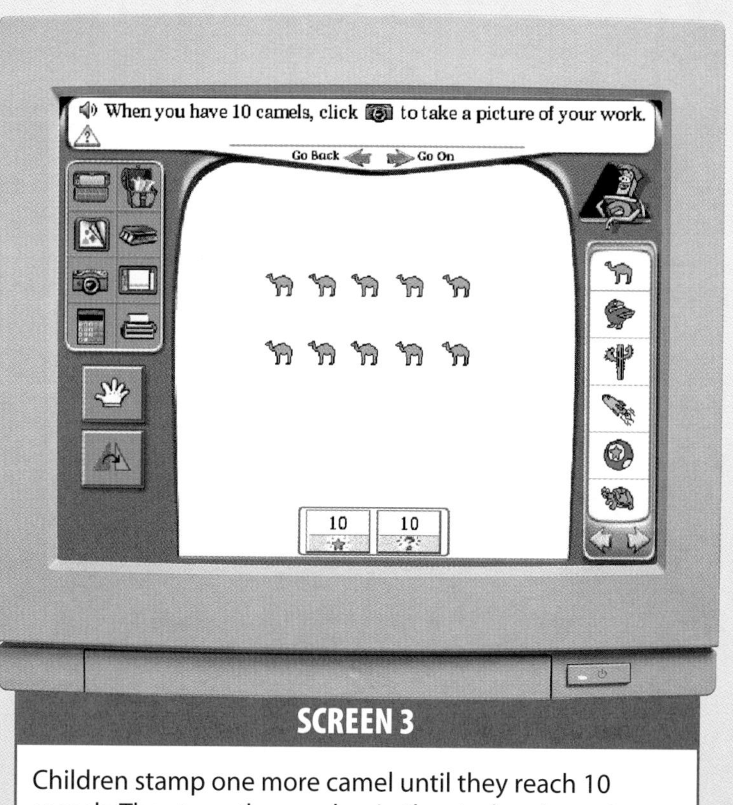

SCREEN 3

Children stamp one more camel until they reach 10 camels. They type the number in the student input box.

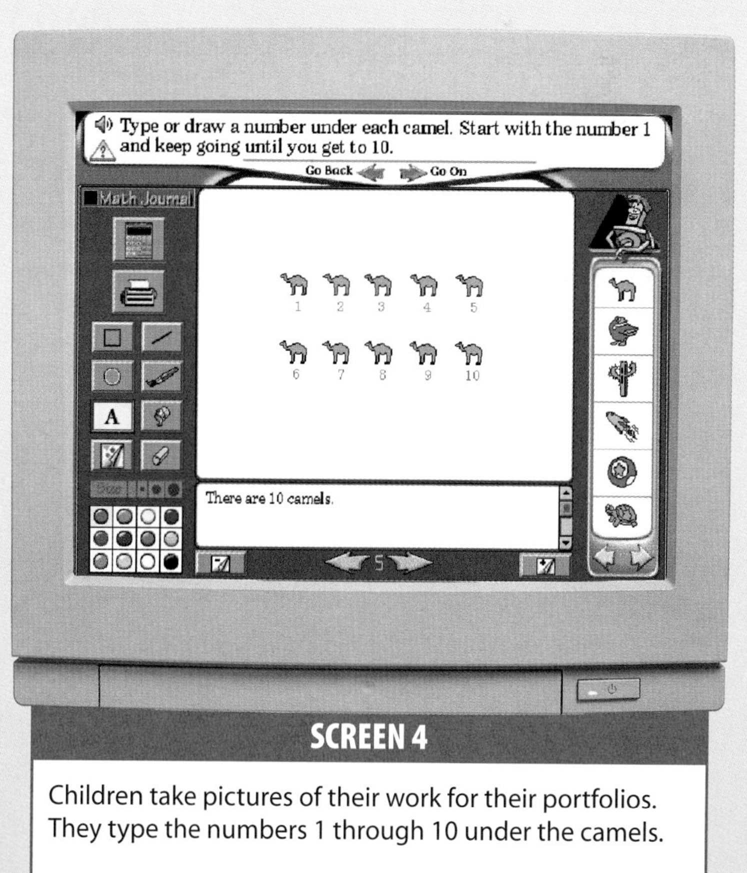

SCREEN 4

Children take pictures of their work for their portfolios. They type the numbers 1 through 10 under the camels.

EXPLORE ACTIVITY

Count Pennies

OBJECTIVES Count sets of pennies, to 10; identify the value of a penny.

Day 1 Explore Activity: Count Pennies

RESOURCE REMINDER
Math Center Cards 8
Practice 10, Reteach 10, Extend 10

SKILLS TRACE	
GRADE K	• Explore counting sets of pennies, to 10. *(Chapter 9)* • Explore identifying the value of a penny. *(Chapter 9)*
GRADE 1	• Explore counting sets of pennies, to 10. • Explore identifying the value of a penny.
GRADE 2	• Identify the value of a penny, nickel, and dime. *(Chapter 4)* • Find the value of a mixed set of coins. *(Chapter 4)*

LESSON RESOURCES

MANIPULATIVE WARM-UP

Cooperative Pairs — **Logical/Analytical**

OBJECTIVE Explore sorting coins.

Materials per pair: play money—pennies, nickels, dimes, and quarters

▶ Give each pair a handful of coins including pennies, nickels, dimes, and quarters. Children sort the coins, creating as many groups as they like.

▶ Pairs display their groups and describe their sorting rules.

▶ Each pair sorts the coins again, this time into two groups, using a different sorting rule. Pairs display their groups. Children guess each others' sorting rules.

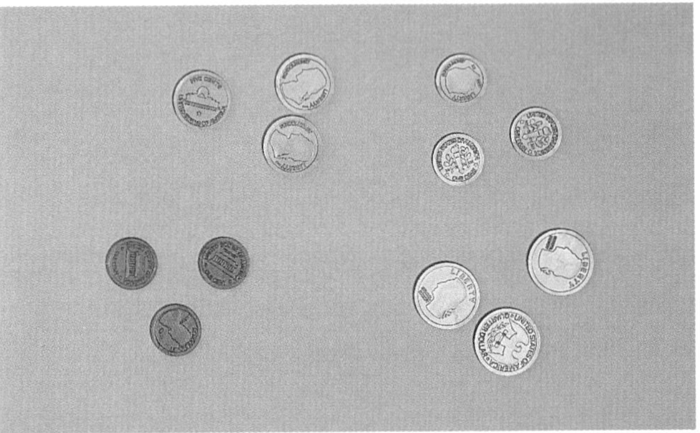

CONNECTION ACTIVITY

Cooperative Pairs — **Visual/Spatial**

OBJECTIVE Connect counting objects with counting money.

Materials per pair: 15 pennies, paper cup

▶ To help children notice the differences between the two sides of a penny, have partners place their pennies in a cup, turn the cup over, and sort the pennies into two groups according to whether they are heads or tails.

▶ Each partner counts and writes the number of pennies in one of the groups.

▶ Partners repeat the activity two more times. Ask volunteers to describe the groups of pennies they counted in the last round. Encourage them to use words they've learned, such as *more* and *fewer*.

DAILY MATH

PREVIOUS DAY QUICK REVIEW

Write the missing number.

1. 7, 8, ___, 10 *[9]*
2. 5, 4, ___, 2 *[3]*
3. 0, ___, 2, 3 *[1]*
4. 2, 3, 4, ___ *[5]*

Problem of the Day • 8

Read aloud to children:

Alex is 6 years old.
How old was he last year?
How old will he be next year?
[5 years old; 7 years old]

TECH LINK

MATH VAN

Tool You may wish to use the Money Models tool with this lesson.

MATH FORUM

Multi-Age Classes Children working at a higher level may show the amounts on page 32 in as many ways as they can, using nickels and dimes in addition to pennies.

Visit our Resource Village at http://www.mhschool.com to see more of the Math Forum.

MATH CENTER

Practice

OBJECTIVE Count pennies.

Materials per child: 10 pennies, crayon, Math Center Recording Sheet (TA 38 optional)

Children pick any number of pennies between 1 and 10, draw each penny, and write the number.
[Check that the drawing matches the number of pennies.]

PRACTICE ACTIVITY 8 — MATH CENTER, On Your Own

Number Sense • Can You Buy It?

YOU NEED: 10 pennies, crayon

- Take some pennies.
- Draw the pennies.
- Write how much.

6¢

Grade Level 1 — McGraw-Hill School Division

Chapter 1, Lesson 8 — Number

NCTM Standards

Problem Solving
✓ Communication
Reasoning
✓ Connections

Problem Solving

OBJECTIVE Compare the number of heads and tails of 10 pennies.

Materials per pair: 1 penny, crayon, Math Center Recording Sheet (TA 38 optional)

Generate, record, and compare the number of heads and tails for sets of 10 pennies. *[Answers may vary. Possible answer: Partner A has 6 heads, 4 tails; Partner B has 3 heads, 7 tails; Partner A has more heads and Partner B has more tails.]*

PROBLEM-SOLVING ACTIVITY 8 — MATH CENTER, Partners

Using Data • (heads) or (tails)?

YOU NEED: penny, crayon

Take turns.

- Flip a penny 10 times and (crayon) what happens.

1. Who has more (heads)?
   Ring who has more.
2. Who has more (tails)?
   Ring who has more.

Do it again.

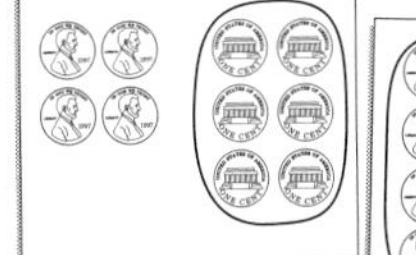
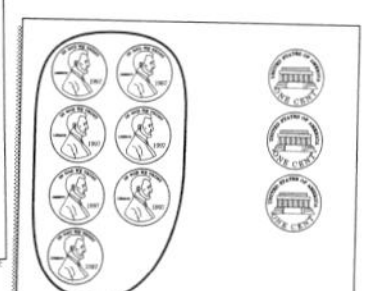

Grade Level 1 — McGraw-Hill School Division

Chapter 1, Lesson 8 — Number

NCTM Standards

✓ Problem Solving
✓ Communication
✓ Reasoning
Connections

Lesson 1.8

DAY 1

EXPLORE ACTIVITY

Count Pennies

OBJECTIVES Children explore counting sets of pennies, to 10; children identify the value of a penny.

Materials per child: 5 pennies

1 Motivate — Whole Class

Materials 10 pennies

Introduce *penny* by displaying the coin and telling children that when you have more than one penny, you say *pennies.* Explain that the penny bears the likeness of President Abraham Lincoln, who was president from 1861 to 1865. Tell children the side showing Lincoln's head is the *heads* side; the side showing the Lincoln Memorial is the *tails* side.

Identify the value of one penny as one *cent;* two pennies as two *cents;* three pennies as three *cents,* and so on.

- **If I have 10 pennies, how many cents do I have?** *[10 cents]*

Show how amounts are written using ¢ instead of writing *pennies* or *cents.*

2 Develop

Page 31

Working Together Make sure children understand that they combine their groups of coins and then count, draw, and write how many cents. Partners use the pocket workmat on one of their pages and record answers on their individual pages.

Critical Thinking
After children have completed the page, ask:

- **If you have 5 cents, how many pennies do you have?** *[5 pennies]*

Page 32

Try These Assign the practice problems.

Cultural Connection Tell children that the pennies shown are from Singapore and Bermuda. Point out these countries on a globe or a world map. Ask children to describe different ways that people store pennies.

3 Close

Check for Understanding by displaying different numbers of pennies and having children write their values. Have children read what they have written.

Name

Explore Activity
Count Pennies

I penny
I¢
I cent

2 pennies
2¢
2 cents

Working Together

You need (penny).

- You show some (penny).
- Your partner shows some (penny).
- Draw all the (penny). Amounts may vary.
- Write how many cents.

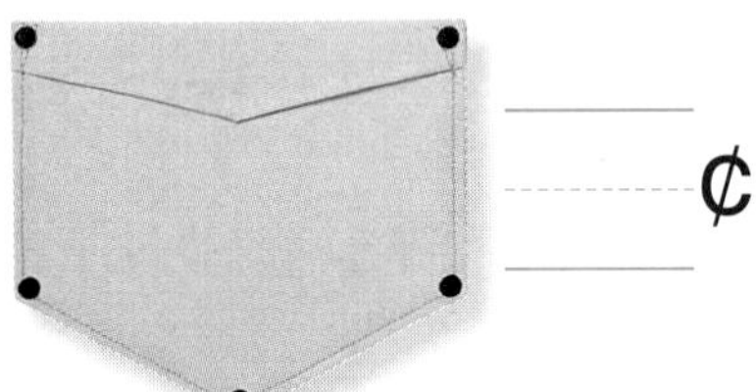
_____ ¢

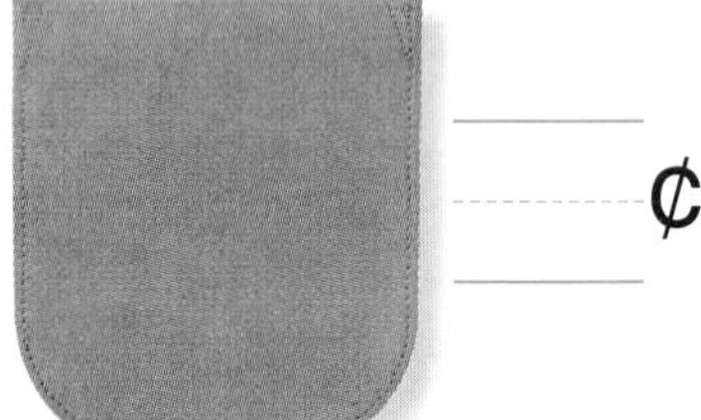
_____ ¢

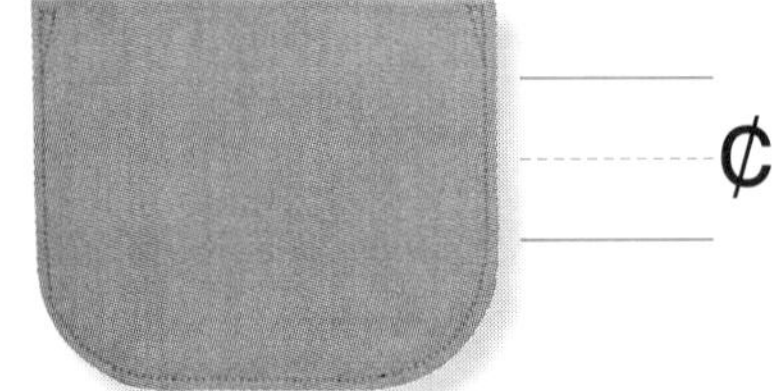
_____ ¢

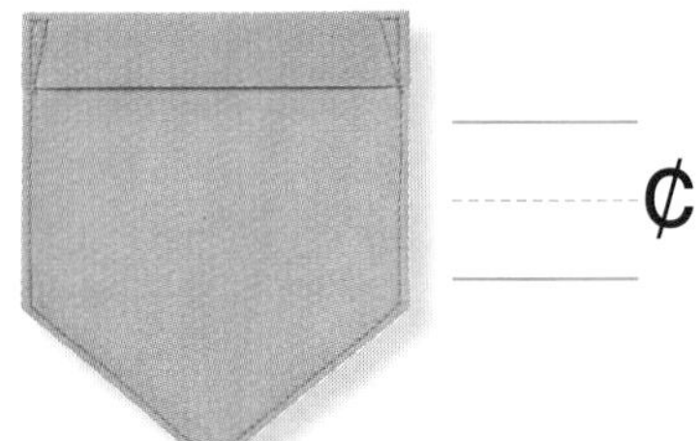
_____ ¢

MEETING INDIVIDUAL NEEDS

EARLY FINISHERS

Children who finish early can examine other coins and find out what is pictured on the heads and tails sides.

EXTRA SUPPORT

Explain to children that a penny is 1 cent, whether it shows heads or tails. Give children 10 pennies each, and have them show 5 heads and 5 tails. Then, have children count all the pennies to show 10 cents.

ONGOING ASSESSMENT

Observation Checklist Determine children's ability to identify the number of objects or pennies in a group to 10 by observing them as they complete the activity.

Follow Up For children having difficulty counting groups of pennies, assign **Reteach 10.**

For children who understand counting pennies, have them show each amount on page 32, trade 5 pennies for 1 nickel, and draw the new set of coins. You may also assign **Extend 10.**

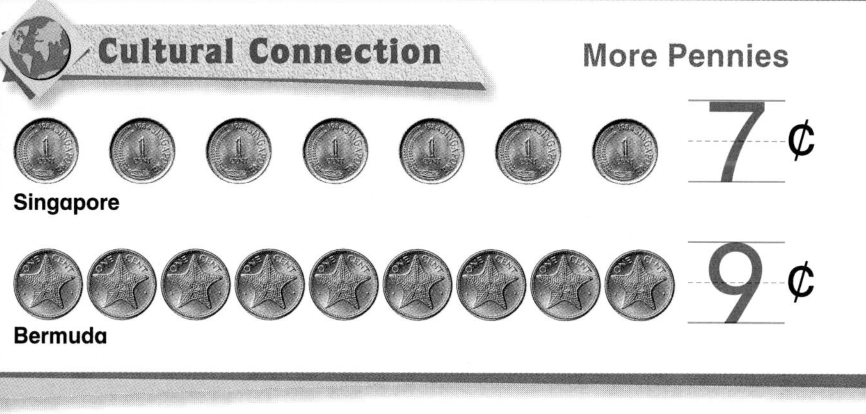

At Home: Hold out from 1 to 10 pennies. Ask your child to count how many cents you have in your hand.

Alternate Teaching Strategy

Materials per group: 50 pennies; blank number cube

Prepare Label three sides of the blank number cube *1*, and label three sides *2*.

Display one or more pennies and review the terms *penny* and *pennies*. Explain that one penny has a value of one *cent;* two pennies, two *cents;* three pennies, three *cents,* and so on. Demonstrate how to write and read money amounts using the cents symbol (¢).

Groups of children take turns rolling the number cube and taking pennies to match the number. On each turn they tell and record how many pennies they have in all and how many cents that is. Continue the activity until one player reaches 10¢.

PRACTICE • 10

RETEACH • 10

EXTEND • 10

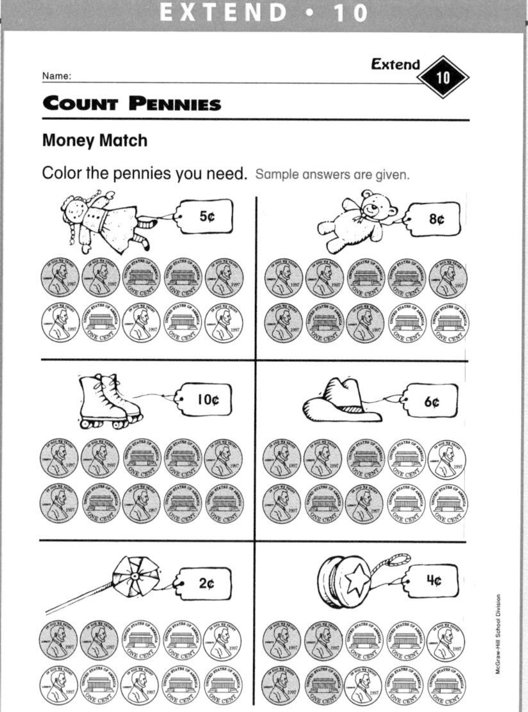

LESSON 1.9

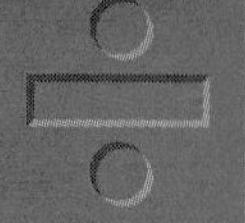

LESSON RESOURCES

Problem Solvers at Work: Number Patterns

OBJECTIVE Write and solve problems by using different representations for a pattern.

Day 1 Problem Solvers at Work: Number Patterns

RESOURCE REMINDER
Math Center Cards 9
Practice 11, Reteach 11, Extend 11

SKILLS TRACE

GRADE K	• Solve problems by making a pattern. *(Chapter 6)*
GRADE 1	• Formulate and solve problems by using different representations for a pattern.
GRADE 2	• Formulate and solve problems by using a pattern. *(Chapter 9)*

WARM-UP

Cooperative Pairs — **Musical**

OBJECTIVE Explore describing patterns with numbers.

Materials classroom instruments (triangles, shakers, cymbals, drums)

▶ Demonstrate a pattern consisting of two actions, such as banging a drum twice and striking a triangle once. Continue the pattern and invite children to join you when they have identified it. Ask them to count the actions as they do them. *[one, two, one; one, two, one].*

- **How many drumbeats? How many chimes?** *[2; 1]*

▶ Change to a 1, 3 pattern (one drumbeat, three chimes). Again, have children copy and count.

- **How many drumbeats? How many chimes?** *[1; 3]*

▶ Have pairs of children create their own two-action patterns. Invite them to demonstrate the patterns for the other children to copy and count. Have children identify the number pattern for each action pattern demonstrated.

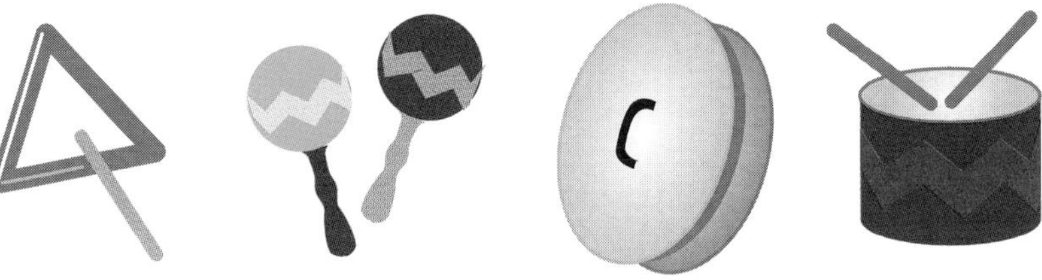

ART

CONNECTION ACTIVITY

Cooperative Pairs — **Visual/Spatial**

OBJECTIVE Connect patterns and art.

Materials per pair: number cube, strips of paper, paint (2 colors), sponges or inkpads (2 colors), rubber stamps

▶ Each child chooses a stamp or sponge. Partners take turns rolling the number cube to see how many imprints to make of the first color. They make the imprints in a row on their paper. Each child rolls again, and makes imprints for the number shown in the second color, continuing the row.

▶ Children repeat the pattern. Have pairs display their designs, and have other pairs tell which numbers they rolled.

DAILY MATH

PREVIOUS DAY QUICK REVIEW

How many cents?

1. 6 pennies *[6¢]*
2. 2 pennies *[2¢]*
3. 10 pennies *[10¢]*
4. 8 pennies *[8¢]*

Problem of the Day • 9

Read aloud to children:

Jake has 7 bananas.
He gets 1 more.
Tim has 9 bananas.
Who has more bananas? *[Tim]*

TECH LINK

MATH VAN

Tool You may wish to use the Counters tool with this lesson.

MATH FORUM

Management Tip I use plastic margarine tubs to store manipulatives. Each is identified by a picture on the lid. I have volunteers sort and put away the items at the end of the day.

Visit our Resource Village at http://www.mhschool.com to see more of the Math Forum.

MATH CENTER

Practice

OBJECTIVE Solve a problem by using numerals to represent a pattern.

Materials per child: crayon, Math Center Recording Sheet (TA 38 optional)

Children choose a number pattern and draw a representation of it.

Make sure children understand the connection between the numerals and the objects they draw. *[Check children's drawing of number pattern.]*

Problem Solving

OBJECTIVE Solve problems by drawing pictorial representations for number patterns.

Materials per child: sheet with number pattern, crayons; have available: pattern blocks

Prepare per child: sheet with a number pattern similar to the one shown on the card.

Children may use pattern blocks as an intermediate step. *[Sample answers given. Number pattern 2, 1, 2, 1, should show color pattern of 1 red, 2 blue, and so on. Second pattern should show shape pattern.]*

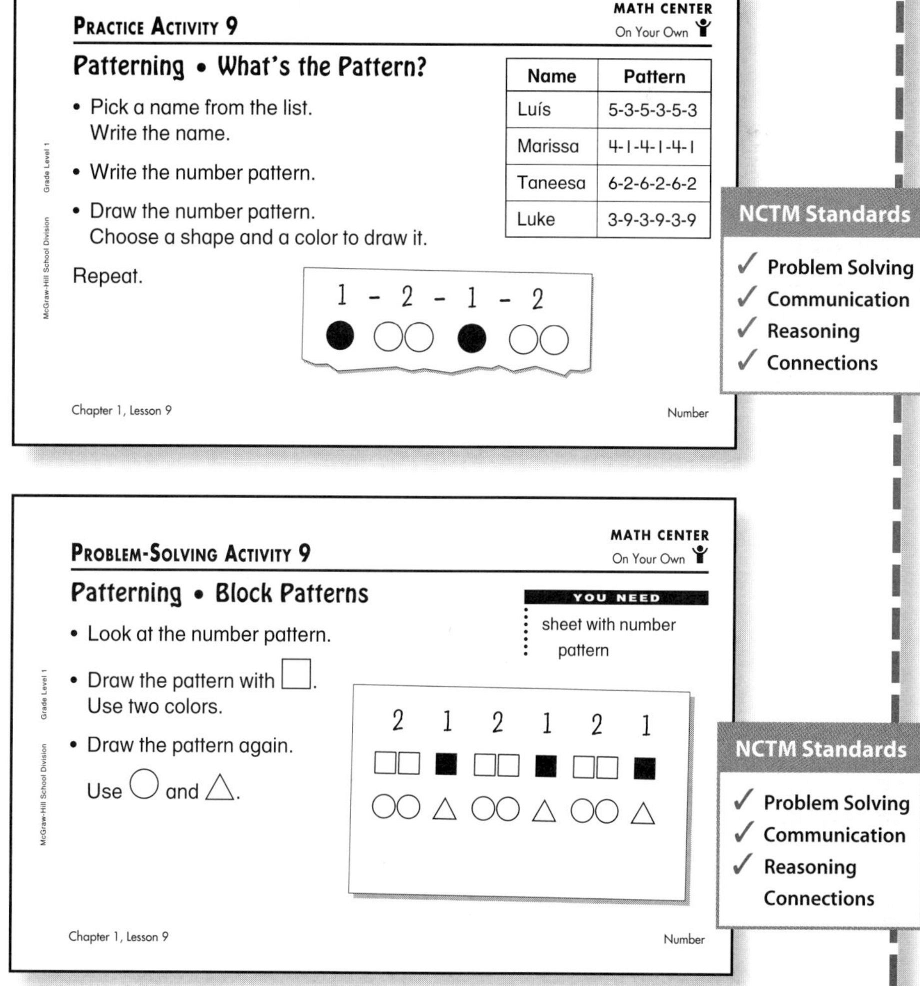

PRACTICE ACTIVITY 9 — MATH CENTER, On Your Own

Patterning • What's the Pattern?

- Pick a name from the list. Write the name.
- Write the number pattern.
- Draw the number pattern. Choose a shape and a color to draw it.

Repeat.

Name	Pattern
Luís	5-3-5-3-5-3
Marissa	4-1-4-1-4-1
Taneesa	6-2-6-2-6-2
Luke	3-9-3-9-3-9

1 - 2 - 1 - 2

Grade Level 1 · McGraw-Hill School Division

Chapter 1, Lesson 9 · Number

NCTM Standards
- ✓ Problem Solving
- ✓ Communication
- ✓ Reasoning
- ✓ Connections

PROBLEM-SOLVING ACTIVITY 9 — MATH CENTER, On Your Own

Patterning • Block Patterns

YOU NEED: sheet with number pattern

- Look at the number pattern.
- Draw the pattern with □. Use two colors.
- Draw the pattern again. Use ○ and △.

2 1 2 1 2 1

Grade Level 1 · McGraw-Hill School Division

Chapter 1, Lesson 9 · Number

NCTM Standards
- ✓ Problem Solving
- ✓ Communication
- ✓ Reasoning
- Connections

Lesson 1.9

DAY 1

Problem Solvers at Work: Number Patterns

OBJECTIVE Children solve a problem by using different representations for a pattern.

Materials have available: two-color counters, connecting cubes

1 Motivate — Whole Class

Materials 6 sheets of red and 6 sheets of yellow construction paper

Use sheets of red and yellow paper to make an AAB pattern, such as 2 red, 1 yellow, 2 red, 1 yellow, and so on. Display it in the chalkboard ledge, and ask children to describe the pattern. Lead them to discover the number that corresponds to the pattern.

- **How can you use words to describe the pattern?** *[red, red, yellow, red, red, yellow, red, red, yellow]*
- **How can you use words and numbers to describe the pattern?** *[2 red, 1 yellow, 2 red, 1 yellow, 2 red, 1 yellow]*
- **How can you use just numbers to describe the pattern?** *[2, 1, 2, 1, 2, 1]*

Repeat the activity using a different pattern such as 3 yellow, 1 red.

2 Develop

Page 33

Read aloud to children the problem found on the reduced Student Book page in this Teacher's Edition. Discuss the steps Jim went through in relation to the Read, Plan, Solve, and Look Back steps. Point out that he solved the problem one way (describing the pattern with color words), then looked back and saw a better way to solve it (describing the pattern using numbers).

Critical Thinking
After students complete the page, ask:

- **How could you show a 6,1, 6, 1, 6, 1 pattern with shapes?** *[Answers may vary. Sample answers: 6 squares, 1 circle; 6 blue cubes, 1 red cube]*

Page 34

Try These Assign the practice problems.

Read aloud the problem at the top of the page. Children may use counters or cubes to show the pattern before drawing it.

3 Close

Check for Understanding by displaying a train of 15 cubes showing a pattern of 2 blue, 3 yellow. Have children describe the pattern using numbers. *[2, 3, 2, 3, 2, 3]*

Name

Problem Solvers at Work

Number Patterns

Listen to the problem.

"Jim made this pattern with cubes. He wrote about it using colors in his journal. That took too long. So he wrote numbers for the pattern."

Read
Plan
Solve
Look Back

Jim's pattern:									
Color pattern:	red	blue	blue	red	blue	blue	red	blue	blue
Number pattern:	1		2	1		2	1		2

The pattern is 1 red 2 blue.

Use numbers to show the pattern.

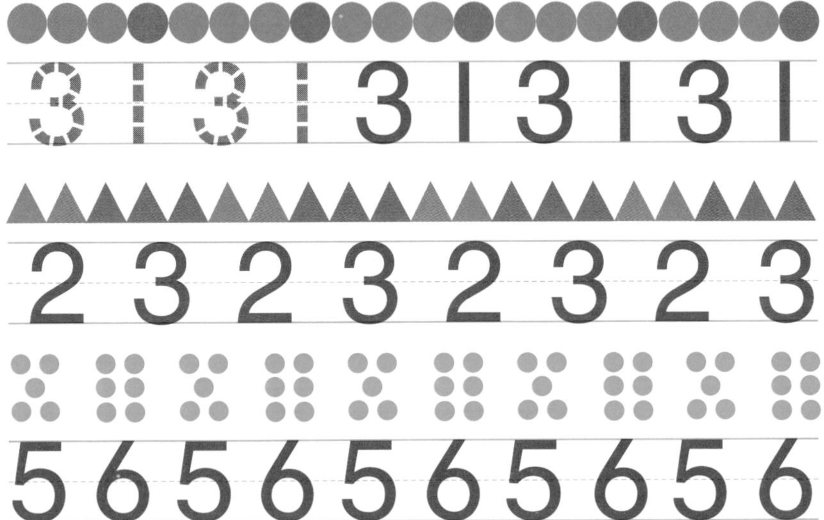

MEETING INDIVIDUAL NEEDS

EARLY FINISHERS

Have children choose one of the number patterns they wrote on page 33 and draw a different picture pattern to represent it.

EXTRA SUPPORT

Children may have difficulty aligning numbers and pattern segments. Draw a vertical line at the end of each pattern segment down to the write-on line below, to indicate where the numbers should be written.

ONGOING ASSESSMENT

Observation Checklist Determine by observation or questioning if children can solve problems that include numbers and patterns.

Follow Up For children who do not understand how to use a pattern to solve a problem, assign **Reteach 11.**

Children who can describe two-color patterns may like to explore creating and describing three-color patterns. You may also assign **Extend 11.**

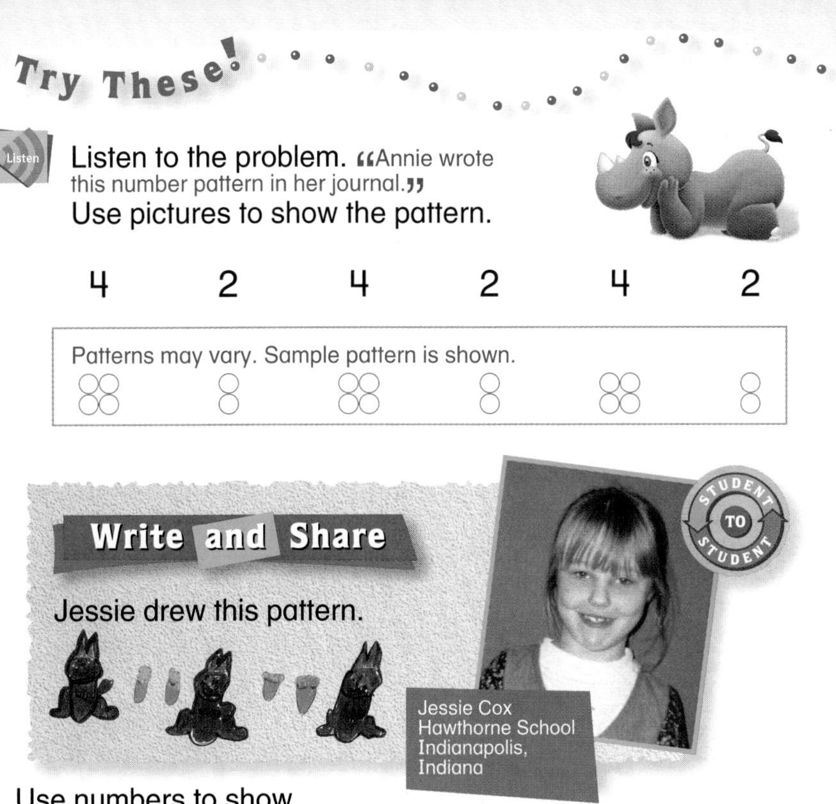

Try These!

Listen to the problem. "Annie wrote this number pattern in her journal."
Use pictures to show the pattern.

4 2 4 2 4 2

Patterns may vary. Sample pattern is shown.

Write and Share

Jessie drew this pattern.

Jessie Cox
Hawthorne School
Indianapolis, Indiana

STUDENT TO STUDENT

Use numbers to show Jessie's pattern.

1 2 1 2 1

Draw a pattern. Your partner writes the numbers.

Patterns may vary.

Your partner's pattern:

Ask your child to show his or her pattern with numbers.

Alternate Teaching Strategy

Materials per pair: 15 red and 15 yellow connecting cubes

Display a cube tower showing a pattern of three red cubes and one yellow cube. Use 12 cubes.

Pose the following problem:

Kim is making this tower with red and yellow cubes. She wants to put on four more cubes. How many of the cubes should be red? yellow?

Ask each pair to copy the cube tower to show Kim's pattern and find the answer.

- **What is the number pattern of Kim's tower?** *[3, 1]*
- **What colors would the next four cubes be?** *[red, red, red, yellow]*
- **How many red cubes is that? How many yellow?** *[3; 1]*

Have children create towers using two colors in different patterns. Have other children identify the number patterns.

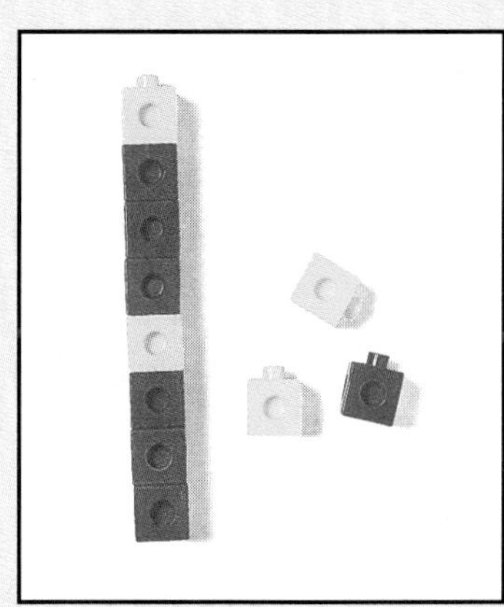

PRACTICE • 11

Practice 11

Name:

PROBLEM SOLVING: NUMBER PATTERNS

Read / Plan / Solve / Look Back

Use numbers to show the pattern.

2 4 2 4 2 4

5 1 5 1 5 1

7 9 7 9 7 9

Draw a pattern.
Your partner writes the numbers. Patterns may vary.

RETEACH • 11

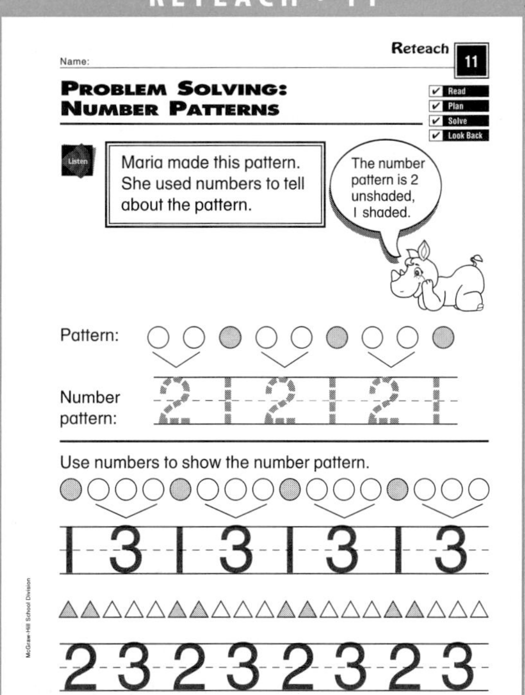

Reteach 11

Name:

PROBLEM SOLVING: NUMBER PATTERNS

Read / Plan / Solve / Look Back

Maria made this pattern. She used numbers to tell about the pattern.

Pattern:

Number pattern: 2 1 2 1 2 1

Use numbers to show the number pattern.

1 3 1 3 1 3 1 3

2 3 2 3 2 3 2 3

EXTEND • 11

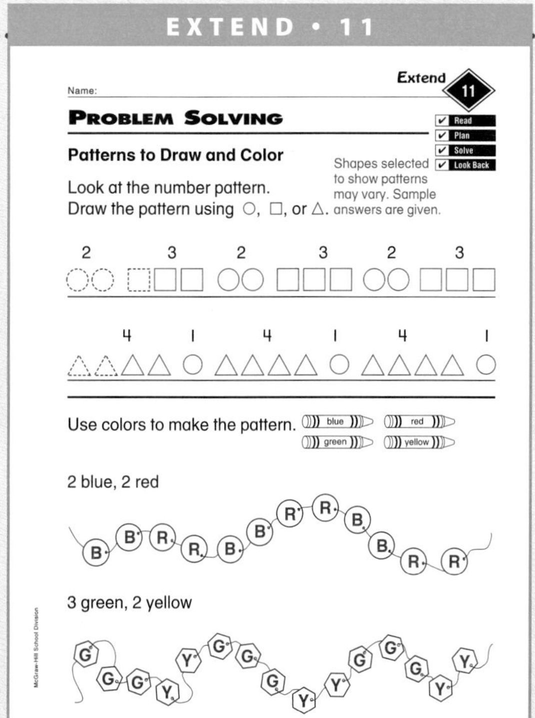

Extend 11

Name:

PROBLEM SOLVING

Read / Plan / Solve / Look Back

Patterns to Draw and Color

Look at the number pattern.
Draw the pattern using ○, □, or △.

Shapes selected to show patterns may vary. Sample answers are given.

2 3 2 3 2 3

4 1 4 1 4 1

Use colors to make the pattern.

2 blue, 2 red

3 green, 2 yellow

CHAPTER REVIEW

PURPOSE Review and assess the concepts, skills, and strategies that children have learned in this chapter.

Materials have available: 2-color counters, 5-frames, and 10-frames

Chapter Objectives

- **1A** Read, write, and represent numbers, 0 to 10
- **1B** Identify the number of objects in a group, including pennies, to 10
- **1C** Order numbers, to 10
- **1D** Solve problems, including those that involve numbers to 10 and patterns

Using the Chapter Review

The **Chapter Review** can be used as a review, practice test, or chapter test.

What Do You Think? This feature gives children an opportunity for self-assessment. Assure children that there are no right or wrong answers. The emphasis is on what they think and how they justify their answers.

JOURNAL Children draw and write about patterns. Most children will draw a pattern and write about it using words and numbers. Some children may define what a pattern is, conveying that it's something that is repeated.

Name

Chapter Review

Write how many.

Write how many cents.

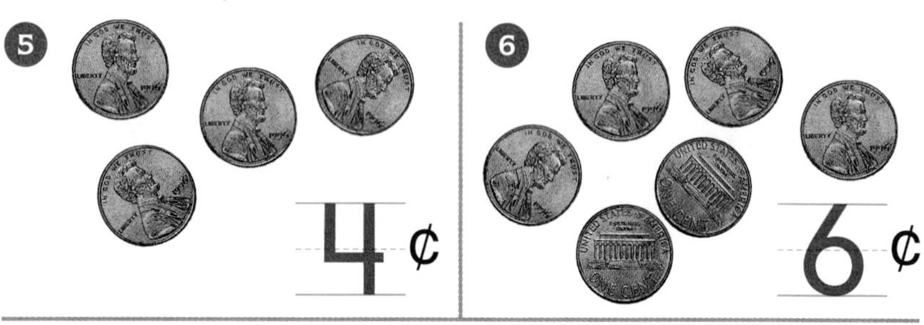

7 Write the numbers in order.

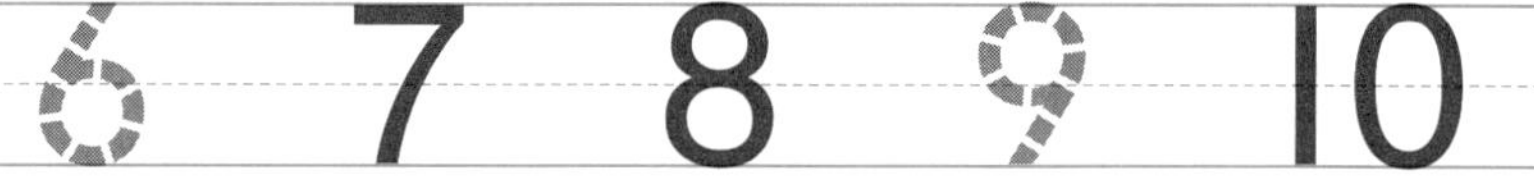

Reinforcement and Remediation

CHAPTER OBJECTIVES	REVIEW ITEMS	STUDENT BOOK PAGES		TEACHER'S EDITION PAGES		TEACHER RESOURCES
		Lessons	Midchapter Review	Activities	Alternate Teaching Strategy	Reteach
1A	1–6	5–10, 13–14, 19–24	15	6A, 12A, 20A	10, 14, 24	1–4, 7
1B	1–6	5–10, 13–14, 19–24, 31–32	15	6A, 12A, 20A, 30A	10, 14, 24, 32	1–4, 7, 10
1C	7	29–30		28A	30	9
1D	8–10	27–28, 33–34		26A, 32A	28, 34	8, 10, 11

Listen to the problems.

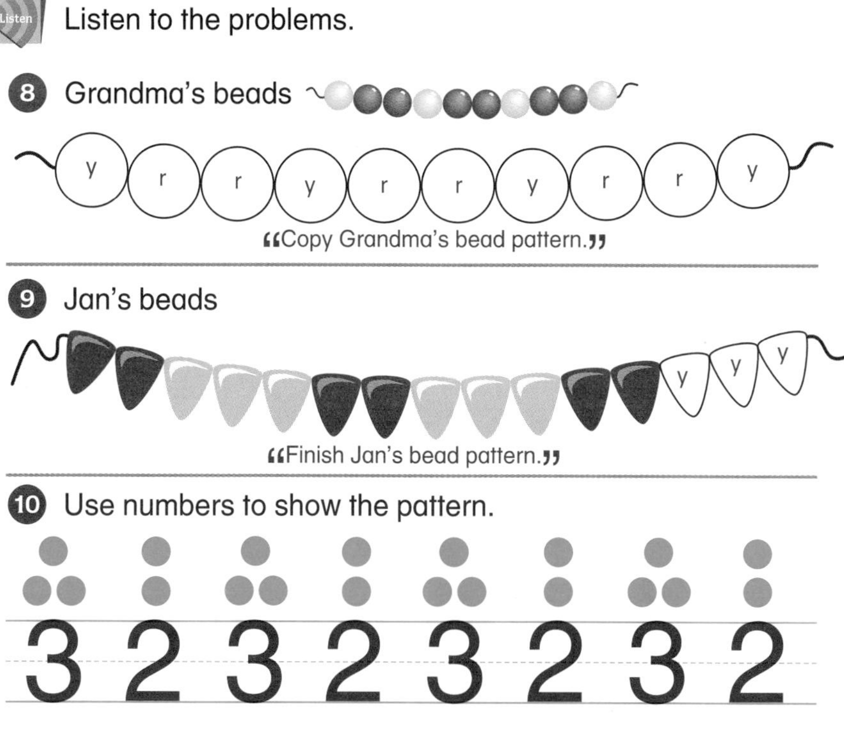

8 Grandma's beads

"Copy Grandma's bead pattern."

9 Jan's beads

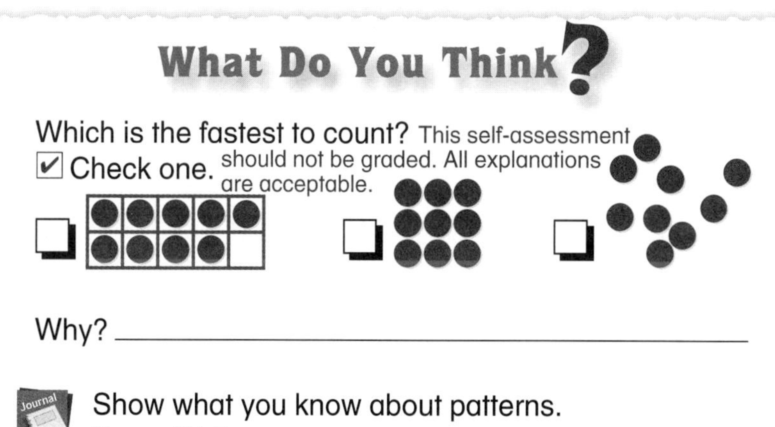

"Finish Jan's bead pattern."

10 Use numbers to show the pattern.

3 2 3 2 3 2 3 2

What Do You Think?

Which is the fastest to count? This self-assessment should not be graded. All explanations are acceptable.
☑ Check one.

☐ ☐ ☐

Why? ______________________

Show what you know about patterns.
Draw. Write. Children's work should demonstrate understanding of the types of patterns taught in the chapter.

CHAPTER TEST

AT A GLANCE

PURPOSE Assess the concepts, skills, and strategies that children have learned in this chapter.

Chapter Objectives

- **1A** Read, write, and represent numbers, 0 to 10
- **1B** Identify the number of objects in a group, including pennies, to 10
- **1C** Order numbers, to 10
- **1D** Solve problems, including those that involve numbers to 10 and patterns

Using the Chapter Test

The **Chapter Test** can be used as a practice test, a chapter test, or as an additional review. The **Performance Assessment** on Student Book page 38 provides an alternate means of assessing children's ability to identify the number of objects in a group, to 10.

The table below correlates the test items to the chapter objectives and to the Student Book pages on which the skills are taught.

Assessment Resources

Test Masters

The Testing Program Blackline Masters provide three forms of the Chapter Test. Form C uses a free-response format. Forms A and B use a multiple-choice format.

Teacher's Assessment Resources

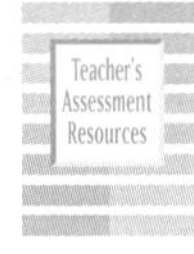

Teacher's Assessment Resources provides resources for alternate assessment. It includes guidelines for Building a Portfolio, page 6, and the Holistic Scoring Guide, page 27.

Name

Chapter Test

Write how many.

1  6

2   8

3  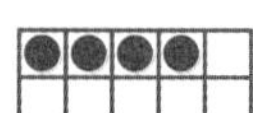  4

Write how many cents.

4  3¢

5  5¢

6  2¢

Write the numbers in order.

7 5 6 7 8 9 10

8 0 1 2 3 4 5

Listen to the problem. "Jeff started this pattern. Color to show which beads come next."

9 Jeff's beads

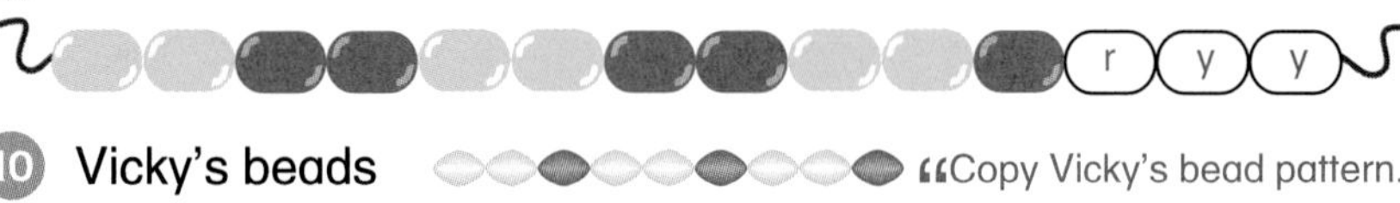

10 Vicky's beads "Copy Vicky's bead pattern."

y y r y y r y y r

Test Correlation		
CHAPTER OBJECTIVES	TEST ITEMS	STUDENT BOOK PAGES
1A	1–3	5–10, 13–14, 19–24
1B	4–6	5–10, 13–14, 19–24
1C	7, 8	29–30
1D	9, 10	27–28, 33–34

Performance Assessment

What Did You Learn?

Listen to the problem. See Teacher's Edition.

Answers may vary.

How many [bird]? 10   How many ? ____

How many ? ____   How many [rhino]? ____

You may want to put this page in your portfolio.

REVIEWING A PORTFOLIO

Have children review their portfolios. Consider including the following items:

- Finished work on a project, page 2F.
- Selected math journal entries, pages 10, 15, and 36.
- Products from investigations, pages 17–18.
- Children's self-selected "best piece" drawn from the work completed during the chapter. Have them attach a note explaining why they chose that piece.
- Any work that you or individual children wish to keep for future reference.

You may wish to take this opportunity to conduct conferences with children.

The Portfolio Analysis Form can help you in the reporting of children's progress. See Teacher's Assessment Resources, page 33.

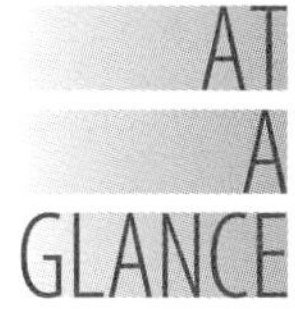

AT A GLANCE

PURPOSE Review and assess the concepts, skills, and strategies that children have learned in this chapter.

Materials per child: 6 blue, 6 yellow, and 6 red rhino counters or connecting cubes; blue, yellow, and red crayons

Using the Performance Assessment

Explain to children that ticks are little insects that bite animals. Tell children that the birds in the picture are tick birds. The rhinos can't get the ticks off by themselves, so they let the tick birds sit on their backs to eat the ticks.

Tell children that each bird in the picture needs a rhino to sit on. Have children use rhino counters in at least two different colors. Check that the children do this.

When children have positioned the rhino counters, read the questions at the bottom of the page and let them answer the questions. As children complete the questions, allow them to draw circles in the three colors to represent their counters so there is a record of their work.

Evaluating Student Work

As you observe the children and read their papers, look for the following:

- *Can the child match each tick bird with a rhino counter?*
- *Can the child count the number of tick birds and the number of each color of counter?*
- *Can the child write the numbers?*

You may wish to use the Holistic Scoring Guide and annotated samples of children's work to assess this task. See pages 29–32 and 37–61 in Teacher's Assessment Resources.

Follow-Up Interviews

Meet with children individually or in small groups to reflect on the Performance Assessment task. You can use the following questions to gain insight into children's thinking and evaluate their level of understanding:

- **Does every tick bird have a rhino to sit on?**
- **How many tick birds are there in the picture?**
- **How many blue rhinos did you use?**
- **How many yellow rhinos did you use?**
- **How many red rhinos did you use?**

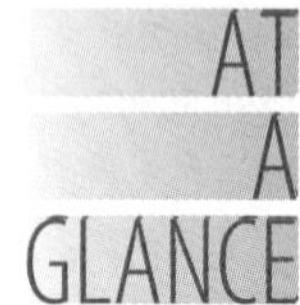

OBJECTIVE Use tally marks.

Using the Math Connection

Demonstrate the use of tally marks by asking ten children a question, such as, "Do you like oranges?" and tallying their responses under *yes* and *no* headings on the chalkboard.

Point out that you can show 5 either by IIIII or ~~IIII~~. Explain that once you have drawn 5 tally marks, you start a new group—like starting a new row in a 10-frame.

You may want to manage the survey by dividing the class into groups of 4 or 5. Designate which groups are to be the interviewers, and which are to be the interviewees. Coordinate the groups' movements around the room. When the interviewers have 10 responses, groups switch roles.

Allow time for children to describe the results of their surveys.

Developing Number Sense Like a filled 5-frame, or a 10-frame with one row filled, the set of 5 tally marks gives children a visual representation of that quantity.

Extending the Activity Children can repeat the survey, recording responses from 10 people outside the classroom.

Name ______________________

Tally Marks

Ask 10 friends.
Use tally marks to show how many.

| = 1 vote
~~IIII~~ = 5 votes

Which animal do you like the best?	
[hippo]	Tallies and totals may vary.
[rhino]	
[tiger]	

Write how many.

 ____  ____  ____

Curriculum Connection

Social Studies

Kamba Counting

The Kamba people have a way to show numbers with their fingers.

1	2	3	4	5
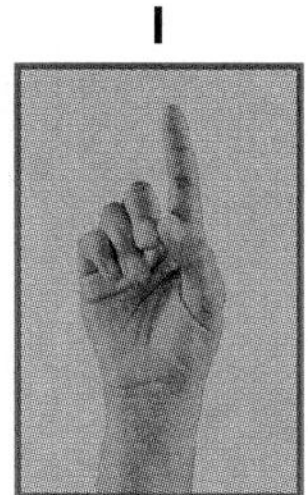	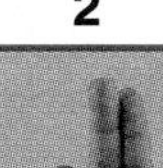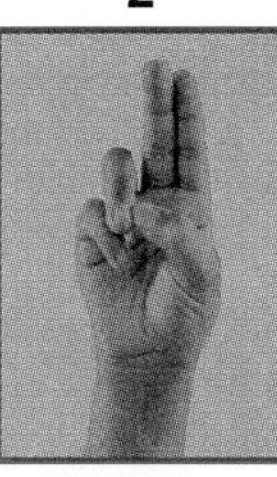	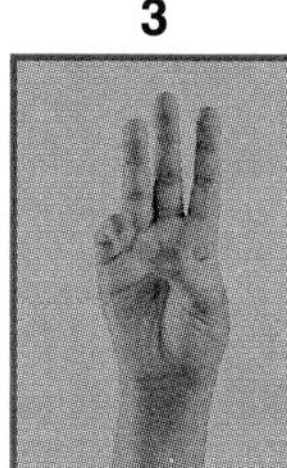	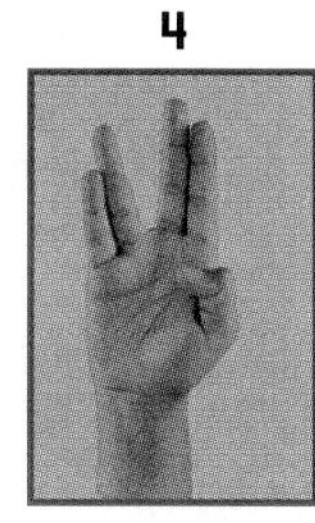	

6	7	8	9	10
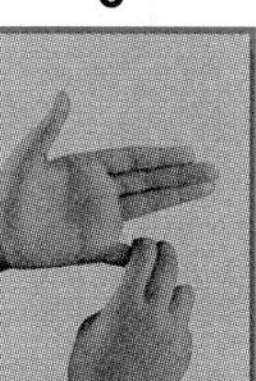	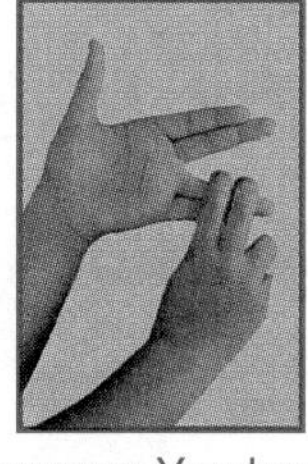	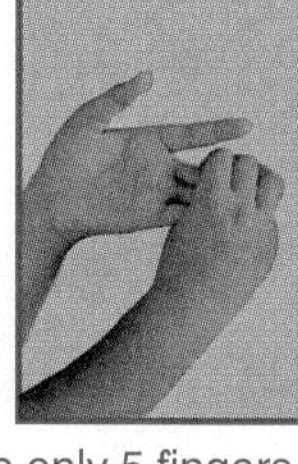	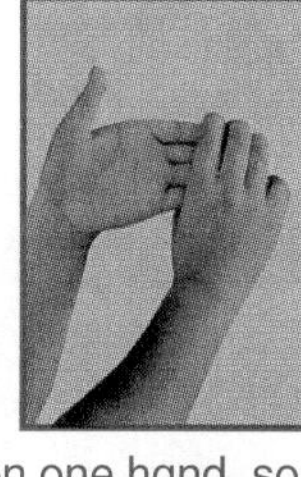	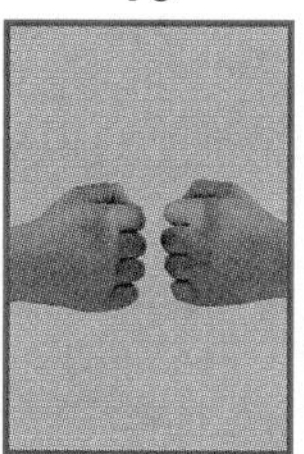

Possible answer: You have only 5 fingers on one hand, so you need one finger from your other hand to show 6.

Talk

Show 6 with your fingers.
Show 6 the Kamba way.
Why do both ways use two hands?

- Think of a number.
  Make it the Kamba way.
- Show your friend.
  Let your friend say the number.

SOCIAL STUDIES CONNECTION

This activity can also be done with children counting aloud using the number words the Kamba people use. The words for numbers 1 to 10 in the Bantu language are:

1—Imwe	**2—Ili**
3—Itatu	**4—Inya**
5—Itaano	**6—Thanthatu**
7—Muonza	**8—Nyaanya**
9—Keenda	**10—Ikumi**

When children are comfortable reciting the numbers in Bantu, ask questions for children to answer using these number words.

AT A GLANCE

OBJECTIVE Show numbers using a finger-counting method.

Using the Curriculum Connection

Make sure children are able to accurately position their hands to make the numbers 1 to 10 as shown in the pictures. Have children identify each number as they represent it.

Extending the Activity Challenge children to count forward, then backward, the Kamba way. You might also encourage children to think of questions that can be answered with numbers, such as:

- **How old are you?**
- **How many sisters do you have?**
- **What is your telephone number?**

Partners can respond using their hands.

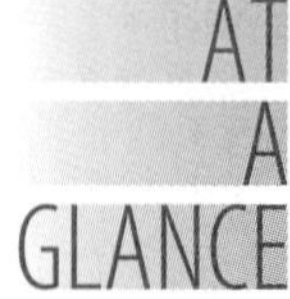

Family Activities

PURPOSE Give family members an opportunity to help children maintain concepts and skills learned in the chapter.

Using the Wrap-Up

Page 41

Tell children that this side of the page will help them show their parents what they have been learning in this chapter.

Explain the rules of the game or demonstrate the game with a volunteer. Children can play together in class to practice.

Name ______________________

The Dotted Giraffe!

PLAYERS 2

MATERIALS 10 pennies

DIRECTIONS Say a number from 1 to 10. Put a penny on the space that shows that number of dots. Play until you cover all the spaces.

Play this game with your child to practice counting from 1 to 10.

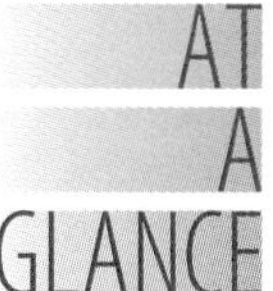

Dear Family,

We are beginning a new chapter in our mathematics book. We will be learning about parts of numbers.

Total	Part	Part
5	3	2

Five can be 3 and 2, or 4 and 1, or just 5.

We will also be talking about transportation and all the ways we can get around. Please help me complete this interview.

Your child,

____
Signature

Interview

Which are your favorite ways to get around?
(You may check more than one.)

- ❑ Car
- ❑ Bus
- ❑ Train
- ❑ Plane
- ❑ Bicycle
- ❑ Truck
- ❑ Other ____________________

If you won a free trip, where would you go?

____

AT A GLANCE

Family Activities

PURPOSE Give family members an opportunity to share in their child's mathematics learning.

Using the Preview

Page 42

Discuss the contents of the page with children and have them sign the letter at the top. Be sure they understand how to conduct an interview with a family member, friend, or neighbor.

Explain to children that they may share what they learn during their next math lesson. You may wish to have children bring back the page.

EXPLORING PART-PART-WHOLE

Planning for Learning

Suggested Pacing : 11–13 days **Theme: Getting Around**

Lesson Title/Description	Pages	Pacing	Real-life Connection	Chapter Objectives	Materials	Reteach/ Practice/Extend	Math Center Cards
Preview	42						
Introduction	43		traveling by bus				
What Do You Know? J P	44						
▶ 1. Cube Trains	45–46	1-day lesson		2A	red and blue connecting cubes, red and blue crayons	12	10
▶ 2. Parts and Totals	47–50	2-day lesson	naming parts of a train	2A	red and blue connecting cubes, red and blue crayons	13–14	11
▶ 3. Problem-Solving Strategy: Act It Out	51–52	1-day lesson		2D	have available: red and blue construction paper	15	12
Midchapter Review J	53				red and blue connecting cubes, red and blue crayons		
Extra Practice Game: Shake and Spill	54				2-color counters, cups, shallow trays or box lids		
Real-life Investigation: Applying Counting P	55–56		observing traffic				
▶ 4. Find the Total Teaching with Technology	57–60	2-day lesson		2B	2-color counters, Workmat 3 (part-part-whole mat)	16–17	13
▶ 5. Find the Missing Part	61–64	2-day lesson		2C	2-color counters, Workmat 3	18–19	14
Extra Practice Game: Guess and Count	65–66				2-color counters, Workmat 3		
▶ 6. Problem Solvers at Work	67–68	1-day lesson		2D	2-color counters, Workmat 3	20	15
ASSESSMENT OPTIONS J P Chapter Review Chapter Test Performance Assessment	 69–70 71 72						
CONNECTIONS MATH: Functions TECHNOLOGY Home Connection	 73 74 75		counting wheels and vehicles				

 = JOURNAL OPPORTUNITY  = PORTFOLIO OPPORTUNITY TA = TEACHER AID

Technology Links	NCTM Standards
Online Exploration, p. 44B Math Forum, p. 44B	4, 7
Math Van: Counters tool Math Forum, p. 46B	7
Math Van: Counters tool Math Forum, p. 50B	1, 2, 3, 4, 8
	1, 2, 3, 4, 6
Math Van: *Floating Total* Math Forum, p. 56B	4, 6, 7
Math Van: Counters tool Math Forum, p. 60D	4, 6, 7
Math Van: Counters tool Math Forum, p. 66B	1, 2, 3, 4
Math Van: Counters tool	1,4,7,8,13

ASSESSMENT OPTIONS

INFORMAL

Ongoing Assessment

- Observation Checklist, pp. 49, 51, 57, 63
- Interview, pp. 45, 61, 67
- Anecdotal Report, pp. 47, 59

Portfolio Opportunities

- Chapter Project, p. 42F
- What Do You Know? p. 44
- Investigation, pp. 55–56
- Journal Writing, pp. 44, 53, 70
- Performance Assessment, p. 72

FORMAL

Chapter Tests

Student Book

- Midchapter Review, p. 53
- Chapter Review, pp. 69–70
- Chapter Test, p. 71

Test Masters

- Free-Response Test: Form C
- Multiple-Choice Test: Forms A and B

Performance Assessment

- What Do You Know? p. 44
- Performance Assessment, p. 72
- Self-Assessment: What Do You Think? p. 69
- Holistic Scoring Guide, Teacher's Assessment Resources, pp. 29–32
- Follow-Up Interviews, p. 72

Teacher's Assessment Resources

- Portfolio Guidelines and Forms, pp. 6–9, 33–36
- Holistic Scoring Guide, pp. 29–32
- Samples of Student Work, pp. 37–61

Chapter Objectives		Standardized Test Correlations
2A	Find parts for a whole	MAT, CAT, SAT, ITBS, CTBS
2B	Find the whole for given parts	MAT, CAT, SAT, ITBS, CTBS
2C	Find a missing part	MAT, CAT, SAT, ITBS, CTBS
2D	Solve problems, including those that involve parts and wholes, and acting it out	MAT, CAT, SAT, ITBS, CTBS

NCTM Standards Grades K–4

1 Problem Solving
2 Communication
3 Reasoning
4 Connections
5 Estimation
6 Number Sense and Numeration
7 Concepts of Whole Number Operations
8 Whole Number Computation
9 Geometry and Spatial Sense
10 Measurement
11 Statistics and Probability
12 Fractions and Decimals
13 Patterns and Relationships

Meeting Individual Needs

LEARNING STYLES

- AUDITORY/LINGUISTIC
- LOGICAL/ANALYTICAL
- VISUAL/SPATIAL
- MUSICAL
- KINESTHETIC
- SOCIAL
- INDIVIDUAL

Children who are talented in art, language, and physical activity may better understand mathematical concepts when these concepts are connected to their areas of interest. Use the following activity to stimulate the different learning styles of some of your children.

Social Learners

Have children work with partners to identify the parts of a total amount.

One child draws or models one part. The other child then draws or shows the missing part.

See Lesson Resources, pp. 44A, 46A, 50A, 56A, 60C, 66A.

GIFTED AND TALENTED

Encourage children who are able to draw part-part-whole models for larger numbers. Have them find all the part-part-whole combinations for the number 10. Encourage children to predict how many combinations they can make for the number 20 and then try them.

See also Meeting Individual Needs, p. 49.

EXTRA SUPPORT

Specific suggestions for ways to provide extra support to children appear in every lesson in this chapter.

See Meeting Individual Needs, pp. 45, 47, 51, 59, 63, 67.

EARLY FINISHERS

Children who finish their class work early may make a festive sign welcoming visitors to Floortown. (See *Chapter Project*, p. 42F.)

See also Meeting Individual Needs, pp. 45, 47, 51, 59, 63, 67.

STUDENTS ACQUIRING ENGLISH

Make number cards, and cards for the words *part* and *whole*. Have children use the cards as they model parts and wholes. Be sure to use the terms as you or your children model.

See also Meeting Individual Needs, p. 49.

INCLUSION

- **For inclusion ideas, information, and suggestions, see pp. 61, T15.**
- **For gender fairness tips, see pp. 57, T15.**

USING MANIPULATIVES

Building Understanding Using a variety of manipulatives for counting and making sets can provide children with the many experiences they need to form number concepts.

Easy-to-Make Manipulatives Dot strips provide an easy and fast way of showing sets of numbers. Children can make them by drawing rows of dots on index cards.

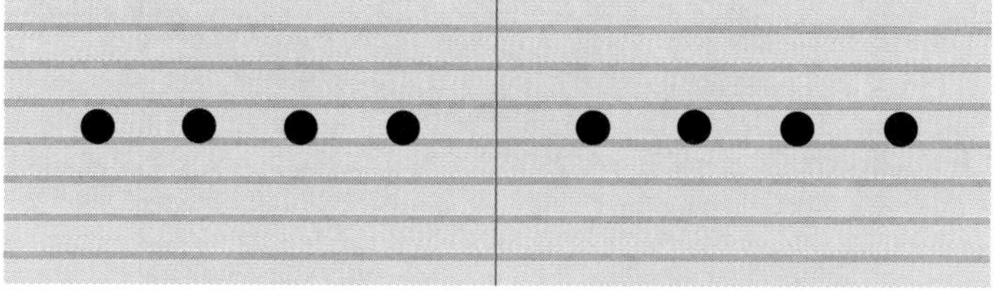

USING COOPERATIVE LEARNING

Line-Ups This strategy allows children to get to know each other quickly, discovering similarities and differences.

- **Children line up according to a shared characteristic (i.e., their birth date).**
- **Children make and discuss mathematical observations about the line-ups.**

USING LITERATURE

Use the Big Book *Bus Stops* to introduce the chapter theme, Getting Around.

Also available in the Read-Aloud Anthology are the poems "Boats," page 23, and "There Are So Many Ways of Going Places," page 24.

EXPLORING PART-PART-WHOLE

Linking Technology

This integrated package of programs and services allows students to explore, develop, and practice concepts; solve problems; build portfolios; and assess their own progress. Teachers can enhance instruction, provide remediation, and share ideas with other educational professionals.

MATH VAN ACTIVITY

In *Floating Total,* students use counters to find out how many sailboats are on a lake. Students can use the online notebook to write what they know about finding totals. To extend the activity, students use the Math Van tools to create and complete their own problem related to the concept. *Available on CD-ROM.*

MATH VAN TOOLS

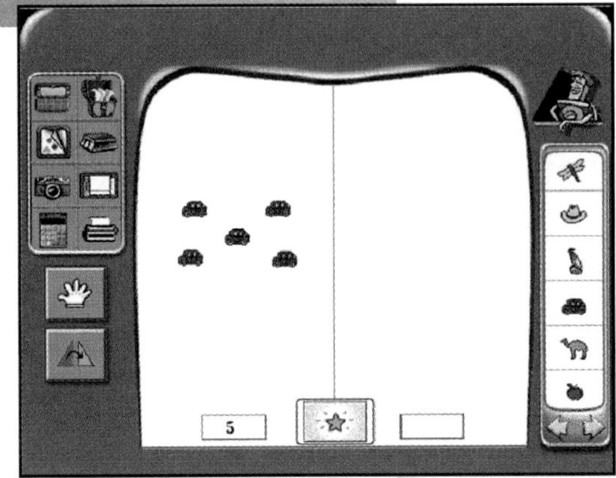

Students can use Math Van's counters to explore the concept of part-part-whole. The Tech Links on the Lesson Resources pages highlight opportunities for students to use this and other tools such as online notes and calculator to provide additional practice, reteaching, or extension. *Available on CD-ROM.*

WEB SITE http://www.mhschool.com

Teachers can access the McGraw-Hill School Division World Wide Web site for additional curriculum support at http://www.mhschool.com. Click on our Resource Village for specially designed activities linking Web sites to finding parts and totals. Motivate children by inviting them to explore Web sites that develop the chapter theme of "Getting Around." Exchange ideas on classroom management, cultural diversity, and other areas in the Math Forum.

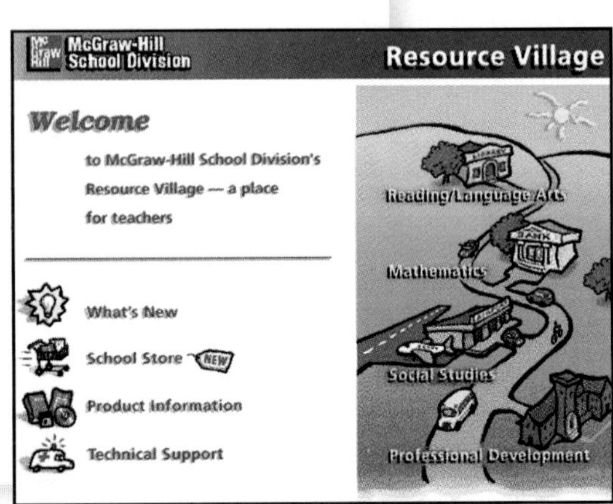

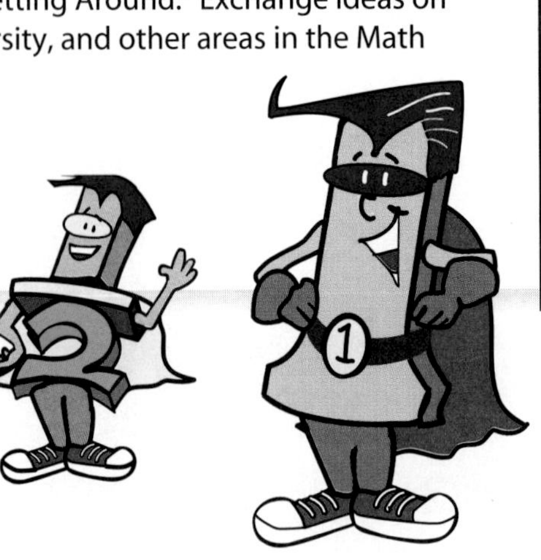

Chapter Project A FLOORTOWN MAP

Highlighting the Math

- count trees, houses, and vehicles
- identify groups of objects as parts and whole
- review sequence

1 Starting the Project

Introduce the idea of making a floor map of an imaginary place called Floortown, and create different kinds of vehicles to travel on it. Have children brainstorm places to include on the map and ways to construct cars, trucks, buses, trees, and houses from scrap materials.

Children can work in pairs painting the map; others can create vehicles for the roads. Consider ways in which family and community members can participate.

2 Continuing the Project

- Pairs of children meet to design the map. Then they take turns drawing and painting the map on long sheets of craft paper taped together.
- Other children make vehicles, trees, and houses. You may wish to have children use two colors for each category created; for example, if there are 8 cars, 5 might be yellow and 3 red.

3 Finishing the Project

Set aside time for children to play with their finished map. Encourage children to count vehicles, trees, and houses and identify them as parts or totals.

Community Involvement

Invite other classes to view the map and have children explain it. Display the map for Parents' Night.

BUILDING A PORTFOLIO

Have children draw and color a picture about the Floortown project. Have each child dictate a caption.

Each child's portfolio should include the picture with a caption, photos (if available), and any notes you made about the child's work.

To assess the work, refer to the Holistic Scoring Guide on page 27 in the Teacher's Assessment Resources.

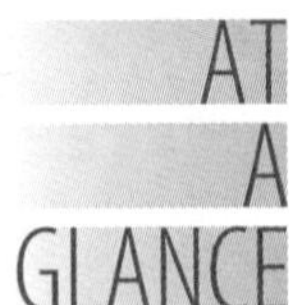

PURPOSE Introduce the theme of the chapter.

Resource Literature Big Book: *Bus Stops*

Using Literature

Page 43

Synopsis of the Book
Bus Stops describes "a day in the life of a bus." As passengers get off at the stops along the route, readers are invited to find something else in each setting. Finally, the driver pulls into the garage where the bus will spend the night.

Read the book to children. After children are familiar with the story, have them act out the sequence of events as you read aloud. You might also have children draw a picture of another stop that the bus will make. Ask:

- **Who will get off the bus? What else will be in the picture?** *[Stories may vary.]*

Developing the Theme

To develop the theme "Getting Around," invite children to remember interesting bus rides they have taken. Where were they going? Who else was on the bus? Ask:

- **What are other ways to get around?** *[Possible answers: car, truck, plane, train, helicopter, horse, bicycle, canoe, roller skates]*

Display children's responses on chart paper and title the list, "How We Get from Here to There." Ask children to share experiences they have had with different types of transportation. The theme will be revisited throughout the chapter on pages 45–48, 51–53, 58, 60, 62, 68, 72, and 74.

Making Cultural Connections

Children may be interested to learn that in some countries, bicycles are the main way of getting around. For example, in the People's Republic of China, more people ride bicycles than drive cars.

Allow time for children to tell about how they use their bicycles. Encourage children to draw pictures of their favorite ways of traveling. Display them on a bulletin board. Use the pictures as a basis for story problems such as, "Michael, Cady, Sam, and Lu each have one blue bike. Jen and Tom each have one red bike. How many bikes are there in all?" *[6]*

Getting Around

Exploring Part-Part-Whole

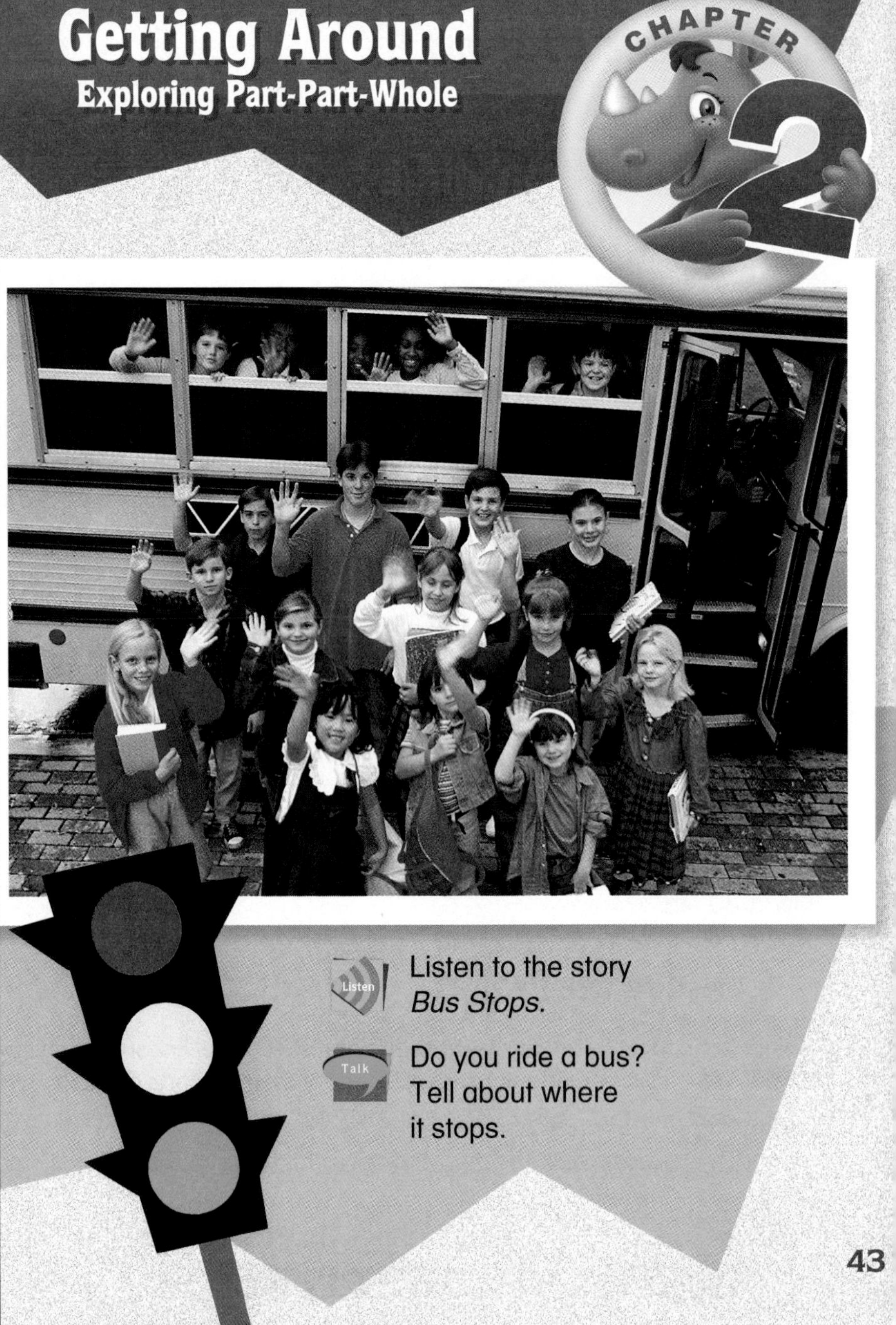

Listen to the story *Bus Stops.*

Do you ride a bus? Tell about where it stops.

43

CHAPTER BIBLIOGRAPHY

How Many Snails? A Counting Book by Paul Giganti. New York: Greenwillow Books, 1988. ISBN: 0–688–06369–1.

Moon Jump: A Countdown by Paula Brown. New York: Viking Children's Books, 1993. ISBN 0-670–84237–0.

The Train to Lulu's by Elizabeth Fitzgerald Howard. New York: Simon & Schuster Books for Young Readers, 1988. ISBN 0–02–744620–4.

COMMUNITY INVOLVEMENT

Take a field trip to a nearby municipal bus stop. If possible, examine a diagram of the entire bus route, and point out and count the bus stops.

Name

What Do You Know?

1

How many ? 3

How many ? 2

2

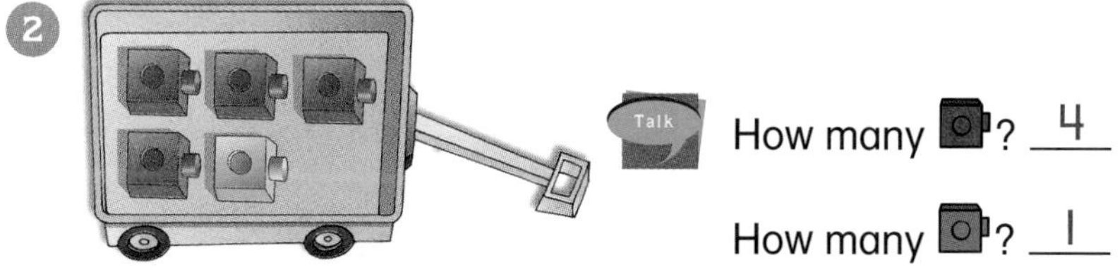

How many ? 4

How many ? 1

Draw some in a wagon.

Write how many .

Write how many .

 Drawings and numbers may vary.

VOCABULARY

These math words will be used in this chapter:

part (p. 45) **total** (p. 45)

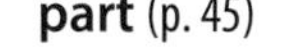

Children may record new words in their math journals. Encourage them to show examples and draw pictures to help tell what the words mean.

PURPOSE Assess children's ability to apply prior knowledge of part-part-total relationships.

Materials have available: red and blue connecting cubes

Assessing Prior Knowledge

Draw a wagon with 3 red connecting cubes and 1 blue connecting cube in it, as shown below.

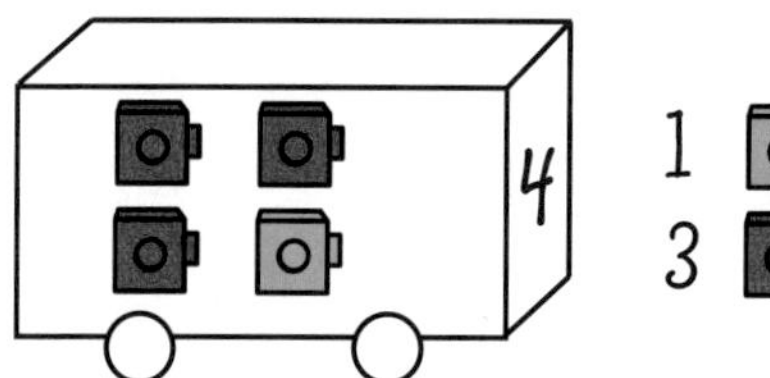

Ask how many cubes are in the wagon. Write the number on the front of the wagon. Ask how many blue cubes are in the wagon and how many red cubes are in the wagon and record those numbers.

Give positive feedback to children on their responses. Tell them that in chapter 2 they will be learning about parts and totals.

Page 44

For items 1 and 2, point out that the number of cubes in the wagon is written on its front. Read the questions in items 1 and 2 to children. If children are having difficulty, ask them to point to the red cubes and then ask them to point to the blue cubes.

Prerequisite Skills

- *Can children count the number of objects in a group of objects?*
- *Can children write the numbers?*

After children have solved the first two problems, review counting objects up to 10, if you feel this would be helpful.

Building a Portfolio

Assign the problem at the bottom of the page. This piece provides an indicator of where children are in their understanding of the part-part-total relationship.

Ask children to draw two wagons with the same number of cubes in each wagon. Tell them that you want a different number of red cubes in each wagon. Also tell them that for each wagon, you want them to show the total number of cubes, the number of red cubes, and the number of blue cubes. Have red and blue connecting cubes available for children who want to use them. Some children may put actual cubes in the rectangles they draw to represent the wagons and then draw the cubes. Others may just draw the cubes.

A Portfolio Checklist for Students and a Checklist for Teachers are provided in Teacher's Assessment Resources, pp. 33–34.

LESSON 2.1

Cube Trains

OBJECTIVE Explore the concept of part-part-whole.

Day 1 Explore Activity: Trains

RESOURCE REMINDER
Math Center Cards 10
Practice 12, Reteach 12, Extend 12

SKILLS TRACE	
GRADE K	• Explore the concept of part-part-whole. *(Chapter 11)*
GRADE 1	• Explore the concept of part-part-whole.
GRADE 2	• Explore finding totals for parts; parts for totals. *(Chapter 1)*

LESSON RESOURCES

MANIPULATIVE WARM-UP

Whole Class — **Visual/Spatial**

OBJECTIVE Explore finding parts for a whole.

Materials per child: 10 red and 10 blue connecting cubes

▶ Use 3 red cubes and 2 blue cubes to demonstrate making a two-color train for 5.

▶ Have each child make a two-color train for 6. Ask a volunteer to show his or her train for 6. Ask:

- **How many parts are red? How many are blue?** *[Answers may vary.]*
- **How do you know you have a train with 6 cars?** *[Possible answers: I counted all the cars, I knew how many red cars there were and then counted on the blue cars.]*

▶ Repeat the activity with other numbers up to 10.

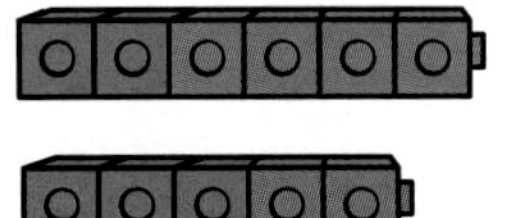

CONNECTION ACTIVITY

Cooperative Pairs — **Kinesthetic**

OBJECTIVE Connect finding parts for a whole with science.

Materials per pair: magnet, 6–10 classroom objects—some that are attracted to a magnet (paper clip, scissors) and some that are not (crayon, paper, plastic toy)

▶ Have pairs of children test whether or not their objects are attracted to, or stick to, a magnet. Ask children to separate their objects into two parts; objects that stick and objects that do not stick.

▶ Let pairs take turns telling how many total objects they have and how many in each part.

▶ Then talk about how the objects that stick to the magnet are similar. *[Possible answer: They are all made of metal.]*

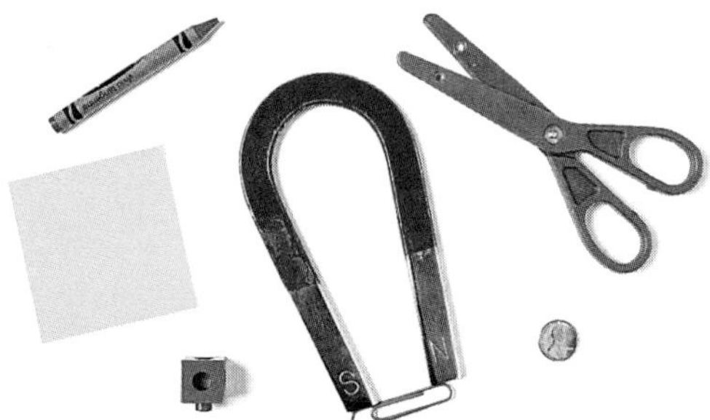

DAILY MATH

PREVIOUS DAY QUICK REVIEW

How many pennies?

1. (8 pennies) *[8]*
2. (3 pennies) *[3]*

Problem of the Day • 10

Read aloud to children:

There are 4 children on the bus.
1 more child gets on at the bus stop.
At the next bus stop, 1 more child gets on.
How many children are on the bus? *[6]*

TECH LINK

ONLINE EXPLORATION

Use our Web-linked activities and lesson plans to connect your students to the real world of transportation.

MATH FORUM

Management Tip For easy distribution, prepackage connecting cubes in plastic zip-closing bags prior to class time. When cleaning up after the lesson, children can count and replace the cubes in the bag.

Visit our Resource Village at http://www.mhschool.com to access the Online Exploration and the Math Forum.

MATH CENTER

Practice

OBJECTIVE Discover and record totals to 9.

Materials 10 red and 10 blue connecting cubes; Math Center Recording Sheet (TA 38 optional), red and blue crayons

Prepare The Math Center Recording Sheet should have 9 blank trains of 9 squares to color.

Children use two colors of connecting cubes to make trains for 9. Then they draw each. *[red and blue in varying combinations: 5 + 4, 6 + 3, 7 + 2, 8 + 1, eight possible trains.]*

Problem Solving

OBJECTIVE Explore the concept of part-part-whole.

Materials magazines, paper, crayon

Prepare Have available magazines or catalogs with pictures. You can also draw several different pictures as samples for children.

Children select a picture that shows a number of objects, and draw part of the picture on each side of a sheet of paper. They find the total. *[Answers may vary. Check pictures and numerals to be sure that parts match the total.]*

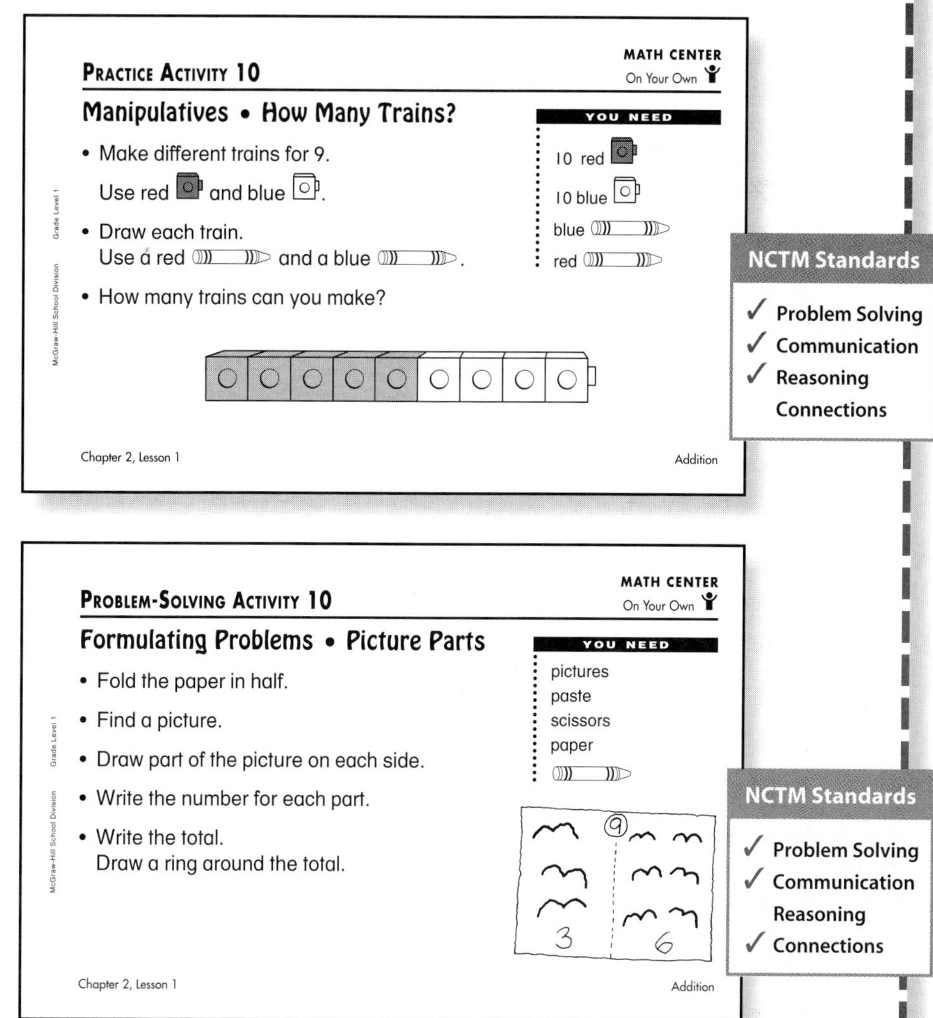

PRACTICE ACTIVITY 10 — MATH CENTER, On Your Own

Manipulatives • How Many Trains?

- Make different trains for 9.
  Use red and blue.
- Draw each train.
  Use a red and a blue.
- How many trains can you make?

YOU NEED: 10 red, 10 blue, blue, red

Grade Level 1 — McGraw-Hill School Division

Chapter 2, Lesson 1 — Addition

NCTM Standards
- ✓ Problem Solving
- ✓ Communication
- ✓ Reasoning
- Connections

PROBLEM-SOLVING ACTIVITY 10 — MATH CENTER, On Your Own

Formulating Problems • Picture Parts

- Fold the paper in half.
- Find a picture.
- Draw part of the picture on each side.
- Write the number for each part.
- Write the total.
  Draw a ring around the total.

YOU NEED: pictures, paste, scissors, paper

Grade Level 1 — McGraw-Hill School Division

Chapter 2, Lesson 1 — Addition

NCTM Standards
- ✓ Problem Solving
- ✓ Communication
- Reasoning
- ✓ Connections

Lesson 2.1

DAY 1

EXPLORE ACTIVITY
Trains

OBJECTIVE Children explore the concept of part-part-whole.

Materials per child: 10 red and 10 blue connecting cubes; red and blue crayons

1 Motivate — Cooperative Pairs

Resources Jumbo Activity Book, page 3; Stickers, sheet 3 (red and blue square counters)

Place 1 red sticker and 3 blue stickers on four consecutive segments of the first track on Jumbo Activity Book page 3. Ask children what is the total number of cars in the train you made, how many cars are in the red part, and how many cars are in the blue part. *[4; 1; 3]* Then call on a volunteer to make a different two-color train for 4 on the second track.

- **How are the trains the same?** *[Both trains have a total of 4 cars, they are the same length.]*
- **How are the trains different?** *[There are different numbers in the parts.]*

Tell partners to take turns making trains for 2 to 10. The one who makes the train describes its parts to a partner.

2 Develop

Page 45

Working Together Partners take turns making a train for 5. They color their trains, but they don't show them to each other. Then they describe their trains to their partner. The partner colors according to the other child's directions. When finished, children compare trains. Repeat for a train for 10.

Talk about the number of cubes in the whole train as the *total* and talk about the *parts.*

CRITICAL THINKING
After children answer the questions on the page, ask:

- **If you and your partner each made a train for 7, how might they be the same?** *[Possible answer: The parts could be the same.]*

Page 46

Try These Assign practice exercises 1–3.

Children should make two different trains for each total.

3 Close

Check for Understanding by having children make a train for 6. Ask:

- **How many cubes are blue? red?** *[Answers may vary.]*
- **What is the total?** *[6]*

Name ______________________

Explore Activity
Trains

Working Together

You need 10 , 10 ▪, a red crayon, and a blue crayon.

Listen to your teacher.

Color. Parts may vary.

1 Your train

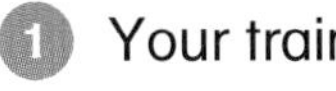

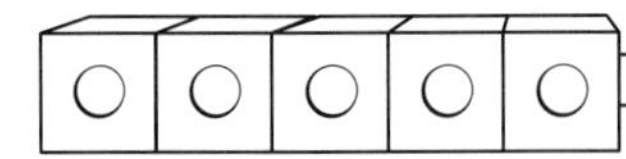

Your partner's train

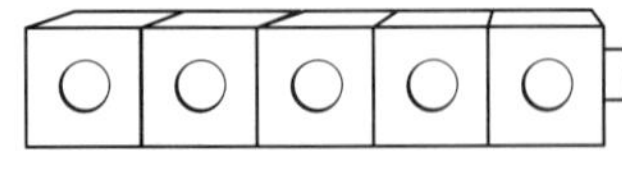

2 Your train

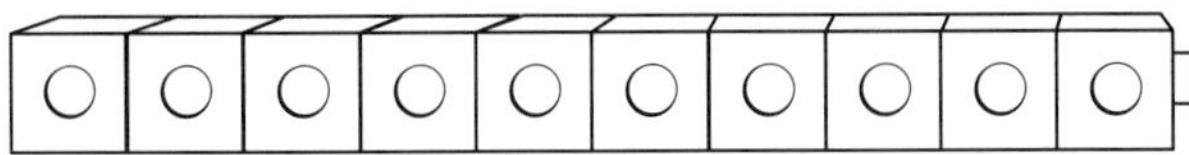

Your partner's train

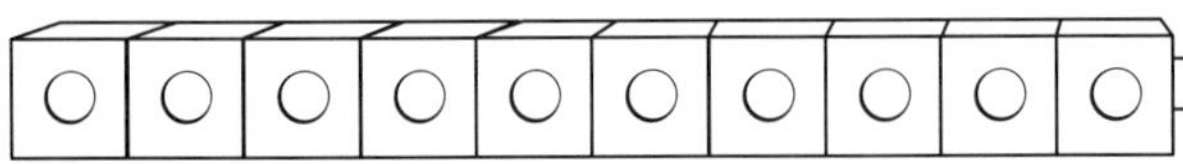

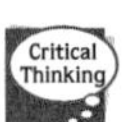

How are the trains for 10 the same? How are the trains for 10 different? Possible answer: Same—the total is the same, they are the same length; different—the colors are in a different order, there are more red than blue or blue than red.

MEETING INDIVIDUAL NEEDS

EARLY FINISHERS

Children can write or dictate a comment about whether they preferred a train for 5 or 10, and why.

EXTRA SUPPORT

Some children may incorrectly count the number of cubes in a part because the cubes are not grouped by color. Encourage these children to sort and group the cubes in their trains by color.

ONGOING ASSESSMENT

Interview Determine if children understand finding parts for a whole by saying:

- **Make a train for 5 with red and blue cubes. Tell me about the parts.** *[Answers may vary but should describe the train.]*

Follow Up Pair children to play "Guess My Train." One child builds a cube train and describes it without showing it. The other child duplicates it. Assign **Reteach 12.**

For children who demonstrate understanding, assign **Extend 12.**

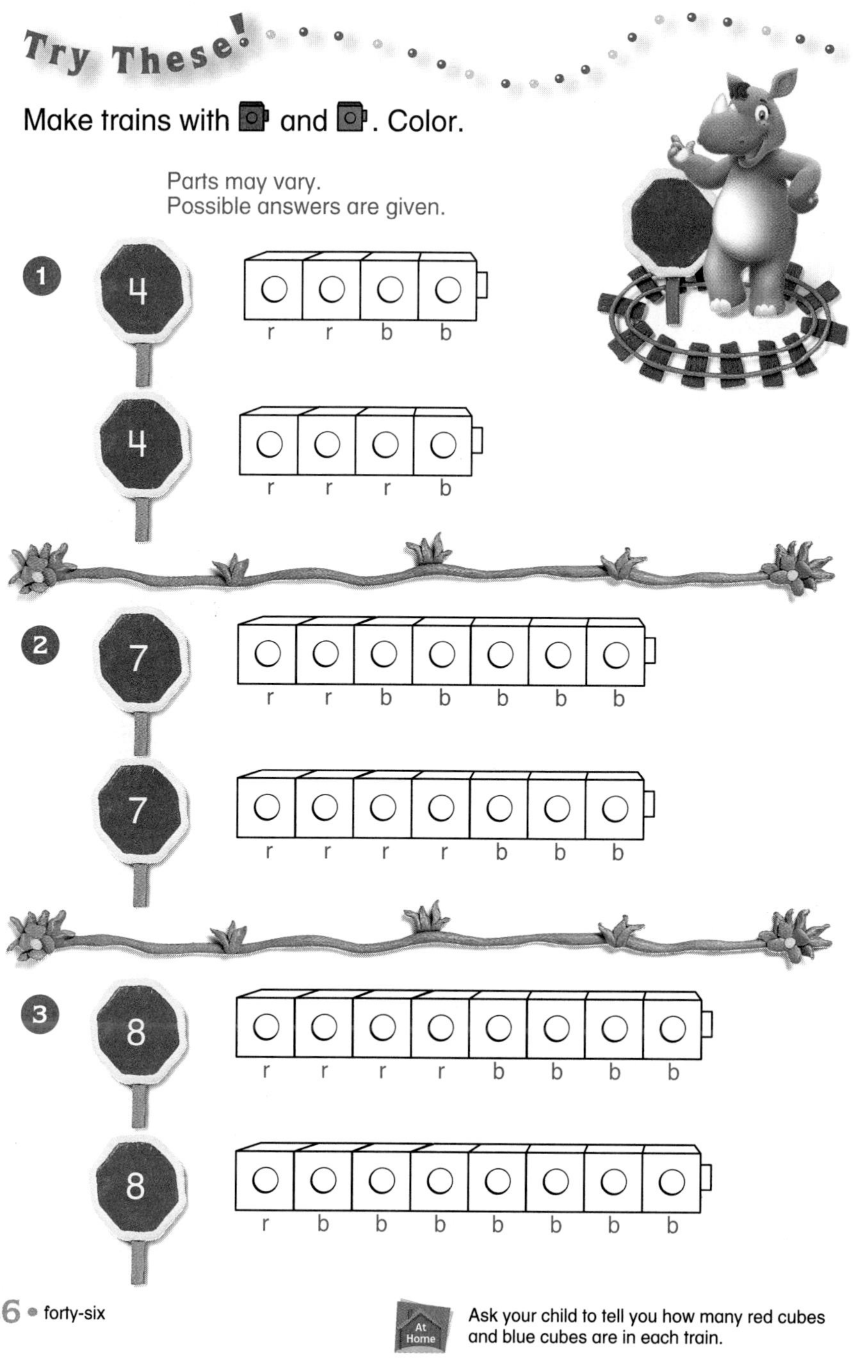

Try These!

Make trains with [cube] and [cube]. Color.

Parts may vary.
Possible answers are given.

1. 4 — r r b b
   4 — r r r b

2. 7 — r r b b b b b
   7 — r r r r b b b

3. 8 — r r r r b b b b
   8 — r b b b b b b b

At Home: Ask your child to tell you how many red cubes and blue cubes are in each train.

Alternate Teaching Strategy

Materials per child: 10 red connecting cubes, 10 blue connecting cubes, 7 5" × 7" index cards

Prepare Make cube-train cards by tracing groups of 2 to 10 connecting cubes on index cards.

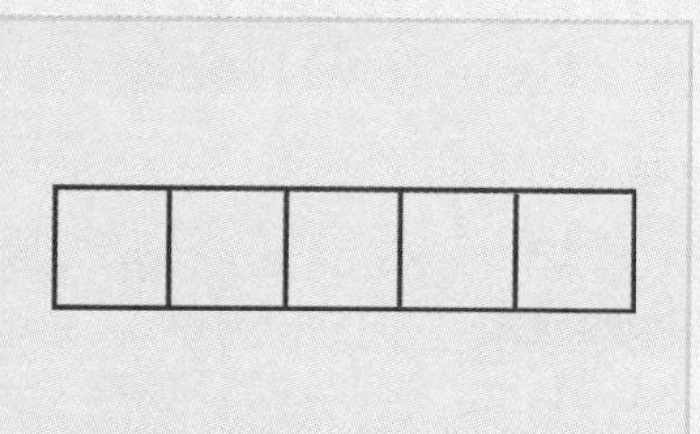

Demonstrate the activity using a cube-train card for 5. Give a volunteer a cube-train card and ask:

- **How many cubes can you put on the drawing?** *[5]*

Make a train using red and blue cubes and place it on the card.

- **How many red cubes did you use? How many blue cubes did you use?** *[Answers may vary.]*
- **What is the total number of cubes you used? How do you know?** *[5; there are five squares on the card, and I put 1 cube on each square.]*

Repeat the activity, using the other cube-train cards.

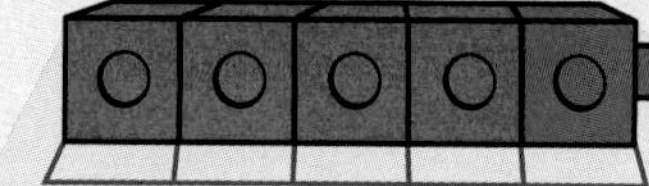

PRACTICE • 12

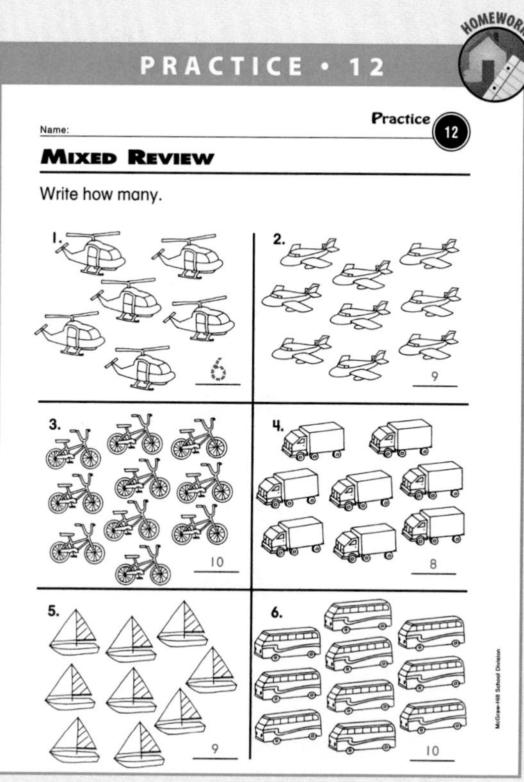

Practice 12

Name:

Mixed Review

Write how many.

1. 6
2. 9
3. 10
4. 8
5. 9
6. 10

RETEACH • 12

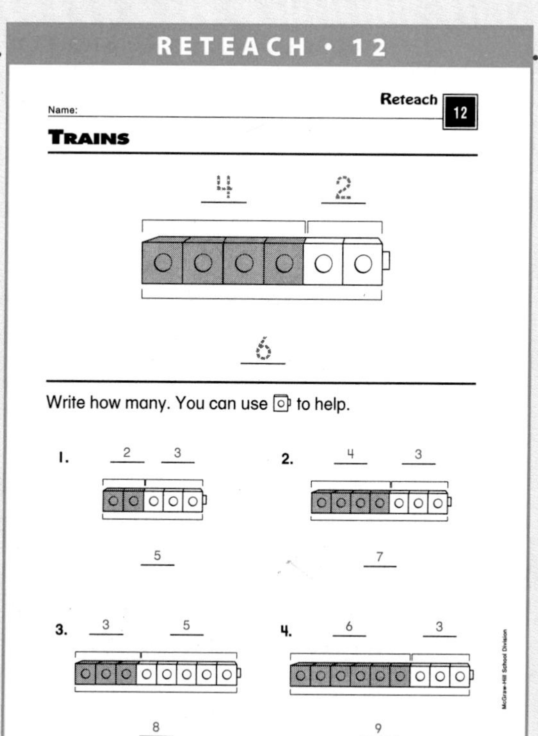

Reteach 12

Name:

Trains

4 2

6

Write how many. You can use [cube] to help.

1. 2 3 — 5
2. 4 3 — 7
3. 3 5 — 8
4. 6 3 — 9

EXTEND • 12

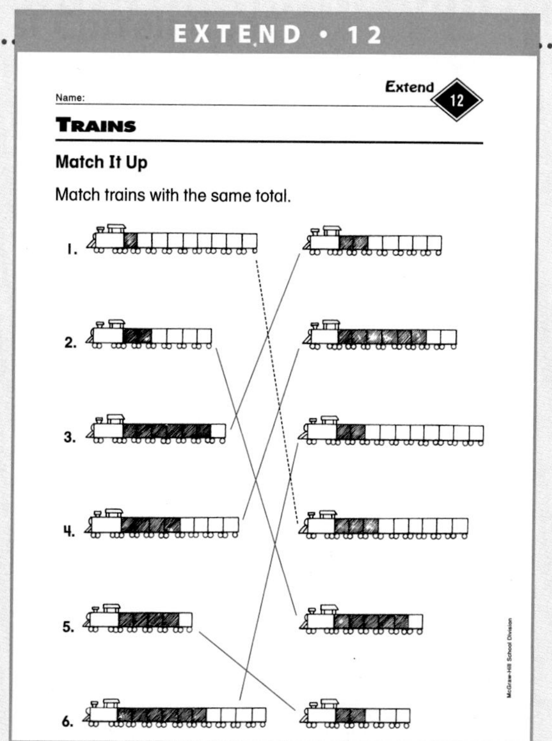

Extend 12

Name:

Trains

Match It Up

Match trains with the same total.

1.
2.
3.
4.
5.
6.

LESSON 2.2

Parts and Totals

OBJECTIVE Find parts for a given whole.

Day 1 Make Cube Trains
Day 2 Parts and Totals

RESOURCE REMINDER
Math Center Cards 11
Practice 13–14, Reteach 13–14, Extend 13–14

SKILLS TRACE	
GRADE K	• Explore finding parts for a given whole. *(Chapter 11)*
GRADE 1	• Find parts for a given whole.
GRADE 2	• Explore finding totals for parts; parts for totals. *(Chapter 1)*

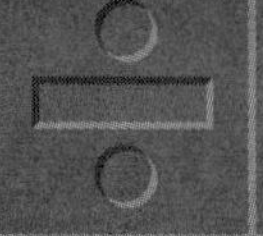

LESSON RESOURCES

MANIPULATIVE WARM-UP

Whole Class — **Kinesthetic**

OBJECTIVE Explore finding parts for a whole.

Resources Jumbo Activity Book, page 3; Stickers, sheet 3 (red and blue square counters)

▶ Write the word *Total* and the numeral 5 on the left side of the first railroad track and write the word *Parts* under the track. Have a volunteer use red and blue stickers to make a train for 5. Ask:

- **How many cars are there of each color?** *[Answers may vary depending on the number of red and blue squares used.]*

▶ Tell the volunteer to write the numeral for each part. Remove the stickers.

▶ Have another volunteer make a different red and blue train for 5. Discuss other ways to make a red and blue train for 5.

▶ Repeat the activity for 6 and 7.

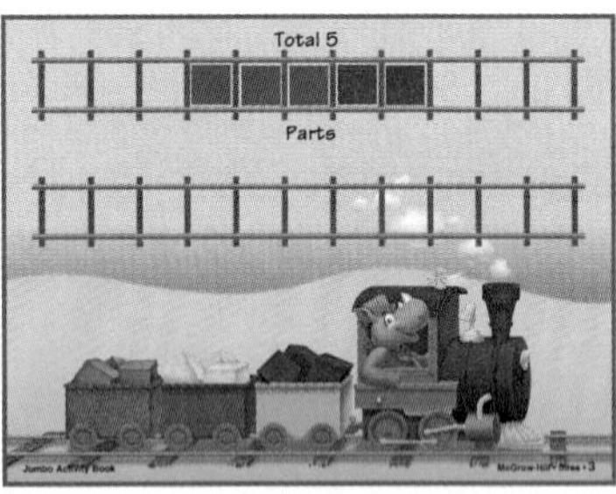

CONNECTION ACTIVITY

Cooperative Pairs — **Social**

OBJECTIVE Connect finding parts for a whole with physical education.

Materials per pair: 12 sheets of construction paper

Prepare Make from construction paper large number cards for 2–10 and motion cards labeled *hop, clap, jump.*

▶ Place the number cards and motion cards face down in separate piles. Pick a number card and a motion card from each pile and show them to the class. Children do the activity in pairs. The first partner performs the motion fewer times than the total number of times written on the number card.

▶ The second partner performs the motion the additional number of times necessary to make the total number.

▶ Repeat the activity using other cards and reversing roles.

DAILY MATH

PREVIOUS DAY QUICK REVIEW

Use red and blue cubes.

1. Make a train for 5.
2. Make a train for 8.
3. Make a train for 6.
4. Make a train for 4.

[Check children's work.]

Problem of the Day • 11

Read aloud to children:

Lee has 5 toy racing cars.
For his birthday he gets 1 racing car from his father.
He gets another from his brother.
How many racing cars does he now have?
[7]

TECH LINK

MATH VAN

Tool You may wish to use counters with this lesson.

MATH FORUM

Multi-Age Classes Some children may be ready to work with larger totals. As children work together, encourage those who are ready to choose larger numbers.

Visit our Resource Village at http://www.mhschool.com to see more of the Math Forum.

MATH CENTER

Practice

OBJECTIVE Find parts for a given whole.

Materials 0–9 spinner (TA7), 10 red connecting cubes, 10 blue connecting cubes, crayons, Math Center Recording Sheet (TA 38 optional)

Prepare Math Center Recording Sheets should have blanks and labels for parts (red cubes and blue cubes) and total. Children spin a number and make a cube train for that number, using red and blue cubes. Then they write the parts and the total. *[Answers may vary.]*

PRACTICE ACTIVITY 11 — MATH CENTER, On Your Own

Number Sense • Spin It!

- Spin a number.
- Make a train for that number. Use red and blue.
- Write the parts and the total.
- Do this 3 times.

YOU NEED: 10 red, 10 blue, red, blue

4 red + 3 blue total 7

Chapter 2, Lesson 2 — Addition

NCTM Standards
✓ Problem Solving
✓ Communication
Reasoning
Connections

Problem Solving

OBJECTIVE Find parts for a given whole.

Materials blank number cube, red and blue crayons, 5 red and 5 blue connecting cubes, part-part-whole mat (TA5); Math Center Recording Sheet (optional)

Prepare Label Recording Sheet with blanks and labels for part-part-total. Label the cube 5, 6, 7, 8, 9, 10. Children roll a number cube and make a cube train using red and blue connecting cubes. Then they write the corresponding number sentence. *[Answers may vary. Check children's work.]*

PROBLEM-SOLVING ACTIVITY 11 — MATH CENTER, On Your Own

Logical Reasoning • Building Trains

- Roll to get a total.
- Use red and blue. Make a train.
- Write the parts and total.

YOU NEED: red, blue, 5 red, 5 blue

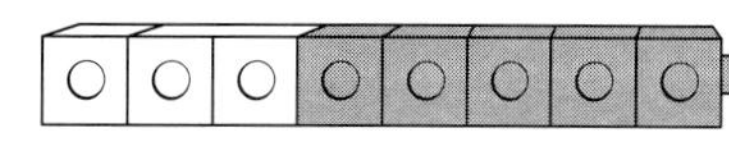

3 + 5 = 8

Chapter 2, Lesson 2 — Addition

NCTM Standards
✓ Problem Solving
✓ Communication
✓ Reasoning
Connections

DAY 1

Make Cube Trains

OBJECTIVE Children count to find parts for a given whole.

Materials per child: 10 red and 10 blue connecting cubes; 1 red crayon, 1 blue crayon

1 Motivate Whole Class

Materials chart paper, 5 red and 5 blue 3" × 3" squares of paper, tape

Draw train tracks as shown:

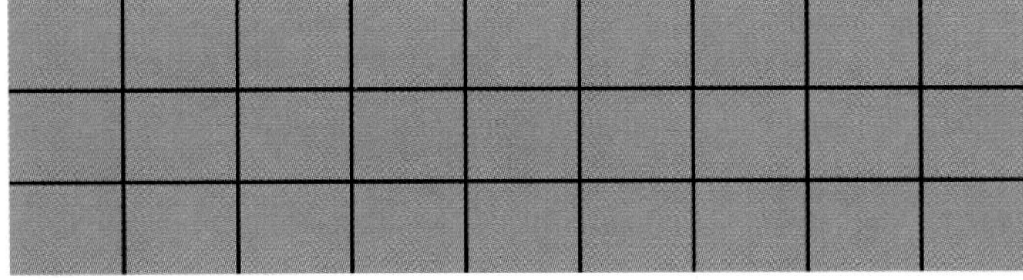

Call out a total, such as 6. Then ask a volunteer to tape red and blue squares onto the track to make a train. Suggest that each child group all the red squares together in one part and all the blue squares in another part.

Ask a volunteer to tell the number of squares in each part. Continue with other numbers.

2 Develop

Page 47

Using red and blue cubes, children make cube trains for given totals on the workspace. Use the vocabulary words *part* and *total* as you explain the page.

Children should group all the red cubes together in one part and all the blue cubes together in another part. Children draw trains and record how many red cubes and blue cubes are in each part.

Critical Thinking

After children discuss the question on the page, ask:

- **How can we find out how many different trains for 6 we made?** *[Possible answer: Put all the trains next to each other.]*

Give children the opportunity to compare their trains for 6.

Name ______________

Make Cube Trains

You need 10 [cube], 10 [cube], a red crayon, and a blue crayon.

Make a train for the total.

Draw. Write how many [cube] and [cube]. Parts may vary. Possible answers are given.

Total | Parts

1  2  1 

2  2  2 

3  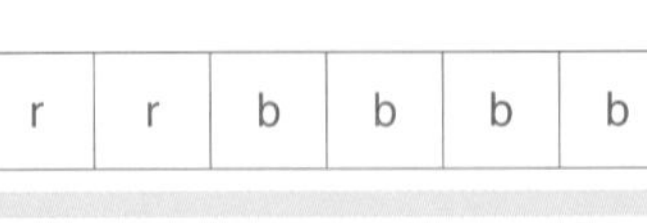 2 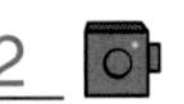 4 

Does everyone have the same train for 6? Why or why not? Probably not since there are seven ways to make parts for the total 6.

MEETING INDIVIDUAL NEEDS

EARLY FINISHERS

Pairs who finish early can discuss the Talk question and compare their findings.

EXTRA SUPPORT

Some children may not be ready to find both parts of a whole. Supply one part until children become more comfortable.

ONGOING ASSESSMENT

Anecdotal Report After children discuss trains with a partner, have them write or draw about parts, colors, or totals. Keep the entry in their portfolios with notes you have made about their meeting.

Follow Up For children having difficulty finding parts for a given whole, assign **Reteach 13.**

For children who demonstrate understanding, assign **Extend 13.**

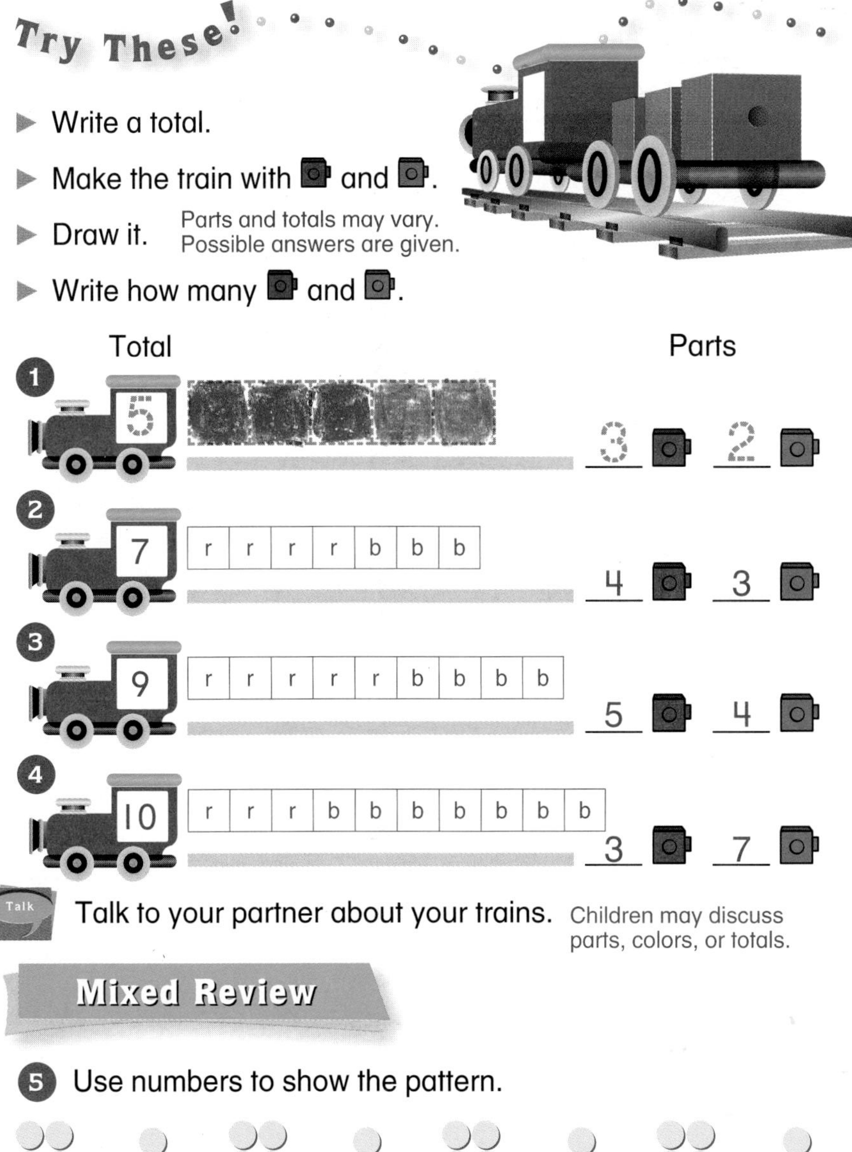
Try These!

- Write a total.
- Make the train with ■ and □.
- Draw it. Parts and totals may vary. Possible answers are given.
- Write how many ■ and □.

	Total	Train	Parts	
1	5	■ ■ ■ □ □	3 ■	2 □
2	7	r r r r b b b	4 ■	3 □
3	9	r r r r r b b b b	5 ■	4 □
4	10	r r r b b b b b b b	3 ■	7 □

Talk to your partner about your trains. Children may discuss parts, colors, or totals.

Mixed Review

5. Use numbers to show the pattern.

4 3 4 3 4 3 4 3

At Home: Your child made trains from connecting cubes. Ask your child to tell about them.

Page 48

Try These Discuss the worked-out example. Assign practice exercises 1–4.

Mixed Review Children review patterning skills from Chapter 1. For additional review, have partners draw and write their own dot and number patterns.

3 Close

Check for Understanding by having the children describe the red part, the blue part, and the total of any cube train they have made or drawn in this lesson.

Tomorrow children find the parts for a given total.

PRACTICE • 13

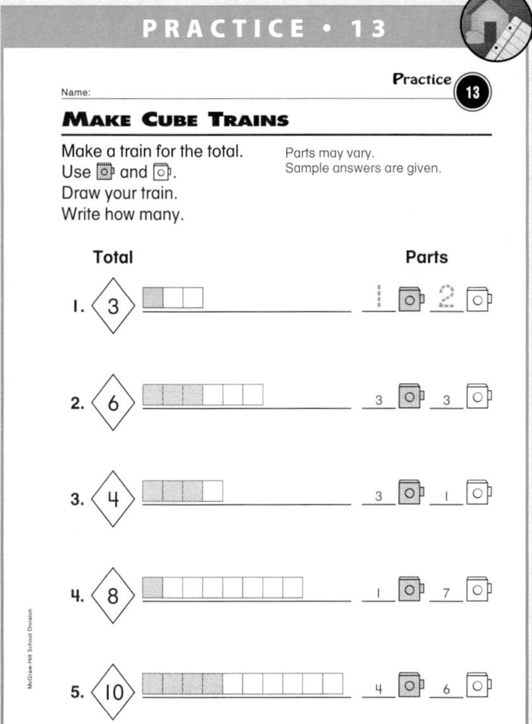
Name: Practice 13

MAKE CUBE TRAINS

Make a train for the total. Use ■ and □. Draw your train. Write how many.

Parts may vary. Sample answers are given.

	Total	Parts	
1.	3	1 ■	2 □
2.	6	3 ■	3 □
3.	4	3 ■	1 □
4.	8	1 ■	7 □
5.	10	4 ■	6 □

RETEACH • 13

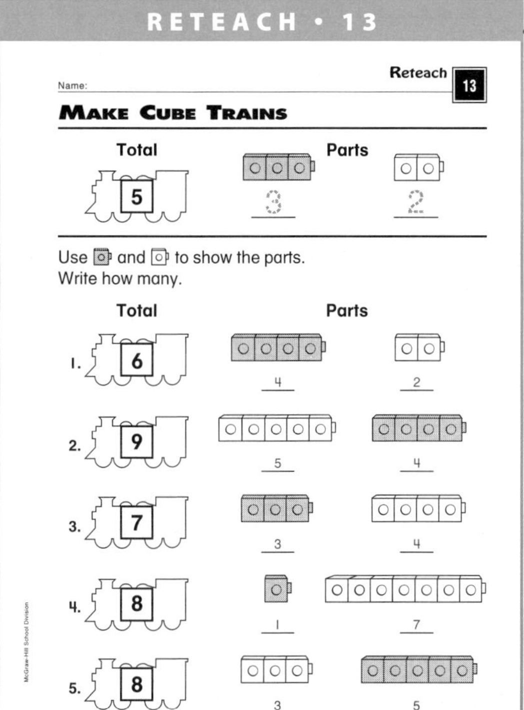
Name: Reteach 13

MAKE CUBE TRAINS

Total	Parts	
5	3	2

Use ■ and □ to show the parts. Write how many.

	Total	Parts	
1.	6	4	2
2.	9	5	4
3.	7	3	4
4.	8	1	7
5.	8	3	5

EXTEND • 13

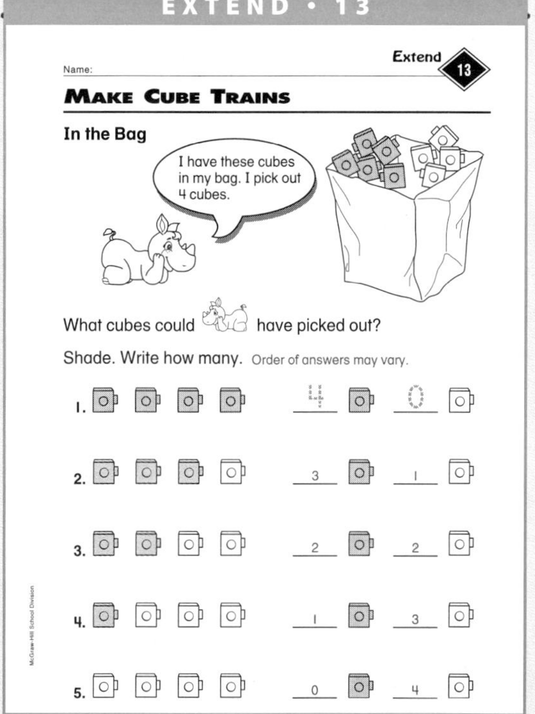
Name: Extend 13

MAKE CUBE TRAINS

In the Bag

What cubes could have picked out?

Shade. Write how many. Order of answers may vary.

	■	□
1.	4	0
2.	3	1
3.	2	2
4.	1	3
5.	0	4

Lesson 2.2

Parts and Totals

OBJECTIVE Children find all the parts for a given total.

Materials per child: 10 red connecting cubes, 10 blue connecting cubes; 1 red crayon, 1 blue crayon

1 Motivate — Whole Class

Materials 10 red connecting cubes, 10 blue connecting cubes

Display the 20 connecting cubes. Ask a volunteer to use red and blue cubes to make a train that has a total of 6 cubes. Suggest that the child group the red cubes together in one part and the blue cubes in another part of the train.

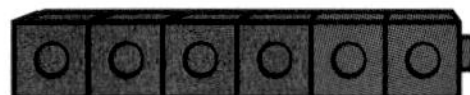

- **How many cubes are in the red part? The blue part?** *[Answers may vary.]*

Call on volunteers to develop other cube trains for 6. Then continue with trains for other totals.

2 Develop

Page 49

Tell children that they are to find as many ways as they can to show 4 with cubes. Children should make their trains with cubes and then color them on the page. Then children write the numbers of the parts and the total.

CRITICAL THINKING
After children discuss the question on the page, ask:

- **How many ways can you make a train for 4?** *[5; 4 red, 0 blue; 3 red, 1 blue; 2 red, 2 blue; 1 red, 3 blue; 0 red, 4 blue]*

Page 50

Try These Discuss and assign practice exercises 1–4.

Cultural Connection Children should copy or discuss the blanket's patterns, and try to copy it with cubes or numerical representation.

3 Close

Check for Understanding by asking children questions about the combinations of colors they found for 3.

- **How did you know what numbers to write for the parts and the total?** *[Possible answers: I counted how many cubes in all; I counted the number of red and blue cubes for each.]*

Name ______________

Parts and Totals

You need 10 red cubes, 10 blue cubes, a red crayon, and a blue crayon.

Make different trains for 4.
Color. Write the parts and total.
Order of answers may vary.

Parts — Total

1. 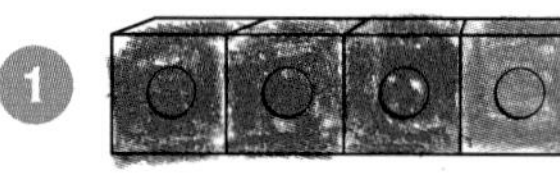  3  1   4
2. 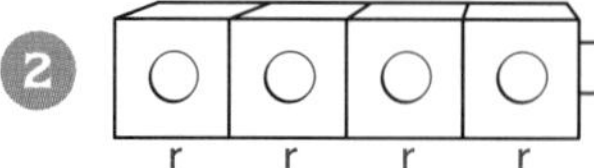 r r r r — 4  0   4
3. 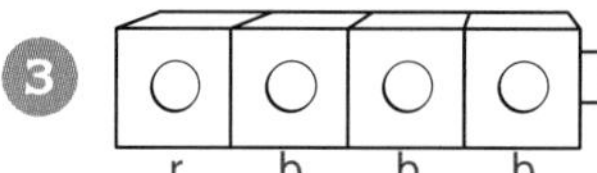 r b b b — 1  3   4
4. 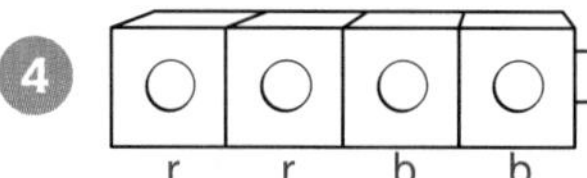 r r b b — 2  2   4
5. 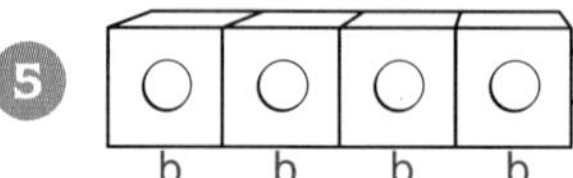 b b b b — 0   4  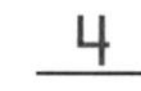 4

Do you think there are more or fewer trains for 7 than 4? Why?

Possible answer: There are more trains for 7; there are more ways to make parts.

MEETING INDIVIDUAL NEEDS

GIFTED AND TALENTED

Challenge children to find as many combinations as they can of red and blue parts for the number 7. *[7 red, 0 blue; 6 red, 1 blue; 5 red, 2 blue; 4 red, 3 blue; 3 red, 4 blue; 2 red, 5 blue; 1 red, 6 blue; 0 red, 7 blue]*

STUDENTS ACQUIRING ENGLISH

Pair children acquiring English with more fluent partners to help them understand the words *part* and *total* as they do the exercises.

ONGOING ASSESSMENT

Observation Checklist Determine if a child understands finding parts for a whole by showing a train with 2 yellow cubes and 3 red and asking for the total. Then show a train with 3 yellow cubes and 2 red and ask whether the total is the same, and if so, why.

Follow Up Have one partner name two numbers from 0 to 5. The other partner uses red and blue cubes to show the total. Assign **Reteach 14.**

For children who demonstrate understanding, assign **Extend 14.**

Try These!

Make different trains for 3 with ▢. Color. Write the parts and total. Order of answers may vary.

		Parts				Total
1	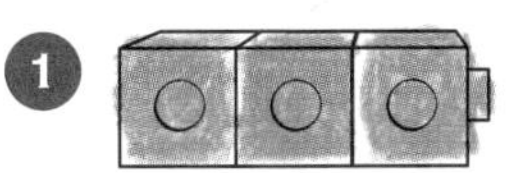	 0	▢	3	▢	3
2	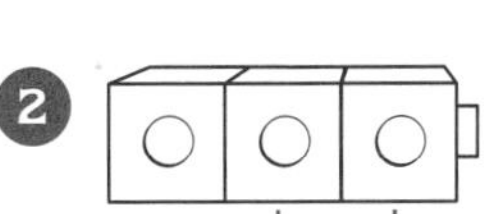 r b b	1	▢	2	▢	3
3	r r b	2	▢	1	▢	3
4	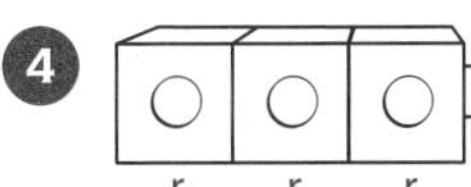 r r r	3	▢	0	▢	3

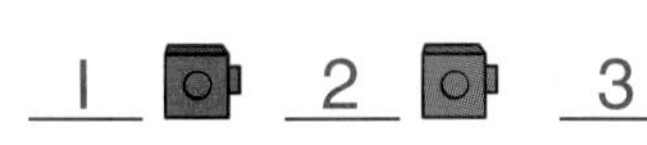

Cultural Connection — Native American Patterns

This blanket was made by Native American weavers.

How many ■? 2

How many ■? 2

How many ■? 1

Total 5

Have your child tell you how to make trains for 3.

Alternate Teaching Strategy

Materials 10 each of red and blue connecting cubes

Show children a two-color cube train for 5.

- **How many cubes are in the red part?**
- **How many cubes are in the blue part?**
- **What is the total number of cubes in the whole train?** *[5]*

Have children record the number of red and blue cubes and the total. Show another train for 5 with a different combination of red and blue cubes. Ask the same questions, and have children record their answers.

Repeat for all combinations of 5. When children can record the combinations for 5, extend the activity for numbers to 10.

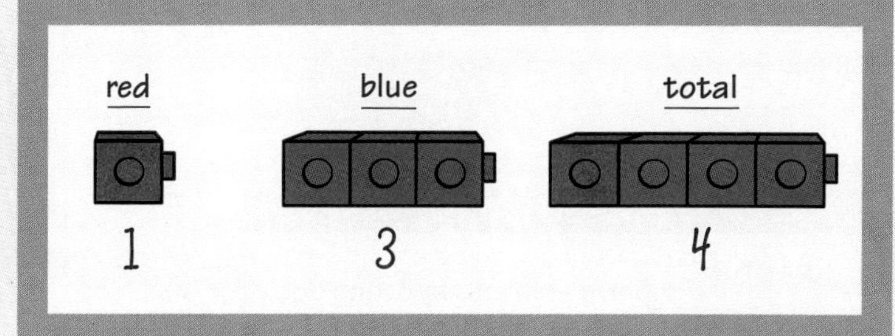

PRACTICE • 14

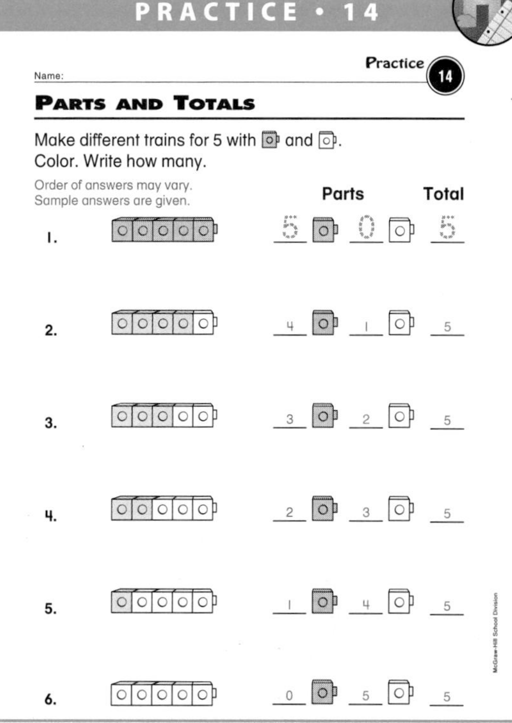

Name: Practice 14

Parts and Totals

Make different trains for 5 with ▢ and ▢. Color. Write how many.

Order of answers may vary. Sample answers are given.

	Parts				Total
1.	5	▢	0	▢	5
2.	4	▢	1	▢	5
3.	3	▢	2	▢	5
4.	2	▢	3	▢	5
5.	1	▢	4	▢	5
6.	0	▢	5	▢	5

RETEACH • 14

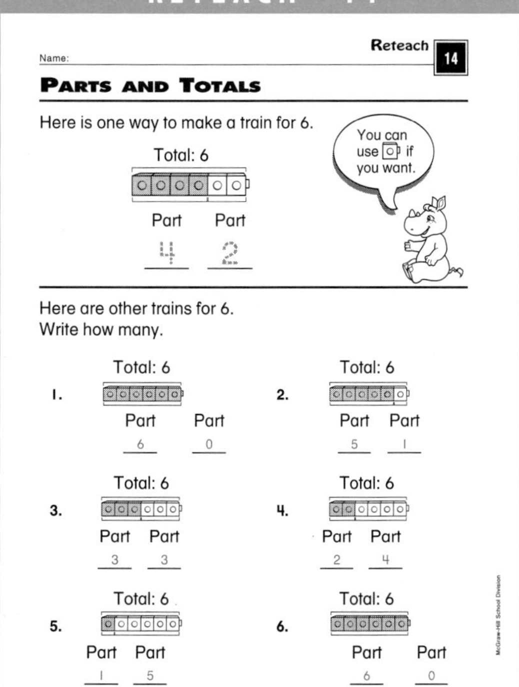

Name: Reteach 14

Parts and Totals

Here is one way to make a train for 6.

Total: 6

Part 4 Part 2

You can use ▢ if you want.

Here are other trains for 6. Write how many.

1. Total: 6 — Part 6, Part 0
2. Total: 6 — Part 5, Part 1
3. Total: 6 — Part 3, Part 3
4. Total: 6 — Part 2, Part 4
5. Total: 6 — Part 1, Part 5
6. Total: 6 — Part 6, Part 0

EXTEND • 14

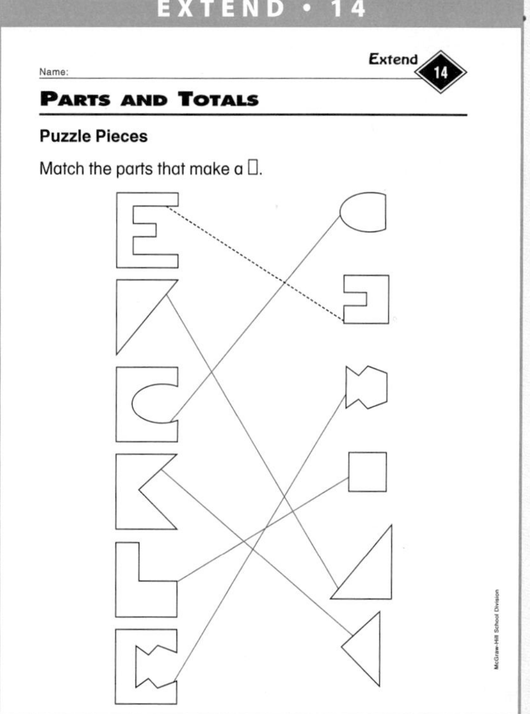

Name: Extend 14

Parts and Totals

Puzzle Pieces

Match the parts that make a ▢.

LESSON 2.3

Problem-Solving Strategy: Act It Out

OBJECTIVE Solve oral problems by acting out part-part-whole situations.

Day 1 Problem-Solving Strategy: Act It Out

RESOURCE REMINDER
Math Center Cards 12
Practice 15, Reteach 15, Extend 15

SKILLS TRACE	
GRADE K	• Solve problems by acting out part-part-whole situations. *(Chapter 11)*
GRADE 1	• Solve problems by acting out part-part-whole situations.
GRADE 2	• Solve problems by acting out part-part-whole situations. *(Chapter 1)*

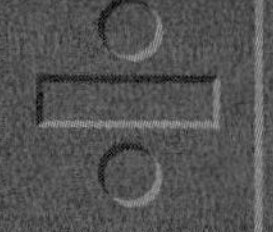

LESSON RESOURCES

MANIPULATIVE WARM-UP

Cooperative Pairs — **Social**

OBJECTIVE Explore solving problems by acting out part-part-whole situations.

Materials per pair: play money—10 pennies; paper plate

▶ Give partners 10 pennies and a paper plate. Tell children to listen carefully to the stories you are going to tell them. After reading each story, have one partner act out the story and the other child check that the answer is correct.

Scott has 3 pennies.
His uncle gives him 1 penny.
How many pennies does he have?
[4]

Kaya has 7 pennies.
She wants to save 4 pennies.
How many pennies can she give her sister? *[3]*

▶ Present similar stories for children to act out.

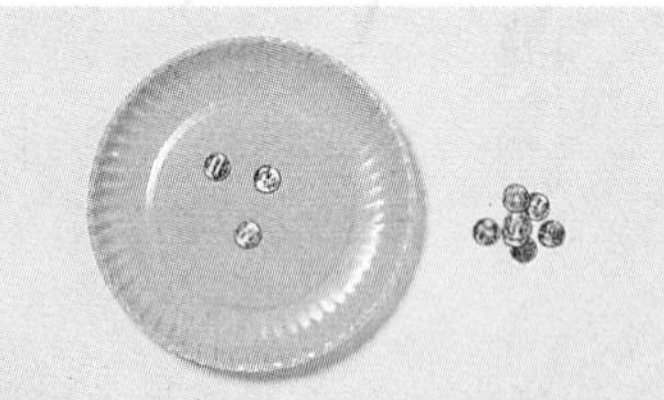

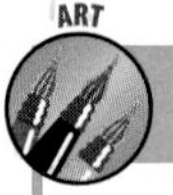

CONNECTION ACTIVITY

Whole Class — **Visual/Spatial**

OBJECTIVE Connect solving problems with art.

Resource Literature Big Book: *Bus Stops*

Materials 11 chairs; crayons

▶ Tell children they are going to make a class "Bus Stops" book. First, set up 11 chairs for the driver and passengers. Then, have children act out illustrations in *Bus Stops* before beginning their own book.

▶ Tell each child to draw a scene from *Bus Stops* to put in the class book. Talk about what they might draw. *[Sample answer: Two children get off the bus, four children are still on the bus.]*

▶ Have children label their illustrations with the appropriate numbers.

DAILY MATH

PREVIOUS DAY QUICK REVIEW

1. What is the red part? *[2]*
2. What is the blue part? *[1]*
3. What is the total? *[3]*

Problem of the Day • 12

Read aloud to children:

There are 7 children on the bus.
No one got on the bus at the bus stop.
How many children are on the bus? *[7]*

TECH LINK

MATH VAN

Tool You may wish to use counters with this lesson.

MATH FORUM

Management Tip Review with children some tips for listening and speaking. For example, children must listen to each complete sentence before deciding what to do.

Visit our Resource Village at http://www.mhschool.com to see more of the Math Forum.

MATH CENTER

Practice

OBJECTIVE Formulate an oral problem using part-part-whole.

Materials 5 red and 5 blue connecting cubes, paper bag, Math Center Recording Sheet (TA 38 optional)

One child puts some connecting cubes of each color in the bag. He or she gives it to the partner, who takes out the cubes and counts them, then makes up a story about the parts. *[Parts and totals may vary.]*

PRACTICE ACTIVITY 12 — MATH CENTER — Partners

Using Data • Part-Part-Whole Stories

Take turns.

- Put some red and blue in a bag.
- Give the bag to your partner. Your partner takes out and counts the parts.
- Your partner tells a story about the parts.

Write the parts and the total.

YOU NEED
5 red
5 blue
bag

Grade Level 1 — McGraw-Hill School Division

Chapter 2, Lesson 3 — Addition

NCTM Standards
- ✓ Problem Solving
- ✓ Communication
- ✓ Reasoning
- ✓ Connections

Problem Solving

OBJECTIVE Solve oral problems by acting out part-part-whole situations.

Materials per pair: 5 red and 5 blue connecting cubes, egg carton

Prepare Remove two sections from each 12-egg carton. Children put red and blue cubes in an egg carton, and make up a problem for their partner to answer. *[Answers may vary. Partners check each other's answers.]*

PROBLEM-SOLVING ACTIVITY 12 — MATH CENTER — Partners

Formulating Problems • Eggs in a Basket

Take turns.

- Put some red in one part of the carton. Put some blue in another part of the carton.
- Make up a problem.
- Tell it to your partner.
- Your partner tells you the answer.

YOU NEED
5 red
5 blue
egg carton

Grade Level 1 — McGraw-Hill School Division

Chapter 2, Lesson 3 — Addition

NCTM Standards
- ✓ Problem Solving
- ✓ Communication
- ✓ Reasoning
- ✓ Connections

Problem-Solving Strategy: Act It Out

OBJECTIVE Solve oral problems by acting out part-part-whole situations.

Materials have available: 3 sheets of red, 4 sheets of blue construction paper

1 Motivate — Whole Class

Read aloud the following word problems and have groups of children act out the problems for the rest of the class to solve.

There are 3 girls standing up.
There are 2 boys standing up.
How many children are standing up? *[5]*

There are 5 children standing up.
There are 4 boys.
How many of the children are girls? *[1]*

After children have acted out these problems, encourage them to make up their own problems to share with the class.

2 Develop

Page 51

Read aloud to children the word problems shown on the reduced Student Book page in this Teacher's Edition. Then have children act out the problems. You may use the chalkboard to help children visualize each situation or have children use simple props such as red and blue construction paper to represent the trains.

CRITICAL THINKING

After children answer the question on the page, ask:

- **What other ways are there to solve problem 1?** *[Possible answers: Use fingers to show each number and count, draw pictures of the children and count.]*

Page 52

Try These Assign practice problems 1–4.

Read aloud to children the problems on the reduced student page. All problems should be acted out.

More to Explore Pair children so that a child who is having difficulty works with a partner who is proficient at making up problems. Have children share their made-up problems and act them out.

3 Close

Check for Understanding by having children explain how they figured out how to present a problem before they solved it.

Name ______

Problem-Solving Strategy

Act It Out

Read | Plan | Solve | Look Back

Listen to the problem.

1

"There are 3 girls on the bus. There are 2 boys on the bus. How many children are on the bus?"

3 girls   2 boys   5 children

2 At the 

"Five children are at the bus stop. Three children are sitting. How many children are standing?"

5 children   3 sitting   2 standing

3 At the 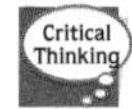

"There are 4 blue trains at the train station. There are 3 red trains at the station. How many red trains and blue trains are at the train station in all?"

4 blue trains   3 red trains   7 trains

Critical Thinking: How can you solve problem 1 using cubes? *Possible answer: 3 red cubes and 2 blue cubes for a total of 5*

CHAPTER 2 *Lesson 3*   fifty-one • 51

MEETING INDIVIDUAL NEEDS

EARLY FINISHERS

Children may write and illustrate their More to Explore problems. Bind the pages together to make a pamphlet. One child can make the cover.

EXTRA SUPPORT

For children who benefit from kinesthetic and auditory cues, reenact "The Wheels on the Bus." For example, sing, "4 people go up and down," then, "2 more people go up and down," for a total of 6.

ONGOING ASSESSMENT

Observation Checklist Determine if children understand the strategy of acting out to solve problems that include parts and wholes. Observe if they place the correct number of counters in each part, and if the solution they supply is the total of the two parts.

Follow Up For children having difficulty, provide a visual cue by placing two-color counters on the picture on page 51 to correspond with the story. Assign **Reteach 15**.

For children who demonstrate understanding, assign **Extend 15**.

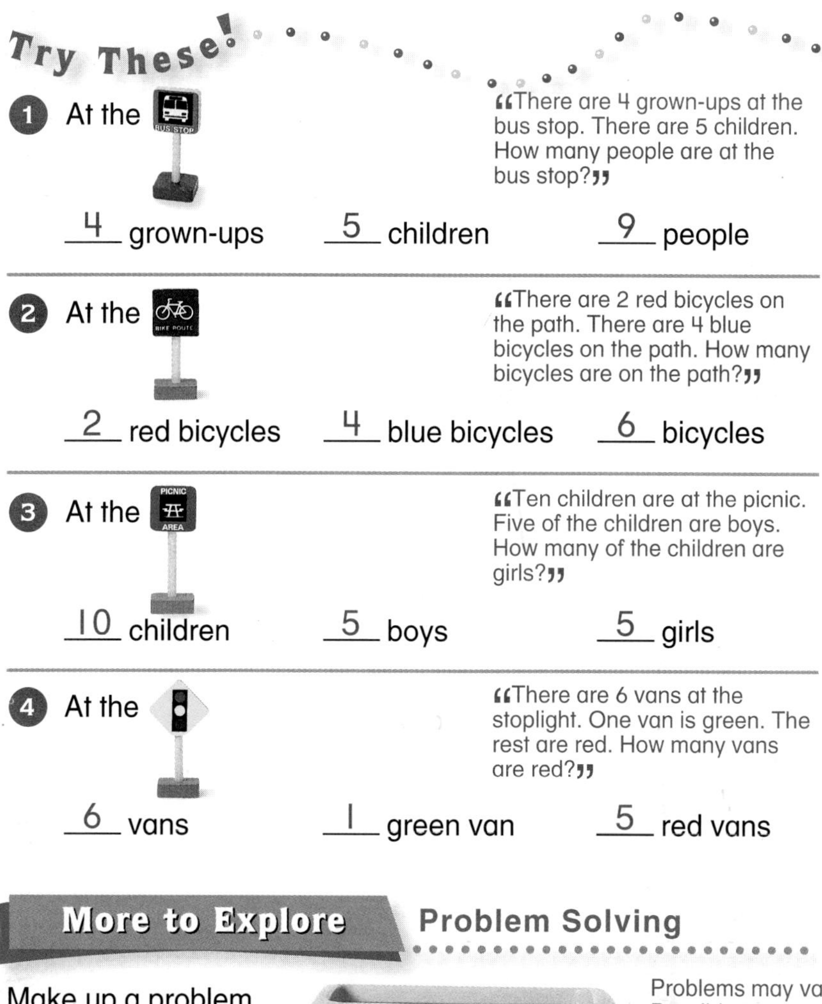

Try These!

1. At the [bus stop sign] "There are 4 grown-ups at the bus stop. There are 5 children. How many people are at the bus stop?"

   4 grown-ups   5 children   9 people

2. At the [bike route sign] "There are 2 red bicycles on the path. There are 4 blue bicycles on the path. How many bicycles are on the path?"

   2 red bicycles   4 blue bicycles   6 bicycles

3. At the [picnic area sign] "Ten children are at the picnic. Five of the children are boys. How many of the children are girls?"

   10 children   5 boys   5 girls

4. At the [stoplight sign] "There are 6 vans at the stoplight. One van is green. The rest are red. How many vans are red?"

   6 vans   1 green van   5 red vans

More to Explore — Problem Solving

Make up a problem.

Problems may vary. Possible answer: There are 3 children at the bus stop. There are 4 children in the bus. How many children in all?

Have your child tell you about the school bus picture above.

Alternate Teaching Strategy

Resources Read-Aloud Anthology, pp. 45–46

Materials per child: 10 two-color counters, sheet of construction paper

Read aloud the verses to "Ten in a Bed" from the Read-Aloud Anthology. Then have children use two-color counters to act out problems. Begin with finding the total for given parts. For example:

There are 2 cats in the bed.
There are 5 cats on the floor.
How many cats are there? *[7]*

Continue with problems about finding a missing part. For example:

There are 8 cats.
If 3 cats are in the bed, how many are on the floor? *[5]*

After you present several problems, have children make up their own problems about cats in the bed.

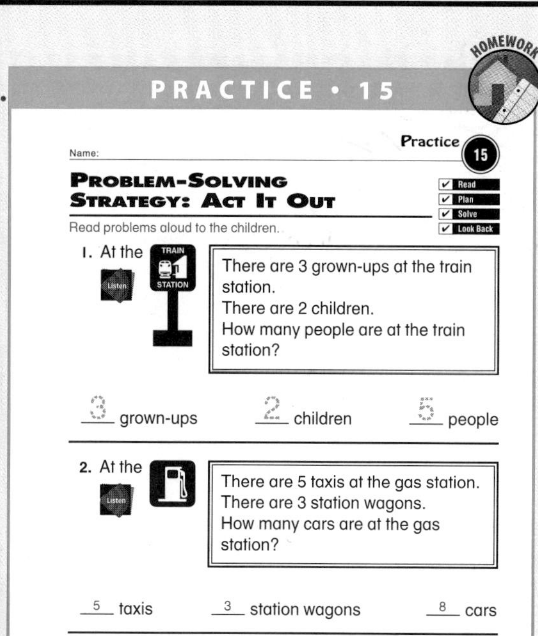

PRACTICE • 15

Practice 15

Name:

Problem-Solving Strategy: Act It Out

Read problems aloud to the children.

1. At the [train station] There are 3 grown-ups at the train station. There are 2 children. How many people are at the train station?

   3 grown-ups   2 children   5 people

2. At the [gas station] There are 5 taxis at the gas station. There are 3 station wagons. How many cars are at the gas station?

   5 taxis   3 station wagons   8 cars

3. At the [pool] 9 children are at the pool. 3 of the children are girls. How many of the children are boys?

   9 children   3 girls   6 boys

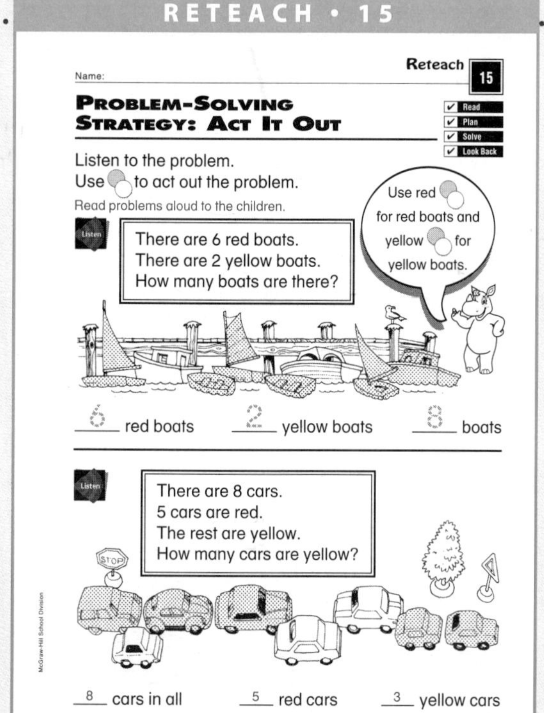

RETEACH • 15

Reteach 15

Name:

Problem-Solving Strategy: Act It Out

Listen to the problem.
Use [counter] to act out the problem.
Read problems aloud to the children.

Use red for red boats and yellow for yellow boats.

There are 6 red boats. There are 2 yellow boats. How many boats are there?

6 red boats   2 yellow boats   8 boats

There are 8 cars. 5 cars are red. The rest are yellow. How many cars are yellow?

8 cars in all   5 red cars   3 yellow cars

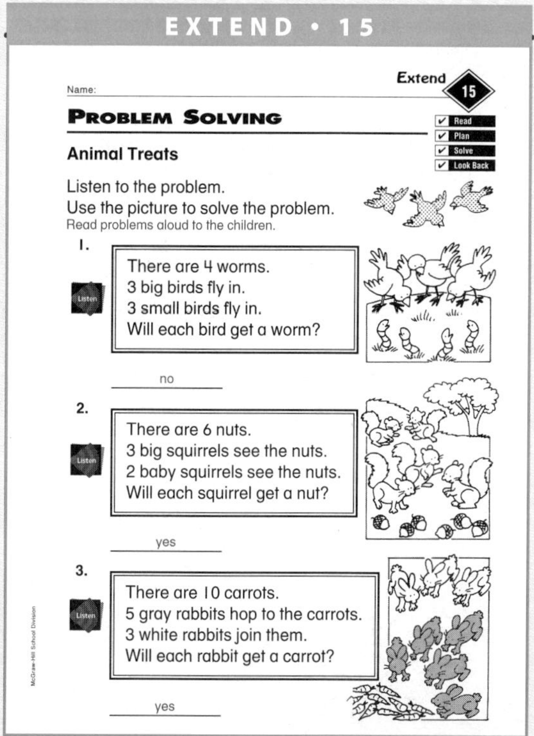

EXTEND • 15

Extend 15

Name:

Problem Solving

Animal Treats

Listen to the problem.
Use the picture to solve the problem.
Read problems aloud to the children.

1. There are 4 worms. 3 big birds fly in. 3 small birds fly in. Will each bird get a worm?

   no

2. There are 6 nuts. 3 big squirrels see the nuts. 2 baby squirrels see the nuts. Will each squirrel get a nut?

   yes

3. There are 10 carrots. 5 gray rabbits hop to the carrots. 3 white rabbits join them. Will each rabbit get a carrot?

   yes

AT A GLANCE

PURPOSE Maintain and review concepts, skills, and strategies that children have learned thus far in the chapter.

Materials per child: 10 red and 10 blue connecting cubes, 10 rhino counters; 1 red crayon, 1 blue crayon

Using the Midchapter Review

Page 53

The **Midchapter Review** may be completed independently or by the class as a whole. Tell children they may use red and blue connecting cubes to make the trains in exercises 1–4. Some children may use cubes or rhino counters to help them understand problem 5.

JOURNAL Have connecting cubes available. Children make, draw, and color as many different trains for 6 as they can. *[6 red; 5 red and 1 blue; 4 red and 2 blue; 3 red and 3 blue; 2 red and 4 blue; 1 red and 5 blue; 6 blue]* Look at children's journals to see how many different trains they draw, how they color them, and whether they write part-part-total numbers to accompany their drawings.

Vocabulary Review

Write the following on the chalkboard:

part **total**

Ask for volunteers to explain, show, or act out the meanings of these words.

Name ______

Midchapter Review

Do your best!

Draw a train.
Write how many ■ and □.

Parts may vary. Possible answers are given.

Total | Parts

1 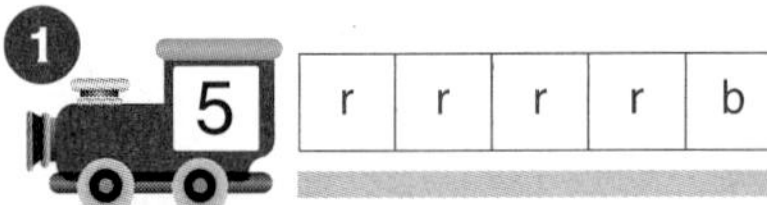 5 r r r r b

4  1

2 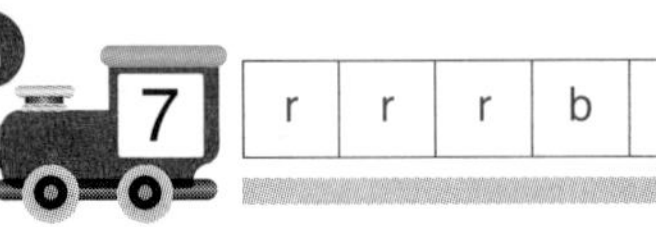 7 r r r b b b b

3 ■ 4 □

Color different trains for 7.
Write the parts and total.

Parts | Total

3 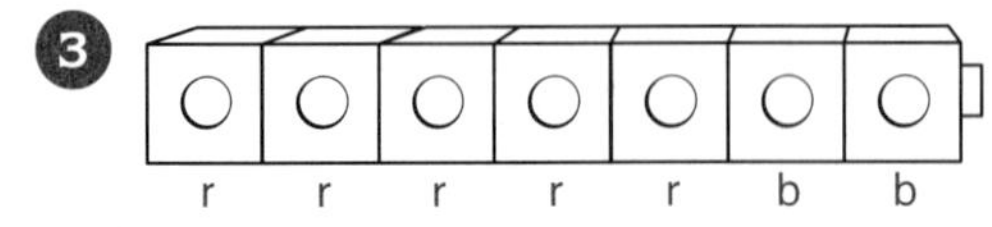 r r r r r b b

5 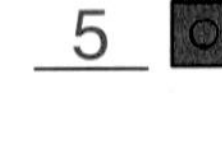 2 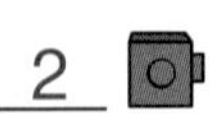 7

4 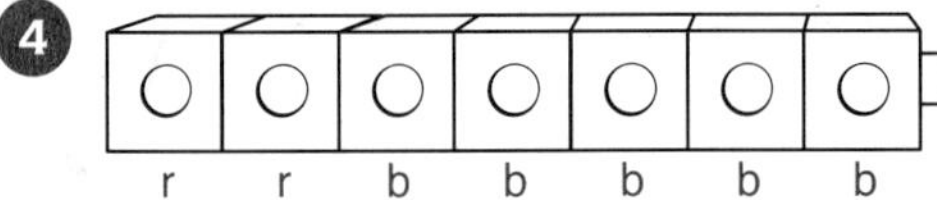 r r b b b b b

2  5 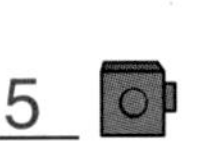 7

5  Listen to the problem.

At the 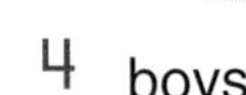

"There are 4 boys at the bus stop. There are 2 girls at the bus stop. How many children are at the bus stop?"

4 boys 2 girls 6 children

 Show as many different trains for 6 as you can.

Children may draw or write numerals for the parts—parts are 6 and 0, 5 and 1, 4 and 2, 3 and 3, 2 and 4, 1 and 5, 0 and 6.

Reinforcement and Remediation

CHAPTER OBJECTIVES	MIDCHAPTER REVIEW ITEMS	STUDENT BOOK PAGES	TEACHER'S EDITION PAGES: Activities	TEACHER'S EDITION PAGES: Alternate Teaching Strategy	TEACHER RESOURCES: Reteach
*2A	1–4	45–50	44A	46	12–14
*2B	5	51–52	50A	52	15
*2D	5	51–52	50A	52	15

*2A Find parts for a whole
*2B Find the whole for given parts
*2C Find a missing part
*2D Solve problems including those that involve parts and wholes, and acting it out

Extra Practice

Game!

Shake and Spill

You need 10 counters and a cup.

- Take turns.
- Put 10 counters in the cup.
- Shake and spill.
- Cross out the row that shows your parts.

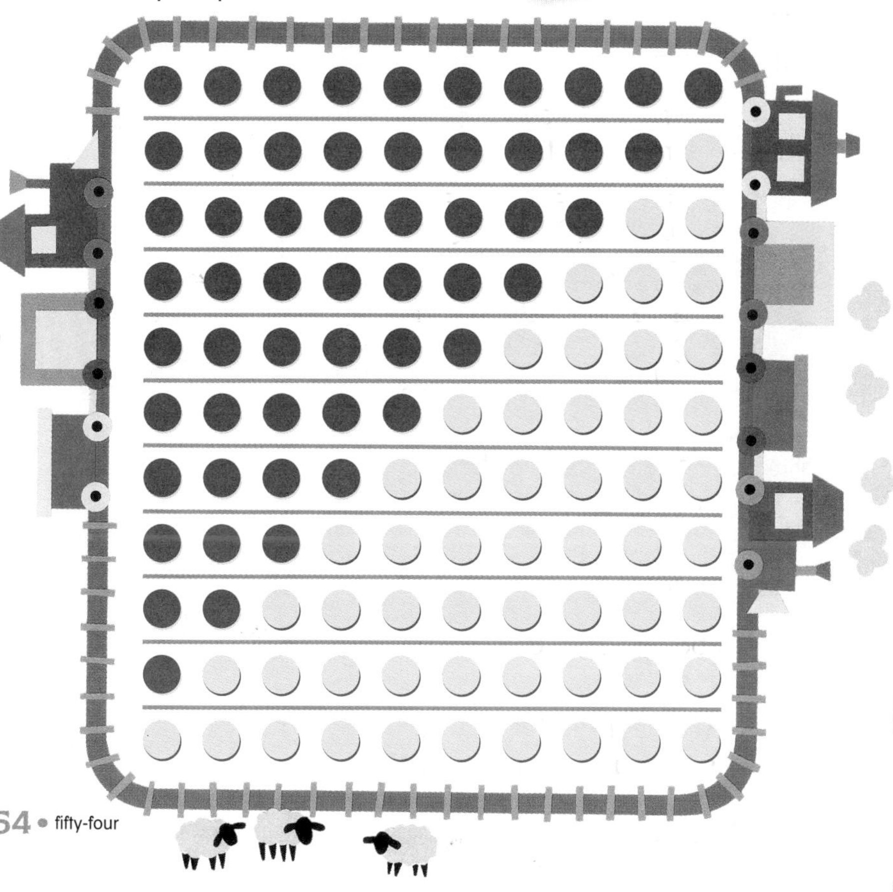

AT A GLANCE

PURPOSE Provide an opportunity for review and practice.

Materials per pair: 10 two-color counters; a cup, a shallow tray or box top

Using the Extra Practice

Page 54

Direct children's attention to the game board.

- **How is a row of 10 counters the same as a cube train for 10? How is it different?** *[Both have parts in 2 different colors, but cubes are connected and counters are not, and the shapes and colors are different.]*

Tell children they will play a game of "Shake and Spill." Explain the rules as you demonstrate with a volunteer.

Players take turns. The first player spills all the counters into a tray. He or she divides them into a red group and a yellow group, and then lines them up—reds first, then yellows. Then the player matches the row of counters to a row on the page and crosses out the row on the page. If that combination has already been crossed out, the player loses a turn.

If time runs out before partners have completed the page, encourage them to continue during free time. After children finish playing, compare results. Then ask:

- **If you wanted to be able to cross out all your rows, how would you change the game board? Why?** *[Possible answers: Don't use the two top rows and the two bottom rows; not many people got those combinations.]*

Using the Additional Practice

The section below provides additional practice that you may want to write on the chalkboard or on a reproducible master.

ADDITIONAL PRACTICE

Write how many in each part. Then write the total.

	Part	Part	Total
1.	*[2]*	*[4]*	*[6]*
2.	*[4]*	*[1]*	*[5]*
3.	*[3]*	*[4]*	*[7]*
4.	*[6]*	*[2]*	*[8]*
5.	*[1]*	*[3]*	*[4]*
6.	*[2]*	*[2]*	*[4]*

Write how many.

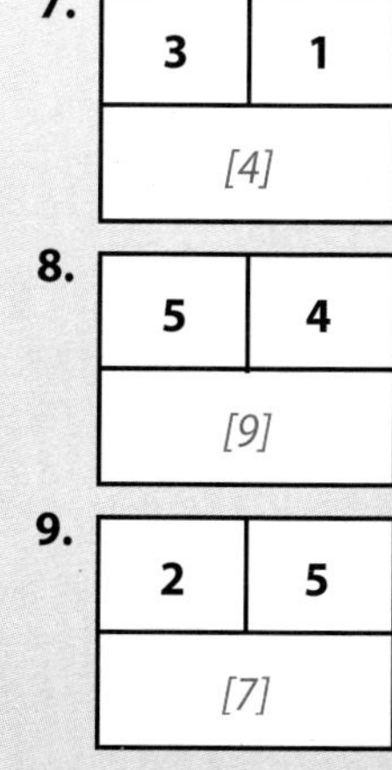

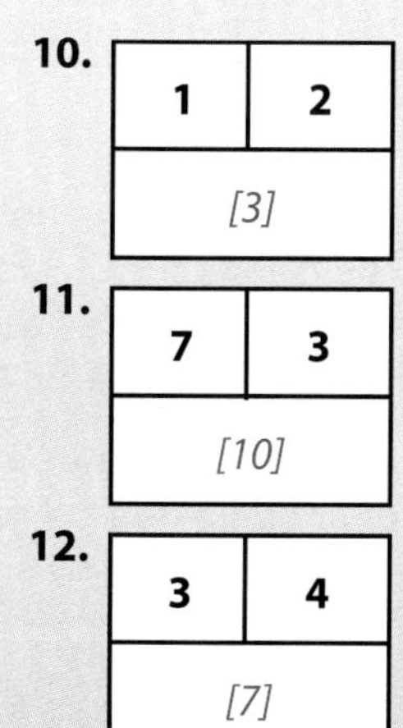

Applying Counting

OBJECTIVE Children use counting in a social studies context.

Materials per group: 25 counters

1 Engage

Tell children that a *survey* is an investigation made in order to answer a question. Explain that children will investigate the question: How do children in this class get to school?

Draw pictures for a tally chart on the chalkboard: a bus, a car, a child walking, a bicycle. Survey children and make tallies on the chart. Then ask questions such as:

- **How many children come to school by bus? by car?**
- **Do more children come by bus or walk?**
- **How do most children in this class get to school?**

Using the Line-ups Strategy, have children line up according to the way they get to school. Children make and discuss mathematical observations about the line-ups.

2 Investigate Cooperative Groups

Page 55

Discuss the meaning of the word *traffic*. *[the movement of vehicles or pedestrians along a street or sidewalk]* Ask children what traffic goes by their school. *[Possible answer: people walking, people riding bicycles, cars, trucks, buses, jeeps]*

Cultural Note Ask children how the bus in the picture is similar to buses they ride or see. *[Possible answers: They have lots of wheels, they carry many people.]*

Working Together Have children work in groups of three to decide what to count and how to record the traffic by their school. You may wish to have each group record a different kind of vehicle. Groups may decide to have each child take a turn observing for 5 minutes to a quarter hour. Children may use counters, make tallies and draw pictures.

3 Reflect and Share

Page 56

Talk about ways each group has counted the vehicles and how the groups could combine the data into one display. Suggest that they make a class graph—a picture graph or a bar graph. Discuss the completed graph.

Write a Report Children can draw pictures to show how they counted and recorded their traffic. They can use numbers and pictures to tell what the graph shows.

Name ____________________

Neighborhood Traffic

What is traffic? Does it go by your school?
Answers may vary.

Working Together

Take a survey.

Decide what to count.

Cultural Note
One way people get around in Haiti is on buses called *tap-taps*.

Show how many your group counted. Answers may vary.
Children can record using pictures, tallies, and so on.

MORE TO INVESTIGATE

Predict Sample answer: At a different time, the traffic could be different, so the numbers could all be different. There could be more cars and fewer trucks. If you counted late at night, the numbers would probably all be smaller.

Explore If possible, choose a time for the new graph when the traffic is likely to be different from the previous time.

Find Discuss possible reasons for differences in the graphs. For example, if the first survey was made in the morning and the second one at lunchtime, the second graph might show more cars because people were going home or somewhere else for lunch.

Bibliography Children may enjoy reading the following book:

Earth Movers by Patricia Armentrout and David Armentrout. Vero Beach, FL: Rourke Book Company, 1989. ISBN 1–55916–131–0.

Decision Making Answers may vary. See Teacher's Edition for sample of children's work.

Decide how to show what you learned about traffic.
You could make a class graph.

Write a report.

1. Show how you counted and recorded.
2. Tell what the class graph shows.

More to Investigate

See Teacher's Edition.

PREDICT What if you counted at a different time. What would the numbers show?

EXPLORE Choose a different time. Take a survey. Make a new class graph.

FIND How are the graphs the same? How are the graphs different?

BUILDING A PORTFOLIO

This assignment will provide insight into children's ability to find data by counting and to organize and interpret the numbers that represent the data.

Allow children to revise their work for the portfolio. Each child's portfolio piece should consist of his or her written report and any notes you made about the child's work.

You may wish to use the Holistic Scoring Guide to assess this task. See page 27 in Teacher's Assessment Resources.

Children's Work

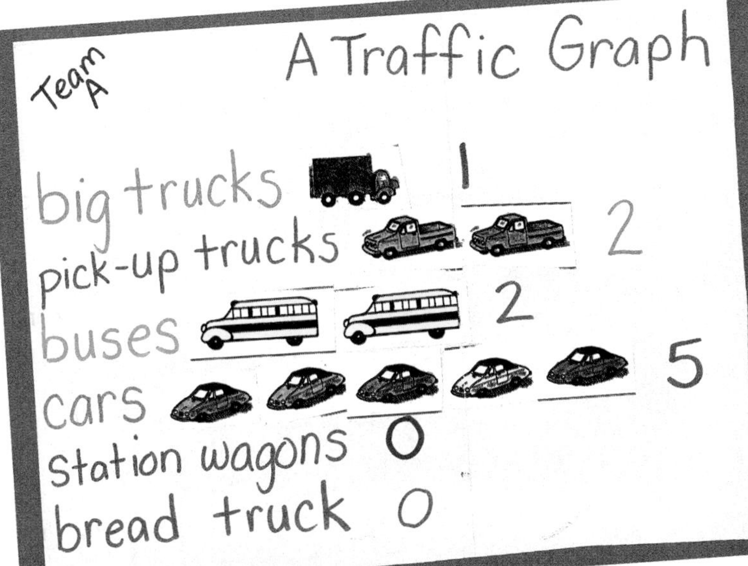

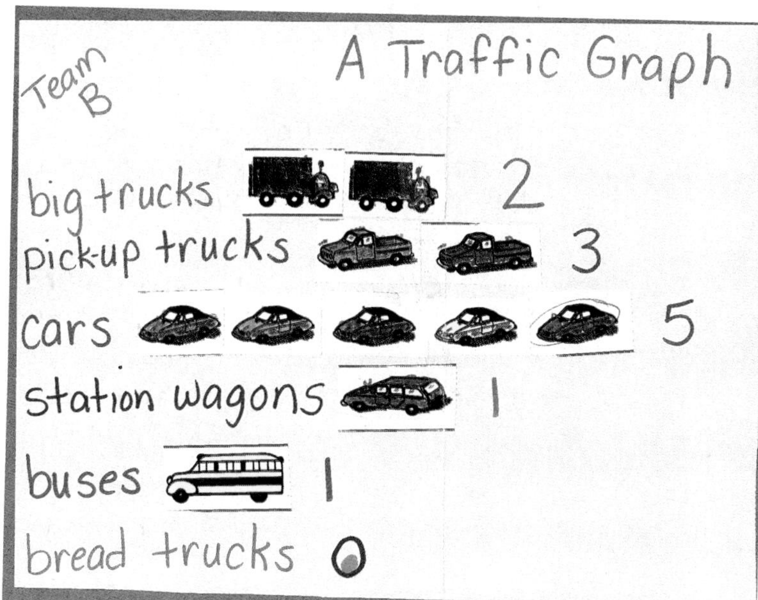

Alex
Snowden school is on a busy street. Team B counted traffic going east. We found out... Team B found more pick-up trucks. Neather team found bread trucks. Team A counted more buses.

Find the Total

OBJECTIVE Find the whole for given parts.

Day 1 More Parts and Totals
Day 2 Find the Total

Teaching with Technology
See alternate computer lesson on pp. 60A–60B.

RESOURCE REMINDER
Math Center Cards 13
Practice 16–17, Reteach 16–17, Extend 16–17

SKILLS TRACE

GRADE K	• Explore finding the whole for given parts. *(Chapter 11)*
GRADE 1	• Find the whole for given parts.
GRADE 2	• Explore finding totals for parts; parts for totals. *(Chapter 1)*

LESSON RESOURCES

WARM-UP

Whole Class | **Visual/Spatial**

OBJECTIVE Explore finding the whole for given parts.

Materials masking tape

▶ Use tape to outline a large part-part-whole mat on the floor. Read to children the following part-part-whole story, and have volunteers act it out by standing in the *Part* sections of the mat.

Three children are building sand castles.
Two more children join them.

▶ Then have the children move to the *Total* section of the mat and ask:

- **How many children are now building sand castles?** *[5]*

▶ Repeat with similar part-part-whole stories.

CONNECTION ACTIVITY

Cooperative Pairs | **Kinesthetic**

OBJECTIVE Connect finding the total for given parts and money.

Materials per pair: play money—10 pennies; Workmat 3 (part-part-whole mat); cup

▶ Have partners identify the "heads" side and the "tails" side of a penny.

▶ One child puts some of the pennies into a cup, and spills the pennies onto the desk. Both children place the coins showing heads on one part of the mat and the coins showing tails on the other part. One child counts the number of heads and the number of tails on the workmat; the other child verifies the count. Together they count all the coins to find the total.

▶ Partners repeat the activity several times.

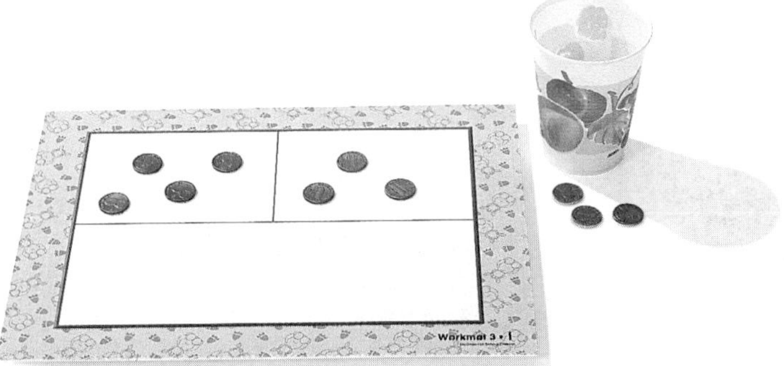

DAILY MATH

PREVIOUS DAY QUICK REVIEW

1. Make 2 different trains for 4. *[Possible trains: 4 red, 0 yellow; 3 red, 1 yellow]*
2. Make 2 different trains for 5. *[Possible trains: 5 red, 0 yellow; 3 red, 2 yellow]*

Problem of the Day • 13

Read aloud to children:

Kayla has 3 red cars.
Janell has 1 yellow car.
Carlos has 1 red car.
How many red cars are there? *[4]*

TECH LINK

MATH VAN

Tool You may wish to use counters with this lesson.

MATH FORUM

Multi-Age Classes I pair children who are ready for work with larger numbers. One child places numbers greater than 10 in the *Part* sections and the other child finds the total.

Visit our Resource Village at http://www.mhschool.com to see more of the Math Forum.

MATH CENTER

Practice

OBJECTIVE Find the whole for given parts.

Materials per child: 10 two-color counters, 3 part-part-whole workmats (TA 5), crayons, cup

Each child puts a handful of counters (any or all of 10) in a cup and spills them to find the parts and the whole. *[Answers may vary. Check the 3 workmats to see that the parts and totals are correct.]*

PRACTICE ACTIVITY 13 — MATH CENTER, On Your Own

Manipulatives • Number Toss

- Put some ◯ in a cup.
- Shake and spill.
- Count how many of each color.
- Put each color on a different part of the workmat.
- Write the parts and the total.
- Do this 3 more times.

YOU NEED: 10 ◯, cup, 3 workmats, crayons

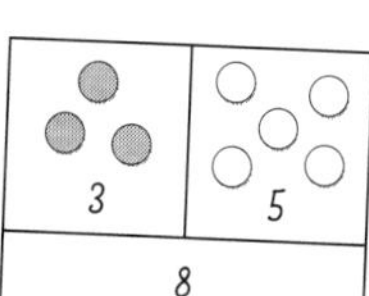

Chapter 2, Lesson 4 — Addition

NCTM Standards
- ✓ Problem Solving
- ✓ Communication
- ✓ Reasoning
- Connections

Problem Solving

OBJECTIVE Find the whole for given parts.

Materials per pair: 10 two-color counters, bag, dot cards (TA 2 and 3), crayon, Math Center Recording Sheet (TA 38 optional)

The number for each part reflects the number of red and yellow sides. *[Check that the parts equal the whole.]*

PROBLEM-SOLVING ACTIVITY 13 — MATH CENTER, On Your Own

Using Data • It's In the Bag

- Put 10 ◯ in the cup.
- Spill some out. That is the total.
- Find two cards that make the same total.
- Draw a picture of the cards and write the total.

Do this 3 more times.

YOU NEED: 10 ◯, cup, set of dot cards, crayon

Chapter 2, Lesson 4 — Addition

NCTM Standards
- ✓ Problem Solving
- ✓ Communication
- ✓ Reasoning
- Connections

More Parts and Totals

OBJECTIVE Children find the whole for given parts.

Materials per child: 10 two-color counters; Workmat 3 (part-part-whole mat)

1 Motivate — Whole Class

Resources Jumbo Activity Book, page 4; Stickers, sheet 1 (red and yellow round counters)

Write the word *Total* in the Total section of the page and *Part* in each Part section. Place 3 red counters and 1 yellow counter in the Part sections. Ask volunteers to count the counters in each Part. Then ask a child to write the total number of counters in the appropriate section of the mat.

Repeat several times, inviting children to suggest the number of red and yellow counters. Use the vocabulary *part* and *total* throughout.

2 Develop

Page 57

Children work individually using red and yellow counters and part-part-whole mats to help them duplicate the exercises. They count to find the total. Do the first exercise with children and write the total 6 as shown.

CRITICAL THINKING

Have children act out the following:

- **Move a yellow counter to a red Part. Does the total change? Why?** *[No; one Part gets 1 more counter and the other Part gets 1 fewer counter, so the total is the same.]*

Children may want to experiment by moving different numbers of counters to see if the results are the same.

Name ____________

More Parts and Totals

You need 10 counters and a part-part-whole mat.

- Show the parts.
- Write the total.

1. Total: 6
2. Total: 3
3. Total: 5
4. Total: 8

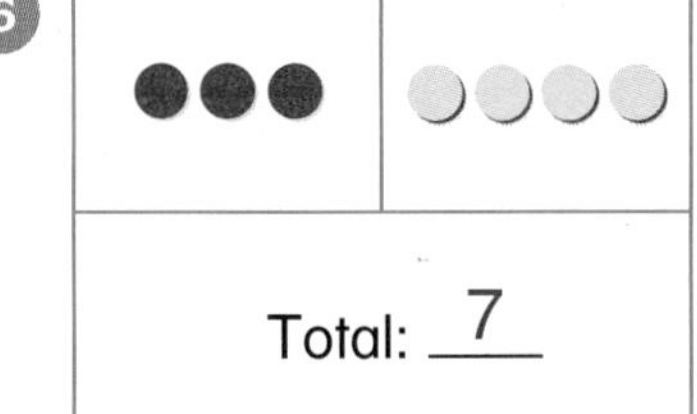

5. Total: 7

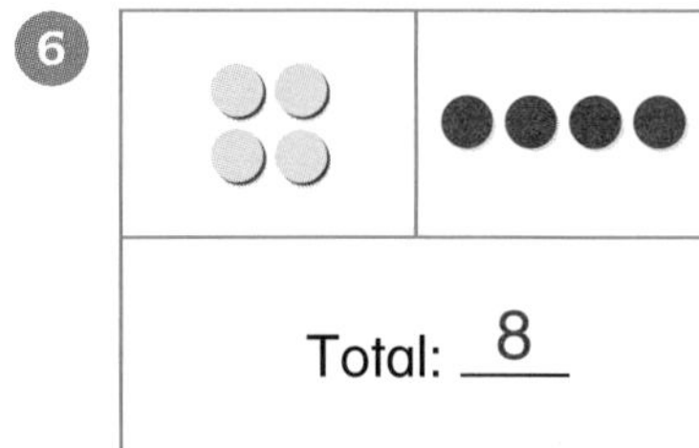

6. Total: 8

Suppose you move a red counter to a yellow part. Does the total change? Why? No; one part gets bigger and the other gets smaller.

MEETING INDIVIDUAL NEEDS

COMMON ERROR

Some children may miscount the counters in each Part of the mat. Suggest that they line up the counters in a row and count on to find the total as they did when they used cube trains.

GENDER FAIRNESS

If some children tend to call out, say "I will call on someone who is raising her or his hand," and do so.

ONGOING ASSESSMENT

Observation Checklist Determine if children understand finding the whole for given parts by observing if they can represent the problems on pages 57 and 58 and then write the correct total on the page.

Follow Up For children having difficulty, encourage them to count the counters and say the total amount. Assign **Reteach 16**.

For children who demonstrate understanding, assign **Extend 16**.

Try These!

How many cars in all?
Find the total.

1  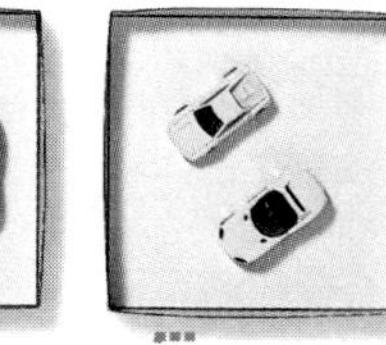
Total: 5

2  
Total: 6

3 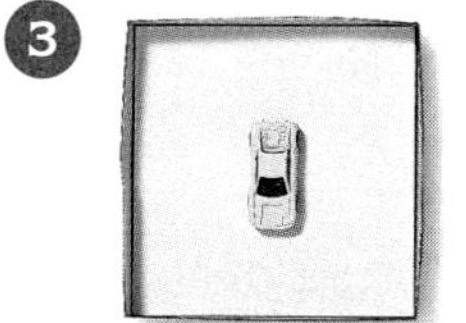 
Total: 4

4  
Total: 7

5 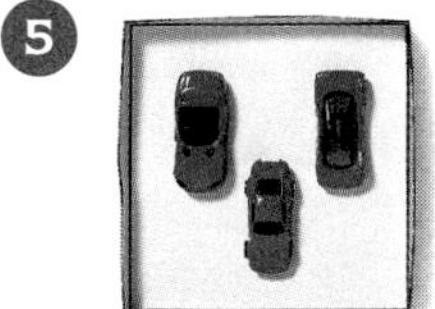 
Total: 6

6  
Total: 8

7  
Total: 7

8 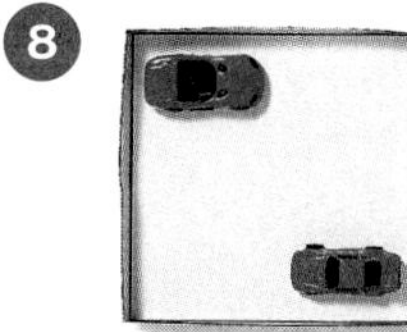 
Total: 2

Ask your child to explain how to find the total number of cars in the pairs of boxes.

Page 58

Try These Assign practice exercises 1–8.

Children may use the red and yellow counters and the part-part-whole mat to complete the exercises.

3 Close

Check for Understanding by asking children how they found the total for any one of the exercises.

- **How did you find the total number of cars for this problem?** *[I counted all the red and yellow cars together.]*

Tomorrow children will continue finding the total for given parts.

PRACTICE • 16

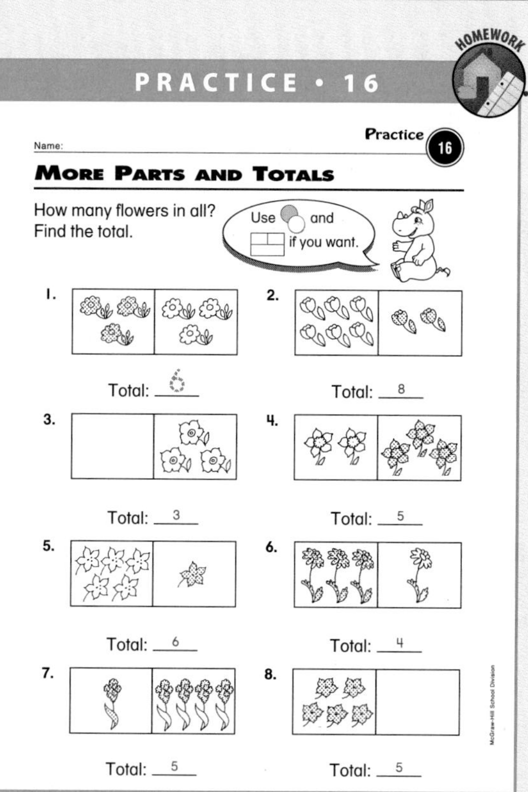
Practice 16

Name:

MORE PARTS AND TOTALS

How many flowers in all?
Find the total.

1. Total: 6
2. Total: 8
3. Total: 3
4. Total: 5
5. Total: 6
6. Total: 4
7. Total: 5
8. Total: 5

RETEACH • 16

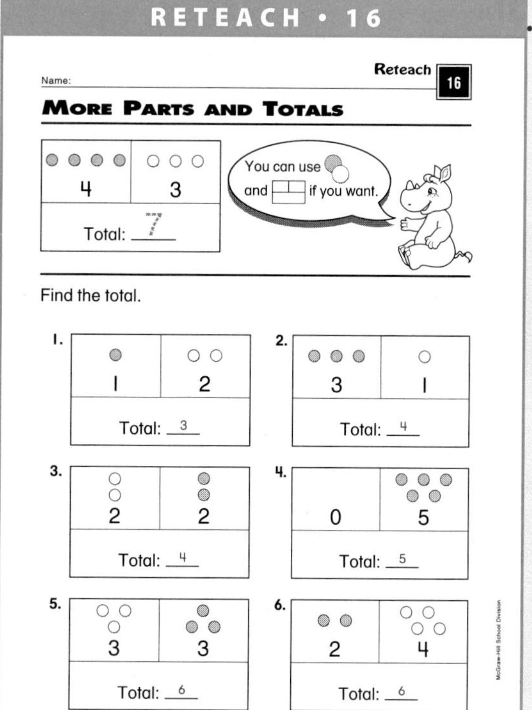
Reteach 16

Name:

MORE PARTS AND TOTALS

4	3
Total: 7	

Find the total.

1. 1 | 2 — Total: 3
2. 3 | 1 — Total: 4
3. 2 | 2 — Total: 4
4. 0 | 5 — Total: 5
5. 3 | 3 — Total: 6
6. 2 | 4 — Total: 6

EXTEND • 16

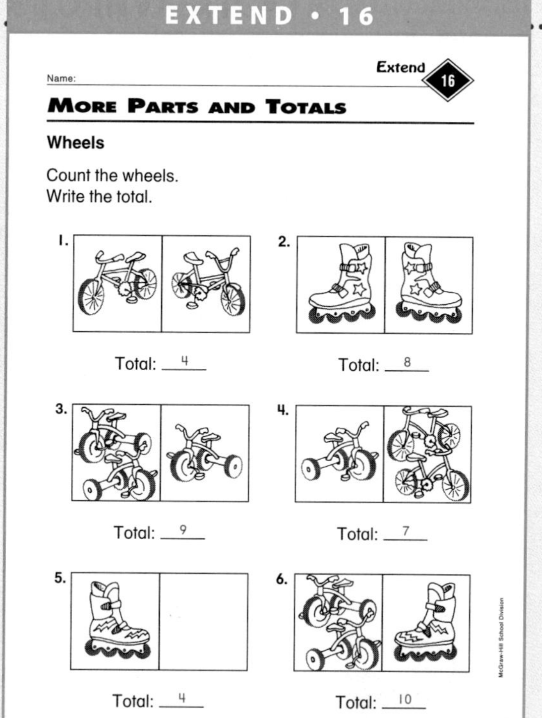
Extend 16

Name:

MORE PARTS AND TOTALS

Wheels

Count the wheels.
Write the total.

1. Total: 4
2. Total: 8
3. Total: 9
4. Total: 7
5. Total: 4
6. Total: 10

DAY 2

Find the Total

OBJECTIVE Children find the whole for given parts.

Materials per child: 10 two-color counters; Workmat 3 (part-part-whole mat)

1 Motivate — Whole Class

Materials Workmat 3 (part-part-whole mat), red chalk, yellow chalk

In this lesson, children make the transition from using manipulatives to writing numbers. Recording is presented in the same basic format (part-part-whole mat) using numbers in both the *Parts* and the *Total* sections of the mat.

Copy Workmat 3 onto the chalkboard. Write 2 in one *Part* section in red and 4 in the other in yellow. Ask:

- **What do you think the numbers 2 and 4 stand for?** *[Possible answer: the counters that we have been putting there]*

Next, have children draw a corresponding number of red and yellow counters next to the number in each *Part* of the mat on the chalkboard. Have another child count all the counters and write the number in the *Total* section.

Repeat the activity with other numbers. Guide children to discover that they can find the total without counters.

2 Develop

Page 59

Children work individually using counters and a workmat to show each part and then count to find the total. Complete the first exercise with children and write the total 7 as shown.

Critical Thinking
Have children use counters to demonstrate the possible combinations for 8. Then refer to exercise 5 and ask:

- **How many ways can you show 6?** *[7 ways—6 + 0, 5 + 1, 4 + 2, 3 + 3, 2 + 4, 1 + 5, 0 + 6]*

Page 60

Try These Assign practice exercises 1–6.

Mixed Review Children review the skill of identifying the number of objects in a group.

3 Close

Check for Understanding by having children tell you how they found the total for any of the exercises 1–6 on page 60.

- **In exercise 3, how did you find the total?** *[Possible answer: I thought of 1 counter and then 4 counters as the parts and then counted in my head.]*

Name ______________________

Find the Total

You need 10 counters and a workmat.

Find the total.

1

2	5
7	

2 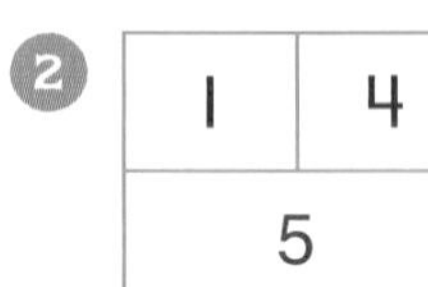

3 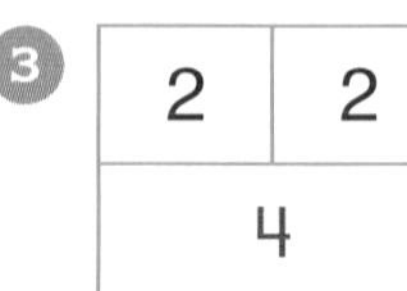

4 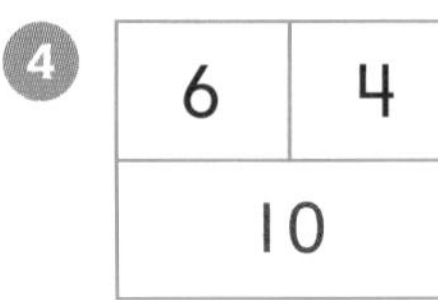

5 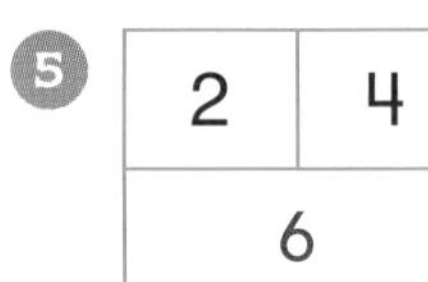

6 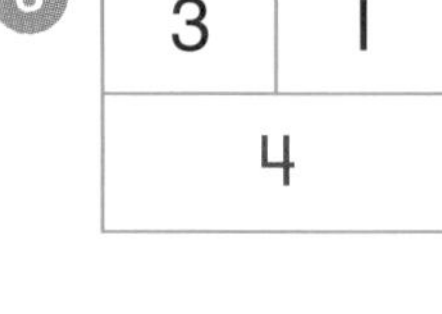

7 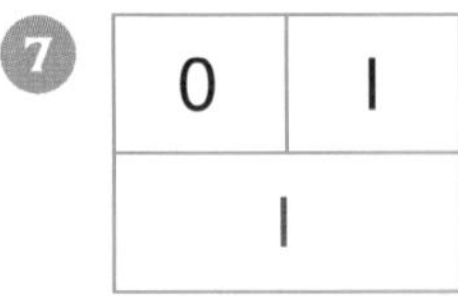

8 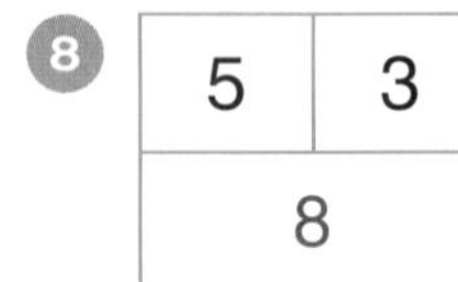

9 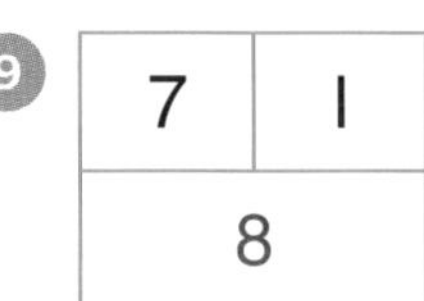

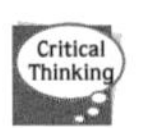

How can you show 8 another way?
Possible answers: 1 and 7, 6 and 2, 4 and 4, 8 and 0, 3 and 5

MEETING INDIVIDUAL NEEDS

EARLY FINISHERS

Have children draw a picture of a number of objects and the corresponding number to reinforce the skill in **Mixed Review.**

EXTRA SUPPORT

List the ways children may have represented parts so far in the chapter: groups of children, cubes, counters. Brainstorm other items and have children use them to act out finding the total.

ONGOING ASSESSMENT

Anecdotal Report Make note of children who have easily made the transition from using counters to using numbers to find the total. Also make note of children who may need more help and practice in order to make this transition.

Follow Up For children having difficulty, assign **Reteach 17** and allow them to use counters to help them find the total.

Children demonstrating success with the exercises on page 60 may work on **Extend 17**.

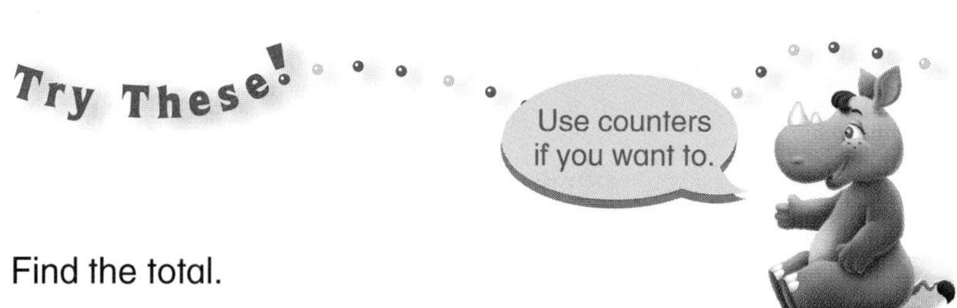

Find the total.

1. 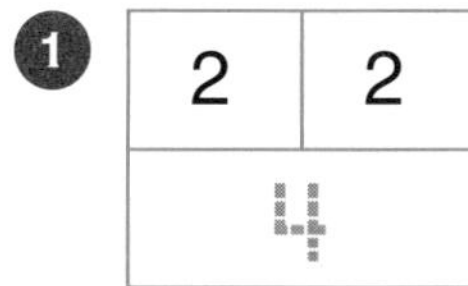
2	2
4	

2. 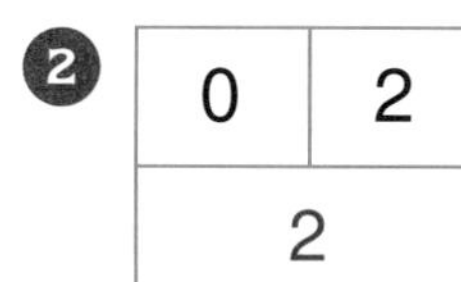
0	2
2	

3. 
1	4
5	

4. 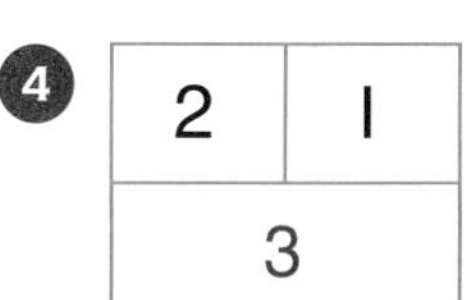
2	1
3	

5. 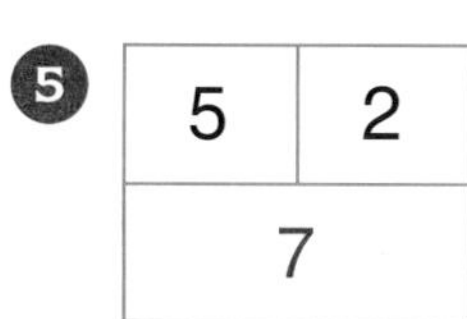
5	2
7	

6. 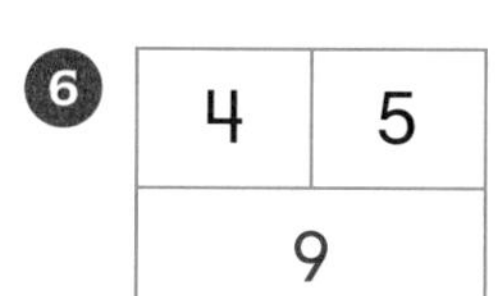
4	5
9	

Mixed Review

Write how many.

7. 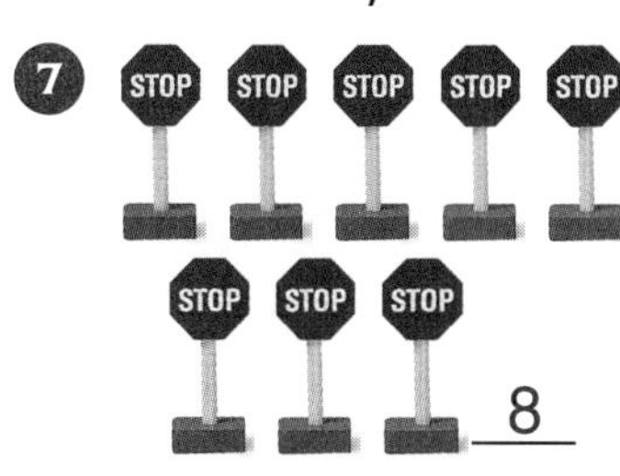

8

8. 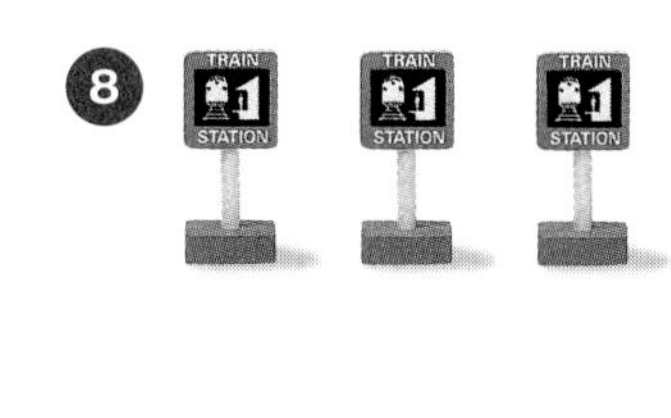

3

9. 
5

10. 
1

Put 3 things in your left hand. Put 2 things in your right hand. Ask your child to find the total.

Alternate Teaching Strategy

Materials per pair: 10 two-color counters; Workmat 3 (part-part-whole mat); number cards 0-10 (TA 9)

Present this problem:

You have 3 red apples in one bowl.
You have 2 yellow apples in another bowl.
How many apples do you have in all? Find the total. *[5]*

Read the problem again as you act it out with the red and yellow counters on Workmat 3. Have a volunteer place the number card for the total on the mat.

Repeat the word problem several times, each time substituting different numbers. Have partners solve each problem using counters to act out the situation.

PRACTICE • 17

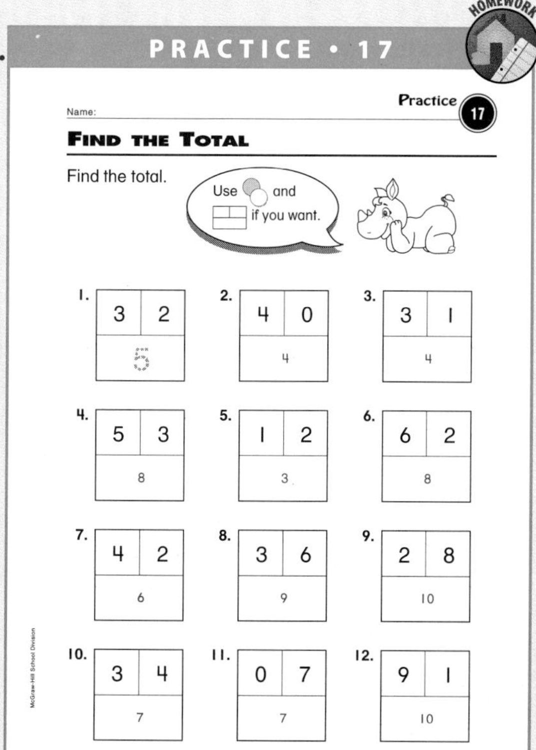

Name:
Practice 17

Find the Total

Find the total.

Use and if you want.

1. 3, 2 — 5	2. 4, 0 — 4	3. 3, 1 — 4
4. 5, 3 — 8	5. 1, 2 — 3	6. 6, 2 — 8
7. 4, 2 — 6	8. 3, 6 — 9	9. 2, 8 — 10
10. 3, 4 — 7	11. 0, 7 — 7	12. 9, 1 — 10

RETEACH • 17

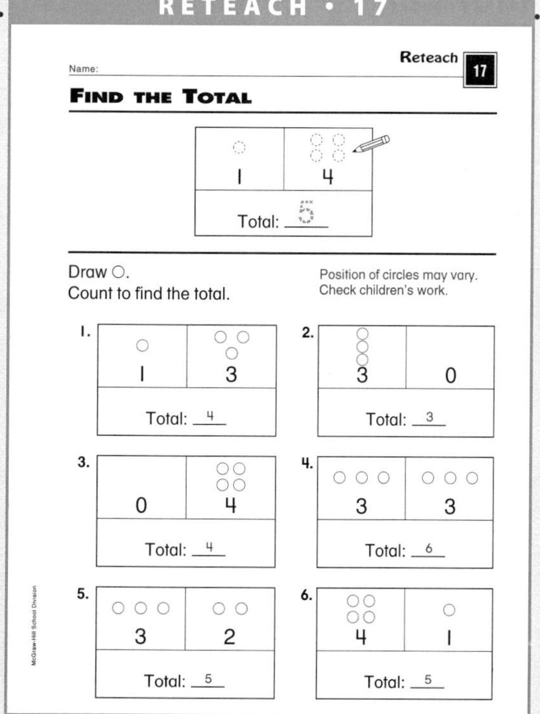

Name:
Reteach 17

Find the Total

1, 4 — Total: 5

Draw ○.
Count to find the total.

Position of circles may vary. Check children's work.

1. 1, 3 — Total: 4	2. 3, 0 — Total: 3
3. 0, 4 — Total: 4	4. 3, 3 — Total: 6
5. 3, 2 — Total: 5	6. 4, 1 — Total: 5

EXTEND • 17

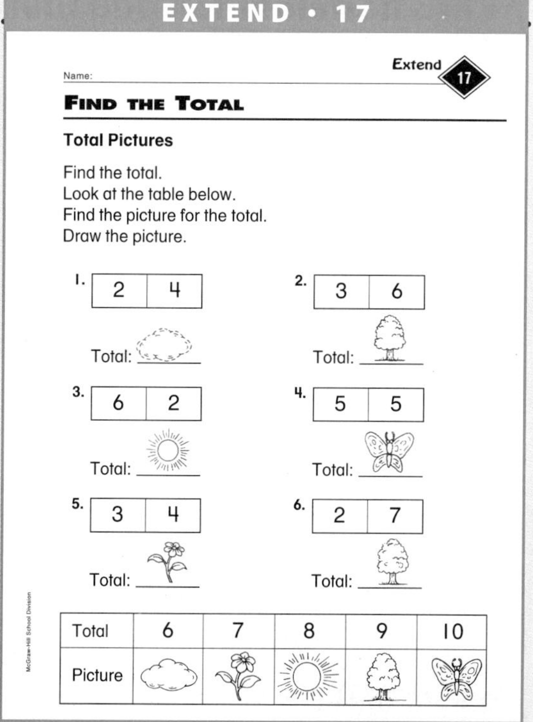

Name:
Extend 17

Find the Total

Total Pictures

Find the total.
Look at the table below.
Find the picture for the total.
Draw the picture.

1. 2, 4 — Total:	2. 3, 6 — Total:
3. 6, 2 — Total:	4. 5, 5 — Total:
5. 3, 4 — Total:	6. 2, 7 — Total:

Total	6	7	8	9	10
Picture					

Teaching With Technology

Find the Total

OBJECTIVE Children find the whole for given parts.

Resource Math Van Activity: *Floating Total*

SET UP

Launch the ***Math Van*** program. Click the right arrow to locate Activity 2, *Floating Total*. After listening to the activity's description, click *Start*.

USING THE MATH VAN ACTIVITY

1 **Getting Started** Allow children to explore the Part-Part-Total Mat within the Counters tool. Ask them to stamp two groups of objects and then find the numbers representing the parts and the total.

2 **Practice and Apply** Children use their knowledge of parts and totals to find out how many sailboats are on a lake. They stamp sailboats on the mat, find the total, and then check their answer by looking at the number in the Total box.

3 **Close** Have children show the pictures from their Math Journal and discuss their work with you, each other, or the class.

Extend Children can create and solve their own parts and totals problems. Have them work with partners and take turns.

TIPS FOR TOOLS

Before children create their own problems, show them how they use the *Start Over* button to clear the screen.

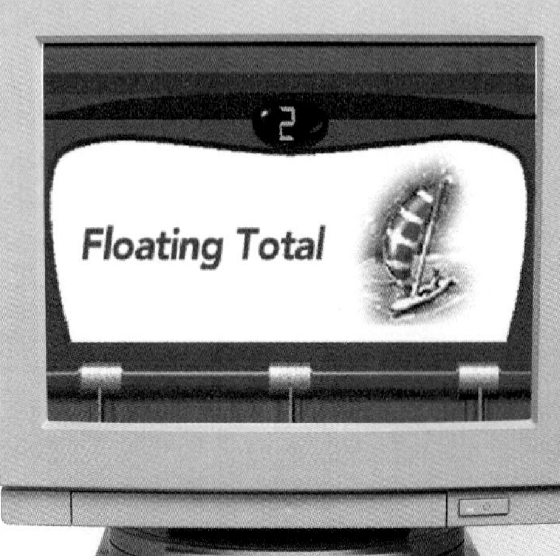

SCREEN 1

Children listen to the *Floating Totals* problem, which asks them to find the total number of sailboats on the lake.

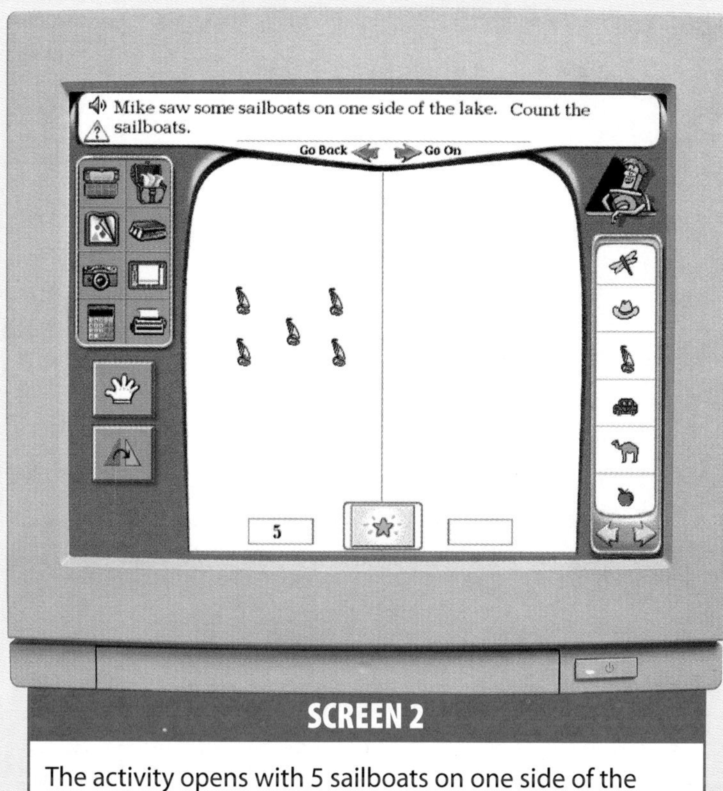

SCREEN 2

The activity opens with 5 sailboats on one side of the Part-Part-Total Mat.

SCREEN 3

Children stamp a second group of sailboats and find the total. They check their answer against the total in the Total box.

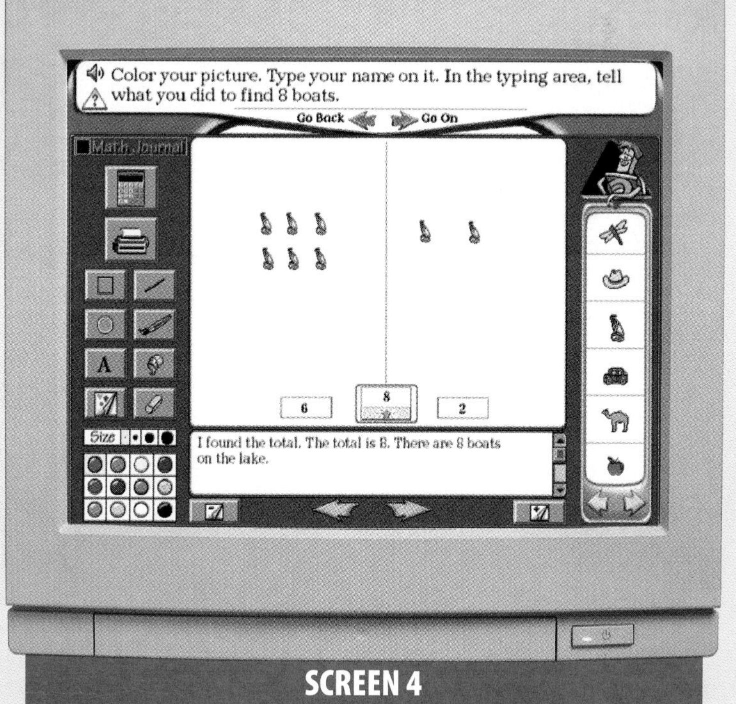

SCREEN 4

Children take a picture of their work. They can draw or type on the picture to explain what they did.

LESSON 2.5

Find the Missing Part

OBJECTIVE Find a part, given a whole and a part.

Day 1 Explore Activity: One Missing Part
Day 2 Find the Missing Part

RESOURCE REMINDER
Math Center Cards 14
Practice 18–19, Reteach 18–19, Extend 18–19

SKILLS TRACE

GRADE K	• Explore finding a part given a whole and a part. *(Chapter 11)*
GRADE 1	• Explore finding a part given a whole and a part.
GRADE 2	• Explore finding totals for parts; parts for totals. *(Chapter 1)*

LESSON RESOURCES

WARM-UP

Whole Class **Logical/Analytical**

OBJECTIVE Explore finding missing parts.

Materials masking tape, chalk

Prepare Using masking tape or chalk, make 4 large Xs on the floor.

▶ Have children count the Xs. Then ask three children to come and each stand on one of the Xs. Ask:

- **How many Xs are there altogether?** *[4]*
- **How many have children standing on them?** *[3]*
- **How many more children should stand on the Xs to make a total of 4?** *[1]*

▶ Challenge children to find and act out other combinations for 4. *[Combinations are 1 and 3, 2 and 2, 4 and 0, 0 and 4.]*

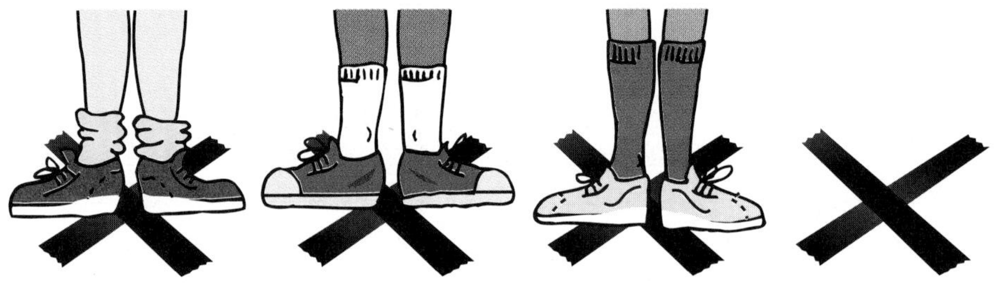

CONNECTION ACTIVITY

Cooperative Pairs **Logical/Analytical**

OBJECTIVE Connect finding a missing part with money.

Materials per pair: play money—10 pennies; 0–9 spinner (TA 7)

▶ One partner counts out 10 pennies. The other partner spins the spinner and covers the number of pennies that the spinner shows. The first partner then counts the number of pennies left in the missing part.

▶ Children continue until they have made all the combinations for 10¢.

DAILY MATH

PREVIOUS DAY QUICK REVIEW

Find the total. Use Workmat 3.

1. 5, 3 *[8]*
2. 3, 6 *[9]*
3. 0, 7 *[7]*
4. 1, 5 *[6]*

Problem of the Day • 14

Read aloud to children:

There are 8 children on the swing.
There are only 6 girls on the swing.
How many boys are on the swing? *[2]*

TECH LINK

MATH VAN

Tool You may wish to use counters with this lesson.

MATH FORUM

Idea I fill zip-closing bags with 2 to 10 beans. Then I draw a line down the middle of the bag. Children show different parts for a total by pushing the beans to either side of the line.

Visit our Resource Village at http://www.mhschool.com to see more of the Math Forum.

MATH CENTER

Practice

OBJECTIVE Find a part given the total and a part.

Materials per pair: blank number cube, part-part-whole workmat (TA 5), 2-color counters

Prepare Label each number cube 3, 4, 5, 6, 7, 8.

The child rolls the cube to get a total number of counters. After he or she writes the total on the part-part-whole mat and puts some counters on the mat, the partner must tell the missing part. *[Partners check each other's answers to see that the parts and total match.]*

Problem Solving

OBJECTIVE Find a part given a whole and a part.

Materials per pair: nine 3" x 5" index cards, counter

Prepare Create a small part-part-whole mat for totals 2 through 10. Make sure the numbers can be covered by a counter.

Children can work on one card together at first, and then separately as their skills improve. *[Students can check their answers as they uncover the counter to look at the hidden number.]*

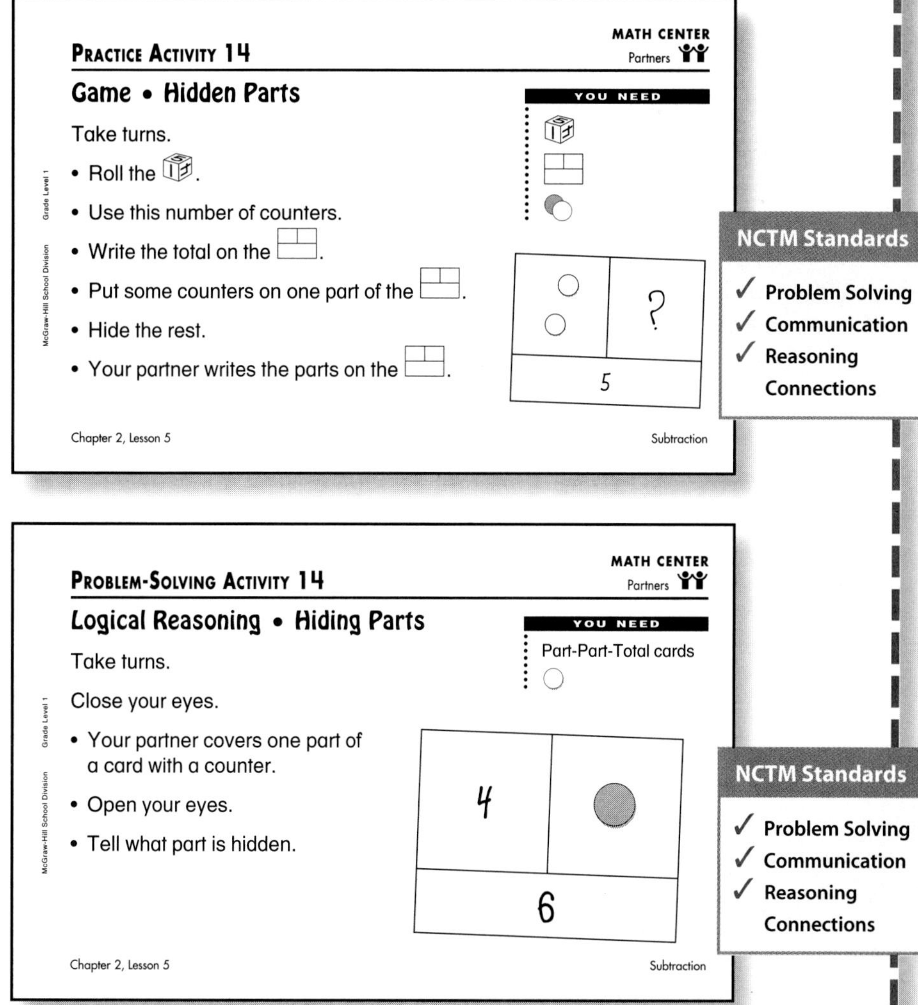
PRACTICE ACTIVITY 14 — MATH CENTER — Partners

Game • Hidden Parts

YOU NEED

Take turns.

- Roll the cube.
- Use this number of counters.
- Write the total on the mat.
- Put some counters on one part of the mat.
- Hide the rest.
- Your partner writes the parts on the mat.

Grade Level 1 — McGraw-Hill School Division

Chapter 2, Lesson 5 — Subtraction

NCTM Standards
✓ Problem Solving
✓ Communication
✓ Reasoning
Connections

PROBLEM-SOLVING ACTIVITY 14 — MATH CENTER — Partners

Logical Reasoning • Hiding Parts

YOU NEED
Part-Part-Total cards

Take turns.

Close your eyes.

- Your partner covers one part of a card with a counter.
- Open your eyes.
- Tell what part is hidden.

Grade Level 1 — McGraw-Hill School Division

Chapter 2, Lesson 5 — Subtraction

NCTM Standards
✓ Problem Solving
✓ Communication
✓ Reasoning
Connections

Lesson 2.5

DAY 1

EXPLORE ACTIVITY

One Missing Part

OBJECTIVE Children explore finding a part, given a whole and a part.

Materials per child: 10 counters; Workmat 3 (part-part-whole mat)

1 Motivate — Whole Class

Materials chart paper, marker, number cards 0–9 (TA 9), counters

Draw one part-part-whole mat on chart paper, and draw six more part-part-whole mats on the chalkboard. Put the number card for 5 in the Total section of the chart-paper mat and write the total 5 in each of the mats that you drew. Ask:

- **In what different ways can you show 5?** *[Answers should include 4 and 1, 1 and 4; 3 and 2, 2 and 3; 5 and 0, 0 and 5.]*

As volunteers show different combinations with counters in the Parts sections on the chart-paper mat, ask a child to record the numbers in the corresponding section of a part-part-whole mat on the chalkboard.

2 Develop

Page 61

Working Together Give each pair of children 10 counters. One child places the pictured number of counters in one part of the workspace. The other child uses counters to show the missing part. Then each child records the number for the missing part in the space provided on his or her page. Together, children should make sure that the two Parts equal the Total.

Critical Thinking
After children answer the question on the page, ask:

- **When can a part and a total be the same?** *[when the missing part is zero]*

Name ______________________

Explore Activity
One Missing Part

Working Together

You need 10 counters.

- Take turns.
- You show one part.
- Your partner shows the missing part.
- Write.

1 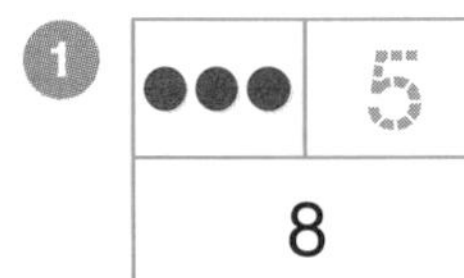 5, 8

2 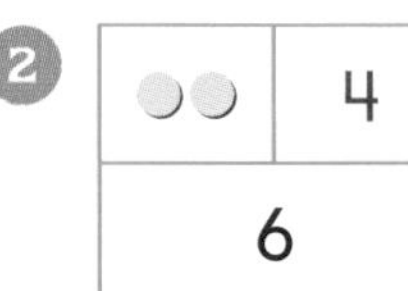 4, 6

3 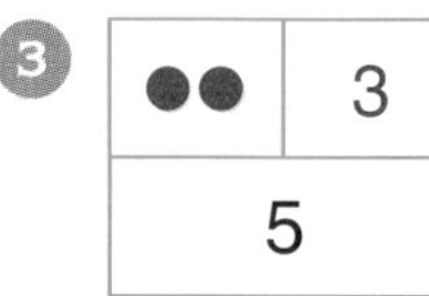 3, 5

4 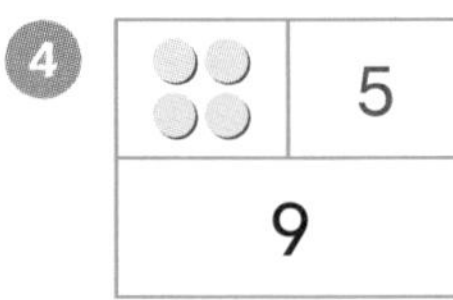 5, 9

5 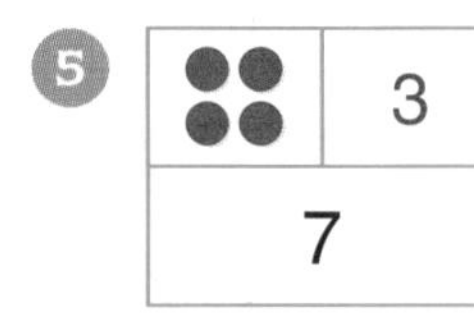 3, 7

6 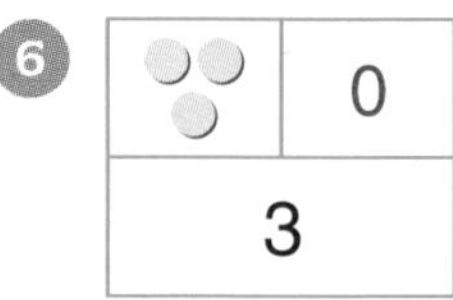 0, 3

When can two parts be the same number? Possible answer: when the total is 2, 4, 6, 8, or 10

MEETING INDIVIDUAL NEEDS

INCLUSION

Check that children understand where the Part and Total sections are on Workmat 3. Write the words *Part* and *Total* in the appropriate sections on the workmat to help them associate the oral and written language with the image.

COMMON ERROR

Children may incorrectly add the part and the total to get a sum of the two numbers. Drawing a heavy red line around the Total section focuses their attention on where the total number is found.

ONGOING ASSESSMENT

Interview Determine if children understand writing a numeral for the missing part by selecting a problem on page 62. Ask:

- **How do you know what number to write?** *[I count how many are there and then how many counters I need.]*

Follow Up Children who are having difficulty should continue to find other missing parts. Assign **Reteach 18.**

For children who demonstrate understanding, challenge them to find all parts for totals 4–10. Assign **Extend 18.**

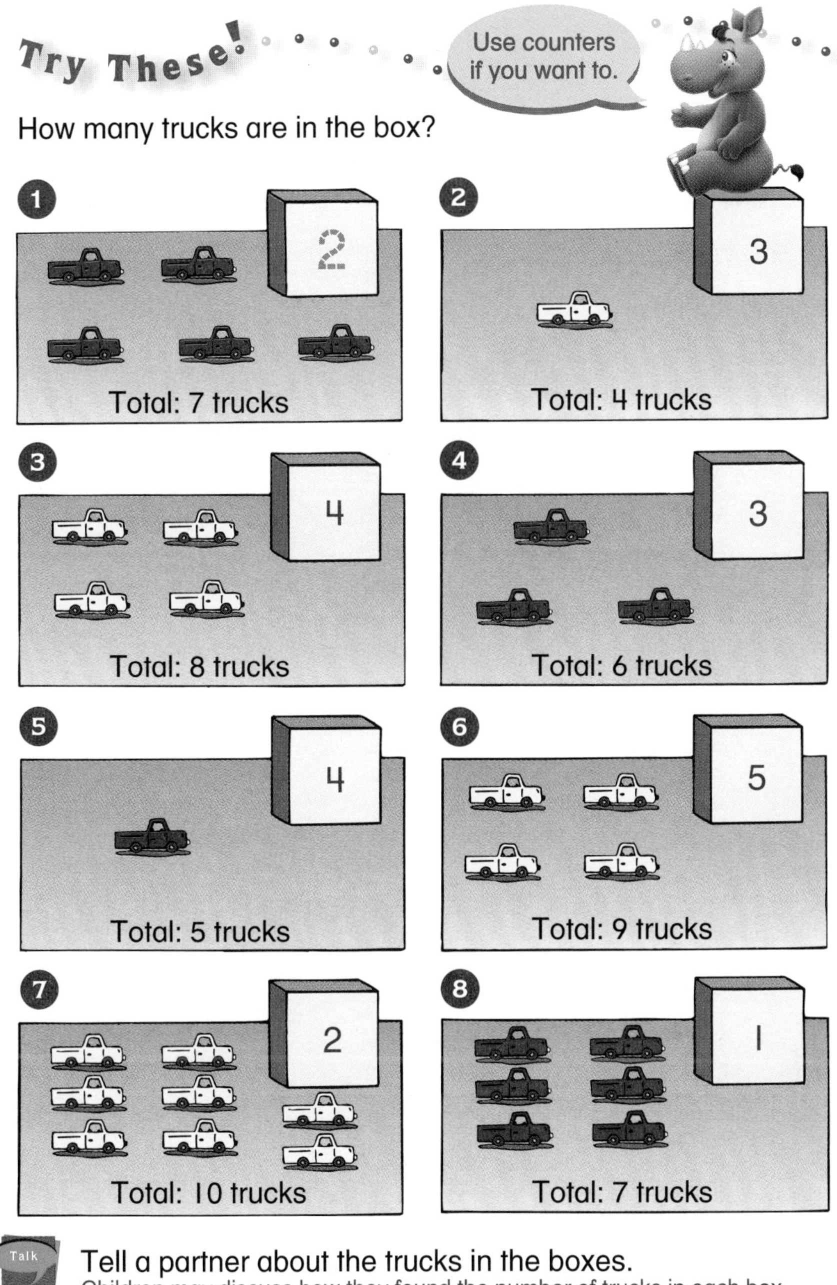

Tell a partner about the trucks in the boxes.

Children may discuss how they found the number of trucks in each box.

At Home: Show your child 8 pennies. Hide some with your hand. Ask your child how many are hidden.

Page 62

Try These Assign practice exercises 1–8.

Children work individually. They may use counters and a part-part-whole mat, or they may draw counters, but they should record the missing part as a number.

3 Close

Check for Understanding by having children explain how they found the missing part. Ask:

- **After you put the given counters and the missing counters on the mat for the total, how do you know which number to write?** *[I count the missing Part counters and write that number as my answer.]*

Tomorrow children will continue finding the missing part, given a whole and a part.

PRACTICE • 18

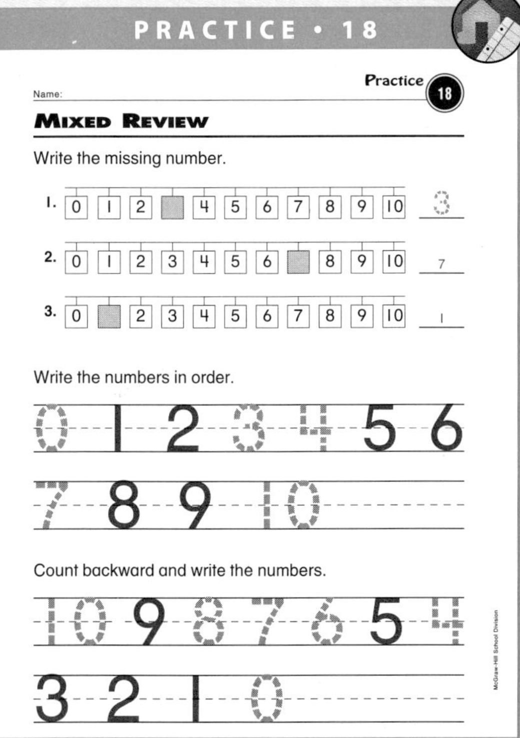

RETEACH • 18

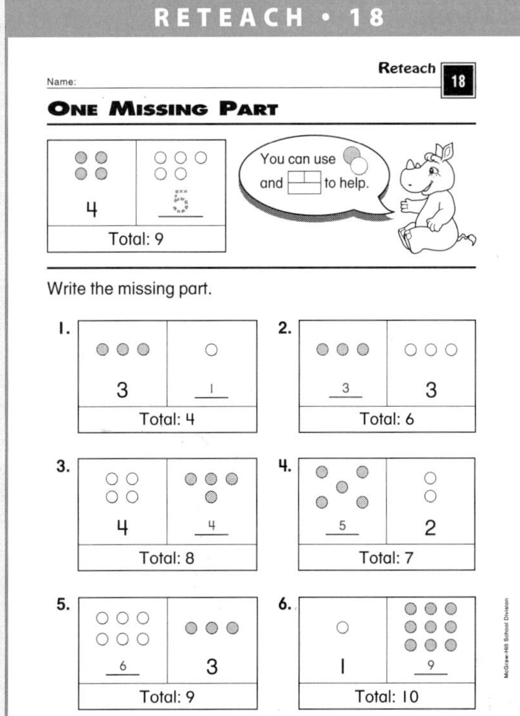

EXTEND • 18

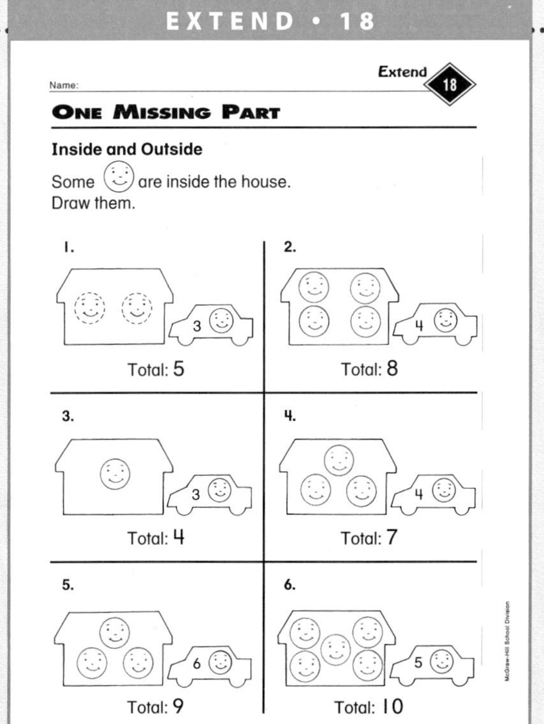

DAY 2 Find the Missing Part

OBJECTIVE Children find a part, given a whole and a part.

Materials per child: 10 two-color counters; Workmat 3 (part-part-whole mat)

1 Motivate — Cooperative Pairs

Materials per pair: Workmat 3 (part-part-whole mat); 10 two-color counters; number cards 0–9 (TA 9)

Demonstrate how to place a number card for 3 in one Part and 7 two-color counters in the Total section on Workmat 3 as children follow along. Point to the 3.

- **How many counters will be in this part?** *[3]*

Have children place 3 counters in one part on their mats. Then have them point to the missing part.

- **How many counters should you put in this part to make a total of 7?** *[4]*

Check that children put 4 counters in the empty Part section. Then have one partner replace the counters with a numeral card for 4. Repeat with other numbers until children no longer have to use counters.

2 Develop

Page 63

For the first exercise, tell children to look at the number in the Total section and place that many counters there. Then ask them to look at the number in the Part section, slide that many counters from the Total section into the Part section, and slide the remaining counters into the other Part section. Children record their answer as a numeral.

CRITICAL THINKING
After children answer the question on the page, ask:

- **When is a missing part zero?** *[when the other part is the same as the total]*

Page 64

Try These Assign practice exercises 1–6.

More to Explore Have partners make up their own word problems telling which object is more than another object. They may dictate the words and draw their own pictures.

3 Close

Check for Understanding by having children explain how to find a missing part in each problem. Ask:

- **If you know the numbers for the total and one part, how can you find the missing part?** *[Possible answer: I can use counters, I can think about the counters.]*

Name

Find the Missing Part

You need 10 counters and a workmat.

- Show the total.
- Show the part.
- Find the missing part.
- Write.

1

2	4
6	

2

5	5
10	

3
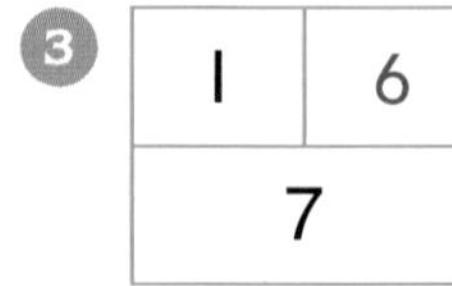

4
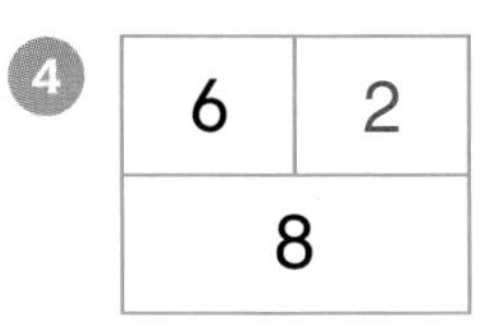

5
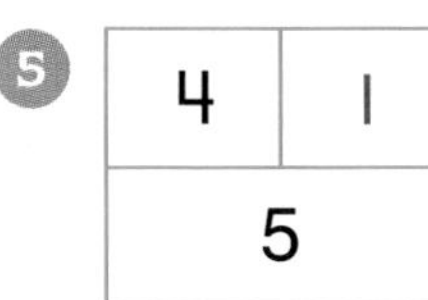

6
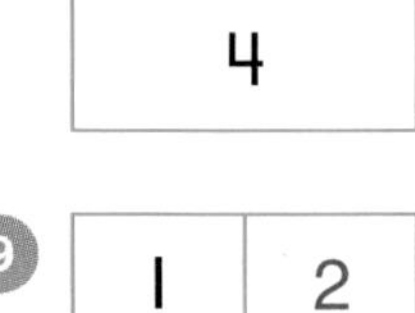

7
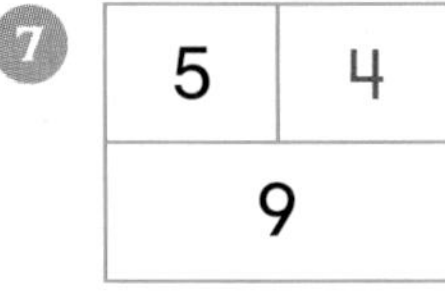

8
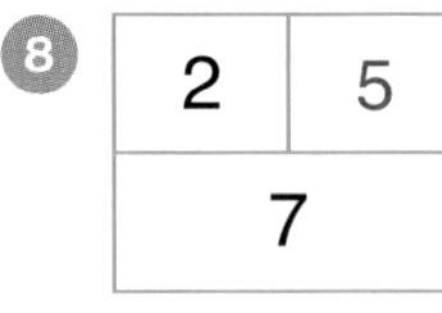

9
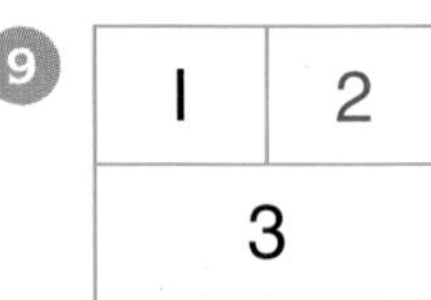

Is the missing part more or less than the total? Why?

The missing part can be the same as or less than the total; it can never be more than the total.

MEETING INDIVIDUAL NEEDS

EARLY FINISHERS

Have children play this game in pairs: one child names a total and a part; the other child names the missing part.

EXTRA SUPPORT

Children with learning disabilities may need to reposition the chart. Help them experiment using Workmat 3 and number cards.

ONGOING ASSESSMENT

Observation Checklist Determine whether children can find a missing part given the whole and a part by noting whether the number they supply is less than the total.

Follow Up For children who are having difficulty, have them place the total number of counters in the Total section of Workmat 3, move part of them to a Part section, and count them aloud. Then repeat to find the missing part. Assign **Reteach 19.**

For children who demonstrate understanding, assign **Extend 19.**

Try These!

Use counters if you want to.

Find the missing part.

1. 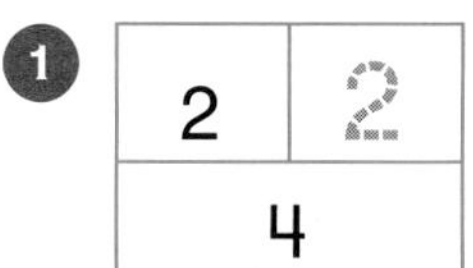

2. 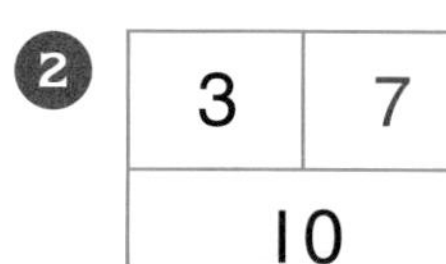

3. 

4. | 2 | 0 |
|---|---|
| 2 | |

5. 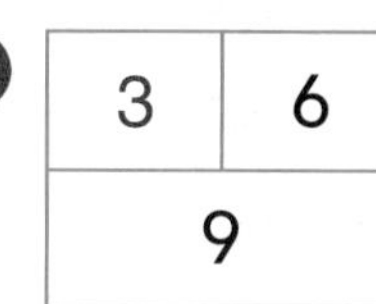

6. | 4 | 4 |
|---|---|
| 8 | |

More to Explore — Logical Reasoning

Ring the correct box.

The box has 2 cars.

It has more trucks than cars.

The box has 3 boats.

It has more boats than planes.

At Home: Ask your child to tell you a math story about one of the animal pictures.

Alternate Teaching Strategy

Materials 10 rhino counters; number cards for 1–10 (TA 9); small bowl; sheet of construction paper

Have children close their eyes. Place the number card for 5, and 3 rhino counters on the sheet of construction paper. Place 2 more rhinos on the construction paper and cover these rhinos with a small bowl. Set aside the remaining counters. Have children open their eyes, and ask:

- **I have 5 rhinos. Some are hiding under the bowl. How may rhinos do you see?** *[3]*
- **How many rhinos are missing?** *[2]*

Have the child turn over the bowl to verify that the number of rhinos hiding there matches the number of rhinos that he or she said were missing.

Repeat the activity until the child can name the missing number without using counters.

PRACTICE • 19

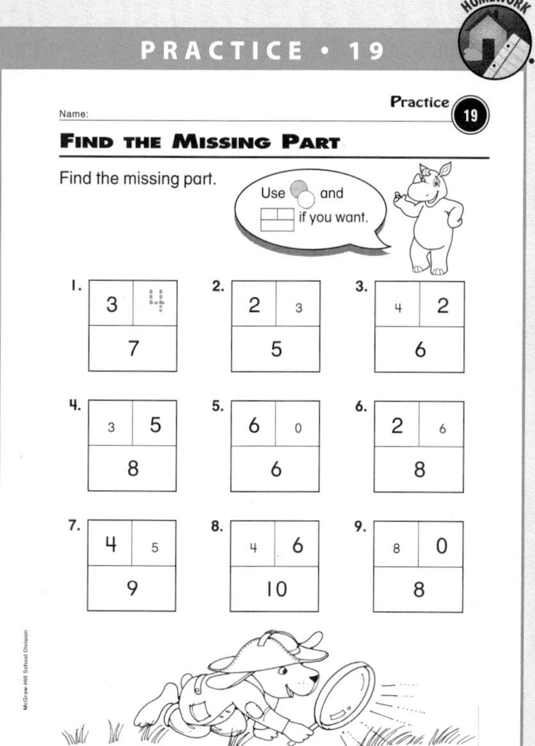

Practice 19

Name:

Find the Missing Part

Find the missing part.

1. 3 | 4 — 7
2. 2 | 3 — 5
3. 4 | 2 — 6
4. 3 | 5 — 8
5. 6 | 0 — 6
6. 2 | 6 — 8
7. 4 | 5 — 9
8. 4 | 6 — 10
9. 8 | 0 — 8

RETEACH • 19

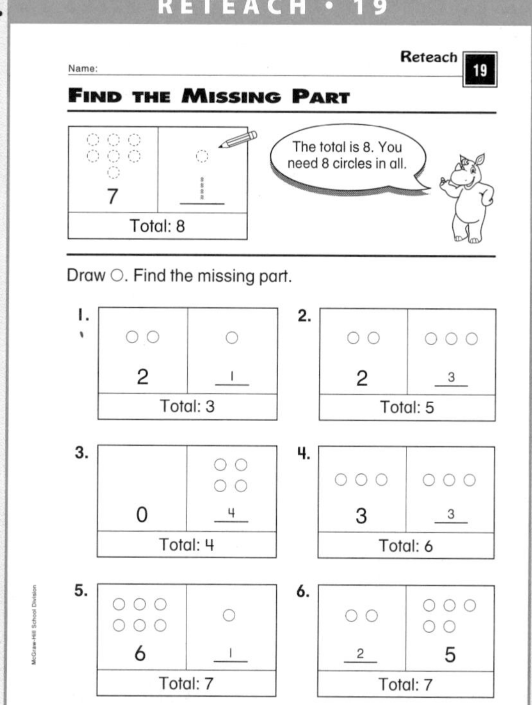

Reteach 19

Name:

Find the Missing Part

7 | 1 — Total: 8

Draw ○. Find the missing part.

1. 2 | 1 — Total: 3
2. 2 | 3 — Total: 5
3. 0 | 4 — Total: 4
4. 3 | 3 — Total: 6
5. 6 | 1 — Total: 7
6. 2 | 5 — Total: 7

EXTEND • 19

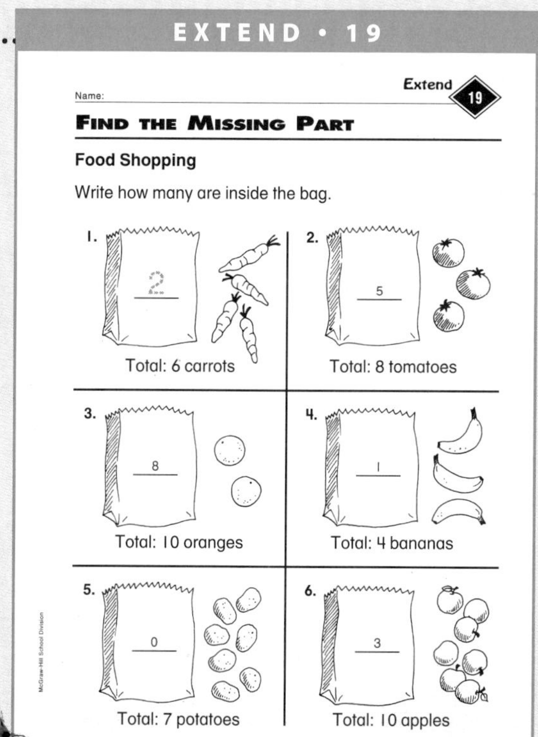

Extend 19

Name:

Find the Missing Part

Food Shopping

Write how many are inside the bag.

1. 2 — Total: 6 carrots
2. 5 — Total: 8 tomatoes
3. 8 — Total: 10 oranges
4. 1 — Total: 4 bananas
5. 0 — Total: 7 potatoes
6. 3 — Total: 10 apples

EXTRA PRACTICE

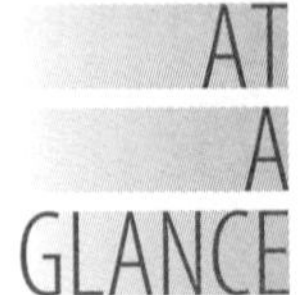

PURPOSE Provide an opportunity for review and practice.

Materials per pair: 10 two-color counters; a sheet of paper

Using the Extra Practice

Page 65

Explain the rules of "Guess and Count" as you demonstrate with a volunteer: The first player closes his eyes. The second player lines up a number of counters, covers some with a piece of paper, and names the total and the part that shows. The first player writes these numbers on his paper and then guesses the missing part. If the guess is correct, she or he writes a check mark.

Players takes turns until they have finished 8 rounds. The winner is the player with the most checks.

After the children finish playing ask:

- **How did you make your guess?** *[Possible answer: I thought about the missing counters in my head.]*

Page 66

Have children complete the exercises independently or in pairs. Children may use counters and Workmat 3 if they wish. For exercises 1–6, children find the total for given parts. For exercises 7–12, children find the missing part for a given total and a given part.

Using the Additional Practice

The section below provides additional practice that you may want to write on the chalkboard or on a reproducible master.

Name

Extra Practice
Game!

Guess and Count

You need paper and 10 .

Listen to the rules.

Winner: the player with the most ✔

Sample recording:

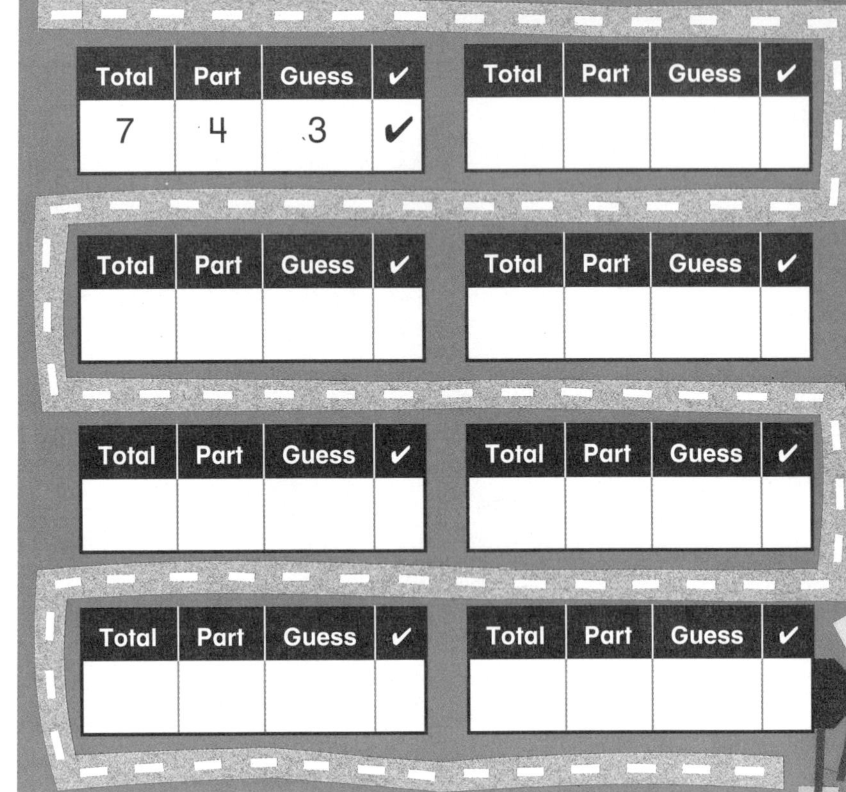

Total	Part	Guess	✔
7	4	3	✔

Total	Part	Guess	✔

Total	Part	Guess	✔

Total	Part	Guess	✔

Total	Part	Guess	✔

Total	Part	Guess	✔

Total	Part	Guess	✔

Total	Part	Guess	✔

ADDITIONAL PRACTICE

Find the total.

1. 5 | 2 — *[7]*

2. 2 | 6 — *[8]*

3. 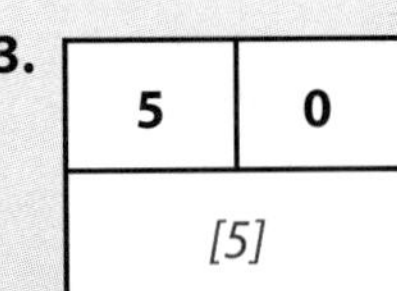
5 | 0 — *[5]*

4. 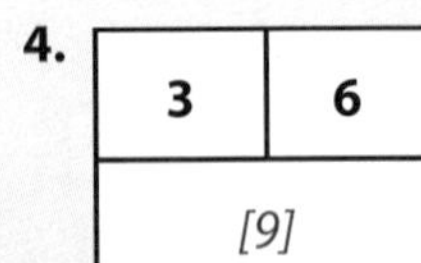
3 | 6 — *[9]*

5. 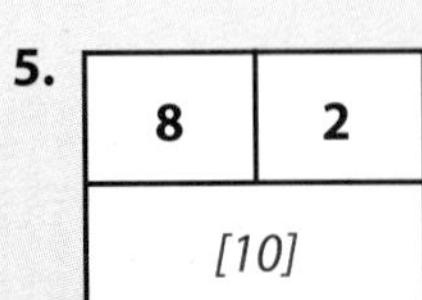
8 | 2 — *[10]*

6. 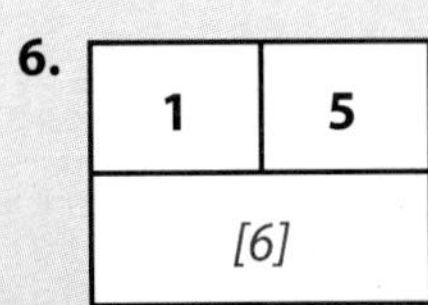
1 | 5 — *[6]*

Find the missing part.

7. *[2]* | 5 — 7

8. 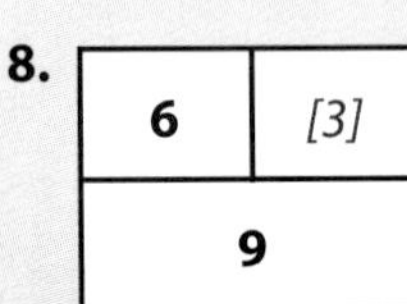
6 | *[3]* — 9

9. 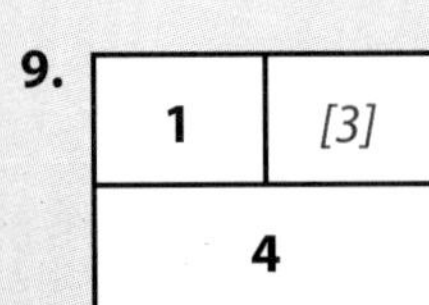
1 | *[3]* — 4

10. *[1]* | 7 — 8

11. *[1]* | 9 — 10

12. 6 | *[0]* — 6

Find the total.

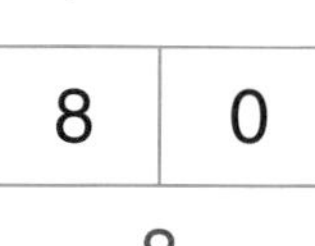

1		2		3	
1	6	8	0	3	2
7		8		5	

4		5		6	
4	5	5	5	2	1
9		10		3	

Find the missing part.

7		8		9	
3	4	5	3	0	4
7		8		4	

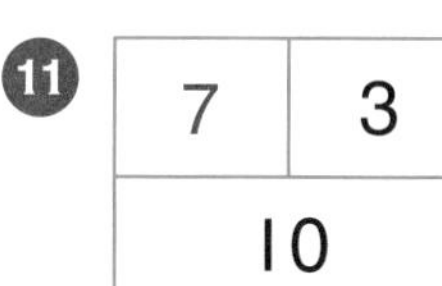

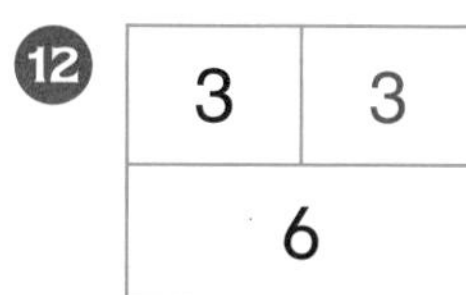

10		11		12	
2	7	7	3	3	3
9		10		6	

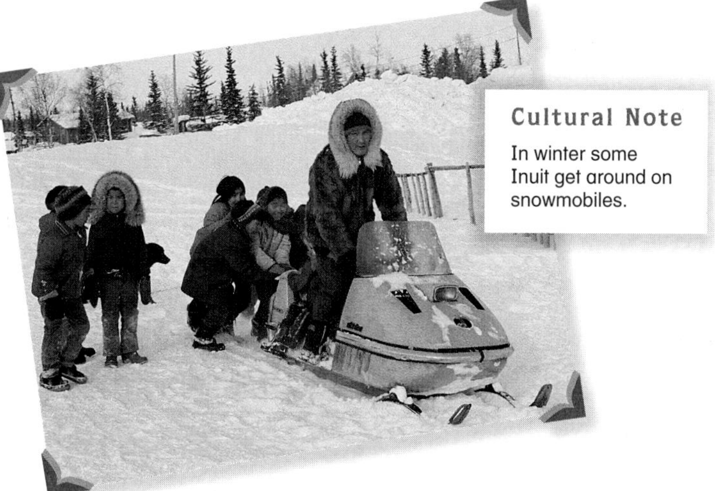

Cultural Note

In winter some Inuit get around on snowmobiles.

Developing Number Sense

This section provides an opportunity to reinforce number sense. You may wish to write the exercises on a chalkboard or on a reproducible master.

Find the pattern. Write in the next two numbers.

1. 1, 2, 1, 2, ___, ___ *[1, 2]*

2. 3, 2, 3, 2, ___, ___ *[3, 2]*

3. 2, 4, 2, 4, ___, ___ *[2, 4]*

Mixed Applications/Problem Solving

Listen. Solve.

1. There are 5 girls on the bus.
There are 4 boys on the bus.
How many children are on the bus? *[9]*

2. Mr. Morris has 10 trucks.
He has 6 trucks in the garage.
How many trucks are not in the garage? *[4]*

3. Brandon has 10 green and red caps.
He has 2 green caps.
How many red caps does Brandon have? *[8]*

4. Alberto had 8 pens.
He lost 5.
How many pens does he have now? *[3]*

5. Sim Bok has 7 pencils.
Two pencils are in his pencil box.
How many pencils are not in his pencil box? *[5]*

6. Dana made 2 bracelets.
Cady made 4 bracelets.
How many bracelets did the girls make? *[6]*

LESSON 2.6

LESSON RESOURCES

Problem Solvers at Work: What is the Question?

OBJECTIVE Write and solve oral problems involving part-part-whole.

Day 1 Problem Solvers at Work: What is the Question?

RESOURCE REMINDER
Math Center Cards 15
Practice 20, Reteach 20, Extend 20

SKILLS TRACE	
GRADE K	• Solve oral problems involving part-part-whole. *(Chapter 11)*
GRADE 1	• Solve oral problems involving part-part-whole.
GRADE 2	• Solve problems by choosing the operation. *(Chapter 2)*

WARM-UP

Whole Class — **Logical/Analytical**

OBJECTIVE Explore solving oral problems for part-part-whole situations.

Materials 3 pairs of children's scissors, 11 crayons, crayon box

▶ Use classroom objects to make up oral problems for children to solve. Show children 3 pairs of scissors and 2 crayons. Present this problem:

There are 3 scissors and 2 crayons.
How many things are there?

Ask children what they need to find. *[how many things: a total]*

▶ Show children 3 crayons and a closed crayon box containing 5 crayons. Pose this problem.

I have 8 crayons.
Here are 3 of my crayons.
How many crayons are left in the box?

Ask children what they need to find. *[how many crayons are in the box: a missing part]*

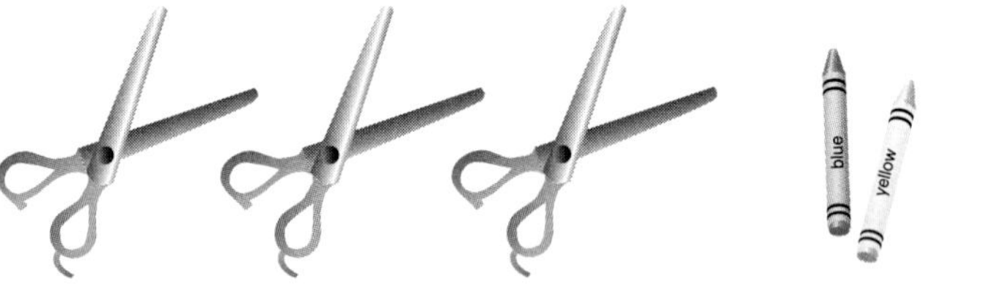

CONNECTION ACTIVITY

Whole Class — **Auditory/Linguistic**

OBJECTIVE Connect solving problems with literature.

Resource Literature Big Book: *Bus Stops*

▶ Show children the page in *Bus Stops* that says, "The bus stops near an old church. Two sightseers get off." Ask:

- **What does the story tell you?** *[how many sightseers get off the bus]*
- **Suppose 6 people are on the bus now. How many people were on the bus before?** *[8]*

▶ Make up more problems based on the book. Then encourage children to make up their own problems to share with classmates.

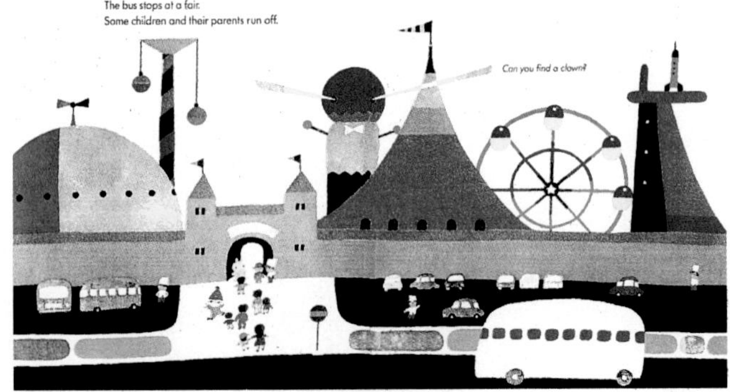

DAILY MATH

PREVIOUS DAY QUICK REVIEW

Find the missing part. Use counters.

	Total	Part	Missing Part
1.	7	4	*[3]*
2.	7	3	*[4]*
3.	7	7	*[0]*

Problem of the Day • 15

Read aloud to children:

There are 8 children riding bikes.
There are 2 children walking.
How many children are not riding bikes? *[2]*

TECH LINK

MATH VAN

Tool You may wish to use counters to teach this lesson.

MATH FORUM

Idea I often record on the chalkboard the variety of answers for a problem and have children defend their choices. Errors can be powerful clarifiers as long as the classroom environment is positive.

Visit our Resource Village at http://www.mhschool.com to see more of the Math Forum.

MATH CENTER

Practice

OBJECTIVE Make up and solve word problems involving part-part-whole.

Materials Part-part-whole mat (TA 5)

The children make up word problems with the pictures on the cards. Partners solve the problems and draw the parts and total on the workmat. *[Answers may vary. Check parts and totals.]*

MATH CENTER
Partners

PRACTICE ACTIVITY 15

Formulating Problems • Story Problems

YOU NEED

Take turns.

- Choose a picture.
- Make up a word problem.
- Tell it to your partner.
- Your partner solves it.
- Your partner draws the objects on .

Grade Level 1

McGraw-Hill School Division

Chapter 2, Lesson 6 — Subtraction

NCTM Standards

- ✓ Problem Solving
- ✓ Communication
- ✓ Reasoning
- ✓ Connections

Problem Solving

OBJECTIVE Solve oral problems involving part-part-whole.

Materials per child: 5 two-color counters

Prepare Sketch a scene with clouds in a sky, and a road or path with bushes and trees on the ground.

Children make up word problems using 2-color counters and a picture. *[Problems may vary. Children should describe the counters as parts of a total.]*

MATH CENTER
Partners

PROBLEM-SOLVING ACTIVITY 15

Formulating Problems • What's Up? What's Down?

YOU NEED

- sheet showing sky and ground
- 5 yellow ◯
- 5 red ◯

Use the picture.

- Put some red ◯ in the sky.
- Put some yellow ◯ on the ground.
- Make up a word problem.
- Tell it to your partner.
- Your partner gives you the answer.

Grade Level 1

McGraw-Hill School Division

Chapter 2, Lesson 6 — Subtraction

NCTM Standards

- ✓ Problem Solving
- ✓ Communication
- ✓ Reasoning
- ✓ Connections

DAY 1

Problem Solvers at Work What is the Question?

OBJECTIVE Children solve oral problems involving part-part-whole.

1 Motivate — Cooperative Pairs

Materials per pair: 10 two-color counters; Workmat 3 (part-part-whole mat)

Tell children that you are going to read two kinds of stories. They are to listen, decide if they have to find a missing part or a total, and act out the stories. Have children work in pairs with counters and Workmat 3.

There are 3 red counters. There are 2 yellow counters. How many counters are there?

Ask children:

- **What does the problem tell you?** *[Possible answers: there are 3 red counters and 2 yellow counters; the parts]*
- **What do you need to find?** *[Possible answers: how many counters there are; total]*

Then read this story aloud:

There are 7 counters. Three of the counters are red. The rest are yellow. How many counters are yellow?

Ask children:

- **What does the problem tell you?** *[a part and the total]*
- **What do you need to find?** *[the missing part]*

2 Develop

Page 67

Read aloud to children each problem found on the Student Book page in this Teacher's Edition. Discuss problems one at a time, focusing on the *Read* step of the problem-solving process.

CRITICAL THINKING

After children finish page 67, ask:

- **How do you know what you need to find in each problem?** *[If something is not given, I have to find it.]*

Page 68

Try These Do word problem 1 orally, and then assign problems 2 and 3.

3 Close

Check for Understanding by having children discuss the problem at the top of page 67. Children often mistake finding a total for two given numbers, not realizing that one of the numbers could be the total.

Name

What Is the Question?

Problem Solvers at Work

Read · Plan · Solve · Look Back

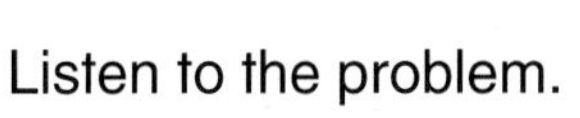

Listen to the problem.

1

How many green cars?

What does the problem tell you?
There are 5 cars and 3 are blue.

5 cars 3 blue cars

What do you need to find?
You need to find how many green cars, or a missing part.

2 green cars

"There are 5 cars parked on this side of the street. Three of the cars are blu[e], the rest are green. How many green cars are there?"

2

How many children?

What does the problem tell you?
There are 4 girls and 2 boys riding bicycles.

4 girls 2 boys

What do you need to find?
You need to find how many children are riding bicycles, or a total.

6 children

"There are 4 girls riding bicycles. There are 2 boys riding bicycles. How many children are riding bicycles?"

MEETING INDIVIDUAL NEEDS

EARLY FINISHERS

Have partners make up additional problems for the pictures on page 67.

EXTRA SUPPORT

If children have difficulty deciding what information they need to find in the problems, make up a few oral problems based on real objects the children select. Let children use the objects to decide.

ONGOING ASSESSMENT

Interview To determine if children understand the importance of the *Read* step in the problem-solving process, ask them questions about the problem they made up on page 68.

- **Why did you write the question (use child's question)?** *[Answers may vary.]*

Follow Up For children having difficulty, use *Bus Stops* to present more oral problems. Assign **Reteach 20.**

For children who demonstrate understanding, have them use *Bus Stops* to make up stories for a friend to read. Assign **Extend 20.**

Try These!

Listen to the problem. "There are 7 trucks. Four of the trucks are red. The rest are blue. How many blue trucks are there?"

1 How many blue trucks?

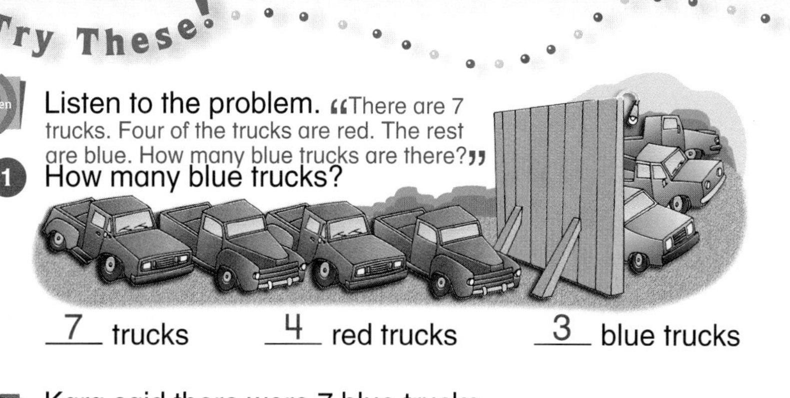

7 trucks 4 red trucks 3 blue trucks

Talk: Kara said there were 7 blue trucks. What did she do wrong? She wrote the total, not the missing part.

2 Solve Gericol's problem. 9 hearts

3 Write: Draw a picture. Write a question.

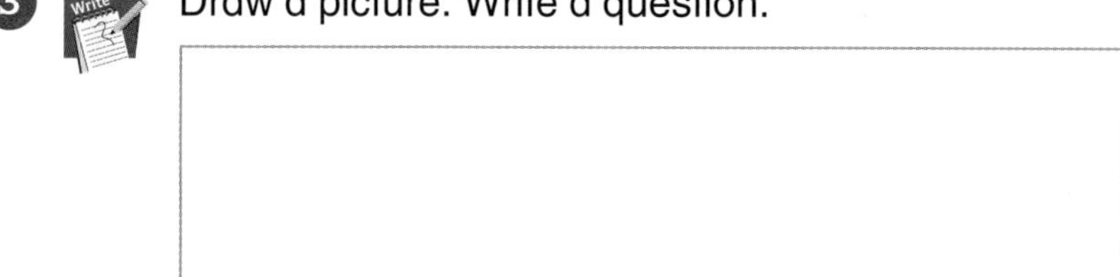

Problems may vary.

Your partner's answer to your question: __________

Your answer to your question: __________

At Home: We are learning to solve oral problems. Have your child make up problems for the pictures and questions on this page.

Alternate Teaching Strategy

Materials 10 two-color counters; a large sheet of construction paper; a small margarine tub

Begin by having children find the total when the parts are given. For example, place 5 red counters and 3 yellow counters in two groups on the construction paper. Ask:

- **What kinds of questions can I ask about these two groups of counters?** *[Answers may vary.]*
- **If I ask "How many counters are there?" what do you need to find, a part or a total?** *[a total]*
- **How many counters are there?** *[8]*

When children have mastered problems about finding the total, advance to finding a missing part. For example, put 6 counters on the construction paper and use the tub to hide 2 of the counters. Ask:

- **What kinds of questions can I ask about these groups of counters?** *[Answers may vary.]*
- **If I say "There are 6 counters but some are hidden" and I ask "How many counters are hidden?," what do you need to find, a part or a total?** *[a part]*
- **How many counters are hidden?** *[2]*

PRACTICE • 20

Practice 20

Name:

PROBLEM SOLVING: WHAT IS THE QUESTION?

Read problems aloud to the children.

1. There are 8 pigs on a farm. 5 are playing and the rest are sleeping. How many pigs are sleeping?

How many are sleeping?

8 pigs 5 pigs playing 3 pigs sleeping

2. There are 6 cows. 2 cows have spots and the rest are black. How many cows are black?

How many cows are black?

6 cows 2 cows with spots 4 black cows

RETEACH • 20

Reteach 20

Name:

PROBLEM SOLVING: WHAT IS THE QUESTION?

Read problems aloud to the children.

There are 7 turtles in the pond. 5 are resting on a rock. The rest are swimming. How many turtles are swimming?

7 turtles in all 5 turtles resting 2 turtles swimming

There are 4 big fish in the pond. There are also 2 small fish. How many fish are there?

4 big fish 2 small fish 6 fish in all

EXTEND • 20

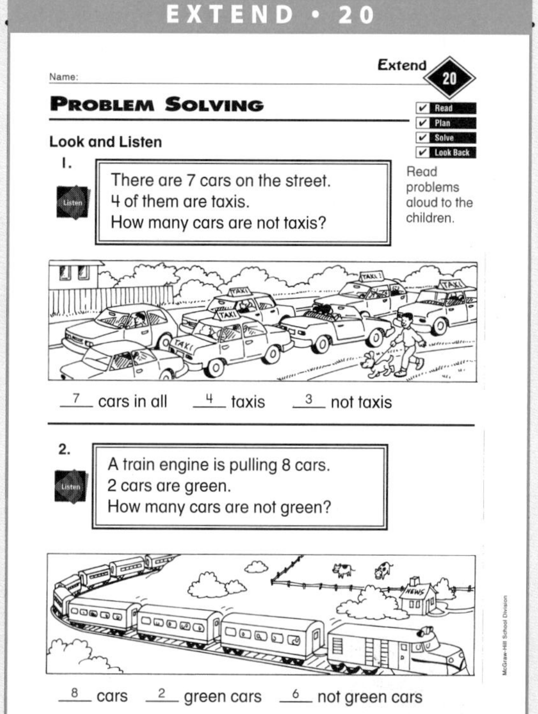

Extend 20

Name:

PROBLEM SOLVING

Look and Listen

Read problems aloud to the children.

1. There are 7 cars on the street. 4 of them are taxis. How many cars are not taxis?

7 cars in all 4 taxis 3 not taxis

2. A train engine is pulling 8 cars. 2 cars are green. How many cars are not green?

8 cars 2 green cars 6 not green cars

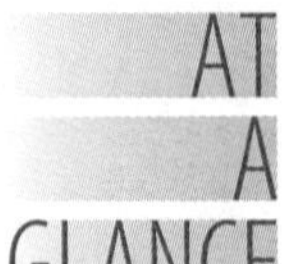

PURPOSE Review and assess the concepts, skills, and strategies that children have learned in this chapter.

Chapter Objectives

- **2A** Find parts for a whole
- **2B** Find the whole for given parts
- **2C** Find a missing part
- **2D** Solve problems, including those that involve parts and wholes and acting it out

Using the Chapter Review

The **Chapter Review** can be used as a review, practice test, or chapter test.

What Do You Think? This feature gives children an opportunity for self-assessment. Assure children that there are no right or wrong answers. The emphasis is on what they think and how they justify their answers

Children copy one of the exercises 3–6 and then draw a picture to show the parts for the total. Encourage children to write the numbers and perhaps a phrase or sentence about their pictures.

Name

Chapter Review

Color different trains for 6. Write the parts and total. Parts may vary. Possible answers are given.

		Parts			Total
1	ⓡ ⓑ ⓑ ⓑ ⓑ ⓑ	1		5	6
2	ⓡ ⓡ ⓡ ⓑ ⓑ ⓑ	3		3	6

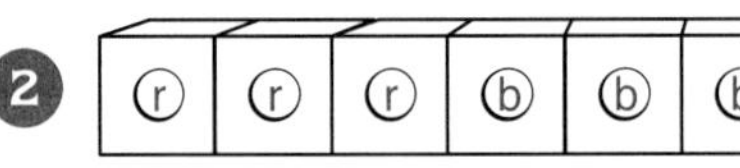

Find the total.

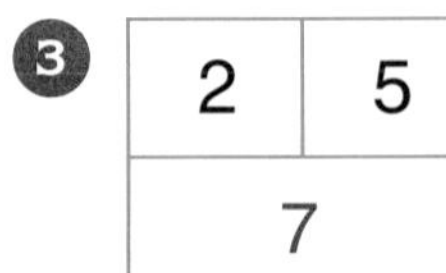

3. | 2 | 5 |, total 7
4. | 8 | 1 |, total 9

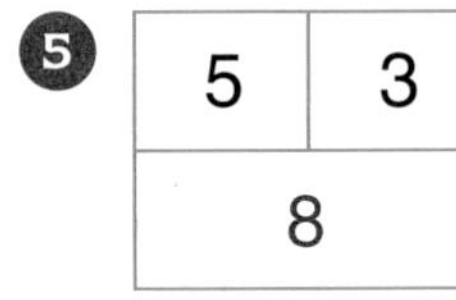

5. | 5 | 3 |, total 8
6. | 4 | 2 |, total 6

Find the missing part.

7. | 6 | 4 |, total 10
8. | 2 | 6 |, total 8

Reinforcement and Remediation

CHAPTER OBJECTIVES	REVIEW ITEMS	STUDENT BOOK PAGES: Lessons	STUDENT BOOK PAGES: Midchapter Review	TEACHER'S EDITION PAGES: Activities	TEACHER'S EDITION PAGES: Alternate Teaching Strategy	TEACHER RESOURCES: Reteach
2A	1–2	45–50	53	44A, 46A, 56A	46, 50, 60	12–14, 16–17
2B	3–6	57–60		60A	64	18–19
2C	7–8	61–64		50A	52	15
2D	9–10	51–52, 67–68	53	66A	68	20

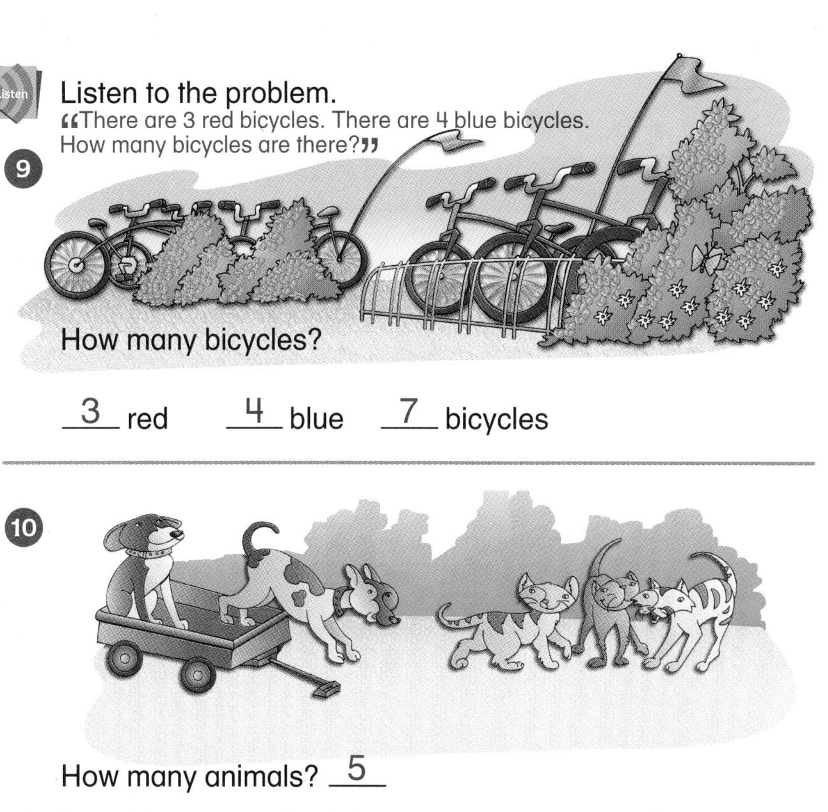

Listen to the problem.

"There are 3 red bicycles. There are 4 blue bicycles. How many bicycles are there?"

9

How many bicycles?

3 red 4 blue 7 bicycles

10

How many animals? 5

What Do You Think?

What do you think about finding parts and totals? This self-assessment should not be graded. All explanations are acceptable.

☑ Check one.

☐ Easy ☐ A little hard ☐ Hard

Why? ______________________________

Choose a total. Children may draw after showing models—parts shown should equal the total.

Show how you find parts for your total.

CHAPTER TEST

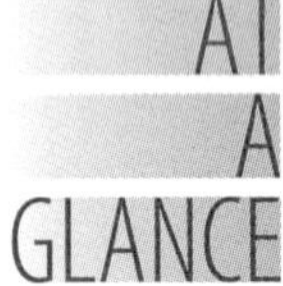

PURPOSE Assess the concepts, skills, and strategies that children have learned in this chapter.

Chapter Objectives

2A Find parts for a whole
2B Find the whole for given parts
2C Find a missing part
2D Solve problems, including those that involve parts and wholes, and acting it out

Using the Chapter Test

The **Chapter Test** can be used as a practice test, a chapter test, or as an additional review. The **Performance Assessment** on Student Book page 72 provides an alternate means of assessing children's ability to understand parts and totals.

The table below correlates the test items to the chapter objectives and to the Student Book pages on which the skills are taught.

Assessment Resources

TEST MASTERS

The Testing Program Blackline Masters provide three forms of the Chapter Test. Form C uses a free-response format. Forms A and B use a multiple-choice format.

TEACHER'S ASSESSMENT RESOURCES

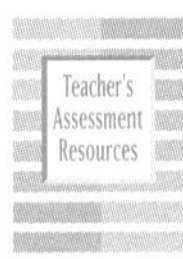

Teacher's Assessment Resources provides resources for alternate assessment. It includes Guidelines for Building a Portfolio, p. 6, and the Holistic Scoring Guide, p. 29.

Name

Chapter Test

Color different trains for 5.
Write the parts and total.

Parts may vary. Possible answers are given.

Parts Total

1 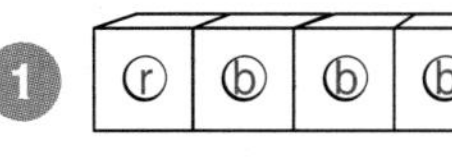 1  4 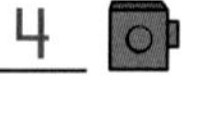 5

2 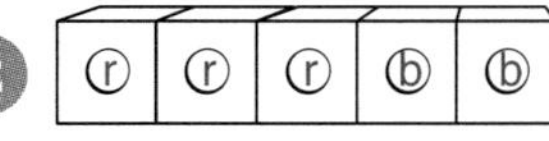 3, 2, 5

Find the total or missing part.

3 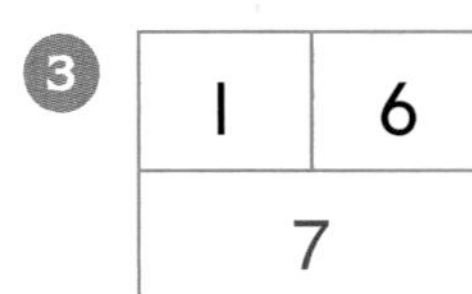
4 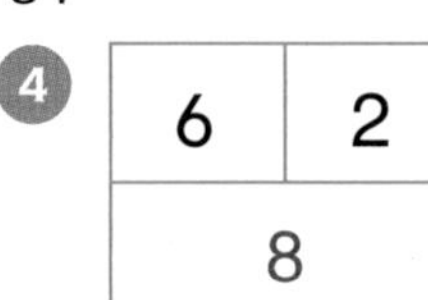
5 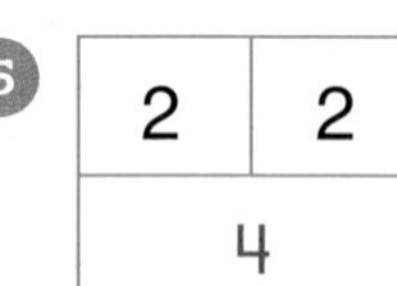

3	1 | 6	4	6 | 2	5	2 | 2
	7		8		4

6 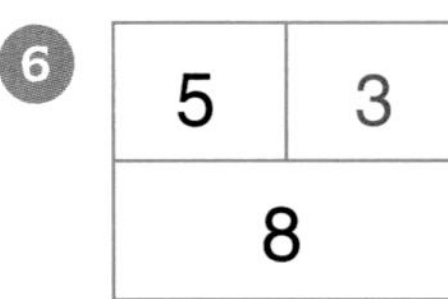
7 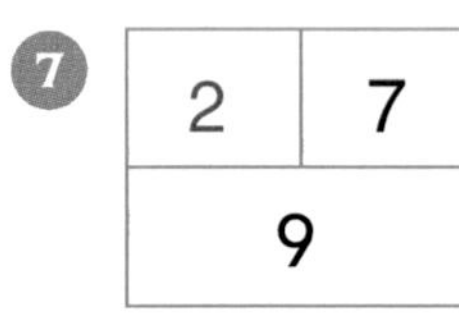
8 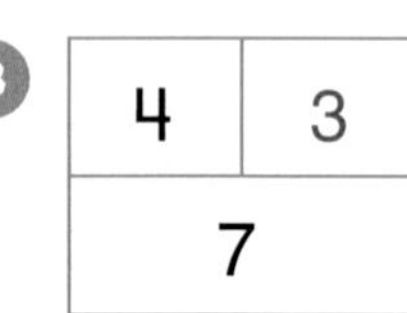

6	5 | 3	7	2 | 7	8	4 | 3
	8		9		7

Listen to the problems.

9  

"There are 4 boys. There are 2 girls. How many children?"

4 boys 2 girls 6 children

10 

"There are 2 red boa[ts.] There are 5 blue boats. How many boats?"

2 red boats 5 blue boats 7 boats

Test Correlation		
CHAPTER OBJECTIVES	TEST ITEMS	STUDENT BOOK PAGES
2A	1–2	45–50
2B	3–5	57–60
2C	6–8	61–64
2D	9–10	51–52, 67–68

Performance Assessment

What Did You Learn?

Listen to the problem. “Seven children want to ride the zoo train. The train has 2 cars. Show how many ways the children can ride in the 2 cars.”

Show trains for 7.

Write how many in each part. Order of parts may vary.

You may want to put this page in your portfolio.

REVIEWING A PORTFOLIO

Have children review their portfolios. Consider including the following items:

- Finished work on a project, page 42F.
- Selected math journal entries, pages 53 and 70.
- Products from investigations, pages 55–56.
- Children's self-selected "best piece" drawn from the work completed during the chapter. Have them attach a note explaining why they chose that piece.
- Any work that you or individual children wish to keep for future reference.

You may wish to take this opportunity to conduct conferences with children.

The Portfolio Analysis Form can help you in the reporting of children's progress. See Teacher's Assessment Resources, page 33.

AT A GLANCE

PURPOSE Review and assess the concepts, skills, and strategies that children have learned in this chapter.

Materials have available: counters

Using the Performance Assessment

Tell children that the zoo train has 2 cars and that 7 children want to ride the zoo train. Have them write over the numbers in the first picture to show that 1 child is in one car and 6 children are in the other car. Ask them to show as many ways as they can how the 7 children can ride in the 2 cars. Have counters available for children who want to use them. Observe children as they work.

Evaluating Student Work

As you read children's papers, look for the following:

- *Can the child write a pair of numbers with a sum of 7 in the cars of at least 2 trains?*
- *How many different pairs can the child find?*
- *Does the child write any pairs with a sum other than 7?*

You may wish to use the Holistic Scoring Guide and annotated samples of children's work to assess this task. See pages 29–32 and 37–61 in Teacher's Assessment Resources.

Follow-Up Interviews

Meet with children individually or in small groups to reflect on the Performance Assessment task. You can use the following questions to gain insight into children's thinking and evaluate their level of understanding:

- **How did you solve this problem? What did you do first?**
- **How did you get these two numbers? (Point to the two numbers on the cars of one of the trains.)**
- **Do you think there are any other ways that 7 children can ride in two cars? Why do you think that?**
- **What if there are no children in one of the cars?**

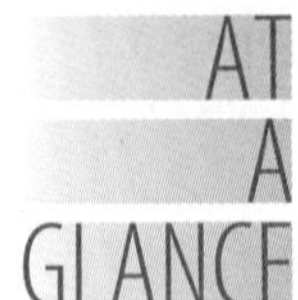

AT A GLANCE

OBJECTIVE Complete a table.

Using the Math Connection

Have children complete the table by recording the number of bikes and wheels. They can continue the pattern of bikes to complete the table.

Observe children as they complete the table. Some children may complete the *Bikes* column before completing the *Wheels* column. Others may complete each row.

After completing the table, have them look for and discuss the pattern for the bikes and wheels. Children should discover that a doubling pattern exists between them.

Some children may use counters to act out the pattern. Have them record the number of bikes first. Then have children put 2 counters on each bike to represent the wheels. Children can count the total number of wheels (counters) by ones or by twos for each bike as they complete each row of the table.

Developing Algebra Sense The table in this activity extends children's understanding of the concept of function.

Extending the Activity Have children make a similar table showing tricycles. Before beginning, you may wish to read "Nine Mice on Tiny Tricycles" from *The New Kid on the Block* by Jack Prelutsky.

Name

Complete a Table

Draw. Complete the table.

Write how many.

	Bikes	Wheels
	1	2
	2	4
	3	6
	4	8
	5	10
	6	12

Technology Connection

Computer

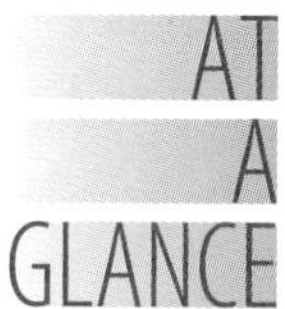

Make a Pattern

You know how to make patterns.

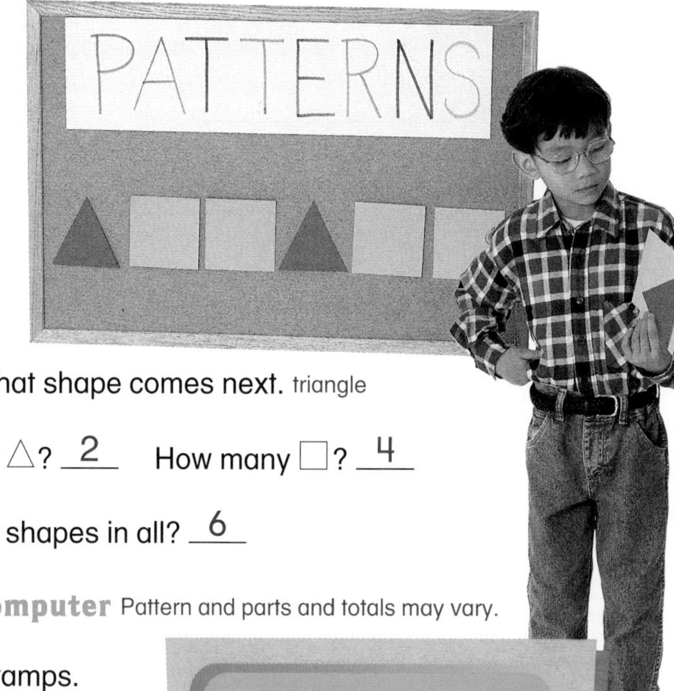

Tell what shape comes next. triangle

How many △? 2 How many □? 4

How many shapes in all? 6

At the Computer Pattern and parts and totals may vary.

1. Use stamps. Make a pattern.
2. Record the parts. Record the total.
3. Make another pattern.

AT A GLANCE

OBJECTIVE Children use a counters program to make patterns.

Materials drawing or geometry program, Math Van Tools

Using the Technology Connection

Have children look at the pattern and tell you what the next shape in the pattern will be. Then have them tell you how many triangles and squares are in the pattern, and the total number of shapes.

Children then use counters to make their own patterns and record the parts and totals.

If computers and software are not available, allow children to use real counters to make patterns.

Extending the Activity Have children work with partners. One partner creates a pattern. The other partner extends it. They continue for a set number of turns. Then they trade roles.

Math Van

Math Van Children may wish to use a variety of different counters in their patterns. Make sure they are comfortable with clicking the arrows to go through the available counters.

AT A GLANCE

Family Activities

PURPOSE Give family members an opportunity to help children maintain concepts and skills learned in the chapter.

Using the Wrap-Up

Page 75

Tell children that this side of the page will help them show their parents what they have been learning in this chapter.

Explain to children that they should look for the number of wheels and vehicles that they see while out with their parents. They should be able to tell whether she or he counted more wheels or vehicles.

Name ____________________

Wheel Count

Where we counted: ____________________

Number of wheels: ____________

Number of vehicles: ____________

We counted more ____________ than ____________.

Take your child to a spot where there are bicycles or cars. Try a parking lot, driveway, garage, or other place. Have your child count the number of vehicles and the number of wheels and tell whether he or she counted more wheels or vehicles.

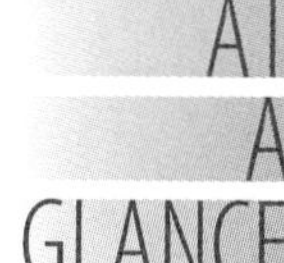

Dear Family,

We are starting a new chapter in our mathematics book. We are going to learn about adding numbers. This is like parts and totals, but we will use pictures and numbers to show addition.

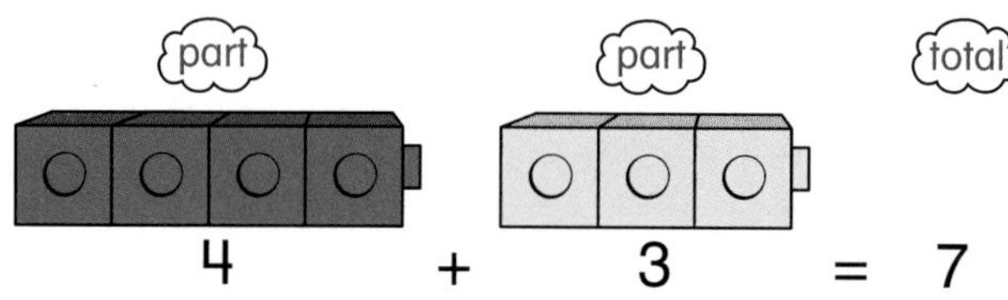

4 + 3 = 7

We will also be talking about favorite foods and shopping for groceries. Please help me complete this interview.

Your child,

____
Signature

Interview

Where do you like to shop for food?
(You may check more than one.)

- ❑ Supermarket
- ❑ Farmer's market
- ❑ Neighborhood store
- ❑ Food club
- ❑ Other ______________________

What is your favorite food? ______________________

AT A GLANCE Family Activities

PURPOSE Give family members an opportunity to share in their child's mathematics learning.

Using the Preview

Page 76

Discuss the contents of the page with children and have them sign the letter at the top. Be sure they understand how to conduct an interview with a family member, friend, or neighbor.

Explain to children that they may share what they learn during their next math lesson. You may wish to have children bring back the page.

BEGINNING TO ADD

Planning for Learning

Suggested Pacing : 10–12 days **Theme: Food for 10**

Lesson Title/Description	Pages	Pacing	Real-life Connection	Chapter Objectives	Materials	Reteach/Practice/Extend	Math Center Cards
Preview	76						
Introduction	77		planning a meal, shopping for food				
What Do You Know? (J) (P)	78						
► 1. Addition Stories (J) Teaching with Technology	79–80	1-day lesson		3A	2-color counters, Workmat 3 (part-part-whole mat)	21	16
► 2. Addition Sentences	81–84	2-day lesson	listing corn products	3A	2-color counters, paper plates	22–23	17
► 3. Problem-Solving Strategy: Write an Addition Sentence	85–86	1-day lesson		3B	rhino counters, connecting cubes	24	18
Midchapter Review (J)	87				have available: rhino counters, 2-color counters		
Extra Practice Game: I Show, You Find	88				rhino counters, connecting cubes		
Real-life Investigation: Applying Addition (P)	89–90		going to an ice-cream store				
► 4. Addition Fact Pairs (J)	91–92	1-day lesson	writing a grocery list	3A	pennies, paper cups	25	19
► 5. Counting On	93–96	2-day lesson		3A	counters, bowls, rhino counters, masking tape, index cards	26–27	20
Extra Practice Game: Supermarket Race	97–98				rhino counters, number cubes		
► 6. Problem Solvers at Work	99–100	1-day lesson	collecting grocery coupons	3B	2-color counters, 1–5 spinners (TA 7)	28	21
ASSESSMENT OPTIONS (J) (P) Chapter Review Chapter Test Performance Assessment	 101–102 103 104				have available: counters, pennies, number lines (TA 11)		
CONNECTIONS MATH: Patterns LANGUAGE ARTS Home Connection	 105 106 109		counting with crackers				
Cumulative Review	107–108						

(J) = JOURNAL OPPORTUNITY

(P) = PORTFOLIO OPPORTUNITY

TA = TEACHER AID

Technology Links	NCTM Standards
Online Exploration, p. 78B Math Van: *Apple Baskets*	4, 8
Math Van: Counters tool Math Forum, p. 80D	8
Math Van: Counters tool Math Forum, p. 84B	1, 2, 3, 4, 8
	1, 2, 3, 4, 8
Math Van: Money Models tool Math Forum, p. 90B	8, 13
Math Van: Counters tool Math Forum, p. 92B	8, 13
Math Van: Counters tool Math Forum, p. 98B	1, 2, 3, 4, 8
	1, 4, 8

ASSESSMENT OPTIONS

INFORMAL

Ongoing Assessment

- Observation Checklist, pp. 83, 85, 91, 93
- Interview, pp. 79, 81, 95
- Anecdotal Report, p. 99

Portfolio Opportunities

- Chapter Project, p. 76F
- What Do You Know? p. 78
- Investigation, pp. 89–90
- Journal Writing, pp. 78, 80, 87, 92, 102
- Performance Assessment, p. 104

Chapter Objectives	Standardized Test Correlations
3A Add, facts to 10	MAT, CAT, SAT, ITBS, CTBS
3B Solve problems, including those that involve addition and writing an addition sentence	MAT, CAT, SAT, ITBS, CTBS

FORMAL

Chapter Tests

Student Book

- Midchapter Review, p. 87
- Chapter Review, pp. 101–102
- Chapter Test, p. 103
- Cumulative Review, pp. 107–108

Test Masters

- Free-Response Test: Form C
- Multiple-Choice Test: Forms A and B

Performance Assessment

- What Do You Know? p. 78
- Performance Assessment, p. 104
- Self-Assessment: What Do You Think? p. 101
- Holistic Scoring Guide, Teacher's Assessment Resources, pp. 29–32
- Follow-Up Interviews, p. 104

Teacher's Assessment Resources

- Portfolio Guidelines and Forms, pp. 6–9, 27–36
- Holistic Scoring Guide, pp. 29–32
- Samples of Student Work, pp. 37–61

NCTM Standards Grades K–4

1 Problem Solving
2 Communication
3 Reasoning
4 Connections
5 Estimation
6 Number Sense and Numeration
7 Concepts of Whole Number Operations
8 Whole Number Computation
9 Geometry and Spatial Sense
10 Measurement
11 Statistics and Probability
12 Fractions and Decimals
13 Patterns and Relationships

Meeting Individual Needs

LEARNING STYLES

- AUDITORY/LINGUISTIC
- LOGICAL/ANALYTICAL
- VISUAL/SPATIAL
- MUSICAL
- KINESTHETIC
- SOCIAL
- INDIVIDUAL

Children who are talented in art, language, and physical activity may better understand mathematical concepts when these concepts are connected to their areas of interest. Use the following activities to stimulate the different learning styles of some of your children.

Musical Learners

Use two kinds of percussion instruments. Beat one instrument a set number of times. Have children record how many times you beat the instrument. Beat the second instrument a set number of times. Have children repeat the recording procedure. Then have them write a number sentence showing the total amount of beats.

Individual Learners

Use two dot cubes with one to six dots. Children toss the two cubes, count and record the number of dots on each cube. Then have children write a number sentence showing the total number.

See Lesson Resources, pp. 78A, 80C, 84A, 90A, 92A, 98A.

GIFTED AND TALENTED

Give children word problems in which the beginning information is unknown and addition is needed to solve the problem.

Juan had some marbles in his pocket.
He gave four to Anna.
Now he has eight marbles left.
How many marbles did he have to begin with?

Problems can be made more challenging by using larger numbers.

Children can be challenged by starting with larger numbers and counting on. For example, they can start with a number like 23 and count on three. Give them more numbers to count three on. Encourage children to notice a pattern.

23 count on 3 = 26	27 count on 3 = 30
33 count on 3 = 36	37 count on 3 = 40
43 count on 3 = 46	47 count on 3 = 50
53 count on 3 = 56	57 count on 3 = 60

See also Meeting Individual Needs, p. 95.

EXTRA SUPPORT

Specific suggestions for ways to provide extra support to children appear in every lesson in this chapter.

See Meeting Individual Needs, pp. 79, 81, 85, 91, 93, 99.

EARLY FINISHERS

Children who finish their class work early may draw, on a paper plate, four foods they like. Have them label each food with the name of the appropriate food group. (See *Chapter Project*, p. 76F.)

See also Meeting Individual Needs, pp. 79, 83, 85, 91, 93, 99.

STUDENTS ACQUIRING ENGLISH

Write the names of numbers and math symbols on cards. Have children place these cards underneath the numbers and symbols, and read the names out loud. As children are reading a number sentence give them a visual model to follow. After repetition and practice, children may begin to read the words independently.

See also Meeting Individual Needs, p. 81.

INCLUSION

- **For inclusion ideas, information, and suggestions, see pp. 83, T15.**
- **For gender fairness tips, see pp. T15.**

USING MANIPULATIVES

Building Understanding Use counters on ten-frame mats to help children model addition problems. Have children place the amount of counters for each addend on two different ten-frame mats. Then have them take the counters from one mat and fill in the other. This will help children count and see a relationship between ten and the numbers they are manipulating.

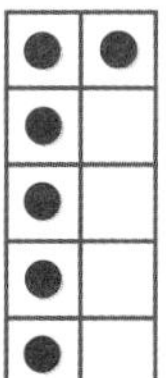

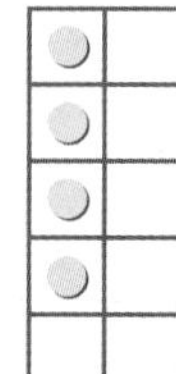

Easy-to-Make Manipulatives Buttons or beans can substitute as counters.

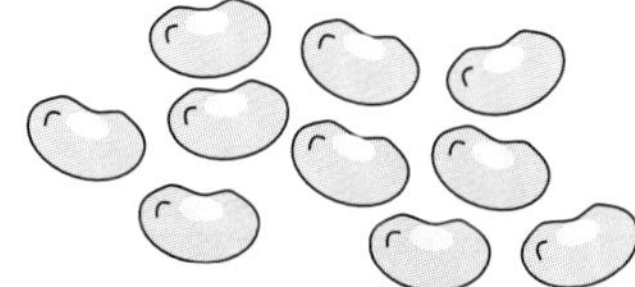

USING COOPERATIVE LEARNING

Think-Check-Step This strategy creates a sense of community by having children reach a consensus.

- **Children stand in line, each holding an answer card.**
- **Teacher asks a question, children THINK about whether they have the right answer, and then CHECK with those on either side of them.**
- **Children who still believe they have the right answer STEP forward, while other students remain in line.**

USING LITERATURE

Use the Big Book *Feast for Ten* to introduce the chapter theme, Food for 10.

Also available in the Read-Aloud Anthology are the poems "Oodles of Noodles," page 25, and "Licorice," page 26.

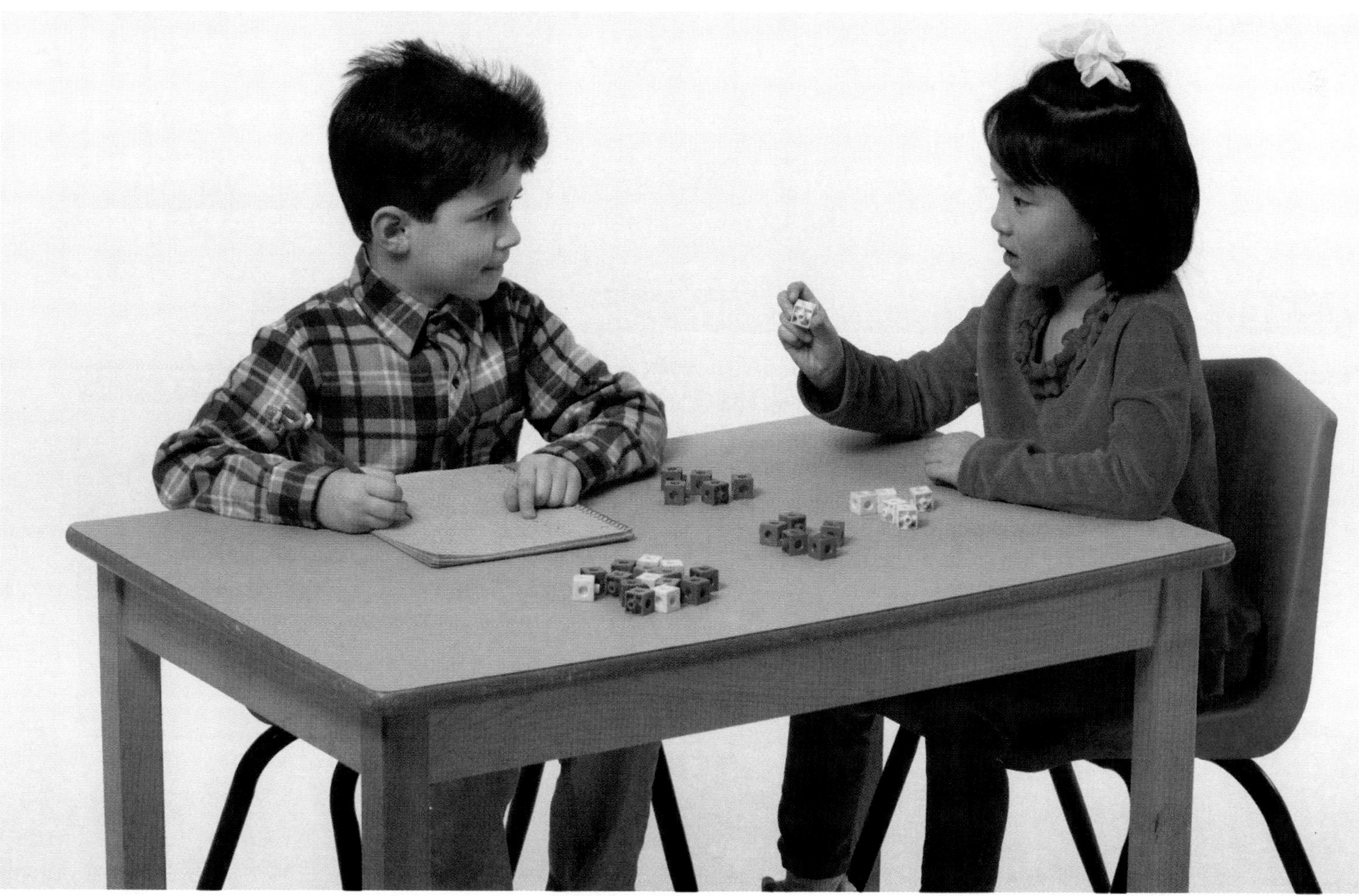

Linking Technology

This integrated package of programs and services allows students to explore, develop, and practice concepts; solve problems; build portfolios; and assess their own progress. Teachers can enhance instruction, provide remediation, and share ideas with other educational professionals.

MATH VAN ACTIVITY

In *Apple Baskets,* students use counters to find the number of apples in two baskets. Students can use the online notebook to write what they know about finding parts from totals. To extend the activity, students use the Math Van tools to create and solve their own addition problems. *Available on CD-ROM.*

MATH VAN TOOLS

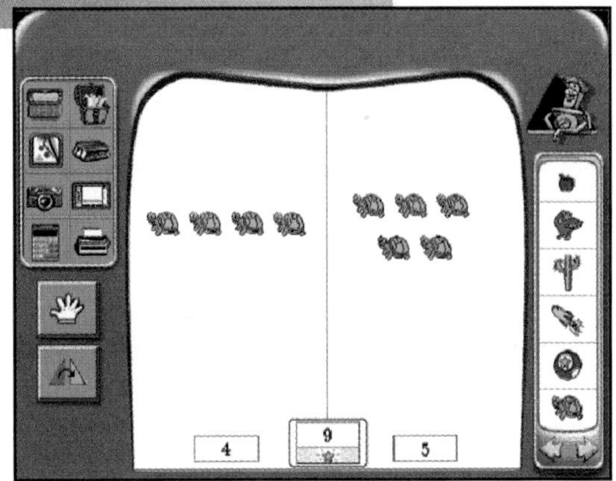

Students can use Math Van's counters to explore the concept of addition. The Tech Links on the Lesson Resources pages highlight opportunities for students to use this and other tools such as money models, online notes, and calculator to provide additional practice, reteaching, or extension. *Available on CD-ROM.*

WEB SITE http://www.mhschool.com

Teachers can access the McGraw-Hill School Division World Wide Web site for additional curriculum support at http://www.mhschool.com. Click on our Resource Village for specially designed activities linking Web sites to addition. Motivate children by inviting them to explore Web sites that develop the chapter theme of "Food for 10." Exchange ideas on classroom management, cultural diversity, and other areas in the Math Forum.

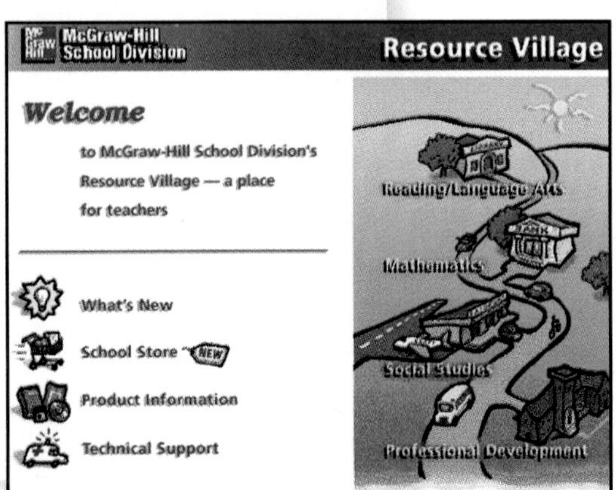

Chapter Project BUILDING A FOOD GUIDE PYRAMID

Highlighting the Math

- read numbers
- count
- find total

2	3
5	

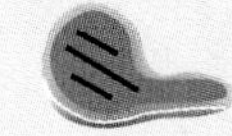

1 Starting the Project

Introduce the idea of working with a Food Guide Pyramid. Create a large Food Guide Pyramid from craft or construction paper. Display it on a bulletin board. Divide the pyramid into six sections, one for each of the food groups. Have children suggest food items found in each food group. List their suggestions on the chalkboard. Consider ways in which family and community members can participate.

2 Continuing the Project

- Children collect magazine pictures or make drawings of food items—at least one food item per food group.
- Label each of 6 large box tops with a food-group name. Set these "food trays" near the bulletin board. Have each child show and tell about one of his or her food pictures and then place it in the appropriate food tray.

3 Finishing the Project

Children sort the rest of the food pictures into the food trays, checking to see that the pictures are correctly placed. Then they attach the food pictures to the pyramid on the bulletin board, and count to find the number of pictures shown for each food group.

Community Involvement

Invite the school nurse or dietitian to visit the class and discuss the Food Guide Pyramid and food choices.

BUILDING A PORTFOLIO

Have each child draw a picture of the pyramid, modeling it after the one on the bulletin board. Have them include one item from each group. Have each child dictate or write a caption for his or her picture.

To assess the work, refer to the Holistic Scoring Guide on page 27 in the Teacher's Assessment Resources.

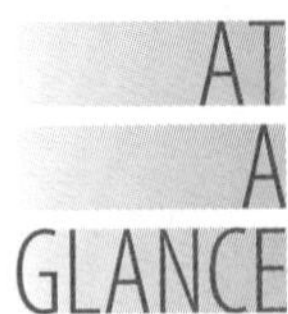

PURPOSE Introduce the theme of the chapter.

Resource Literature Big Book: *Feast for 10*

Using Literature

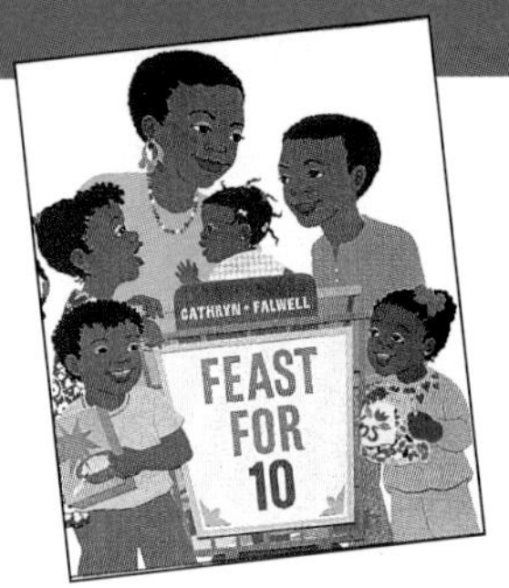

Page 77

Synopsis of the Book
In *Feast for 10* by Cathryn Falwell, the numbers 1 to 10 are used to show how many people and how many types of food are used to plan a special meal. Then the family enjoys the banquet they have prepared. The importance of teamwork, cooperation, and sharing is reinforced as adults, older children, and younger children all play valued roles in the success of the feast.

Read the story aloud to children. Then reread it, pausing to let children look at each page more closely. Talk about the food and the family members. Then have children count various objects, foods, and people on each page. Later they can use this information to create and solve word problems.

Discuss what children know about shopping for food. Have them talk about how foods are packaged, how many items are in a package, shopping lists, food prices, paying for groceries, shopping lists, aisle numbers, and so on.

Developing the Theme

The theme of the chapter is "Food for 10." Lead a discussion about food groups (fruits, vegetables, meat, milk, breads) and "healthy foods." Ask children to find healthy foods in the story.

Then extend the discussion to children's favorite healthy foods.

Have children find magazine pictures of healthy foods to include on a chart entitled "A Healthy Feast for (the number of people in the class)."

The theme will be developed throughout the chapter. (See pages 79, 83, 84, 93, 94, 97, 99, 100, and 106.)

Making Cultural Connections

Food is a basic part of every culture. Help children realize that local food resources and traditions determine what foods people eat. You may wish to focus on one category in the Food Guide Pyramid, such as Bread, Cereal, Rice, and Pasta. Collect pictures, drawings, and photographs of a variety of breads, including pita (Middle East), chappatties (India), and baguettes (France). The foods that children suggest can be included in the Food Guide Pyramid project.

Invite parents to bring to the class different bread products for children to sample.

Food for 10

Beginning to Add

Listen to the story *Feast for 10.*

Tell what you know about shopping for food.

CHAPTER BIBLIOGRAPHY

Dinner at the Panda Palace by Stephanie Calmenson. New York: HarperCollins Children's Books, 1991. ISBN: 0–06–021010–1.

Mouse Count by Ellen S. Walsh. San Diego: Harcourt Brace & Company, 1991. ISBN 0–15–256023–8.

This Is the Way We Eat Our Lunch: A Book About Children Around the World by Edith Baer. New York: Scholastic Inc., 1995. ISBN 0–590–46887–1.

COMMUNITY INVOLVEMENT

Invite the school nurse or dietician to visit the class to discuss the USDA Food Guide Pyramid and food choices with children.

Name

What Do You Know?

You need 10 counters.

Show parts here.

Write the total.

1

3	2
5	

5	1
6	

4	6
10	

2

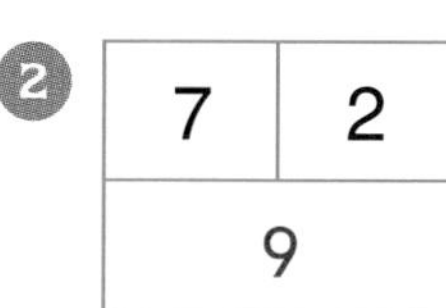

7	2
9	

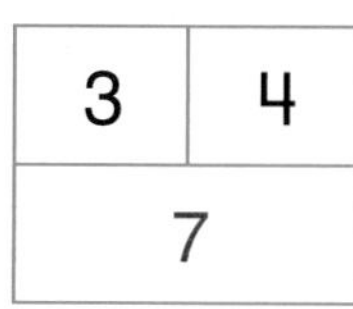

3	4
7	

3	5
8	

Show parts for your favorite number.

VOCABULARY

These math words will be used in this chapter.

- **parts** (page 78)
- **total** (page 78)
- **add** (page 81)
- **addition sign** (page 81)
- **equals** (page 81)
- **equal sign** (page 81)
- **plus** (page 81)
- **addition sentence** (page 83)
- **in all** (page 83)
- **sum** (page 83)
- **order** (page 92)
- **mental math** (page 93)

Children may record new words in their math journals. Encourage them to draw pictures or diagrams to help them tell what the words mean.

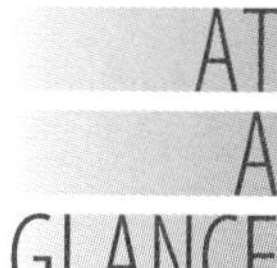

PURPOSE Assess children's ability to apply prior knowledge of part-part-whole relationships.

Materials have available: counters

Assessing Prior Knowledge

Draw a mat like the one at the top of the Student Book page on an overhead or the board.

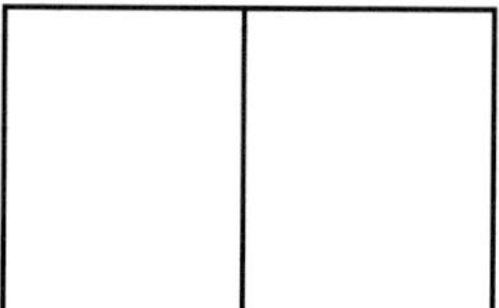

Have children look at the first item in row 1 on the Student Book page. Copy it on the overhead. Tell children you want to use counters to show the two parts on the mat and find the total.

Use counters to model what the children are to do. Begin by pointing to the left side of the mat on the overhead and asking how many counters you should put on that part. When children agree there should be 3, place 3 counters on the left side of the mat on the overhead. Have children put 3 counters on the left side of their mats on the Student Book page. Continue in this way to complete the problem.

Page 78

Tell children that you want them to do the rest of the problems in rows 1–2 in the same way that you just did the first problem together. They are to show the two parts on the mat and find the total. Observe children as they work. Some children may use other strategies without using the counters. For example, some may count on.

Give positive feedback to children on what they already know about parts and totals. Tell them that in chapter 3 they will be learning more about parts and totals and about adding.

Prerequisite Skills

- *Can children count?*
- *Can children write the numbers?*
- *Can children find the total given the two parts?*

After children have solved the problems in the first two rows, ask volunteers to share their solutions and methods. Ask children what they think of the methods that are different from the ones they used.

BUILDING A PORTFOLIO

Assign the problem at the bottom of the page. This piece provides an indicator of where children are in their understanding of the part-part-whole relationship.

A Portfolio Checklist for Students and a Checklist for Teachers are provided in Teacher's Assessment Resources, pp. 33–34.

LESSON 3.1

EXPLORE ACTIVITY

Addition Stories

OBJECTIVE Explore the concept of addition through part-part-whole stories.

Day 1 Explore Activity: Addition Stories

Teaching with Technology
See alternate computer lesson, pp. 80A–80B.

RESOURCE REMINDER
Math Center Cards 16
Practice 21, Reteach 21, Extend 21

SKILLS TRACE	
GRADE K	• Explore the concept of addition through part-part-whole stories. *(Chapter 11)*
GRADE 1	• Explore the concept of addition through part-part-whole stories.
GRADE 2	• Explore finding totals for parts and parts for totals. *(Chapter 1)*

LESSON RESOURCES

MANIPULATIVES

MANIPULATIVE WARM-UP

Whole Class — **Kinesthetic**

OBJECTIVE Explore the concept of addition through part-part-whole stories.

Materials 5 oranges, 5 apples, 5 bananas, 2 bowls

▶ Display 2 oranges in one bowl and 3 oranges in the other bowl. Ask children how many oranges are in each bowl. Then ask them for the total number of oranges in both bowls. *[5]* Ask how they knew how to find the total number of oranges. *[Counted how many in both bowls.]*

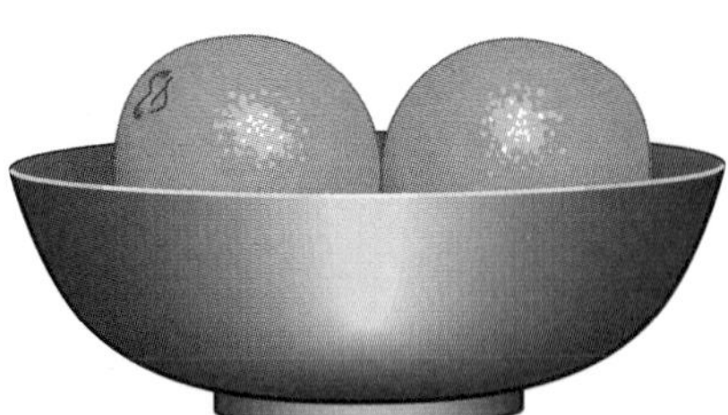

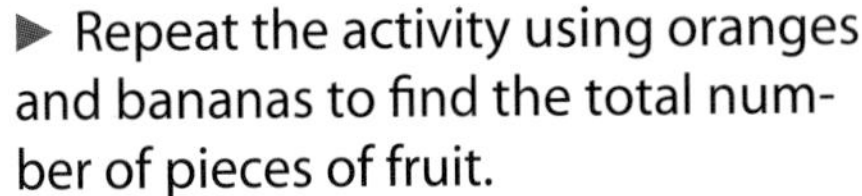

▶ Repeat the activity using oranges and bananas to find the total number of pieces of fruit.

▶ Challenge children to make up part-part-total stories about the fruit bowls for their classmates to solve.

MONEY

CONNECTION ACTIVITY

Cooperative Pairs — **Auditory/Linguistic**

OBJECTIVE Connect the concept of part-part-whole with money.

Materials per pair: Workmat 3 (part-part-whole mat), 10 pennies

▶ Tell the following story problem:
Juan has 3 pennies. His father gives him 5 more pennies. How many pennies does Juan have in all?

▶ Ask children to put pennies in each Part on their workmats as you repeat the story. Then ask partners to solve the problem by counting both Parts to find the Total. *[Juan has 8 pennies in all.]*

▶ Continue the activity with similar stories, using parts for totals to 10.
Karen spends 4 pennies on a banana. She spends 3 pennies on a cookie. How many pennies does Karen spend altogether? *[7 pennies]*

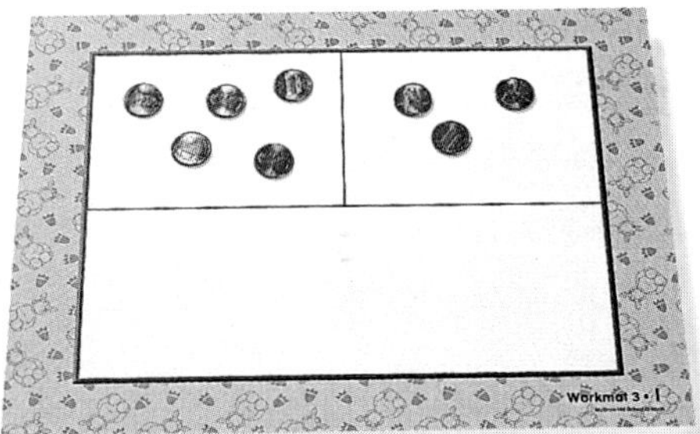

DAILY MATH

PREVIOUS DAY QUICK REVIEW

Make cube trains to show each number.

1. 5 *[5 cubes]*
2. 7 *[7 cubes]*
3. 10 *[10 cubes]*
4. 6 *[6 cubes]*

Problem of the Day • 16

Read aloud to children:

Kenny has 6 apples.
Some are green.
Some are red.
How many green apples could Kenny have?
How many red apples could he have? *[Possible answers: 1 green, 5 red; 2 green, 4 red; 3 green, 3 red; 4 green, 2 red; 5 green, 1 red]*

TECH LINK

ONLINE EXPLORATION

Use our Web-linked activities and lesson plans to connect children to the real world of food.

MATH VAN

Activity You may wish to use *Apple Baskets* to teach this lesson.

Visit our Resource Village at http://www.mhschool.com to access the Online Exploration.

MATH CENTER

Practice

OBJECTIVE Make up addition story problems.

Materials per pair: 10 two-color counters, part-part-whole mat (TA 5), Math Center Recording Sheet (TA 38 optional)

Prepare Label the two parts of each part-part-whole mat *box* and *bag.*

Children choose a fruit and use two-color counters to show the number in each part, make up a word problem about the fruit, and record the parts and total. *(apples: 2, 2, 4; oranges, 1, 3, 4; strawberries 6, 4, 10]*

PRACTICE ACTIVITY 16 — MATH CENTER, Partners

Manipulatives • How Much Fruit?

YOU NEED: 10 counters, part-part-whole mat

Take turns and use counters.

- Show how many bananas are in the box.
- Show how many bananas are in the bag.
- Write how many counters are in each part.
- Your partner makes up a word problem. Your partner writes the total.
- Check your partner's total. Then pick another fruit.

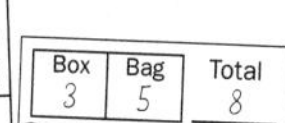

Box	Bag	Total
3	5	8

Chapter 3, Lesson 1 — Addition

NCTM Standards
- Problem Solving
- ✓ Communication
- Reasoning
- Connections

Problem Solving

OBJECTIVE Make up word problems involving addition.

Materials per pair: 5 red and 5 yellow connecting cubes, 2 yellow and 2 red crayons, Math Center Recording Sheet (TA 38 optional)

Children choose from one to five connecting cubes of each color, draw and color the parts, and make up a word problem. They solve and record the total. *[Check that the sums are correct.]*

PROBLEM-SOLVING ACTIVITY 16 — MATH CENTER, Partners

Formulating Problems • Tell a Story

YOU NEED: 5 yellow, 5 red, yellow crayon, red crayon

- Make a train with yellow cubes. Write how many cubes are in the train.
- Make a train with red cubes. Write how many cubes are in the red train.
- Make up a story about both trains.
- Add the cubes with your partner. Check your work.

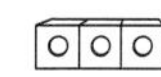

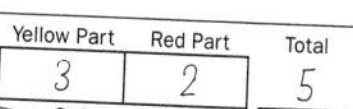
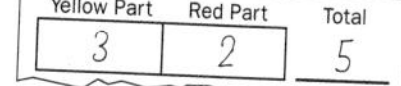

Yellow Part	Red Part	Total
3	2	5

Chapter 3, Lesson 1 — Addition

NCTM Standards
- ✓ Problem Solving
- ✓ Communication
- ✓ Reasoning
- ✓ Connections

Lesson 3.1

EXPLORE ACTIVITY
Addition Stories

OBJECTIVE Children explore the concept of addition through part-part-whole stories.

Materials per child: 10 two-color counters

1 Motivate — Cooperative Pairs

Resources Jumbo Activity Book, page 4; Sticker sheet 1 (two-color counters)

Materials per pair: 10 two-color counters; Workmat 3 (part-part-whole mat)

Give each pair of children a part-part-whole mat and 10 counters. Tell partners to prepare a "plate of fruit" using the red counters as apples and the yellow counters as lemons.

Demonstrate using Jumbo Activity Book page 4 and the red and yellow counter stickers as children use their workmats. Have one child put the apples on one Part of the mat, the other child put the lemons on the other Part of the mat.

Have children name the parts, combine them, and then tell the total number of pieces of fruit. Continue the activity to include all children in telling about their plates of fruit.

2 Develop

Page 79

Working Together Read aloud to children the first word problem found on the reduced student page in this Teacher's Edition. Work through the first problem together. Ask children to name the parts and the total.

Then read aloud each word problem and allow children to complete it before going on to the next one. Encourage partners to check each other's work and talk about what the correct answers should be.

CRITICAL THINKING
After children discuss the Critical Thinking question ask:

- **If your totals are different, what can you do?** *[Possible answers: Check the parts, count again.]*

Page 80

Try These Assign practice exercises 2–4.

Check children's journals to see if they understand the concept of part-part-total.

3 Close

Check for Understanding by having children make up stories about parts and totals to 10 using combinations of classroom objects or manipulatives.

Name ____________

Explore Activity
Addition Stories

Working Together
You need 10 .

Listen to the story.
Show the parts. Draw.
Write the total.

	Part	Part	Total
1	2	4	"I have a bowl with 2 apples. I have a bowl with 4 apples. How many apples do I have?" 6  
2	3	1	"I have a bowl with 3 oranges. I have a bowl with 1 orange. How many oranges do I have?" 4  
3	5	4	"I have 5 red bowls. I have 4 green bowls. How many bowls do I have in all?" 9  

Drawings may vary.

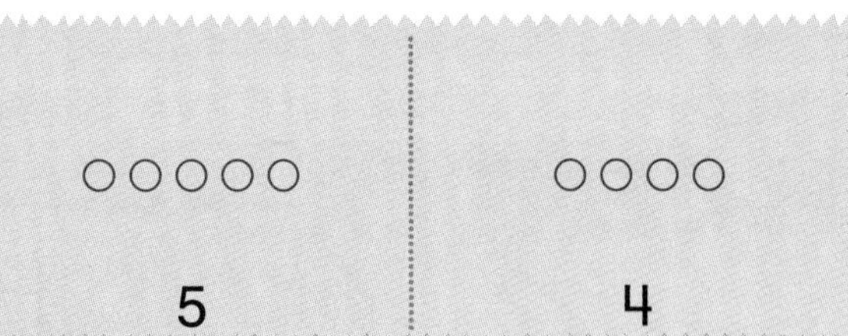

 Why do you get the same totals as your partner? Possible answer: We drew the same parts.

MEETING INDIVIDUAL NEEDS

EARLY FINISHERS

Children may collect magazine pictures or make drawings of food items needed for building the Food Guide Pyramid. (See page 76F of this Teacher's Edition.)

EXTRA SUPPORT

Some children may make the error of counting objects in the two Parts and then placing that many objects in the Total. Have children move the counters from the Part sections into the Total section before they count.

ONGOING ASSESSMENT

Observation Checklist Observe if children listen carefully to their partner's opinions and talk about what the correct answers should be in the activity.

Follow Up Ask children who are not listening carefully to their partner to repeat what their partner says.

Try These!

Take turns.

You tell a story about parts. Your partner draws the parts and writes the total.

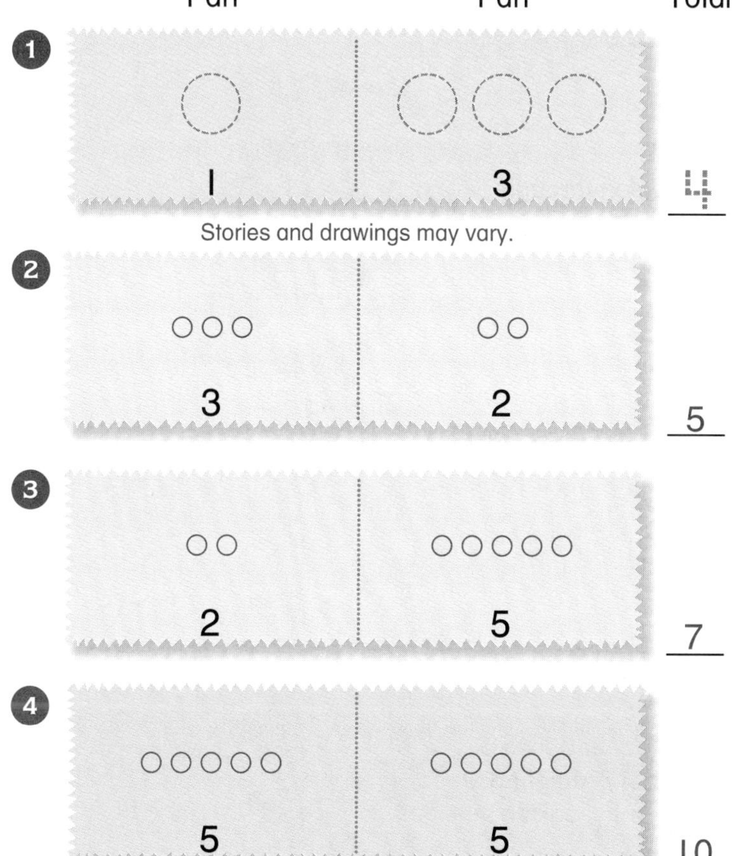

	Part	Part	Total
1	1	3	4
2	3	2	5
3	2	5	7
4	5	5	10

Stories and drawings may vary.

Journal: **Draw and write to show parts and a total.** The parts that children draw should match the total.

At Home: Ask your child to tell you a story about exercise 1 above.

Alternate Teaching Strategy

Materials per pair: 10 two-color counters, 1 paper cup

Have children work in pairs. One child puts 1 to 10 counters in the paper cup. The other child overturns the cup so the counters fall onto a desk or table. Then they both make up a vegetable or fruit part-part-total story using the red and yellow counters.

For example, for 3 red and 4 yellow counters, they could tell a story like this one:

- **I see 3 tomatoes and 4 onions. What is the total number of vegetables?** *[7]*

Do this activity several times. Invite pairs of children to share their stories with the class. You may wish to record them and have children illustrate each story for a class book.

PRACTICE • 21 (HOMEWORK)

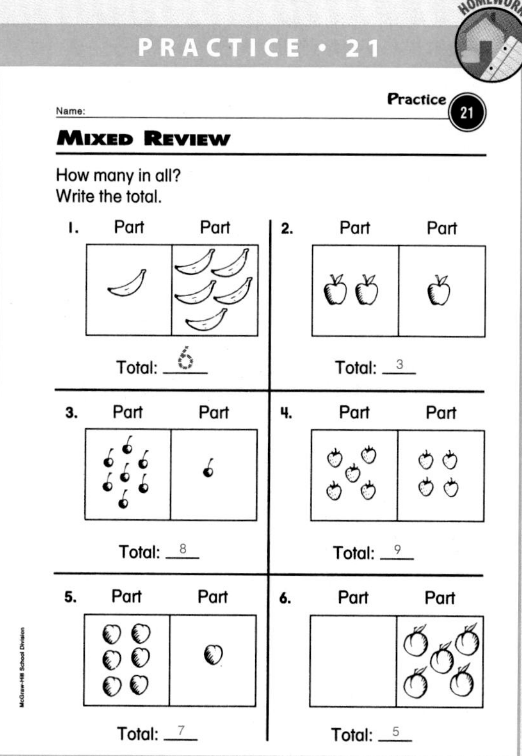

Name: Practice 21

Mixed Review

How many in all? Write the total.

Exercise	Part	Part	Total
1.	1	5	6
2.	2	1	3
3.	7	1	8
4.	5	4	9
5.	6	1	7
6.	0	5	5

RETEACH • 21

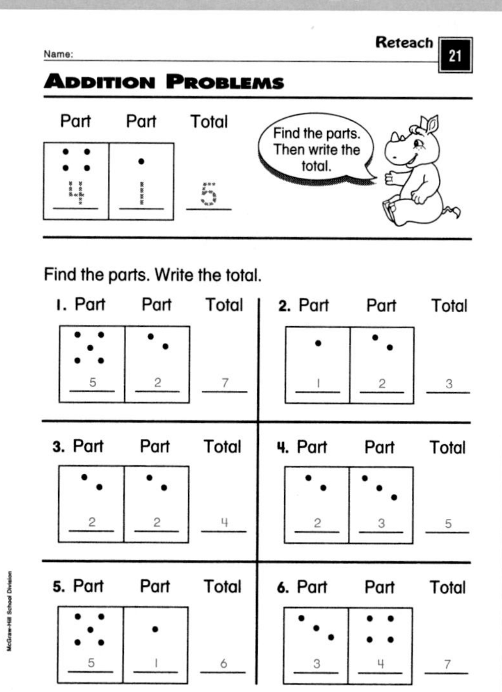

Name: Reteach 21

Addition Problems

Part	Part	Total
4	1	5

Find the parts. Then write the total.

Find the parts. Write the total.

Exercise	Part	Part	Total
1.	5	2	7
2.	1	2	3
3.	2	2	4
4.	2	3	5
5.	5	1	6
6.	3	4	7

EXTEND • 21

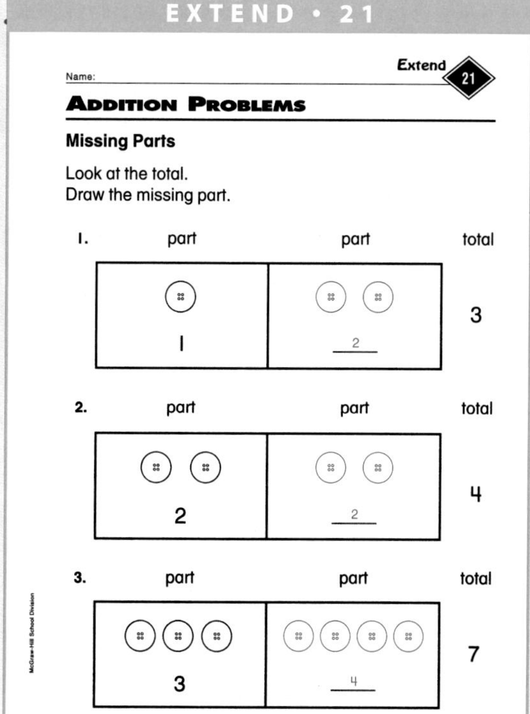

Name: Extend 21

Addition Problems

Missing Parts

Look at the total. Draw the missing part.

Exercise	part	part	total
1.	1	2	3
2.	2	2	4
3.	3	4	7

Teaching With Technology

Addition Stories

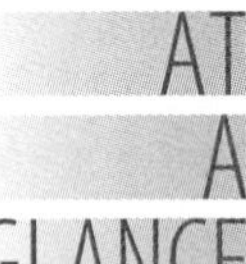

OBJECTIVE Children explore the concept of addition through part-part-whole stories.

Resource Math Van Activity: *Apple Baskets*

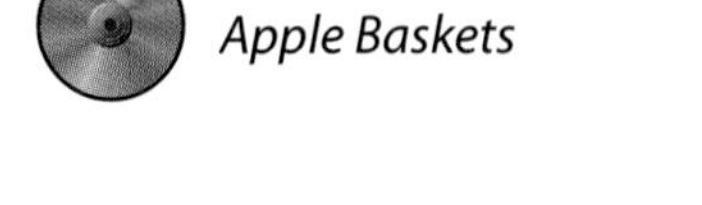

SET UP

Launch the ***Math Van*** program. Click the right arrow to locate Activity 3, *Apple Baskets.* After listening to the activity's description, click *Start.*

Using the Math Van Activity

1 Getting Started Have children review the use of the Part-Part-Total Mat within the Counters tool.

2 Practice and Apply Children listen to a story about two baskets of apples and then use stamps to model the story. After finding the total number of apples, they check their answers by looking at the number in the Answer box.

3 Close Have children show the pictures from their Math Journal and discuss their work with you, each other, or the class.

Extend Children can create their own stories and solve their own parts and totals problems. Have them work with partners and take turns. The first child tells a story about two groups of objects. The second child stamps the two groups on the mat and then finds the total.

TIPS FOR TOOLS

Before children create their own problems, show them how to scroll through the Stamp Palette to access all the available stamp pictures for their stories.

SCREEN 1

Children listen to the *Apple Baskets* problem, which asks them to find the total number of apples in two baskets.

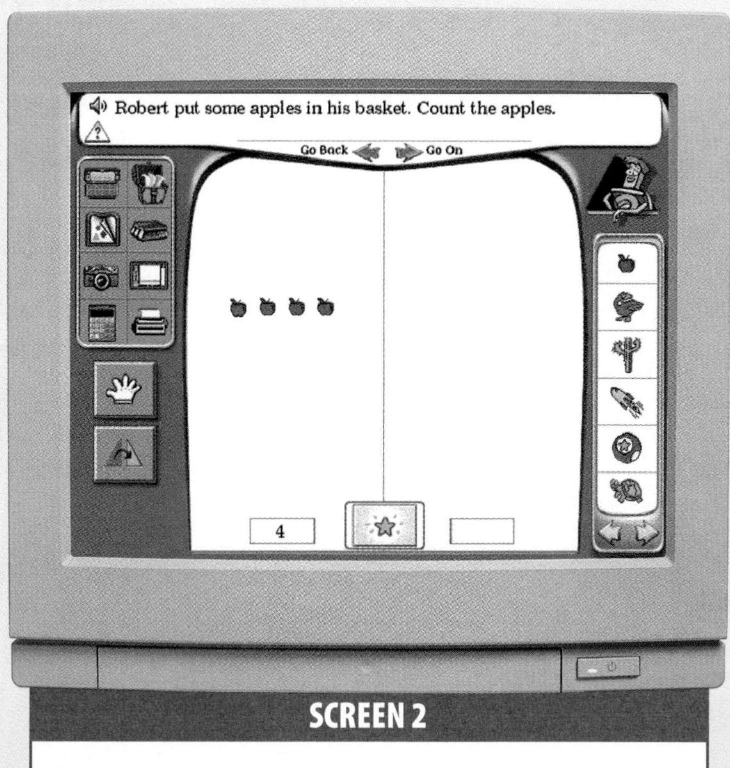

SCREEN 2

The activity opens with a group of apples on one side of a Part-Part-Total Mat.

SCREEN 3

Children stamp another group of apples and then find the total. They check their answer by looking at the number in the total box.

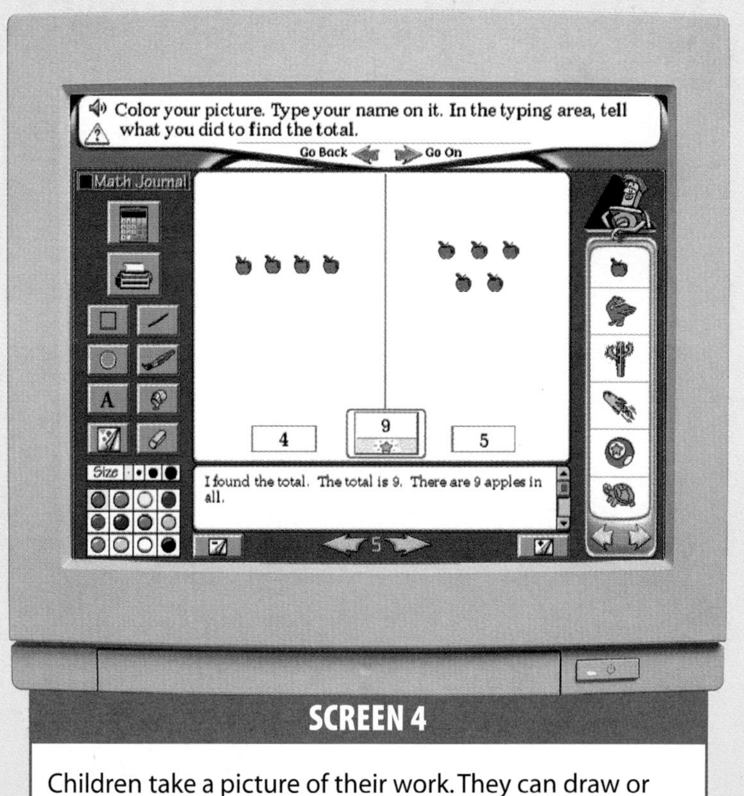

SCREEN 4

Children take a picture of their work. They can draw or type on the picture to explain what they did.

Addition Sentences

OBJECTIVE Complete or write addition sentences.

Day 1 Addition Sentences

Day 2 More Addition Sentences

RESOURCE REMINDER
Math Center Cards 17
Practice 22–23, Reteach 22–23, Extend 22–23

SKILLS TRACE

GRADE K	• Explore completing or writing an addition sentence. *(Chapter 11)*
GRADE 1	• Complete or write an addition sentence.
GRADE 2	• Complete or write an addition sentence. *(Chapter 1)*

LESSON RESOURCES

MANIPULATIVE WARM-UP

Cooperative Pairs **Kinesthetic**

OBJECTIVE Explore completing addition sentences.

Materials per pair: 2 paper plates, 10 pieces of popped popcorn

▶ To begin the activity, have one child put 6 popcorn pieces on one plate and the other child put 3 popcorn pieces on the other plate. Ask:

- **What is the total number of pieces of popcorn on the plates?** *[9]*
- **Write the sentence "6 and 3 are ___" on the chalkboard. Read it aloud and then ask children to fill in the blank.**

▶ Repeat the activity, having partners make up popcorn addition problems with the paper plates. Have them fill in the blanks for "___ and ___ are ___" on the chalkboard.

CONNECTION ACTIVITY

Cooperative Pairs **Musical**

OBJECTIVE Connect writing an addition sentence with a song.

Resource Math Songs audiocassette, Side 2, Selection 2

▶ Have the children listen to and then sing the song "Ten Little Fingers." Then tell partners to take turns playing a finger adding game.

▶ One child raises some fingers on one hand and some fingers on the other hand as he or she sings the last line "I can hold them just so." The other child says and then writes the addition sentence on a sheet of paper for the number of fingers the first child's hands show.

DAILY MATH

PREVIOUS DAY QUICK REVIEW

Make cube trains. Find the total.

1. 1 blue and 3 red *[4]*
2. 2 blue and 2 red *[4]*
3. 0 blue and 4 red *[4]*
4. 3 blue and 2 red *[5]*

Problem of the Day • 17

Read aloud to children:

Halle ate 4 plums.
Cal ate 5 plums.
Who ate more plums?
How many did they eat in all? *[Cal; 9]*

TECH LINK

MATH VAN

Tool You may wish to use the Counters tool with this lesson.

MATH FORUM

Cultural Diversity I encourage children to draw pictures of foods that they like from their cultures. They draw on white paper plates. When they are finished, I have them show their paper plate drawings to the class and tell something about the food.

Visit our Resource Village at http://www.mhschool.com to access the Math Forum.

MATH CENTER

Practice

OBJECTIVE Write addition sentences.

Materials per child: paper bag, 5 blue and 5 red connecting cubes, 5 index cards

Prepare Make five addition number frame cards as shown.

Children put the connecting cubes into a bag, and then take some cubes out of the bag. They make red and blue cube trains, and write an addition sentence to find the sum. *[Check that children's drawings and number agree.]*

PRACTICE ACTIVITY 17 — MATH CENTER On Your Own

Number Sense • Blue Train, Red Train

YOU NEED: bag of blue and red cubes; cards

- Take some red and blue cubes from the bag.
- Make a train with red cubes. Make a train with blue cubes.
- Write how many red cubes. Write how many blue cubes.
- Write the sum.
- Put the cubes back.

Play 4 more times.

2 + 4 = 6

Grade Level 1 — McGraw-Hill School Division — Chapter 3, Lesson 2 — Addition

NCTM Standards
- Problem Solving
- ✓ Communication
- ✓ Reasoning
- ✓ Connections

Problem Solving

OBJECTIVE Count cubes and add to find a total.

Materials per child: 6 plastic bags, 22 red and 46 yellow connecting cubes, six 5" × 8" index cards

Prepare Cut index cards in half lengthwise. Label with write-on lines, plus and equal signs. Set up 6 plastic bags: 6 red, 2 yellow; 3 red, 3 yellow; 2 red, 5 yellow; 5 red, 4 yellow; 2 red, 8 yellow; 4 red, 3 yellow. Number the bags 1–6.

Children write the addition sentences on the number frame cards. *[Check children's work.]*

PROBLEM-SOLVING ACTIVITY 17 — MATH CENTER On Your Own

Spatial Reasoning • How Many?

YOU NEED: 6 bags of cubes; 6 cards

- Look at the cubes in Bag 1.
- Count the red cubes.
- Count the yellow cubes.
- Write an addition sentence.
- Tell how many cubes in all.

Do the same for bags 2, 3, 4, 5, and 6.

4 + 6 = 10

Grade Level 1 — McGraw-Hill School Division — Chapter 3, Lesson 2 — Addition

NCTM Standards
- ✓ Problem Solving
- ✓ Communication
- Reasoning
- ✓ Connections

DAY 1

Addition Sentences

OBJECTIVE Children complete addition sentences.

Materials per child: 10 two-color counters

1 Motivate — Whole Class

Materials per child: 10 two-color counters, 2 paper plates

Draw 3 apples and 2 apples on the chalkboard. Ask children to tell what is the total number of apples. *[5]* Write the sentence "3 and 2 are 5" on the chalkboard. Tell children there is another way to write that sentence. Write 3 + 2 = 5 under the first sentence.

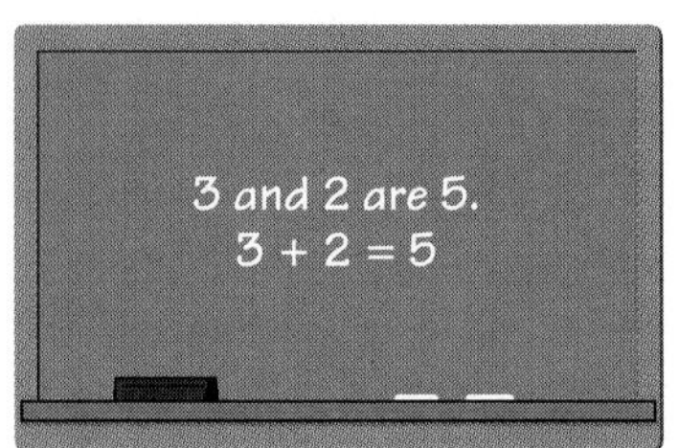

Read the second sentence, pointing to each number and symbol.

- **Three plus two equals five.**

Explain that this sentence shows that you *add* 3 and 2 and get the total 5.

Point to the *addition sign* and say it stands for the word "plus." Explain that the *equal sign* stands for the word "equals." Call on volunteers to point out the addition sign and the equal sign in the number sentence.

Call on volunteers to say other number sentences for parts you show.

2 Develop

Page 81

Work through the example with children. Explain that the drawing in exercise 1 shows cookies on two plates. Have children use counters to show the two parts, find the total, and complete the number sentence. Then work through exercises 2–6 with children, having them show the parts on the 2 plates, draw, then find the sum.

Note that some children may need to point to each part of the addition sentence and be told to read from left to right. Read the sentences aloud with children. Review the vocabulary as necessary.

Critical Thinking

After children finish the exercises on the page, ask:

- **How many different number sentences can you think of to show a total of 5?** *[Possible answers: 1 + 4 = 5, 2 + 3 = 5, 3 + 2 = 5, 4 + 1 = 5; some children may include 0 + 5 = 5 and 5 + 0 = 5.]*

Name ____________

Addition Sentences

You need 10 counters.

Draw. Add.
Drawings may vary.

1. 

2. 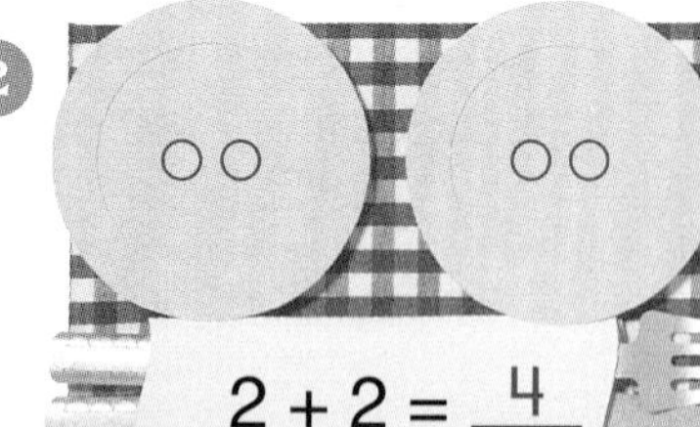

3. 

4. 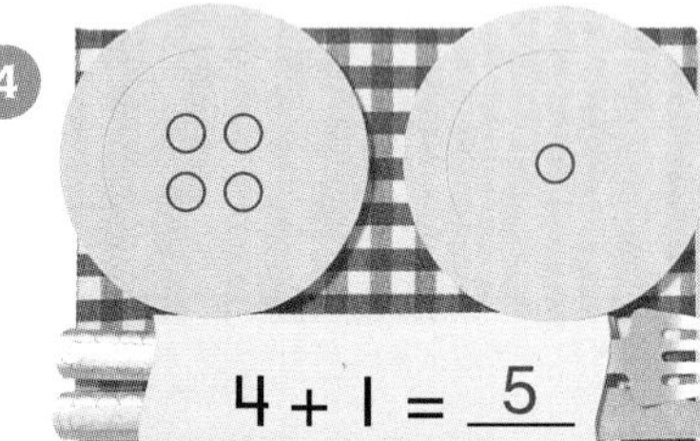

5. 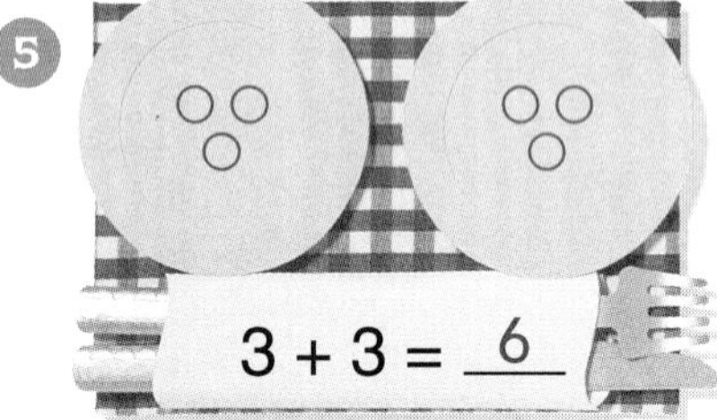

6. 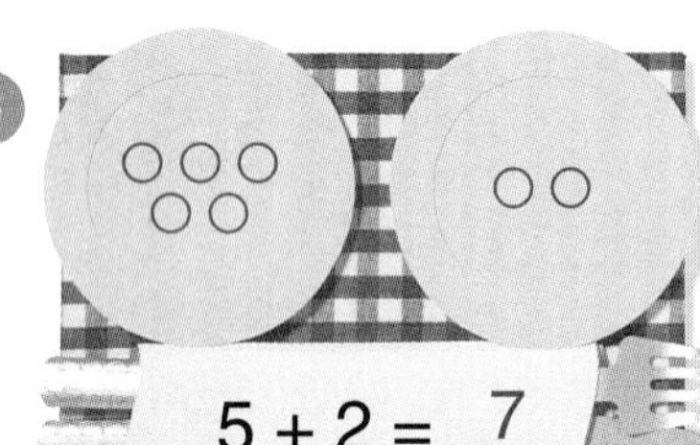

MEETING INDIVIDUAL NEEDS

EXTRA SUPPORT

Make addition number sentence flash cards for children to practice with. Write the sums on the back of the flash cards.

STUDENTS ACQUIRING ENGLISH

The concept of adding in Spanish is expressed using the word *màs* ("more"). Help Spanish-speaking children to understand addition sentences by expressing them in Spanish.

ONGOING ASSESSMENT

Interview Determine if children can complete an addition sentence. Write 3 + 1 = ___ on the chalkboard, draw 3 circles and 1 circle above the number sentence, and ask:

- **What is the total?** *[4]*
- **Read this addition sentence.** *[Three plus one equals four.]*

Follow Up Allow children having difficulty completing addition sentences to use counters. Then assign **Reteach 22.**

For children who are adept at completing addition number sentences, assign **Extend 22.**

Try These!

Add.

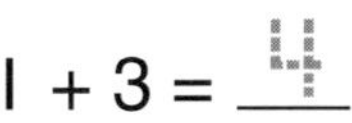

1 + 3 = 4

3 + 4 = 7

4 + 4 = 8

1 + 5 = 6

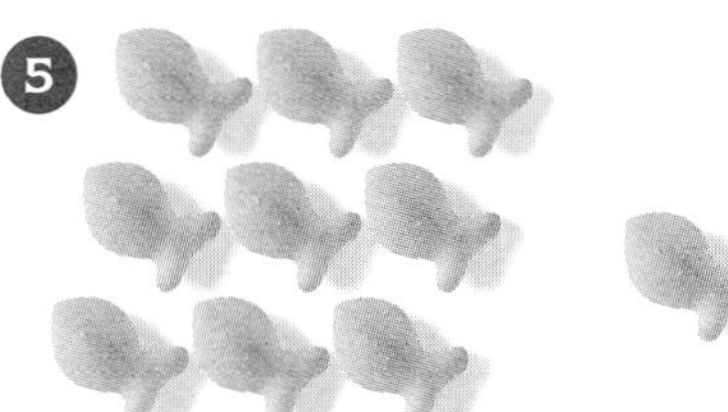

9 + 1 = 10

3 + 3 = 6

Mixed Review

Write the numbers in order.

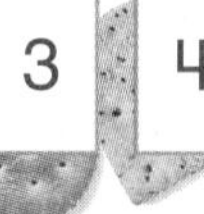
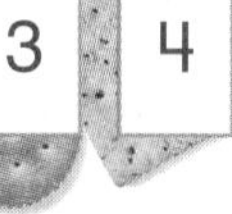
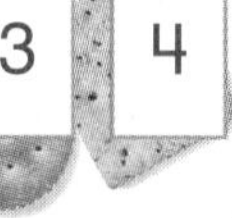
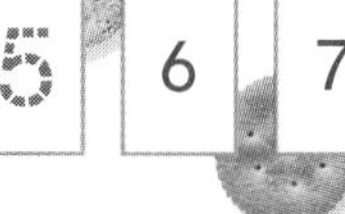
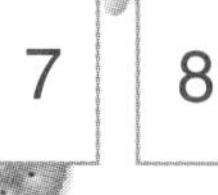
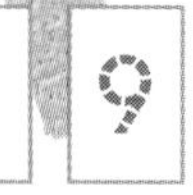

7. 1 2 3 4 5 6 7 8 9 10

At Home: Your child has begun to add. Have your child tell you about the addition exercises on this page.

Page 82

Try These Assign practice exercises 1–6.

Work through the first exercise with children. Allow them to point to each part of the number sentence. Remind them to read from left to right. Then reread the number sentences aloud with the children.

Mixed Review Children review skills from Chapter 1 by writing numbers 1 to 10 in order.

3 Close

Check for Understanding by having children use counters to illustrate addition sentences and then complete the sentences.

Tomorrow children will write addition sentences.

PRACTICE • 22

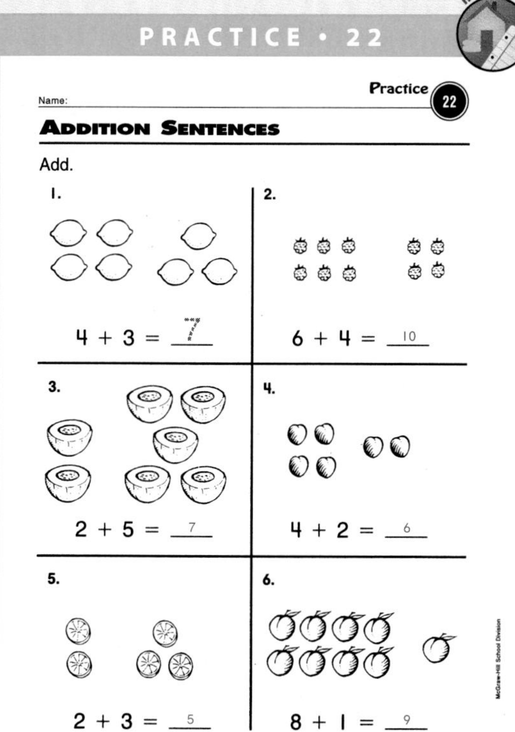

RETEACH • 22

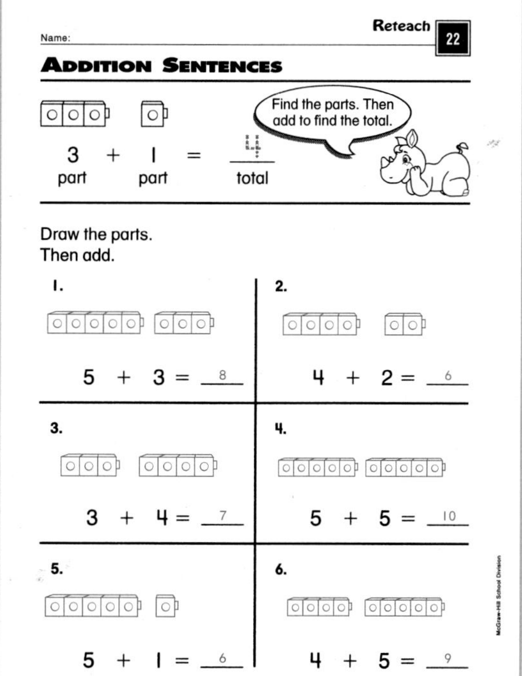

EXTEND • 22

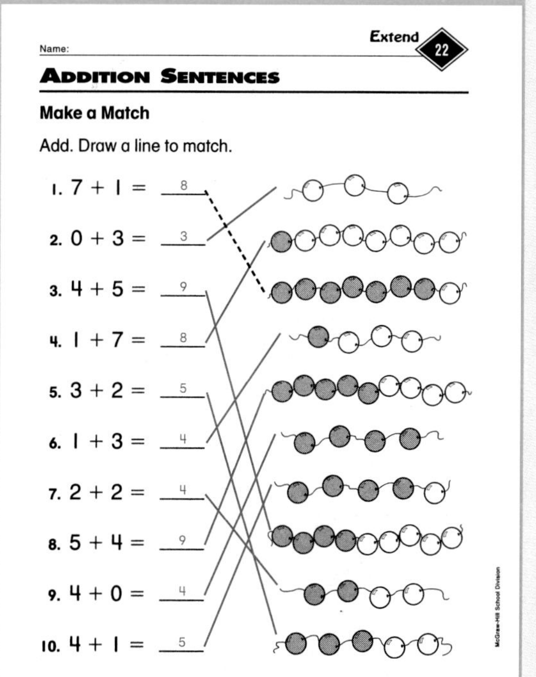

More Addition Sentences

OBJECTIVE Children write addition sentences.

1 Motivate — Whole Class

Resources Jumbo Activity Book, page 5; Sticker, sheets 5 (numerals, symbols) and 6 (vegetables)

Place corn stickers on Jumbo Activity Book page 5 as you present this problem:

Zena gave 7 ears of corn to her big pig and 2 ears of corn to her little pig. How many ears of corn did she give both pigs?

Construct the addition sentence 7 + 2 = 9 on the page as children answer the following questions:

- **What can you write to show how many ears of corn there are in the parts?** *[numbers 7 and 2]*
- **What do you write to show adding?** *[addition sign]*
- **What do you write after the second number?** *[equal sign]*
- **What is the total number of ears of corn?** *[9]*

Explain that another word for *total* is *sum.* Tell children that 7 + 2 = 9 is an *addition sentence.*

2 Develop

Page 83

Discuss the cornstalk picture problem and the addition sentence at the top of the page. Point out that 3 is the sum. Work through the first two exercises with children.

Critical Thinking

After children discuss the Critical Thinking question, ask:

- **Why can you use numbers to stand for pictures?** *[Possible answer: It's a shorter way to tell how many things are in a group.]*

Page 84

Try These Assign practice exercises 1–6.

More to Explore Help children to identify the pattern by asking them to look at the addition sentences and read all the first numbers. *[0, 1, 2, 3, 4, 5]*

- **What number are you adding to each number?** *[0]*
- **What addition sentence comes next in the pattern? How do you know?** *[6 + 0 = 6; explanations will vary.]*

3 Close

Check for Understanding by having children write an addition sentence for a simple addition picture: 4 + 3 = ____. *[7]*

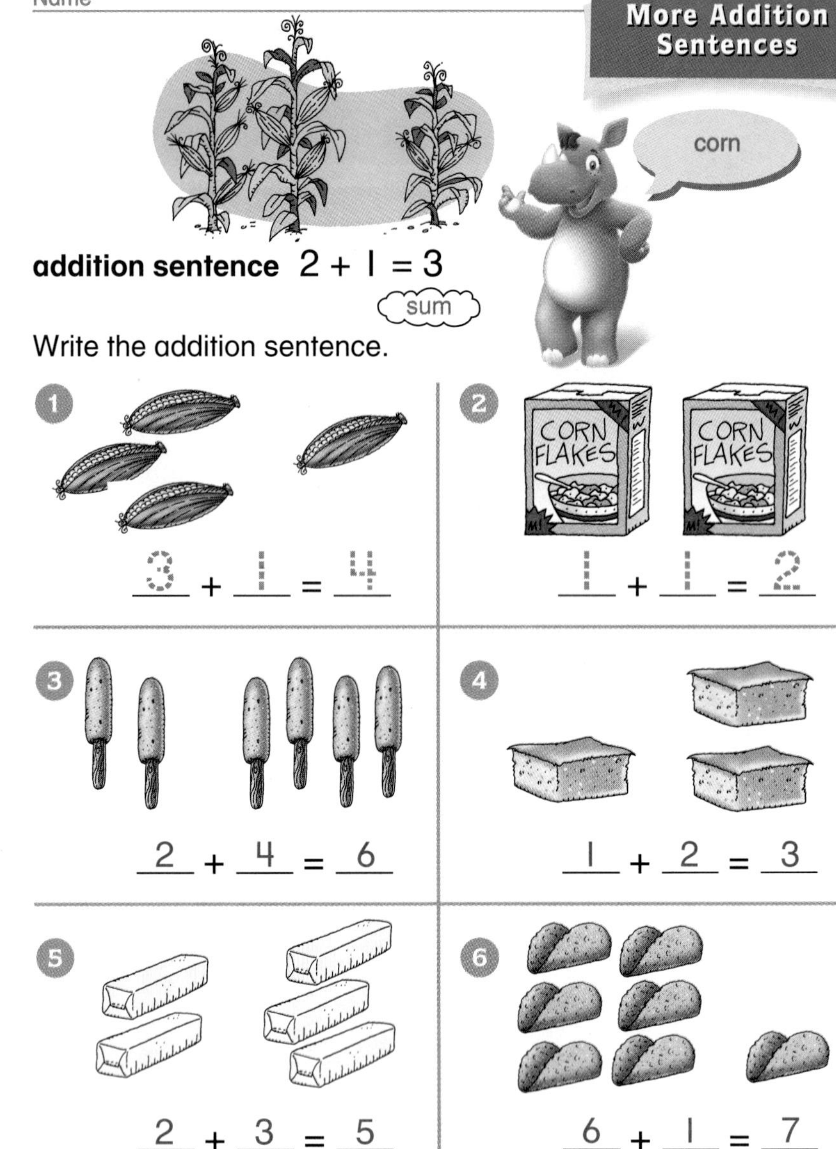
Name

More Addition Sentences

addition sentence 2 + 1 = 3

(sum)

Write the addition sentence.

1. 3 + 1 = 4
2. 1 + 1 = 2
3. 2 + 4 = 6
4. 1 + 2 = 3
5. 2 + 3 = 5
6. 6 + 1 = 7

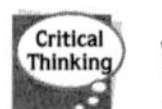

What is an addition story you can tell about 3 + 1?

Possible answer: I picked 3 ears of corn. I picked 1 more ear of corn. I picked 4 ears of corn in all.

CHAPTER 3 *Lesson 2* — eighty-three • 83

MEETING INDIVIDUAL NEEDS

EARLY FINISHERS

Have children make drawings showing two groups of their favorite foods, exchange their drawings with classmates, and write addition sentences for the drawings.

INCLUSION

Provide several sets of number cards for zero through 10 and operation cards for + and =. Let children use the cards to compose addition sentences before writing them. (Use TA 9.)

ONGOING ASSESSMENT

Observation Checklist Observe children's understanding of addition facts to 10 as they write addition sentences from picture problems.

Follow Up For children having difficulty with addition facts to 10, have them use counters to help them add. Assign **Reteach 23.**

For children who can add facts to 10 and write addition sentences, assign **Extend 23.**

Write the addition sentence.

1
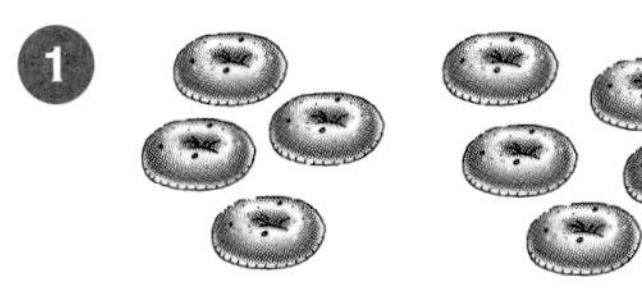

4 + 5 = 9

2

3 + 2 = 5

3
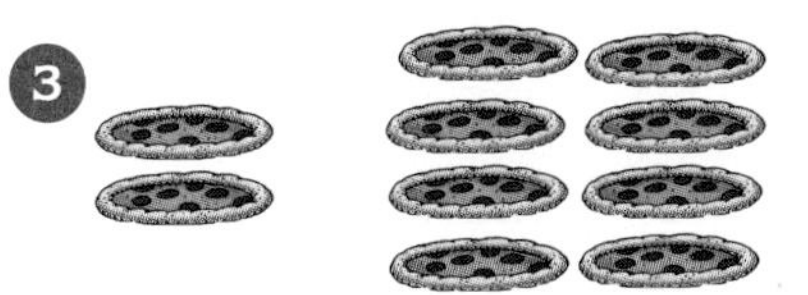
2 + 8 = 10

4

6 + 2 = 8

5
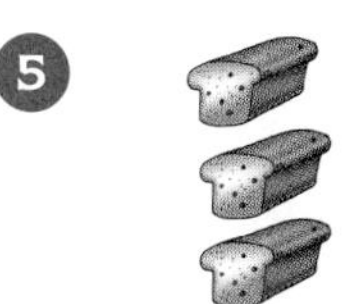
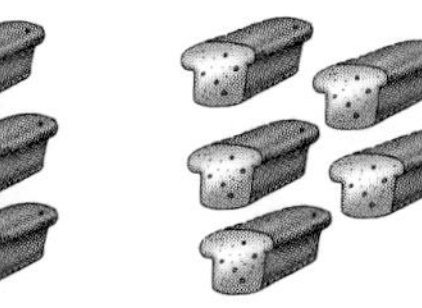

3 + 5 = 8

6

5 + 5 = 10

More to Explore Patterns

Look for a pattern. Complete.

0 + 0 = 0	1 + 0 = 1	2 + 0 = 2
3 + 0 = 3	4 + 0 = 4	5 + 0 = 5

We are learning to write addition sentences. Have your child tell you about the exercises on this page.

Alternate Teaching Strategy

Materials per pair: 5 blue and 5 red connecting cubes, paper bag

Give each pair of children 5 blue and 5 red connecting cubes and a paper bag. Partners take turns doing the following activity: One child, without looking into the bag, picks a handful of cubes, separates them into groups of blue and red, and shows them to the other child. The other child says and then writes an addition sentence that describes that number of cubes.

Do an example or two with children. Allow them to make a blue train and a red train before they write their addition sentences if they wish, and then put them together to find the sum. Emphasize the vocabulary: *plus, equals, sum, addition sentence.*

PRACTICE • 23

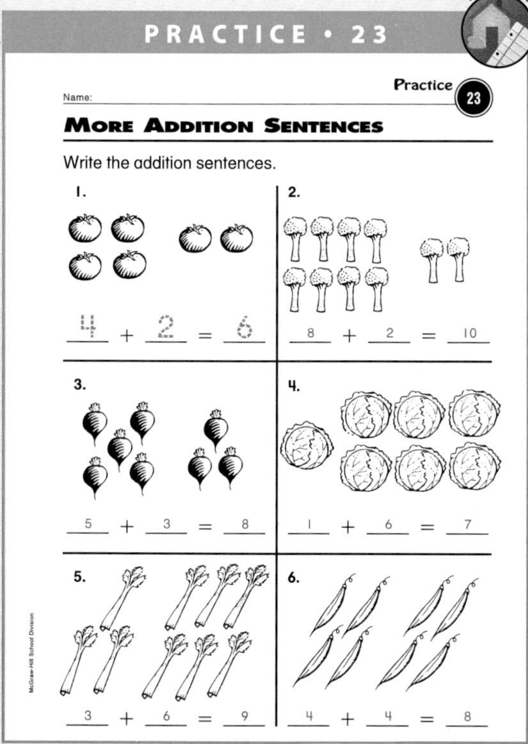

Name: Practice 23

More Addition Sentences

Write the addition sentences.

1. 4 + 2 = 6
2. 8 + 2 = 10
3. 5 + 3 = 8
4. 1 + 6 = 7
5. 3 + 6 = 9
6. 4 + 4 = 8

RETEACH • 23

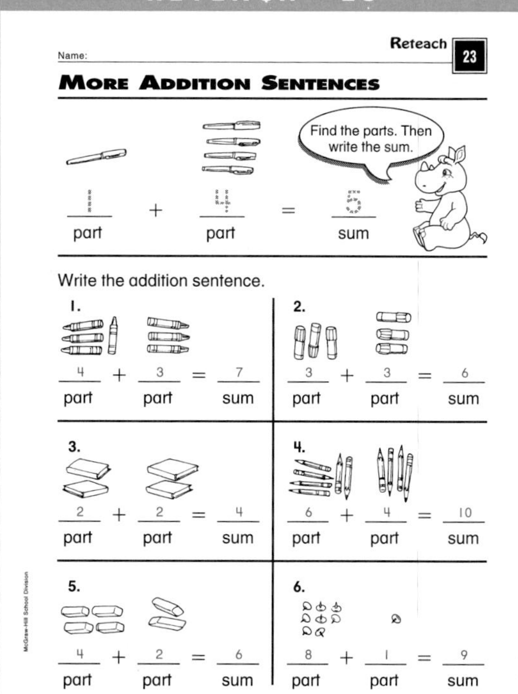

Name: Reteach 23

More Addition Sentences

1 + 4 = 5
part part sum

Write the addition sentence.

1. 4 + 3 = 7 (part part sum)
2. 3 + 3 = 6 (part part sum)
3. 2 + 2 = 4 (part part sum)
4. 6 + 4 = 10 (part part sum)
5. 4 + 2 = 6 (part part sum)
6. 8 + 1 = 9 (part part sum)

EXTEND • 23

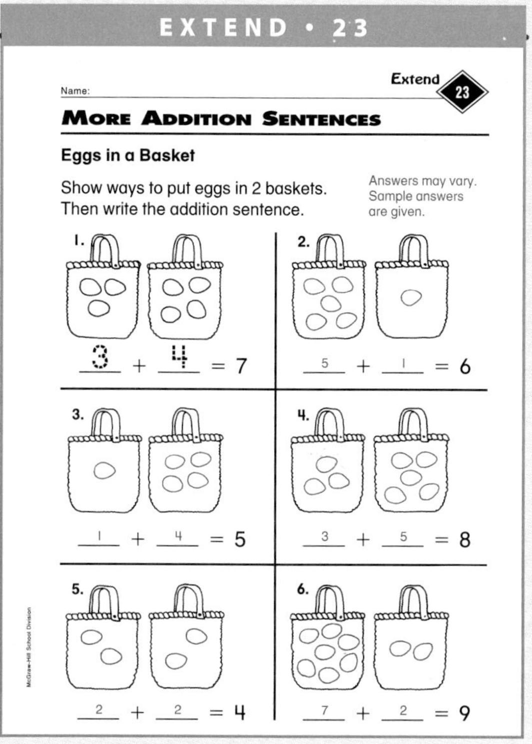

Name: Extend 23

More Addition Sentences

Eggs in a Basket

Show ways to put eggs in 2 baskets. Then write the addition sentence.

Answers may vary. Sample answers are given.

1. 3 + 4 = 7
2. 5 + 1 = 6
3. 1 + 4 = 5
4. 3 + 5 = 8
5. 2 + 2 = 4
6. 7 + 2 = 9

Problem-Solving Strategy: Write an Addition Sentence

OBJECTIVES Solve addition problems; write addition sentences to show solutions.

Day 1 Problem-Solving Strategy: Write an Addition Sentence

RESOURCE REMINDER
Math Center Cards 18
Practice 24, Reteach 24, Extend 24

SKILLS TRACE

GRADE K	• Solve an addition problem by completing an addition sentence. *(Chapter 11)*
GRADE 1	• Solve an addition problem and write an addition sentence to show the solution.
GRADE 2	• Solve problems by writing an addition sentence. *(Chapter 1)*

WARM-UP

Whole Class — **Kinesthetic**

OBJECTIVES Explore addition by acting out addition stories and writing addition sentences.

Materials name tags for various storybook characters

▶ Tell children a simple story such as:
Little Bear has a birthday party. First to come are Little Red Riding Hood, Little Bo Peep, and Goldilocks. Then come the Three Little Pigs. How many friends come to Little Bear's party?

▶ Give volunteers name tags and let them act out the story to find the answer. Write the addition sentence on the chalkboard: **3** + **3** = **6.** Read the sentence with the children.

▶ Continue the activity using other storybook characters such as the Three Bears, the Big Bad Wolf, Little Jack Horner, and Tom, the Piper's Son.

CONNECTION ACTIVITY

Whole Class — **Auditory/Linguistic**

OBJECTIVE Connect writing an addition sentence with poetry.

Materials butcher paper, markers or crayons

▶ Display the following poem:

Bears Everywhere
1 dreamy bear, walking by.
2 hungry bears, eating pie.
3 sleeping bears, taking naps.
4 dancing bears, wearing caps.
5 playful bears, trying to hide.
6 happy bears, smiling wide.

▶ Read the poem aloud and ask children to point to words that rhyme. Have volunteers draw bears for each group on butcher paper.

▶ Ask children to pick two groups of bears and write an addition sentence.

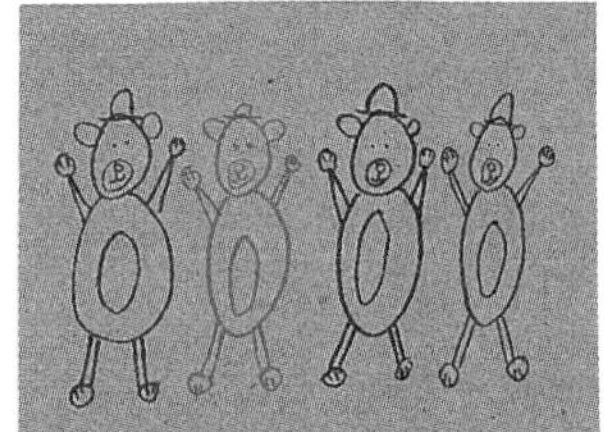

DAILY MATH

PREVIOUS DAY QUICK REVIEW

1. 5 + 4 = __ *[9]*
2. 8 + 2 = __ *[10]*
3. 6 + 3 = __ *[9]*
4. 5 + 5 = __ *[10]*

FAST FACTS

1. 1 + 1 *[2]*
2. 1 + 2 *[3]*
3. 1 + 3 *[4]*
4. 1 + 4 *[5]*

Problem of the Day • 18

Read aloud to children:

Maya has 5 red beads, 2 green beads, and 4 blue beads.
How many red beads and blue beads does she have in all? *[9 beads]*
How many green beads and blue beads does she have in all? *[6 beads]*

TECH LINK

MATH VAN

Tool You may wish to use the Counters tool with this lesson.

MATH FORUM

Combination Classes I have children at the second-grade level write addition sentences. I have first grade children use counters or pictures to represent the addition sentences.

Visit our Resource Village at http://www.mhschool.com to see more of the Math Forum.

MATH CENTER

Practice

OBJECTIVE Use an addition sentence to solve a word problem.

Materials per pair: 2 five-part spinners (TA 7), 10 connecting cubes, ten 5" × 8" index cards

Prepare Label spinners 1–5. Cut index cards in half lengthwise, and label as shown.

Children spin for two numbers, use connecting cubes to show the numbers, and make up a word problem.

Partners solve the word problem by writing an addition sentence. Partners check each other's work.

PRACTICE ACTIVITY 18

MATH CENTER
Partners

Formulating Problems • Spin It!

Take turns.

- Spin a spinner to get a number. Use cubes to show the number.
- Spin and show another number.
- Make up a word problem about the numbers.
- Your partner writes an addition sentence to solve it.
- Check your partner's work. Then spin again.

YOU NEED
2 (spinners)
10 (cubes)
frame cards

4 + 3 = 7

Grade Level 1 · McGraw-Hill School Division

Chapter 3, Lesson 3 · Addition

NCTM Standards
- ✓ Problem Solving
- ✓ Communication
- Reasoning
- ✓ Connections

Problem Solving

OBJECTIVE Write an addition sentence.

Materials per child: 30 connecting cubes–10 yellow, 10 red, 10 blue; two 5" × 8" index cards

Prepare Cut each index card in half lengthwise, and label as shown. Include separate write-on line and *in all* on each card.

Children use counters to solve addition problems and then write the solutions as addition sentences. *[Check that children's number stories match their connecting cubes.]*

PROBLEM-SOLVING ACTIVITY 18

MATH CENTER
On Your Own

Using Data • Vegetable Soup

Rabbit and Bear made soup.
They used carrots and onions.

- Show Rabbit's carrots with cubes.
- Show Bear's carrots with cubes.
- Write a number story for the carrots.
- Write a number story for the onions.

YOU NEED
10 yellow
10 red
10 blue
2 number frame cards

Rabbit · Bear
Carrots
Onions

2 + 3 = 5
5 in all

Grade Level 1 · McGraw-Hill School Division

Chapter 3, Lesson 3 · Addition

NCTM Standards
- ✓ Problem Solving
- ✓ Communication
- Reasoning
- ✓ Connections

Lesson 3.3

Problem-Solving Strategy: Write an Addition Sentence

OBJECTIVES Children solve addition problems; children write addition sentences to show solutions.

Materials per child: 10 rhino counters; have available: 10 connecting cubes

1 Motivate — Whole Class

Resources Jumbo Activity Book, page 5; Sticker sheets 2 (rhinos), 5 (numerals and symbols)

As you tell children a rhino story, have them put the rhino stickers on Jumbo Activity Book page 5.

4 rhinos are in the park. 3 more rhinos join them. How many rhinos are in the park? *[7 rhinos]*

Then help children show the addition sentence 4 + 3 = 7 with stickers. Point out the "____ *in all*" answer blank. Tell them the sum (or total) is to be written in the answer blank.

Challenge children to think of rhino stories and solve them.

2 Develop

Page 85

Read aloud to children the first word problem found on the reduced student page in this Teacher's Edition. Have them use rhino counters to show the problem on the workspace at the top of the page. Help them to write the addition sentence. Discuss the **Talk** question.

Read aloud word problems 2 and 3, allowing time for children to find the answers and write the addition sentences.

CRITICAL THINKING

After children finish the problems on the page, ask:

- **How can you find answers to problems another way?** *[Possible answer: I can act them out or draw pictures.]*

Page 86

Try These Work through problem 1 and assign practice problems 2–3.

More to Explore Children may find this problem very challenging. You may need to point out that there are 2 hidden connecting cubes in the left-hand group, which brings that group's total to 7. Suggest that children build the structures to solve the problems.

3 Close

Check for Understanding by having children make up addition problems that ask how many rhinos in all. Then ask them to write addition sentences to go with their problems.

Name __________

Problem-Solving Strategy

Write an Addition Sentence

You need 10 .

Listen to the problem.

Find how many in all.

1. At the store _5_ in all
"There are 3 rhinos at the store. Two more rhinos come in. How many rhinos in all?"
_3_ + _2_ = _5_

Tell how you found the answer.
I showed 3 counters, showed 2 more, and counted 5 rhinos.

2. At the party _6_ in all
"There are 4 rhinos at the party. Two more rhinos join them. How many rhinos in all?"
_4_ + _2_ = _6_

3. At school _5_ in all
"One rhino is at school. Four more rhinos come to school. How many rhinos in all?"
_1_ + _4_ = _5_

MEETING INDIVIDUAL NEEDS

EARLY FINISHERS

Have pairs make 2 groups with their rhino counters and write a number sentence to show the addition. Partners take turns grouping and recording.

EXTRA SUPPORT

Allow children to use a part-part-whole mat (Workmat 3) to act out the problems using counters.

ONGOING ASSESSMENT

Observation Checklist Determine if children understand how to write an addition sentence by observing whether they write the correct numbers for the parts and sum.

Follow Up Have children use counters to show the addition and then use number cards to make the addition sentence. Also assign **Reteach 24.**

For children who can write addition sentences, assign **Extend 24.**

Try These!

Make up a problem for the picture.
Find how many in all.

1

4 in all

3 + 1 = 4

2

7 in all

5 + 2 = 7

3

4 in all

2 + 2 = 4

More to Explore — Spatial Sense

Find how many [cube] in all.

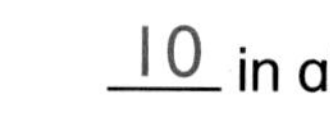

10 in all

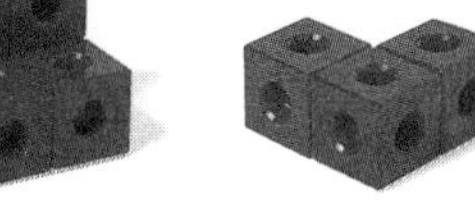

7 + 3 = 10

Ask your child to tell you a story about one of these pictures.

Alternate Teaching Strategy

Materials 10 to 15 manila folders, drawing paper, rhino stamp, ink pad, counters

Prepare For each folder, stamp groups of rhino shapes on 2 sheets of paper to show an addition fact to 10.

Place the closed folders on a table. Tell each pair of children to choose a folder.

Have one partner tell the other a story about the two groups of rhinos. Then both children help each other solve the problem and write an addition sentence for it. Have counters available for children to use.

Walk around the room asking children about their stories and checking their addition sentences. When finished with a folder, pairs can exchange with other pairs.

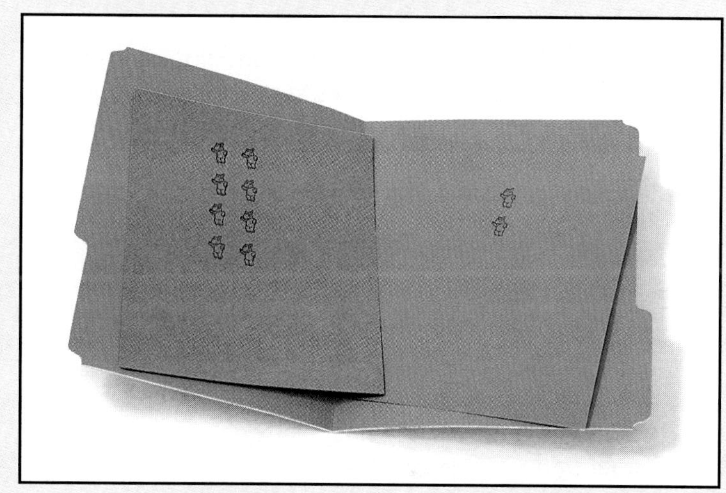

PRACTICE • 24

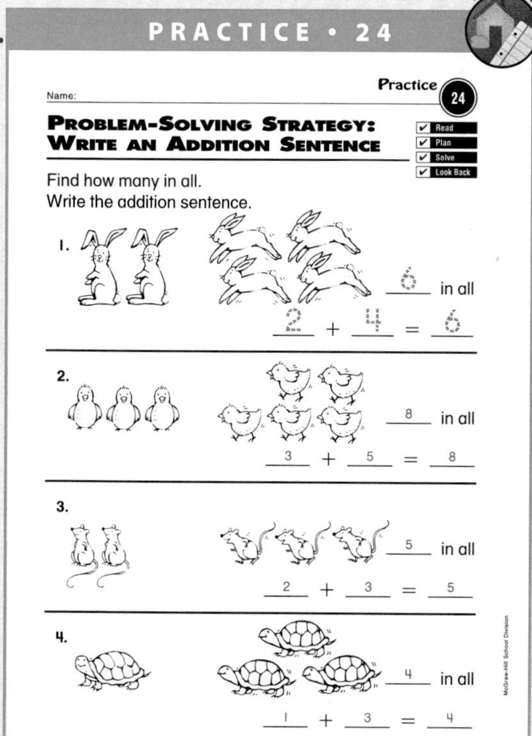

HOMEWORK

Name:

Practice 24

PROBLEM-SOLVING STRATEGY: WRITE AN ADDITION SENTENCE

Read / Plan / Solve / Look Back

Find how many in all.
Write the addition sentence.

1. 6 in all — 2 + 4 = 6

2. 8 in all — 3 + 5 = 8

3. 5 in all — 2 + 3 = 5

4. 4 in all — 1 + 3 = 4

McGraw-Hill School Division

RETEACH • 24

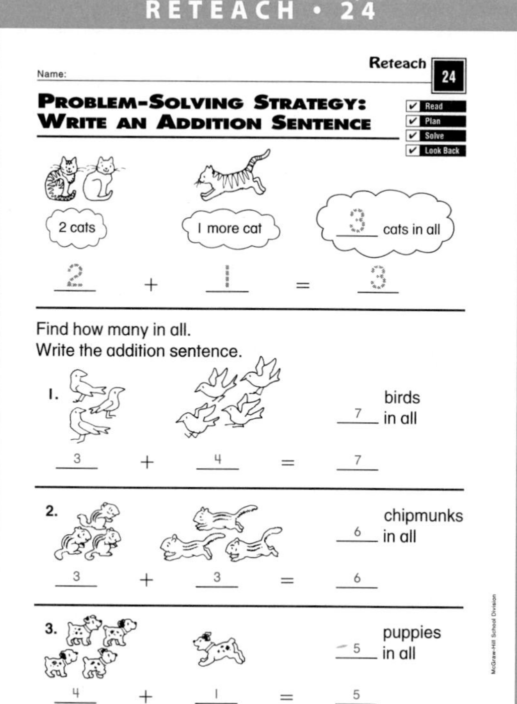

Name:

Reteach 24

PROBLEM-SOLVING STRATEGY: WRITE AN ADDITION SENTENCE

Read / Plan / Solve / Look Back

2 cats — 1 more cat — 3 cats in all

2 + 1 = 3

Find how many in all.
Write the addition sentence.

1. 7 birds in all — 3 + 4 = 7

2. 6 chipmunks in all — 3 + 3 = 6

3. 5 puppies in all — 4 + 1 = 5

McGraw-Hill School Division

EXTEND • 24

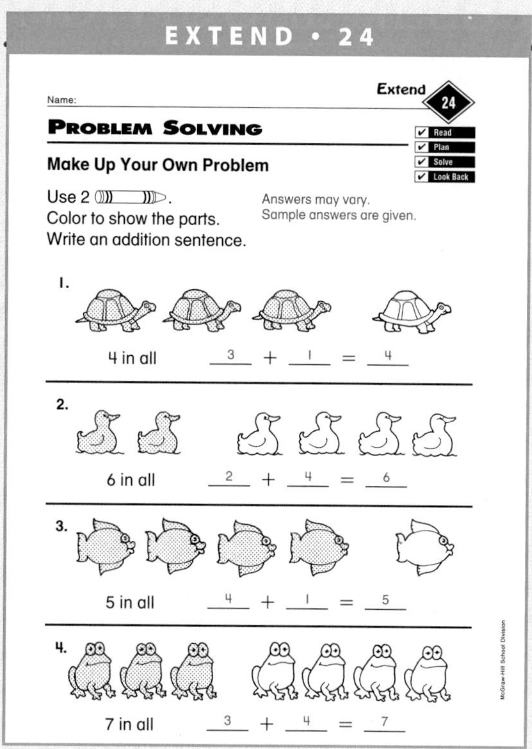

Name:

Extend 24

PROBLEM SOLVING

Read / Plan / Solve / Look Back

Make Up Your Own Problem

Use 2 [crayons].
Color to show the parts.
Write an addition sentence.

Answers may vary.
Sample answers are given.

1. 4 in all — 3 + 1 = 4

2. 6 in all — 2 + 4 = 6

3. 5 in all — 4 + 1 = 5

4. 7 in all — 3 + 4 = 7

McGraw-Hill School Division

PURPOSE Maintain and review the concepts, skills, and strategies that children have learned thus far in the chapter.

Materials have available: rhino counters, two-color counters

Using the Midchapter Review

Page 87

The **Midchapter Review** may be completed independently or by the class as a whole. Explain to children that they can use words, numbers, and pictures to show the meaning of item 10. Some children might prefer answering verbally.

Read aloud to children the word problem for item 1, found on the reduced student page of this Teacher's Edition. Then allow children to do the rest of the page.

Children draw pictures to show addition. Some may draw two separate pictures to show the parts being added together, to match the illustrations in the book. Other children may put the two separate parts together in a third picture that shows the total.

Vocabulary Review

Write the following on the chalkboard:

add	**in all**
addition sentence	**parts**
addition sign	**plus**
equal sign	**sum**
equals	**total**

Ask for volunteers to explain, show, or act out the meaning of the words.

Name

Midchapter Review

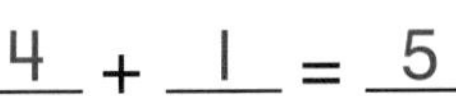

"Four rhinos are having a party. One more rhino joins them. How many rhinos in all?"

Find how many in all.

1 At the party 5 in all

4 + 1 = 5

Add.

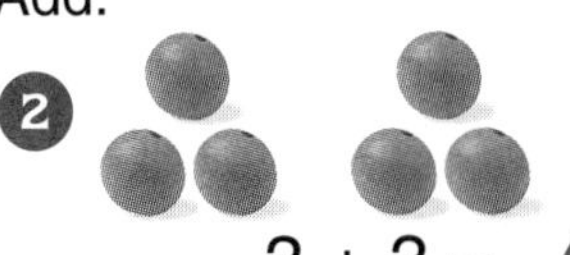

2 3 + 3 = 6

3 1 + 5 = 6

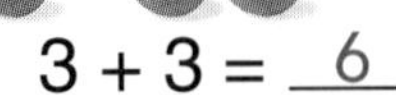

4 6 + 2 = 8

5 5 + 4 = 9

Write the addition sentence.

6 3 + 1 = 4

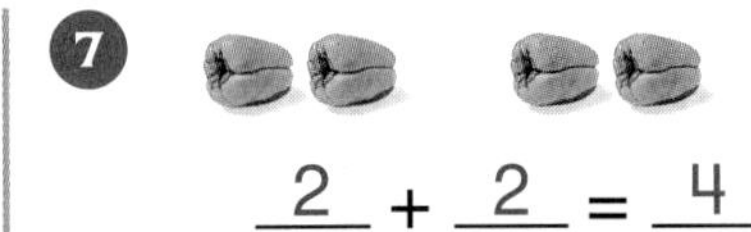

7 2 + 2 = 4

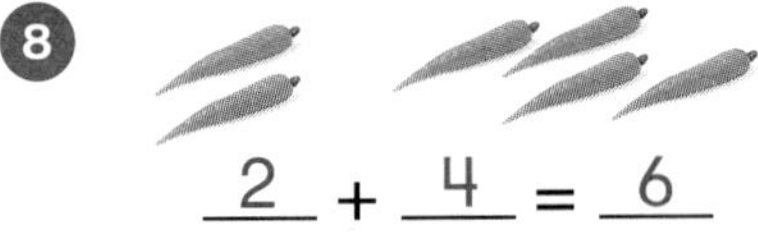

8 2 + 4 = 6

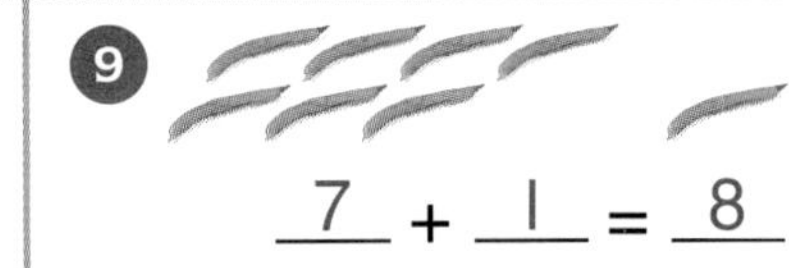

9 7 + 1 = 8

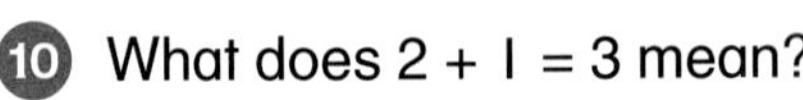

10 What does 2 + 1 = 3 mean?

Possible answer: There are 2 and 1 more, and that is 3.

Draw a picture that shows addition. Children may show groups of objects or action pictures.

CHAPTER 3 *Midchapter Review* eighty-seven • 87

Reinforcement and Remediation

CHAPTER OBJECTIVES	MIDCHAPTER REVIEW ITEMS	STUDENT BOOK PAGES	TEACHER'S EDITION PAGES		TEACHER RESOURCES
			Activities	Alternate Teaching Strategy	Reteach
*3A	1–5	79–82	78A, 80C	80	21–22
*3B	6–10	83–86	84A	84, 86	23

*3A Add, facts to 10
*3B Solve problems, including those that involve addition, and writing an addition sentence

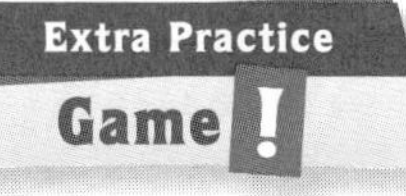

I Show, You Find

You need 2 rhino counters and 10 connecting cubes.

Listen to the rules.

Take turns.

- You put rhino counters on 2 numbers.
- Your partner adds.
- Score 1 point if the sum is correct.

Play until you get 10 points.

Use  to keep score.

AT A GLANCE

OBJECTIVE Provide an opportunity for review and practice.

Materials per pair: 2 rhino counters, 10 connecting cubes

Using the Extra Practice

Page 88

Read aloud to children the rules for the game. Demonstrate how to play, with a volunteer's help. Place one rhino counter on a red game board square and another counter on an orange square. Have the volunteer use connecting cubes to find the sum.

One point is scored for a correct response. Review how to use tally marks to keep score. You might want each child to write his or her name in their score box.

After children finish playing, ask:

- **Which numbers were easiest for you to add? Why?** *[Answers may vary. Possible answers: It's easiest to add the red numbers, the smaller numbers, or 1 or 2.]*

Using the Additional Practice

The section below provides additional practice that you may want to write on the chalkboard or a reproducible master.

ADDITIONAL PRACTICE

Add.

1. 1 + 2 = __ *[3]*   3 + 3 = __ *[6]*

2. 2 + 5 = __ *[7]*   4 + 4 = __ *[8]*

3. 6 + 3 = __ *[9]*   1 + 4 = __ *[5]*

4. 3 + 4 = __ *[7]*   6 + 1 = __ *[7]*

5. 2 + 3 = __ *[5]*   2 + 2 = __ *[4]*

6. 5 + 3 = __ *[8]*   1 + 7 = __ *[8]*

7. 4 + 2 = __ *[6]*   6 + 2 = __ *[8]*

8. 5 + 5 = __ *[10]*   4 + 6 = __ *[10]*

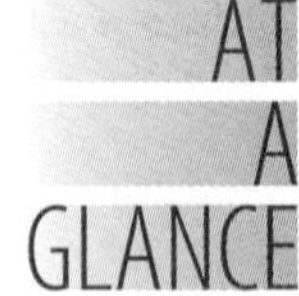

Applying Addition

OBJECTIVE Children use addition and counting in order in a social studies context.

Materials per pair: 3 paper circles—brown, pink, yellow; crayons of the same color

1 Engage

Ask two children to form a line, one standing behind the other. Ask children who is first and who is second in line. Record the names on the chalkboard. Ask:

- **What other way could the two children be in line, one behind the other?** *[They could switch places.]*

Using the Think-Check-Step Strategy, have children think about whether they have the right answer, and then check with those on either side of them.

Have children switch places, and write the names in the new order. Repeat the activity, using three children. Ask:

- **How many different ways are there with (Child A) first in line?** *[2]*
- **How many with (Child B) first in line?** *[2]*
- **How many with (Child C) first in line?** *[2]*
- **How many different ways in all?** *[6]*

2 Investigate — Cooperative Pairs

Page 89

Distribute the brown, pink, and yellow paper circles to pairs of children. Discuss making 3-scoop ice-cream cones. In this investigation, each of the scoops will be a different flavor. The brown circle stands for chocolate, the pink is strawberry, and the yellow is vanilla.

Working Together Have children work in pairs to find all the different ways to stack the 3 scoops. Children color the pictured circles to record their arrangements.

3 Reflect and Share

Page 90

Materials have available: calculators

Have children choose 3 colors, then find and record ways of stacking the ice cream. Some children may draw and color sets of dots; linguistic learners may write the color words in columns.

Write a Report After children have completed the second set of arrangements, have them begin their portfolio reports. To see if they have found all the ways of stacking the ice cream, children can check to see if each color is used 2 times on the top, 2 times on the bottom, and 2 times in the middle.

Name ____________________

Ice Cream Time

Make an ice cream cone.

Working Together

You need 1 , 1 , 1 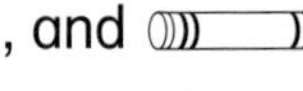, and crayon.

▶ Find different ways to stack the ●, ●, and 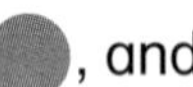.

▶ Color to show each way. Order of arrangements may vary.

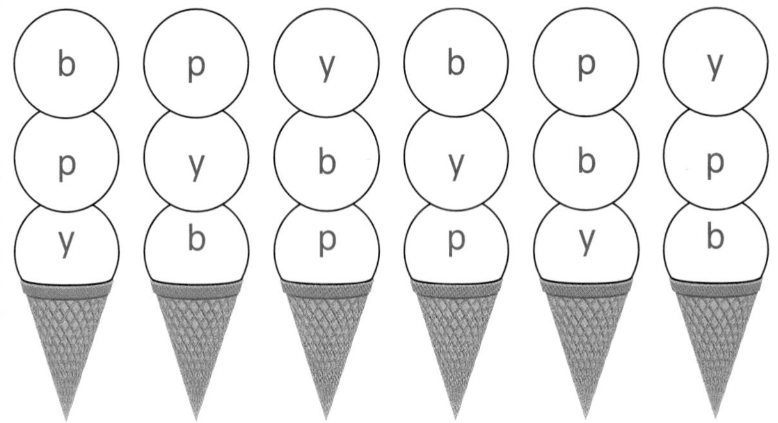

How many ways to stack? 6

MORE TO INVESTIGATE

Predict Sample answer: There will be 4 ways.

Explore As children work, observe how they organize their investigation. You may want to suggest they start by finding all the ways that have the same color at the bottom.

Find Sample answer: There are 4 ways to stack the ice cream. There are 2 colors of cones, and 2 colors of ice cream. For each cone you can stack the ice cream in 2 different ways. This gives a total of 4 ways to stack the ice cream.

Bibliography Children may enjoy reading the following books:

If You Give a Mouse a Cookie by Laura Joffe Numeroff. New York: HarperCollins Children's Books, 1985. ISBN 0–06–024586–7.

10 for Dinner by Jo Ellen Bogart. New York: Scholastic, Inc., 1989. ISBN 0–590–73173–4.

Decision Making Answers may vary. See Teacher's Edition for sample of children's work.

1. Choose your own 3 colors. Find different ways to stack the ice cream.

Write a report.

2. Tell how many ways you found to stack each time.
3. How do you know you found all the ways to stack?

More to Investigate

See Teacher's Edition.

PREDICT What if you have a ⚪, ⚫, ▼, and ▽. How many ways to stack?

EXPLORE Try it. Color to show each way.

FIND Did you find all the ways? How do you know?

BUILDING A PORTFOLIO

This assignment will provide insight into children's ability to organize counting arrangements and their reasoning skills for finding all the possible arrangements.

Allow children to revise their work for the portfolio. Each child's portfolio piece should consist of his or her written record of the arrangements and written report and any notes you made about the child's work.

You may wish to use the Holistic Scoring Guide to assess this task. See page 27 in Teacher's Assessment Resources.

Children's Work

Addition Fact Pairs

OBJECTIVES Add zero using money amounts; use the Order Property with money amounts.

Day 1 Addition Fact Pairs

RESOURCE REMINDER
Math Center Cards 19
Practice 25, Reteach 25, Extend 25

SKILLS TRACE	
GRADE K	• Explore completing or writing an addition sentence. *(Chapter 11)*
GRADE 1	• Add zero using money amounts. • Use the Order Property with money amounts.
GRADE 2	• Explore adding money amounts, including 3 addends. *(Chapter 7)*

MANIPULATIVE WARM-UP

Whole Class — **Kinesthetic**

OBJECTIVE Explore the order property of addition.

Materials 10 counters; 2 paper cups

▶ Show 3 counters and then 2 counters. Ask children for the sum. Write the addition sentence 3 + 2 = 5 on the chalkboard.

▶ Cover up each group of counters with the paper cups. Switch places of the cups with counters under them. Lift up the cups. Ask children how many counters they see in each group, and then ask for the sum.

▶ Ask whether the sum was the same before the switch, and why. *[Yes; changing the order in which you add the numbers doesn't change the sum.]* Write the addition sentence 2 + 3 = 5 under the first addition sentence.

▶ Repeat the activity, having children take turns being the magician and recorders of the addition sentences.

CONNECTION ACTIVITY

Whole Class — **Kinesthetic**

OBJECTIVE Connect the order property and money.

Materials 10 pennies; per pair: play money—1 penny, 1 nickel, 1 dime

▶ Give each pair of children a penny, a nickel, and a dime. Discuss how United States coins are alike and different from each other. Discuss the relative value of coins.

▶ Then give a volunteer 4 pennies and a second volunteer 6 pennies.
- **If (name of child) gives me 4 pennies and (name of another child) gives me 6 pennies, how many pennies will I have?** *[10]*

▶ Have the volunteers trade coins. Ask:
- **If (name of child) gives me 6 pennies and (name of another child) gives me 4 pennies, will I have the same number as before?** *[yes]*

▶ Repeat with other combinations of coins, including addends of zero coins.

DAILY MATH

PREVIOUS DAY QUICK REVIEW

Find the total.

1. 5 + 3 = __ *[8]*
2. 4 + 4 = __ *[8]*
3. 2 + 6 = __ *[8]*
4. 7 + 1 = __ *[8]*

FAST FACTS

1. 3 + 0 *[3]*
2. 4 + 0 *[4]*
3. 0 + 4 *[4]*
4. 0 + 3 *[3]*

Problem of the Day • 19

Read aloud to children:

There are 3 girls swimming.
There are 2 boys fishing.
There are 2 girls hiking.
How many girls are there in all? *[5 girls]*

TECH LINK

MATH FORUM

Management Tip I manage the distribution and collection of pennies by designating several children as Penny Collectors. As each child counts his or her 10 pennies in front of a Penny Collector, they also get a chance to review counting to 10.

Visit our Resource Village at http://www.mhschool.com to see more of the Math Forum.

MATH CENTER

Practice

OBJECTIVE Add zero and reinforce the Order Property of Addition.

Materials per child: blank number cube, 10 pennies, one 5" × 8" index card

Prepare Cut the index card in half, lengthwise. Copy the number frame card format shown on the Math Center Card. Label the number cube 0–5.

After children write the first addition sentence, they write another using the same addends in a different order. If they roll the same number twice, they roll again.

PRACTICE ACTIVITY 19 — MATH CENTER On Your Own

Number Sense • Penny Facts

YOU NEED: 10 pennies, cards

- Roll the cube for a number.
  Use pennies to show the number.
- Roll again and show the number.
  Try again if you get the same number.
- Write the numbers. Find the sum.
- Use the same parts.
  Write another addition sentence.

5 + 3 = 8
3 + 5 = 8

Grade Level 1 — McGraw-Hill School Division

Chapter 3, Lesson 4 — Addition

NCTM Standards
- Problem Solving
- Communication
- ✓ Reasoning
- ✓ Connections

Problem Solving

OBJECTIVE Use the Order Property of Addition.

Materials per child: 10 pennies, three 5" × 8" index cards

Prepare Cut index cards in half lengthwise, and label with write-on lines and plus and equal signs.

Children choose two fruits that add up to 10¢. They use pennies to show the price of each fruit, and write a pair of addition facts to solve the problem. *[Order may vary. 3 + 7 = 10, 7 + 3 = 10; 1 + 9 = 10, 9 + 1 = 10]*

PROBLEM-SOLVING ACTIVITY 19 — MATH CENTER On Your Own

Decision Making • All for 10¢

YOU NEED: 10 pennies, cards

You have 10¢.

Which 2 fruits can you buy?

- Use pennies to show what you buy.
- Write an addition sentence.
  Tell how many pennies in all.
- Then add another way to show the sum.
- Find more fruits for 10¢.

Play 2 more times.

4¢ 7¢ 6¢ 8¢ 2¢

2¢ + 8¢ = 10¢
8¢ + 2¢ = 10¢

Grade Level 1 — McGraw-Hill School Division

Chapter 3, Lesson 4 — Addition

NCTM Standards
- ✓ Problem Solving
- ✓ Communication
- ✓ Reasoning
- ✓ Connections

Lesson 3.4

DAY 1

Addition Fact Pairs

OBJECTIVES Children add zero using money amounts; children use the Order Property with money amounts.

Materials per child: 10 pennies

1 Motivate — Cooperative Pairs

Materials per pair: 10 pennies, 2 paper cups

Give each pair of children 10 pennies and 2 paper cups. Call out two amounts of pennies; for example, 5 cents and 3 cents. The 5 cents are to be put into a cup by one child and the 3 cents are to be put in the other cup by the other child. Tell them to spill out the pennies and count to find the total.

Write the addition sentence 5¢ + 3¢ = 8¢ on the chalkboard. Then write 3¢ + 5¢ = 8¢ under the first addition sentence. Ask which sentence describes the pennies in their two cups. Children should conclude that both addition sentences are correct and that the order of the numbers does not change the sum.

2 Develop

Distribute 10 pennies to each child. Real pennies are a better manipulative than play money or counters. Children respond to the "real-life" quality they imply.

Work through exercise 1 with the children and discuss why the order of the numbers does not change the sum. *[Possible answer: You are still adding the same two numbers.]*

Also work through exercise 2. Ask:

- **If you put together the pennies in both purses, would you have more than 5 pennies? Explain.** *[No; there is nothing in the other purse to add to the 5 pennies.]*

Have children complete exercises 3–7.

CRITICAL THINKING
After children discuss the question on the page, ask:

- **What is 0¢ + 0¢? Why?** *[0¢; no cents and no cents is no cents.]*

Page 92

Try These Assign practice exercises 1–10.

Check children's journals to see how they are drawing the pennies and writing addition sentences for them.

3 Close

Check for Understanding by showing some pennies in your right hand and some pennies in your left hand. Ask for the total. Then ask if the total will change if you switch hands. *[No.]*

Name ______________________

Addition Fact Pairs

You need 10 pennies.

Show pennies here.

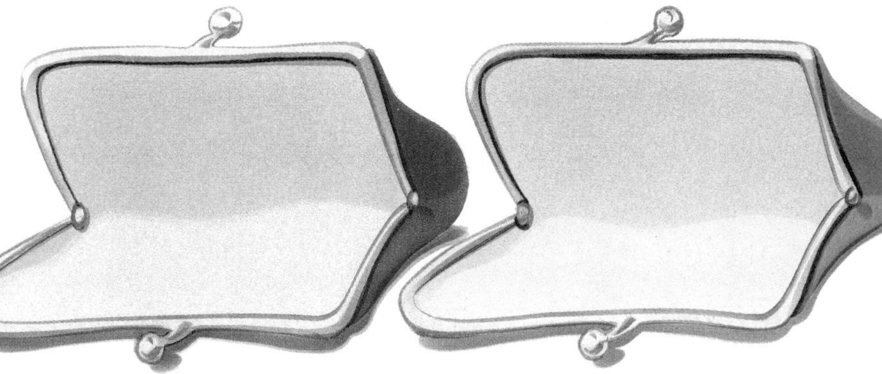

Find how many cents in all.

1. 2¢ + 4¢ = 6 ¢ 4¢ + 2¢ = 6 ¢

Why is the sum the same? The parts are the same.

2. 5¢ + 0¢ = 5 ¢ 0¢ + 5¢ = 5 ¢
3. 3¢ + 4¢ = 7 ¢ 4¢ + 3¢ = 7 ¢
4. 1¢ + 2¢ = 3 ¢ 2¢ + 1¢ = 3 ¢
5. 0¢ + 3¢ = 3 ¢ 3¢ + 0¢ = 3 ¢
6. 2¢ + 5¢ = 7 ¢ 5¢ + 2¢ = 7 ¢
7. 9¢ + 0¢ = 9 ¢ 0¢ + 9¢ = 9 ¢

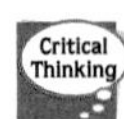

What happens when you add 0? The sum (total) is the same as the other number (part).

MEETING INDIVIDUAL NEEDS

EXTRA SUPPORT

Have children draw pictures of different ways to show two purses of money for 10¢.

EARLY FINISHERS

Have pairs of children spill 5 to 10 pennies out of a paper cup, count the heads and tails, and then write an addition sentence for the pennies.

ONGOING ASSESSMENT

Observation Checklist Determine if children understand the concept of adding zero to another number by observing them as they complete this lesson.

Follow Up For children who need more practice adding zero to a number, assign **Reteach 25.**

For children who demonstrate understanding of this lesson, assign **Extend 25.**

Try These!

Use pennies if you want to.

1. $1¢ + 4¢ = \underline{5}¢$

2. $4¢ + 5¢ = \underline{9}¢$ — $5¢ + 4¢ = \underline{9}¢$
3. $2¢ + 0¢ = \underline{2}¢$ — $0¢ + 2¢ = \underline{2}¢$
4. $6¢ + 1¢ = \underline{7}¢$ — $1¢ + 6¢ = \underline{7}¢$
5. $3¢ + 2¢ = \underline{5}¢$ — $2¢ + 3¢ = \underline{5}¢$
6. $0¢ + 4¢ = \underline{4}¢$ — $4¢ + 0¢ = \underline{4}¢$
7. $5¢ + 2¢ = \underline{7}¢$ — $2¢ + 5¢ = \underline{7}¢$
8. $2¢ + 2¢ = \underline{4}¢$ — $0¢ + 0¢ = \underline{0}¢$
9. $4¢ + 4¢ = \underline{8}¢$ — $3¢ + 3¢ = \underline{6}¢$
10. $5¢ + 5¢ = \underline{10}¢$ — $1¢ + 1¢ = \underline{2}¢$

Journal: Show how you add (penny).  Children may draw pennies or write addition sentences.

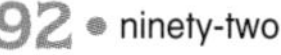

At Home: Ask your child to show you how $4¢ + 1¢$ is like $1¢ + 4¢$.

Alternate Teaching Strategy

Materials per pair: 10 pennies, Workmat 3 (part-part-whole mat)

Have children put pennies on their workmats to act out this story:

Keisha has 4 pennies in her left pocket and 2 pennies in her right pocket. How many pennies does she have? *[6 pennies]*

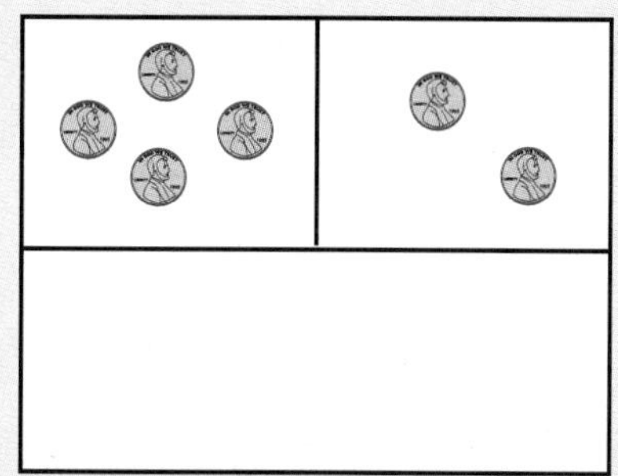

Write 4¢ + 2¢ = 6¢ on the chalkboard and read the addition sentence aloud. Continue the story:

Keisha switches the pennies so that she has 2 pennies in her left pocket and 4 pennies in her right pocket. How many pennies does she have? *[6 pennies]*

Have children switch the pennies on their workmats. Write 2¢ + 4¢ = 6¢ on the chalkboard and read the addition sentence aloud.

- **Does changing the order of the numbers change the sum?** *[No; there still is the same number of pennies.]*

Repeat the activity, using zero pennies and 8 pennies.

- **When you add zero to a number, what is the sum? Explain.** *[Possible answer: The sum is that number; zero does not add anything.]*

PRACTICE • 25

HOMEWORK

Name: ______ Practice 25

ADDITION FACT PAIRS

Add.

1. Use (penny) if you want.

$2¢ + 6¢ = \underline{8}¢$

2. $3¢ + 5¢ = \underline{8}¢$ $5¢ + 3¢ = \underline{8}¢$	3. $6¢ + 4¢ = \underline{10}¢$ $4¢ + 6¢ = \underline{10}¢$
4. $0¢ + 6¢ = \underline{6}¢$ $6¢ + 0¢ = \underline{6}¢$	5. $3¢ + 1¢ = \underline{4}¢$ $1¢ + 3¢ = \underline{4}¢$
6. $5¢ + 1¢ = \underline{6}¢$ $1¢ + 5¢ = \underline{6}¢$	7. $0¢ + 8¢ = \underline{8}¢$ $8¢ + 0¢ = \underline{8}¢$
8. $3¢ + 6¢ = \underline{9}¢$ $6¢ + 3¢ = \underline{9}¢$	9. $0¢ + 7¢ = \underline{7}¢$ $7¢ + 0¢ = \underline{7}¢$

RETEACH • 25

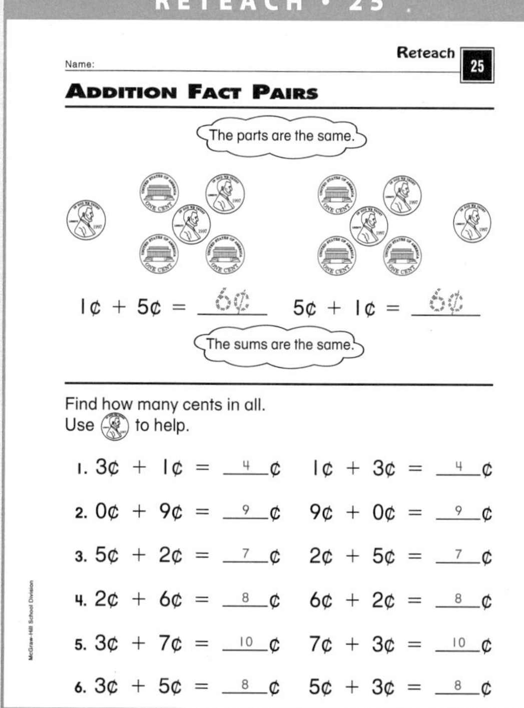

Name: ______ Reteach 25

ADDITION FACT PAIRS

The parts are the same.

$1¢ + 5¢ = \underline{6¢}$ — $5¢ + 1¢ = \underline{6¢}$

The sums are the same.

Find how many cents in all. Use (penny) to help.

1. $3¢ + 1¢ = \underline{4}¢$ — $1¢ + 3¢ = \underline{4}¢$
2. $0¢ + 9¢ = \underline{9}¢$ — $9¢ + 0¢ = \underline{9}¢$
3. $5¢ + 2¢ = \underline{7}¢$ — $2¢ + 5¢ = \underline{7}¢$
4. $2¢ + 6¢ = \underline{8}¢$ — $6¢ + 2¢ = \underline{8}¢$
5. $3¢ + 7¢ = \underline{10}¢$ — $7¢ + 3¢ = \underline{10}¢$
6. $3¢ + 5¢ = \underline{8}¢$ — $5¢ + 3¢ = \underline{8}¢$

EXTEND • 25

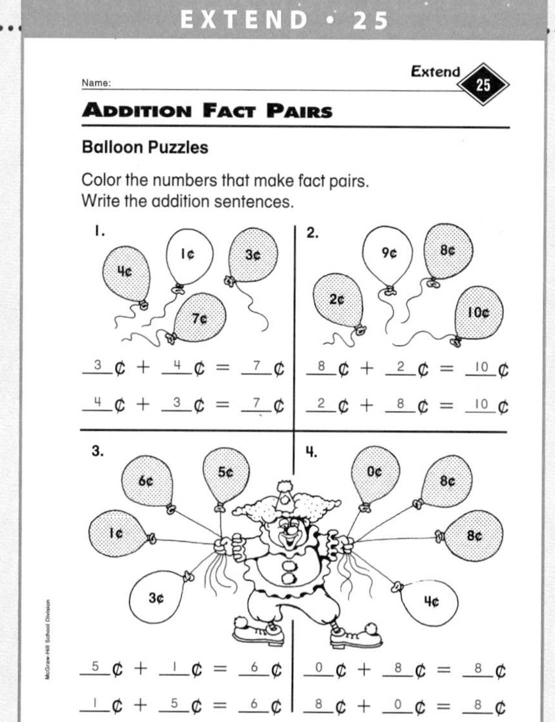

Name: ______ Extend 25

ADDITION FACT PAIRS

Balloon Puzzles

Color the numbers that make fact pairs. Write the addition sentences.

1.

$\underline{3}¢ + \underline{4}¢ = \underline{7}¢$
$\underline{4}¢ + \underline{3}¢ = \underline{7}¢$

2.

$\underline{8}¢ + \underline{2}¢ = \underline{10}¢$
$\underline{2}¢ + \underline{8}¢ = \underline{10}¢$

3.

$\underline{5}¢ + \underline{1}¢ = \underline{6}¢$
$\underline{1}¢ + \underline{5}¢ = \underline{6}¢$

4.

$\underline{0}¢ + \underline{8}¢ = \underline{8}¢$
$\underline{8}¢ + \underline{0}¢ = \underline{8}¢$

LESSON 3.5

Count On

OBJECTIVE Use a counting-on strategy to add.

Day 1 Counting On
Day 2 More Counting On

RESOURCE REMINDER
Math Center Cards 20
Practice 26–27, Reteach 26–27, Extend 26–27

SKILLS TRACE	
GRADE K	• Explore counting-on. *(Chapter 12)*
GRADE 1	• Use a counting-on strategy to add.
GRADE 2	• Use counting-on and related facts to find sums to 12. *(Chapter 1)*

LESSON RESOURCES

MANIPULATIVE WARM-UP

Whole Class — Logical/Analytical

OBJECTIVE Explore the counting-on strategy to add 1, 2, and 3.

Materials 10 pennies, 7 sheets of pink construction paper

Prepare Make piggy bank cards labeled 1¢ to 7¢.

▶ Mix up the piggy bank cards and place them face down on a table. Have a child choose a card, for example 6¢, and give her or him 2 pennies. Write on the chalkboard: **6¢** + **2¢** = ___ **¢**

▶ Ask the child for the total amount of money and how they got the answer.
- **If you see 6¢ and 2 pennies, how do you know the total is 8¢?** *[Possible answer: I can imagine 6 pennies in my head, and then add on 2 more.]*
- **If you started at 6¢, how could you count on to find the total amount?** *[Possible answer: I would say 7¢ and then 8¢ for the 2 pennies.]*

▶ Give children the opportunity to use the piggy bank cards several times.

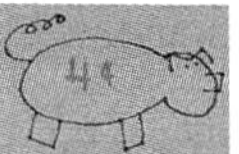

CONNECTION ACTIVITY

Whole Class — Auditory/Linguistic

OBJECTIVE Connect the counting-on strategy with language arts.

Resource Read-Aloud Anthology, page 22

▶ Have children learn the Mexican rhyme "The Graceful Elephant," found in the Read-Aloud Anthology, which is about the concept of *one more*. The verse is always the same except for the first number.

(1–5) elephant(s) balanced gracefully
Upon a spider's web.
But when the web bounced him (them) all around
He (they) called on another to help hold it down.

▶ After each verse, ask how many elephants there are. Then write an addition sentence for the verse. *[Possible answer: 2 + 1 = 3]* You may wish to change the last line of the rhyme to practice adding on 2 to a number.

DAILY MATH

PREVIOUS DAY QUICK REVIEW

1. 5¢ + 3¢ = __ *[8¢]*
2. 3¢ + 5¢ = __ *[8¢]*
3. 7¢ + 0¢ = __ *[7¢]*
4. 0¢ + 7¢ = __ *[7¢]*

FAST FACTS

1. 5 + 1 *[6]*
2. 6 + 1 *[7]*
3. 7 + 1 *[8]*
4. 8 + 1 *[9]*

Problem of the Day • 20

Read aloud to children:

3 children are eating lunch.
2 friends join them.
Then 1 more friend joins them.
How many children are eating lunch?
[6 children]

TECH LINK

MATH VAN

Tool You may wish to use the Counters tool with this lesson.

MATH FORUM

Idea During the week, I have each child make a counting-on cube train. They start on Monday with one cube. By Friday they each will have a cube train for 5.

Visit our Resource Village at http://www.mhschool.com to see more of the Math Forum.

MATH CENTER

Practice

OBJECTIVE Use the counting-on strategy to add.

Materials per pair: 0–10 number line (TA 11), 2 two-color counters, blank number cube, blank spinner

Prepare Label each number cube 1, 1, 2, 2, 3, 3. Label each spinner 0–7.

Children use a number line and numbers generated by a number cube and spinner to count on. *[Check that children count on correctly.]*

PRACTICE ACTIVITY 20 — MATH CENTER, Partners

Game • Counting On

YOU NEED: 2 counters, number cube, spinner

- Spin to get a number. Look for it on the number line. Put your counter on the number.
- Roll the number cube. Use the number to count on. Put your counter on the total.
- Your partner takes a turn. Who has a greater total?

0 1 2 3 4 5 6 7 8 9 10

Chapter 3, Lesson 5 — Addition

NCTM Standards
- ✓ Problem Solving
- ✓ Communication
- Reasoning
- ✓ Connections

Problem Solving

OBJECTIVE Use a table and count on to determine sums.

Materials per pair: 10 connecting cubes, blank number cube, Math Center Recording Sheet (TA 38 optional)

Prepare Label the number cube 1, 1, 2, 2, 3, 3.

Children use a table to find a number and count on by the number they roll to find a sum. They record the addition sentence. *[Check that the sums are correct.]*

PROBLEM-SOLVING ACTIVITY 20 — MATH CENTER, Partners

Using Data • Help Your Partner

YOU NEED: connecting cubes, number cube

Look at the table.
It tells how many stickers the children have.

STICKERS			
Lauren	6	Kevin	7
Sarah	5	Michael	4

- Lauren has 6 stickers. Roll the cube for a number. It tells how many more stickers she buys.
- Count on to find how many she has in all.
- Your partner writes an addition sentence for Lauren.
- Check your partner's work.

Play again for Sarah, Kevin, and Michael.

Chapter 3, Lesson 5 — Addition

NCTM Standards
- ✓ Problem Solving
- ✓ Communication
- ✓ Reasoning
- ✓ Connections

Lesson 3.5

DAY 1

Counting On

OBJECTIVE Children count on 1, 2, or 3 using models.

Materials have available per child: 10 counters, bowl

1 Motivate — Cooperative Pairs

Materials per pair: 10 counters, bowl

Tell children to suppose that the counters are eggs. Explain the activity: One child puts 1 to 8 eggs in the bowl, and the partner decides whether to add 1 or 2 eggs. Both children tell how many eggs are in the bowl. Then partners exchange tasks.

Notice the strategies children use to find the sums. Then explain that you can use *mental math* when adding 1 or 2 by just thinking of the first number and then *counting on* the second number to find the sum.

Use counters to demonstrate adding 2 to 5 and say:

- **Think five and count on, saying: six, seven. What is the sum?** *[7]*

Encourage children to use mental math as they continue the activity.

2 Develop

Page 93

Encourage children to use counters and bowls to count on 1, 2, or 3 as they complete exercises 1–6.

Critical Thinking

After children discuss the Critical Thinking question on the page, ask:

- **Why is using counting on to add a kind of mental math?** *[Possible answer: I remember the first number in my head.]*

Name ____________________

Counting On

You can **count on** to add.
Start at 4. Count on 2.

4 + 2 = 6

Do you have to count the 4 eggs first? Why? No; you know there are 4, so you can just start with 4.

Count on to add.

1. 

3 + 1 = 4

2. 

6 + 2 = 8

3. 

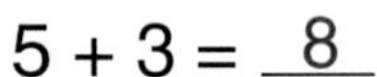

5 + 3 = 8

4. 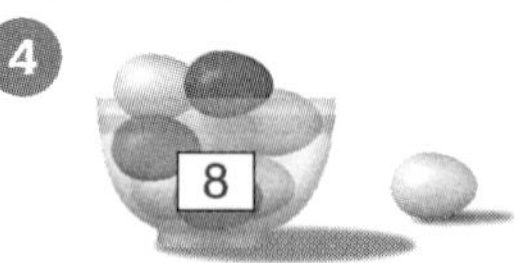

8 + 1 = 9

5. 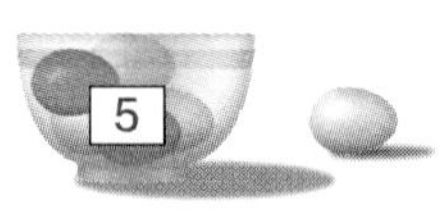

5 + 1 = 6

6. 

3 + 3 = 6

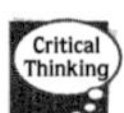

Why can you count on to add? When you add you have to find a total, and you can count to find a total.

MEETING INDIVIDUAL NEEDS

EARLY FINISHERS

Have children write addition sentences for each problem in the **Mixed Review**.

EXTRA SUPPORT

Suggest that children put their finger on each model as they count on.

ONGOING ASSESSMENT

Observation Checklist Determine if children understand counting on by observing if they count on from the other addend. If children must count from 1 each time, they do not understand the concept.

Follow Up For children who do not understand the concept of counting on, assign **Reteach 26.**

For children who can mentally count on to add, assign **Extend 26.**

Try These!

Count on to add.

1 (6) (7)

$6 + 1 = $ 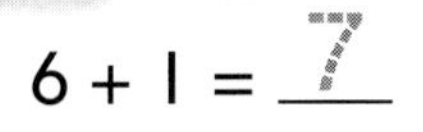

2 (4) (5) (6) (7)

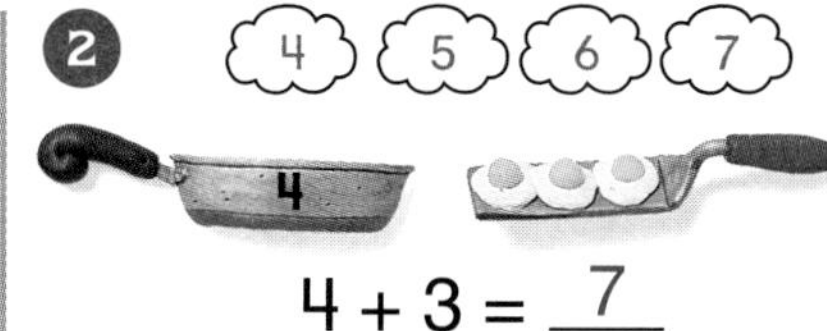

$4 + 3 = 7$

3	$5 + 2 = 7$	$3 + 1 = 4$	$2 + 3 = 5$
4	$6 + 3 = 9$	$2 + 2 = 4$	$7 + 1 = 8$
5	$8 + 2 = 10$	$9 + 1 = 10$	$4 + 2 = 6$
6	$3 + 3 = 6$	$5 + 3 = 8$	$2 + 0 = 2$
7	$8 + 1 = 9$	$6 + 2 = 8$	$7 + 3 = 10$

Mixed Review

Write parts for the total. Parts may vary. Sample answers are given.

8

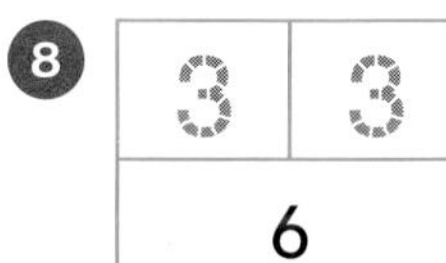

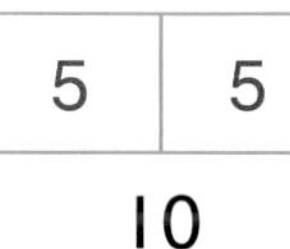

3	3
6	

5	5
10	

4	3
7	

9

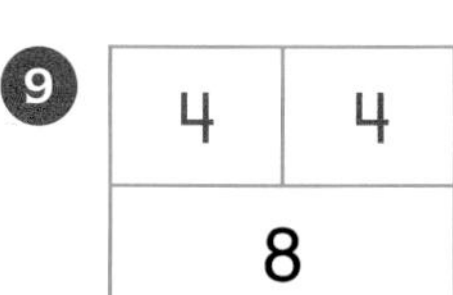

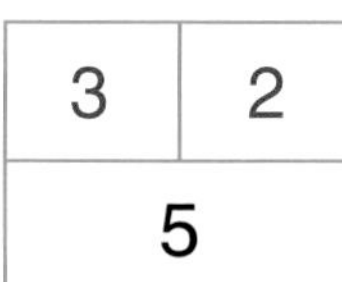

4	4
8	

3	2
5	

5	4
9	

Ask your child to tell you about counting on to add.

Page 94

Try These Discuss the first two examples and then assign practice exercises 3–7.

Mixed Review Children write two parts for each given total, reviewing a skill from Chapter 2.

3 Close

Check for Understanding by asking children:

- **How many people are in your family? How many would be in your family if you had 2 more brothers or 2 more sisters?** *[Answers may vary, but should correctly reflect a number and then that number plus 2 more.]*

Tomorrow children will count on using a number line.

PRACTICE • 26

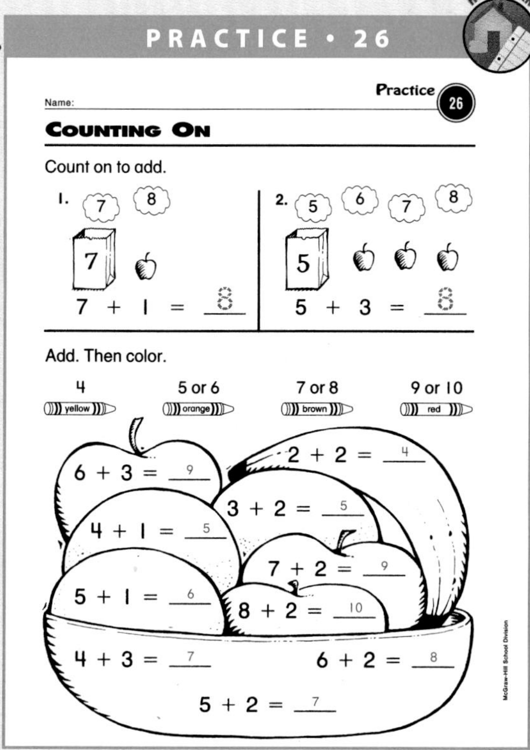

Practice 26

Name:

Counting On

Count on to add.

1. (7) (8) $7 + 1 = 8$

2. (5) (6) (7) (8) $5 + 3 = 8$

Add. Then color.

4 yellow | 5 or 6 orange | 7 or 8 brown | 9 or 10 red

$6 + 3 = 9$
$2 + 2 = 4$
$3 + 2 = 5$
$4 + 1 = 5$
$7 + 2 = 9$
$5 + 1 = 6$
$8 + 2 = 10$
$4 + 3 = 7$
$6 + 2 = 8$
$5 + 2 = 7$

RETEACH • 26

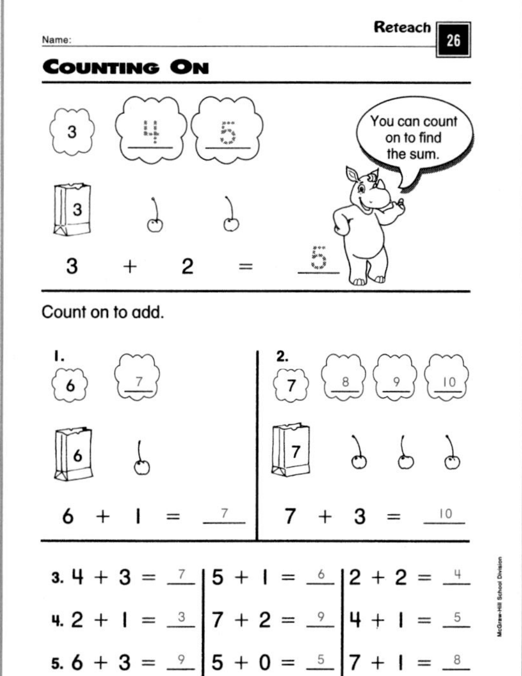

Reteach 26

Name:

Counting On

(3) (4) (5)

$3 + 2 = 5$

You can count on to find the sum.

Count on to add.

1. (6) (7) $6 + 1 = 7$

2. (7) (8) (9) (10) $7 + 3 = 10$

3. $4 + 3 = 7$ | $5 + 1 = 6$ | $2 + 2 = 4$

4. $2 + 1 = 3$ | $7 + 2 = 9$ | $4 + 1 = 5$

5. $6 + 3 = 9$ | $5 + 0 = 5$ | $7 + 1 = 8$

EXTEND • 26

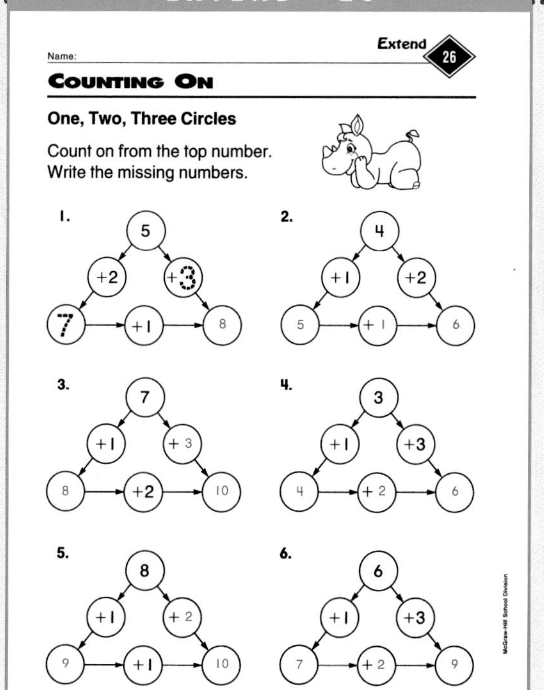

Extend 26

Name:

Counting On

One, Two, Three Circles

Count on from the top number. Write the missing numbers.

1. 5; +2, +3; 7, +1, 8
2. 4; +1, +2; 5, +1, 6
3. 7; +1, +3; 8, +2, 10
4. 3; +1, +3; 4, +2, 6
5. 8; +1, +2; 9, +1, 10
6. 6; +1, +3; 7, +2, 9

DAY 2

More Counting On

OBJECTIVE Children count on 1, 2, or 3 on a number line.

Materials per child: 1 rhino counter

1 Motivate — Whole Class

Materials masking tape, 11 index cards

Prepare Write the numbers 0 to 10 on the index cards. Use masking tape to create a floor number line by taping the cards at equal intervals along a line on the floor.

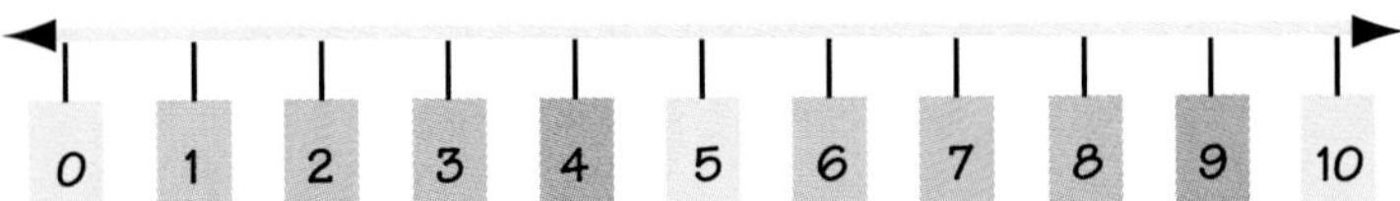

Introduce the *number line*. Tell children that the numbers are read from left to right. Explain that using a number line is another way to count on. Give each child an opportunity to step along the number line to practice counting on from numbers you tell them.

2 Develop

Page 95

Children may use their fingers or a rhino counter to "jump" or "take steps" on the number line at the top of the page. Point out that the dashed lines show how to count on. Then have children complete exercises 1–6.

CRITICAL THINKING
After children complete the page, ask:

- **How is counting on with a number line different from counting on with pictures? How is it the same?** *[Possible answer: On a number line you count jumps, with pictures you count objects; you still count on the same number.]*

Page 96

Try These Discuss the first two examples and then assign practice exercises 2–5.

Cultural Connection The Incas, who ruled a great empire in South America 500 years ago, invented the *quipu* (KEY poo) as a way to keep important records. The *quipu* is made of knotted cotton cords of different colors. The knots represent numbers.

3 Close

Check for Understanding by asking children to use a number line to solve 5 + 3, 3 + 1, and 6 + 2. *[8, 4, and 8]*

Name

More Counting On

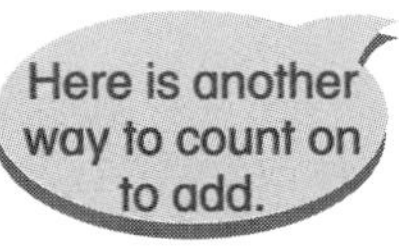

Start at 6. Count on 3.

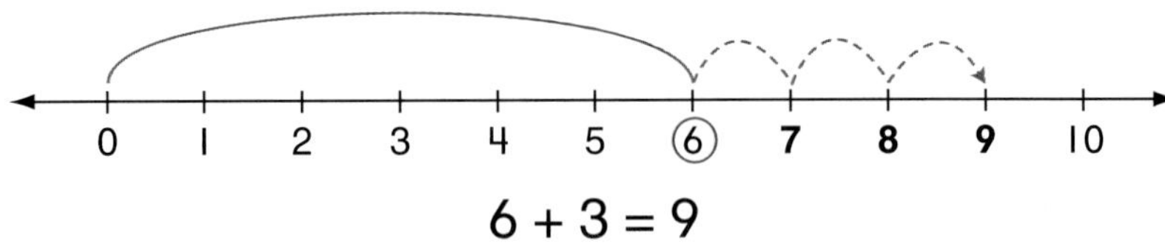

6 + 3 = 9

Count on to add.

1.
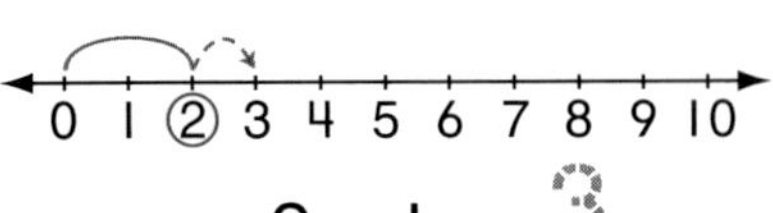

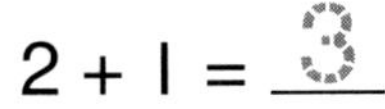
2 + 1 = 3

2.
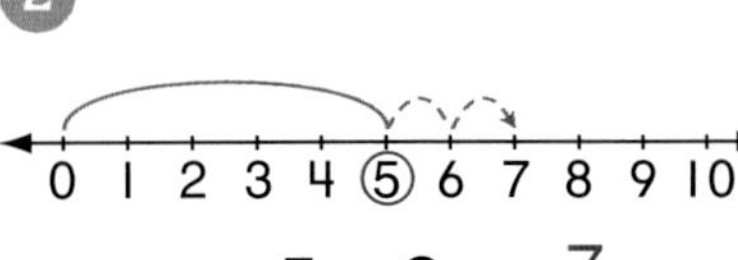

5 + 2 = 7

3.
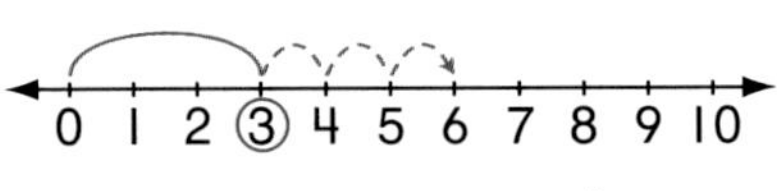

3 + 3 = 6

4.
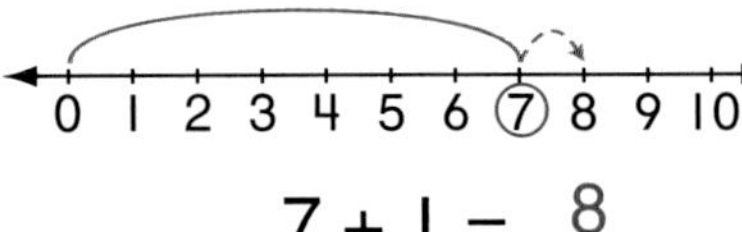

7 + 1 = 8

5.
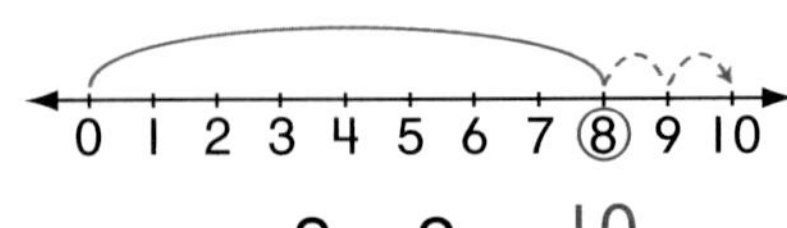

8 + 2 = 10

6.
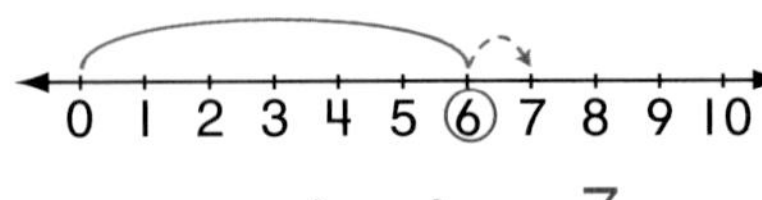

6 + 1 = 7

MEETING INDIVIDUAL NEEDS

COMMON ERROR

Children may say the first addend as part of the counting-on procedure and get an incorrect sum. For 5 + 2, "think five," count on 2: "six, seven."

GIFTED AND TALENTED

Have children make up and solve problems in pairs, adding 1, 2, or 3 to numbers 10 and greater. One partner poses the problem and uses a number line to check the others' answer.

ONGOING ASSESSMENT

Interview Determine if children understand how to use a number line to count on to solve an addition problem. Ask:

- **Can you show how to add 6 and 2 on the number line?** *[Find 6 and then count on 7, 8.]*

Follow Up For children who need help understanding the strategy, assign **Reteach 27.**

For children who can use a number line to count on to find a sum, assign **Extend 27**.

Try These!

Add.

0 1 2 3 4 5 6 7 8 9 10

1. 7 + 1 = 8   5 + 2 = 7   4 + 1 = 5
2. 6 + 2 = 8   4 + 3 = 7   1 + 1 = 2
3. 2 + 1 = 3   8 + 1 = 9   7 + 2 = 9
4. 3 + 2 = 5   7 + 3 = 10   4 + 0 = 4
5. 5 + 3 = 8   9 + 1 = 10   6 + 1 = 7

Cultural Connection — The Ancient Inca

This is an old way to count.

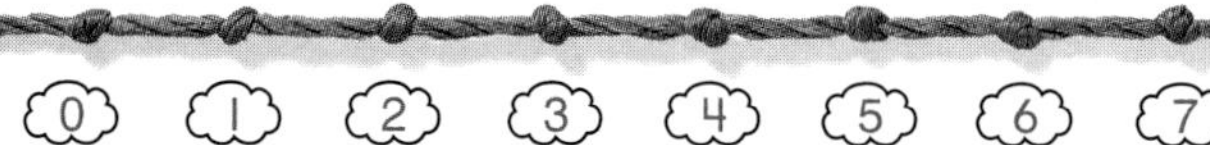

0 1 2 3 4 5 6 7 8 9 10

Add on the rope.

3 + 2 = 5   5 + 1 = 6   6 + 3 = 9

5 + 2 = 7   7 + 2 = 9   8 + 1 = 9

3 + 0 = 3   3 + 1 = 4   8 + 2 = 10

Ask your child to show you how to count on to add on the number line.

Alternate Teaching Strategy

Resources Jumbo Activity Book page 7, Sticker sheet 3 (square counters)

Materials per child: 10 small beans, number line (TA 11)

Write 5 + 2 = __ on Jumbo Activity Book page 7. Then have the class count aloud as you place a bean on each of the numbers 1 to 5. Ask children how many beans there are to start. *[5]* Place 2 more beans on the number line. Demonstrate *counting on* from 5. Say, "Six, seven; the sum is seven."

- **I don't have to go back to 1 and count all the counters. Why?** *[Possible answer: You know the first number is 5; you can start there.]*

Explain that you are using *mental math* to find the sum. Complete the addition sentence, 5 + 2 = 7.

Practice counting on with children to solve 8 + 1, 7 + 3, 7 + 1, and 6 + 2. *[9, 10, 8, 8]* Children use beans on a number line to count on.

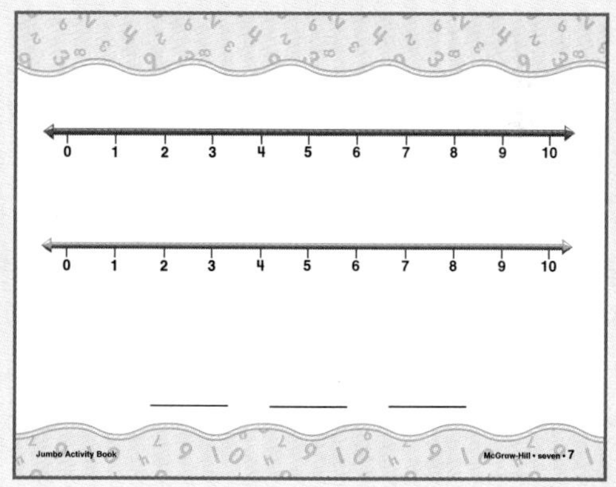

PRACTICE • 27

Practice 27

Name:

More Counting On

Add.
Use a number line to count on.

0 1 2 3 4 5 6 7 8 9 10

Color sums 4 and 5 yellow. Color sums 6 and 7 green. Color sums 8 and 9 purple. Color sum 10 red.

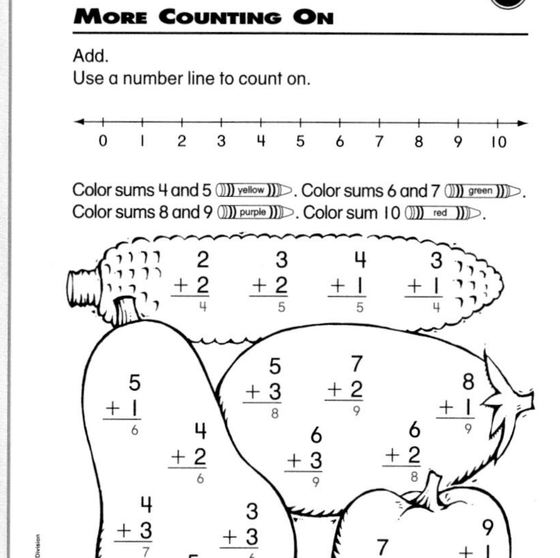

RETEACH • 27

Reteach 27

Name:

More Counting On

EXTEND • 27

Extend 27

Name:

More Counting On

How Many More?

Add. Then complete the number line to match the addition sentence.

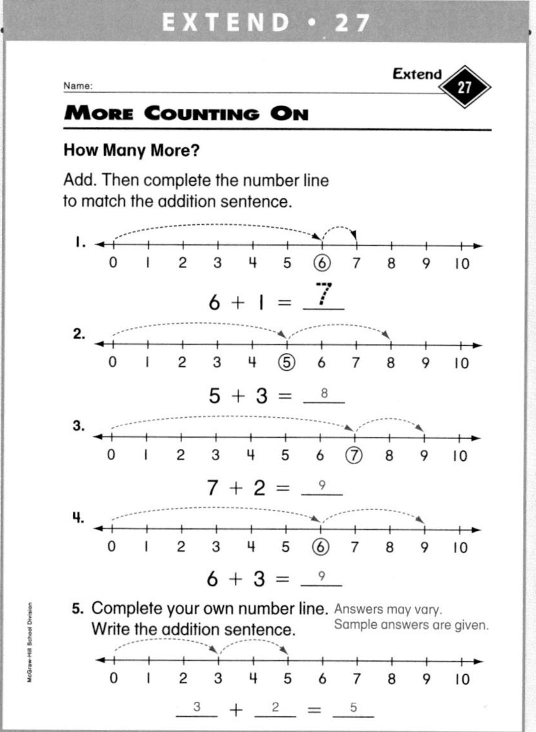

EXTRA PRACTICE

AT A GLANCE

PURPOSE Provide an opportunity for review and practice.

Materials per pair: 2 rhino counters, number cube; have available per pair: 10 connecting cubes, number line (TA 11)

Using the Extra Practice

Page 97

Explain and demonstrate how to play the game. Have children toss the cube for the first move. Children may use connecting cubes or number lines to add. On all turns after that, players solve the addition problem and move the number of spaces indicated by the sum. Suggest that partners check each other's work.

Page 98

Have children complete the exercises independently or in pairs. Children may use counters or number lines.

After children finish playing, ask:

- **Which spaces were best to land on? Why?** *[Possible answers: The ones with the biggest sums—6 + 3, 7 + 2, 6 + 2, 7 + 1, 5 + 3; I can move more spaces when I land on the spaces with the biggest sums.]*

Using the Additional Practice

The section below provides additional practice that you may wish to write on the chalkboard or on a reproducible master.

Name

Extra Practice

Game !

Supermarket Race

You need 2 rhino counters and a number cube.

Take turns.

- ▶ Roll the number cube.
- ▶ Move that many spaces.
- ▶ Next turn. Add.
- ▶ Move that many spaces.

Winner: first player to get to **Checkout**

Start

3 + 2

6 + 2

5 + 1 | 3 + 1 | 7 + 2 | 2 + 2

1 + 1

1 + 0 | 4 + 2 | 5 + 0 | 3 + 3 | 4 + 1 | 1 + 2 | 4 + 3

7 + 1

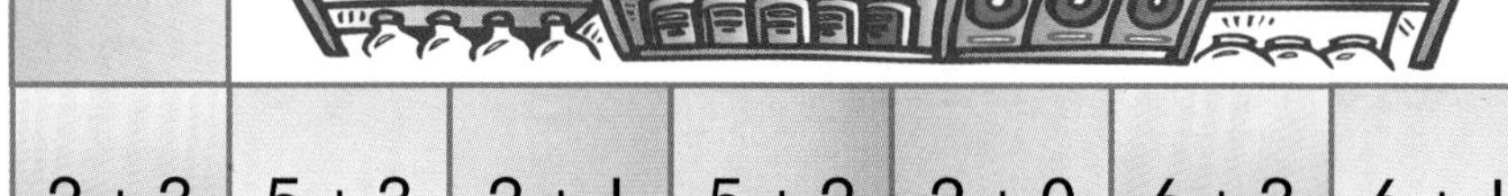

2 + 3 | 5 + 3 | 2 + 1 | 5 + 2 | 2 + 0 | 6 + 3 | 6 + 1

Checkou

CHAPTER 3 *Extra Practice* ninety-seven • 97

ADDITIONAL PRACTICE

Add.

1. 4 + 1 = __ *[5]* 2 + 4 = __ *[6]*

2. 3 + 5 = __ *[8]* 4 + 4 = __ *[8]*

3. 6 + 4 = __ *[10]* 5 + 4 = __ *[9]*

4. 0 + 7 = __ *[7]* 8 + 2 = __ *[10]*

5. 8 + 0 = __ *[8]* 1 + 9 = __ *[10]*

6. 3 + 7 = __ *[10]* 6 + 3 = __ *[9]*

7. 4¢ + 5¢ = __ *[9¢]* 7¢ + 0¢ = __ *[7¢]*

8. 3¢ + 3¢ = __ *[6¢]* 3¢ + 5¢ = __ *[8¢]*

Add.

Use counters if you want to.

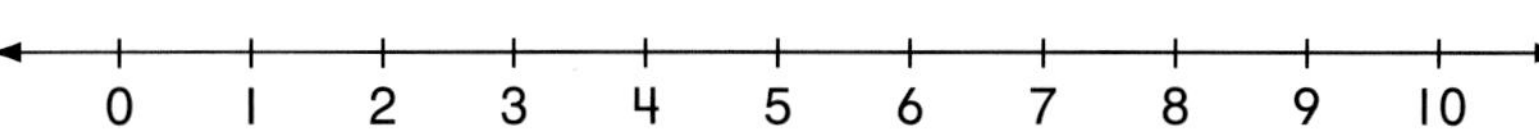

1	4 + 3 = 7	1 + 0 = 1	4 + 1 = 5
2	6 + 2 = 8	8 + 1 = 9	2 + 2 = 4
3	1 + 1 = 2	5 + 1 = 6	1 + 3 = 4
4	6 + 3 = 9	3 + 2 = 5	5 + 3 = 8
5	4 + 2 = 6	8 + 2 = 10	6 + 1 = 7
6	7 + 1 = 8	2 + 0 = 2	2 + 1 = 3
7	1 + 2 = 3	9 + 1 = 10	5 + 2 = 7
8	3 + 0 = 3	3 + 1 = 4	2 + 3 = 5

Find how many in all.

9

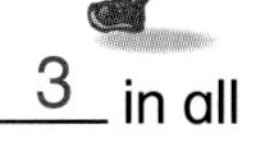

3 in all

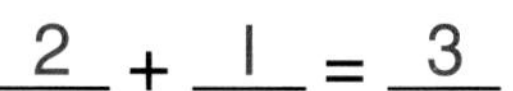

2 + 1 = 3

10

5 in all

3 + 2 = 5

Developing Algebra Sense

This section provides another opportunity to reinforce algebraic ideas. You may want to write these exercises on the chalkboard or on a reproducible master.

Find the missing number.

1. __ + 1 = 4 *[3]*	**2.** 4 + __ = 4 *[0]*	**3.** __ + 2 = 3 *[1]*
__ + 1 = 5 *[4]*	__ + 0 = 5 *[5]*	__ + 2 = 4 *[2]*
__ + 1 = 6 *[5]*	__ + 0 = 6 *[6]*	__ + 2 = 5 *[3]*
__ + 1 = 7 *[6]*	7 + __ = 7 *[0]*	__ + 2 = 6 *[4]*

Mixed Applications/Problem Solving

1. 7 girls are eating lunch.
3 boys are eating lunch.
How many children are eating lunch? *[10 children]*

2. Elly has 5¢.
She found 3¢ more.
How much money does she have? *[8¢]*

3. Carlos has 5 red peppers.
He also has 2 green peppers.
How many peppers does he have? *[7 peppers]*

4. Don has 8 pennies.
Gene has 2 pennies.
How many pennies do they have altogether? *[10 pennies]*

5. There are 5 blue boats on the pond.
There are 5 yellow boats on the pond.
How many boats are on the pond? *[10 boats]*

6. 6 boys are playing.
3 girls are playing.
How many children are playing? *[9 children]*

LESSON 3.6

Problem Solvers at Work: Can You Add to Solve?

OBJECTIVE Write and solve problems including those involving addition.

Day 1 Problem Solvers at Work: Can You Add to Solve?

RESOURCE REMINDER
Math Center Cards 21
Practice 28, Reteach 28, Extend 28

SKILLS TRACE	
GRADE K	• Solve problems, including those that involve addition. *(Chapter 11)*
GRADE 1	• Formulate and solve problems, including those that involve addition.
GRADE 2	• Formulate and solve problems, including those that involve addition. *(Chapter 1)*

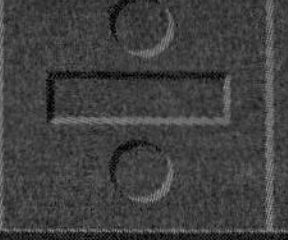

LESSON RESOURCES

WARM-UP

Whole Class — **Visual/Spatial**

OBJECTIVE Decide if addition is needed to solve a problem.

▶ Arrange 4 girls and 3 boys in a line in front of the class. Ask:

- **How many children in all?** *[7 children]*
- **Did you add to find the answer?** *[Yes.]*

▶ Arrange the same 7 children in a girl-boy pattern. Ask:

- **How is this arrangement different from the other one?** *[Possible answer: There is a girl-boy pattern.]*
- **If I ask another child to stand at the end of the line, would it be a boy or a girl?** *[a boy]*
- **Did you add to find the answer?** *[No.]*
- **When do you add to solve a problem?** *[Possible answer: when there are two parts and I want to find how many in all.]*

CONNECTION ACTIVITY

Whole Class — **Logical/Analytical**

OBJECTIVE Connect solving addition problems with consumerism.

Materials price tags (TA 12), cutouts of lemon, apple, orange, banana shapes

Prepare Mark each fruit with a price tag: lemon—2¢, apple—3¢, orange—4¢, banana—5¢

▶ Display the fruits with price tags on a table. Tell children to pretend they are shopping in a grocery store.

- **How much do you have to pay for an apple?** *[3¢]*
- **What costs 2¢?** *[a lemon]*

▶ Present some addition problems.

- **How much does an apple and an orange cost?** *[7¢]*
- **How much would 2 bananas cost?** *[10¢]*

▶ Encourage children to think of some addition problems for the fruit. Also ask them to write addition sentences for their problems.

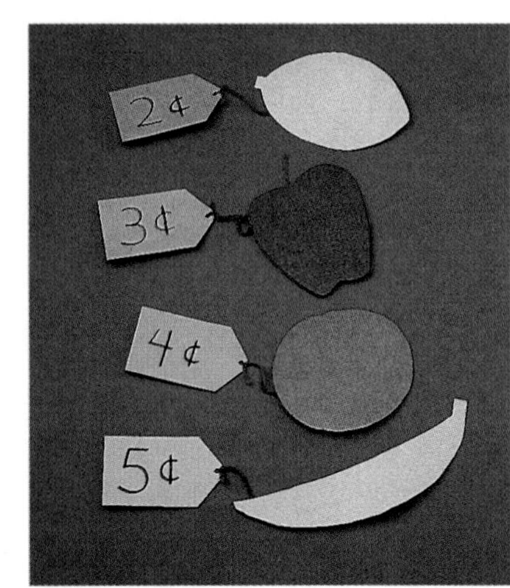

DAILY MATH

PREVIOUS DAY QUICK REVIEW

How many in all?

1. 2 red trucks and 3 green trucks *[5 trucks]*
2. 2 blue houses and 2 yellow houses *[4 houses]*

FAST FACTS

1. 5 + 3 *[8]*
2. 3 + 3 *[6]*
3. 3 + 1 *[4]*
4. 6 + 2 *[8]*

Problem of the Day • 21

Read aloud to children:

Luna has 4 apples, 3 carrots, and 5 bananas.
How many pieces of fruit does she have?
[9 pieces]

TECH LINK

MATH VAN

Tool You may wish to use the Counters tool with this lesson.

MATH FORUM

Multi-Age Classes When having partners make up problems to solve, I pair children who have more proficient language skills with children who are less skilled.

Visit our Resource Village at http://www.mhschool.com to see more of the Math Forum.

MATH CENTER

Practice

OBJECTIVE Decide if addition is needed to solve a problem.

Materials Math Center Recording Sheet (TA 38 optional)

Children solve problems. For the addition problems, they write addition sentences. *[**1.** 3, 5; 5; **2.** 6, 4; 6; 6 + 4 = 10; **3.** 7, 2; 7 + 2 = 9]*

PRACTICE ACTIVITY 21 — MATH CENTER, On Your Own

Decision Making • Can I Add?

Solve. Write a number sentence if you add.

1. Write how many pears in each box. Ring which is more.

2. Write how many grapes in each box. Ring which is more. How many grapes in all?

3. Write how many peaches in each box. How many peaches in all?

Grade Level 1 · McGraw-Hill School Division

Chapter 3, Lesson 6 — Addition

NCTM Standards
- ✓ Problem Solving
- Communication
- ✓ Reasoning
- Connections

Problem Solving

OBJECTIVE Decide whether or not to use addition to solve word problems.

Materials per child: Math Center Recording Sheet (TA 38 optional)

Children solve problems using a variety of methods. If addition is necessary, children write number sentences. *[**1.** Paul; **2.** 5 + 4 = 9; **3.** 1 orange, 2 bananas]*

PROBLEM-SOLVING ACTIVITY 21 — MATH CENTER, Partners

Logical Reasoning • Fruit Problems

Solve. Write a number sentence if you add.

1. Paul has 3 grapes. Maria has 7 grapes. Who has fewer grapes?
2. Nina picks 5 apples. Jamal picks 4 apples. How many apples do they have in all?

3. Look at the oranges and bananas. Show what comes next.

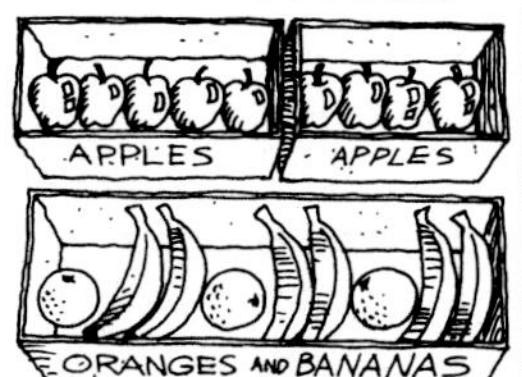

Grade Level 1 · McGraw-Hill School Division

Chapter 3, Lesson 6 — Addition

NCTM Standards
- ✓ Problem Solving
- Communication
- ✓ Reasoning
- Connections

Problem Solvers at Work: Can You Add to Solve?

OBJECTIVE Children write and solve problems including those involving addition.

Materials per child: 10 counters

1 Motivate — Whole Class

Materials 1–5 spinner (TA 7); per child: 10 two-color counters

Spin the spinner. Write the number on the chalkboard. Spin again and write that number.

- **What is the total of these two numbers? How did you find the answer?** *[Possible answers: I added in my head, I used counters.]*
- **Which number is greater? How did you find the answer?** *[Possible answer: I lined up counters for each number and compared the two lines of counters.]*

Show this number pattern on the chalkboard: 2, 1, 2, 1, 2, 1, 2.

- **What comes next?** *[1]* **How did you find the answer?** *[Possible answer: The pattern is 2, 1, so 1 comes after 2.]*

2 Develop

Page 99

Read aloud to children the first word problem found on the reduced student page in this Teacher's Edition. Discuss the fact that the children need to compare the number of green and red apples to discover which group has more.

Read the other two word problems aloud and have children solve them.

CRITICAL THINKING

After children have finished the page, ask:

- **What kinds of problems can you solve by adding?** *[Possible answers: problems about joining groups of things, problems about knowing the parts and finding the total]*

Page 100

Try These Assign practice exercises 1–4.

3 Close

Check for Understanding by showing a stack of 3 books and a stack of 5 books. Ask:

- **How many books are there in all?** *[8 books]* **How did you find the answer?** *[Possible answer: I added 3 and 5.]*

Show this pattern with connecting cubes: green, red, green, red, green.

- **What comes next?** *[red]* **How did you find the answer?** *[Possible answer: I looked at the pattern and saw that 1 red cube always comes after 1 green cube.]*

Name ____________

Problem Solvers at Work

Can You Add to Solve?

Listen to the problem.

1 "Jerry has 4 green apples and 3 red apples. Does he have more green apples or red apples?"

What do you need to find? Whether he has more green apples or red apples.

Can you add to find the answer? No.

Write how many. Ring which is more. (4) 3

2 At the store "Kara bought 7 brown pears and 3 green pears. How many pears did she buy in all?" 10 in all

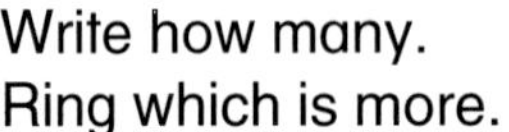

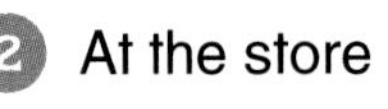

7 + 3 = 10

3 In school "The cafeteria workers show bananas and oranges in a pattern. Show the next two fruits in the pattern."

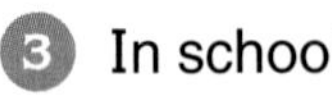

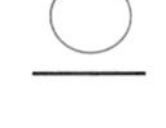

MEETING INDIVIDUAL NEEDS

EARLY FINISHERS

Children who have collected pictures or made drawings for the Food Guide Pyramid should begin sorting them into food groups before they attach them to the bulletin-board display.

EXTRA SUPPORT

Some children may make the error of adding the numbers in a problem without understanding what the problem is asking. Encourage them to use manipulatives and to think about what the problem tells and asks.

ONGOING ASSESSMENT

Anecdotal Report Make notes about how children solve problems: Can they decide when to add or when to use another strategy?

Follow Up For children who need more work on the lesson concepts, assign **Reteach 28**.

For children who understand when to add and when not to, assign **Extend 28**.

1. How many in all?

9 in all

5 + 4 = 9

2. Show what comes next.

3. Solve Diane's problem. 3 + 3 = 6, 6 animals in all

How did you solve Diane's problem? Possible answers: Added, counted, counted on 3 from 3.

4. 

Write a problem.
Have a partner solve it. Problems and answers may vary.

Your partner's answer: ______

Ask your child to tell you about the problem he or she wrote.

Alternate Teaching Strategy

Materials per pair: 10 blue and 10 red connecting cubes

Make a train with 4 red connecting cubes and a train with 5 blue connecting cubes.

- **How many blue cubes?** *[5]* **How many red cubes?** *[4]*
- **How many cubes are there in all?** *[9]*
- **Did you add to find out? Explain.** *[Possible answers: Yes; no, I counted the cubes.]*

Next, make this pattern out of connecting cubes: blue, red, blue, red, blue.

- **What comes next?** *[red]*
- **Did you add to find out? Explain.** *[No; I didn't need to find out how many.]*

Have children use cubes to create similar problem situations involving cube trains and patterns. Discuss methods of solving the problems and the strategies children used when they added.

PRACTICE • 28

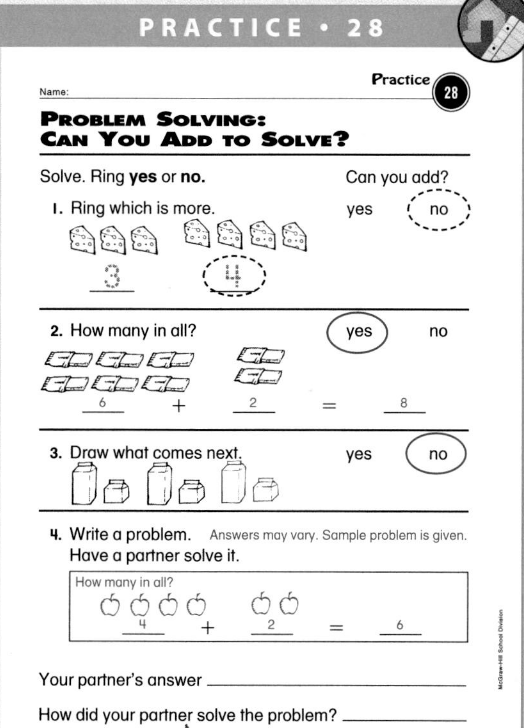

Name: Practice 28

Problem Solving: Can You Add to Solve?

Solve. Ring **yes** or **no**. Can you add?

1. Ring which is more. yes (no)
3 (4)

2. How many in all? (yes) no
6 + 2 = 8

3. Draw what comes next. yes (no)

4. Write a problem. Answers may vary. Sample problem is given.
Have a partner solve it.
How many in all?
4 + 2 = 6

Your partner's answer ______

How did your partner solve the problem? ______

RETEACH • 28

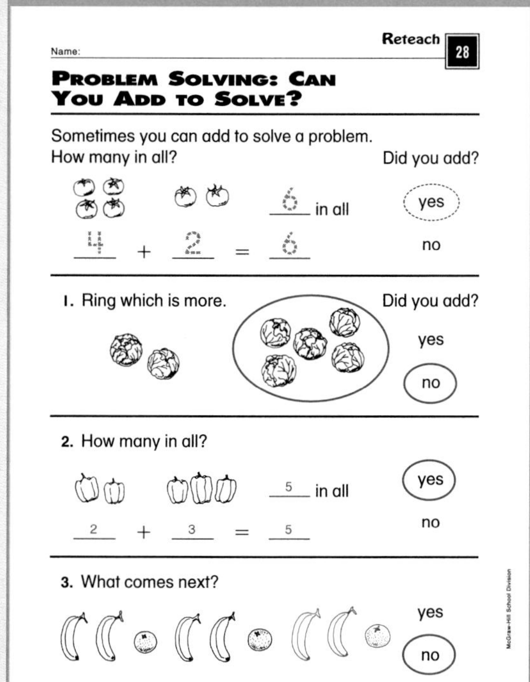

Name: Reteach 28

Problem Solving: Can You Add to Solve?

Sometimes you can add to solve a problem.
How many in all? Did you add?

6 in all (yes)
4 + 2 = 6 no

1. Ring which is more. Did you add?
yes
(no)

2. How many in all?
5 in all (yes)
2 + 3 = 5 no

3. What comes next?
yes
(no)

EXTEND • 28

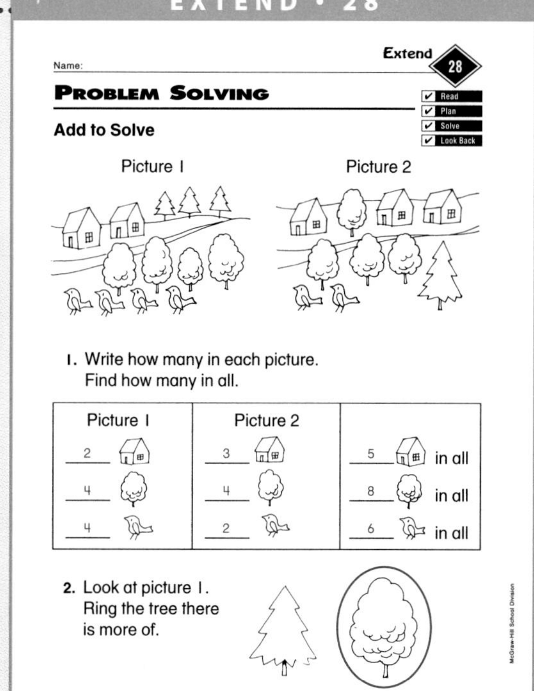

Name: Extend 28

Problem Solving

Add to Solve

Read / Plan / Solve / Look Back

Picture 1 Picture 2

1. Write how many in each picture.
Find how many in all.

Picture 1	Picture 2	
2	3	5 in all
4	4	8 in all
4	2	6 in all

2. Look at picture 1.
Ring the tree there is more of.

CHAPTER REVIEW

AT A GLANCE

PURPOSE Review and assess the concepts, skills, and strategies that children have learned in this chapter.

Materials have available: counters, pennies, number lines (TA 11)

Chapter Objectives

3A Add, facts to 10

3B Solve problems, including those that involve addition and writing an addition sentence

Using the Chapter Review

The **Chapter Review** can be used as a review, practice test, or chapter test.

Read aloud to children the word problems found on the reduced Student Book page 102 in this Teacher's Edition.

What Do You Think? This feature gives children an opportunity for self-assessment. Assure children that there are no right or wrong answers. The emphasis is on what they think and how they justify their answers.

Children draw a picture to show an addition problem and write an addition sentence for the picture. You may wish that children dictate their problems to an adult or older student.

Name

Chapter Review

Write the addition sentence.

1  

2 + 3 = 5

2 

4 + 2 = 6

Add.

3 

5 + 3 = 8

4 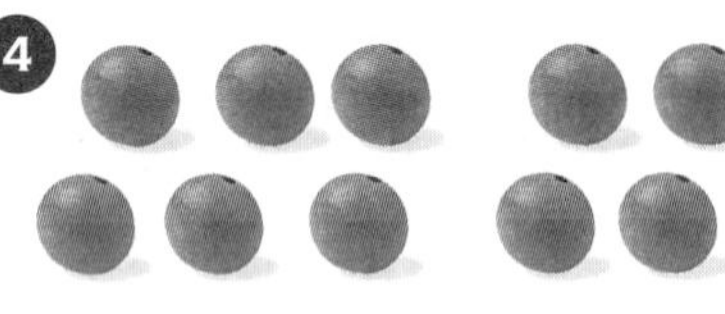

6 + 4 = 10

5 3 + 1 = 4

6 3 + 3 = 6

7 6 + 3 = 9

8 4 + 0 = 4

9 2 + 2 = 4

10 5 + 1 = 6

11 3 + 2 = 5

12 1 + 1 = 2

13 6 + 1 = 7

14 2 + 1 = 3

15 5¢ + 2¢ = 7¢

16 8¢ + 2¢ = 10¢

Reinforcement and Remediation

CHAPTER OBJECTIVES	REVIEW ITEMS	STUDENT BOOK PAGES		TEACHER'S EDITION PAGES		TEACHER RESOURCES
		Lessons	Midchapter Review	Activities	Alternate Teaching Strategy	Reteach
3A	1–16	79–84, 91–96	87	78A, 80A, 90A, 92A	80, 84, 92, 96	21, 23, 25–27
3B	17–20	85–86, 99–100	87	84A, 92A, 98A	86, 100	24–28

Find how many in all.

"Two children are sitting on a bench. Two more children join them. How many children in all?"

4 in all

2 + 2 = 4

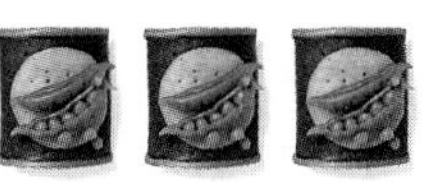

"Joe bought 3 cans of peas and 1 can of corn. How many cans did he buy?"

4 in all

3 + 1 = 4

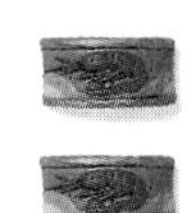

"Terry bought 6 cans of tuna fish and 2 cans of shrimp. How many cans did she buy?"

8 in all

6 + 2 = 8

20 Show what comes next.

What Do You Think?

How do you add 7 + 2? This self-assessment should not be graded. All explanations are acceptable.

✓ Check one.

 With   With 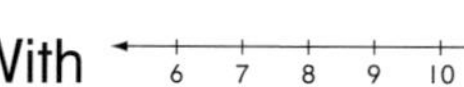 ☐ In my head

Why? ______________________________

Draw an addition picture.

Write the addition sentence. Children's pictures and sentences should show the same addition.

CHAPTER TEST

AT A GLANCE

PURPOSE Assess the concepts, skills, and strategies that children have learned in this chapter.

Chapter Objectives

3A Add, facts to 10

3B Solve problems, including those that involve addition and writing an addition sentence

Using the Chapter Test

The **Chapter Test** can be used as a practice test, a chapter test, or as an additional review. The **Performance Assessment** on Student Book page 104 provides an alternate means of assessing children's understanding of addition and addition sentences.

Assessment Resources

TEST MASTERS

The Testing Program Blackline Masters provide three forms of the Chapter Test. Form C uses a free-response format. Forms A and B use a multiple-choice format.

TEACHER'S ASSESSMENT RESOURCES

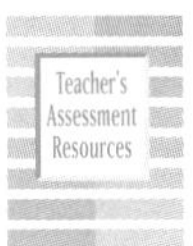

Teacher's Assessment Resources provides resources for alternate assessment. It includes Guidelines for Building a Portfolio, page 6, and the Holistic Scoring Guide, page 27.

Name

Chapter Test

Write the addition sentence.

1.  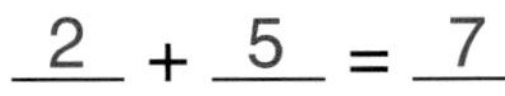
2 + 5 = 7

2. 
3 + 1 = 4

Add.

3. 
4 + 5 = 9

4.  
3 + 4 = 7

5. 8 + 0 = 8

6. 7 + 3 = 10

7. 4¢ + 2¢ = 6 ¢

8. 6¢ + 3¢ = 9 ¢

Find how many in all.

9. 
7 in all

"Ellen bought 4 apples and 3 pears. How many pieces of fruit did she buy in all?"

4 + 3 = 7

10.   
8 in all

"Aaron bought 2 bottles of apple juice and 6 bottles of grape juice. How many bottles of juice did he buy in all?"

2 + 6 = 8

Test Correlation

CHAPTER OBJECTIVES	TEST ITEMS	STUDENT BOOK PAGES
3A	1–8	79–84, 91–96
3B	9, 10	85–86, 99–100

Performance Assessment

What Did You Learn?

You and your partner need a 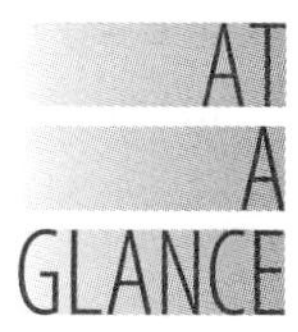, 10 counters, and a number line.

- Spin.
- Write the number.
- Add.

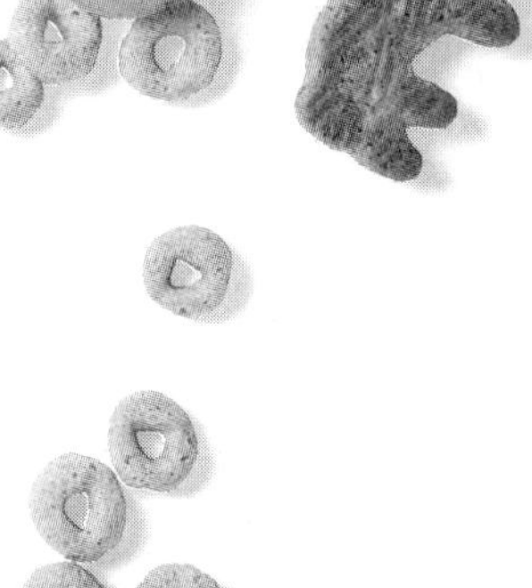

3 + ___ = ___

4 + ___ = ___

2 + ___ = ___

6 + ___ = ___

7 + ___ = ___

5 + ___ = ___

Addition facts may vary.

Tell how you added.
Children may have used counting on, the number line, or counters to add.

You may want to put this page in your portfolio.

REVIEWING A PORTFOLIO

Have children review their portfolios. Consider including the following items:

- Finished work on a project, page 76F.
- Selected math journal entries, pages 80, 87, 92, and 102.
- Products from **investigations,** pages 89–90.
- Children's self-selected "best piece" drawn from the work completed during the chapter. Have them attach a note explaining why they chose that piece.
- Any work that you or individual children wish to keep for future reference.

You may wish to take this opportunity to conduct conferences with children.

The Portfolio Analysis Form can help you in the reporting of children's progress. See Teacher's Assessment Resources, page 33.

AT A GLANCE

PURPOSE Review and assess the concepts, skills, and strategies that children have learned in this chapter.

Materials per pair: blank 5-part spinner (TA 7), 10 two-color counters, number line (TA 11)

Using the Performance Assessment

Divide children into pairs. Have each pair make a spinner by writing the numbers 0, 1, 2, 3, and 4 in the parts of a 5-part blank spinner and following the directions at the bottom of Teaching Aid 7. (They don't need to color the spinner.)

Explain to children that they are to spin the spinner, write down the number after one of the plus signs on the Student Book page, and then add. They are to repeat until all the addition sentences are completed. Suggest that the partners take turns spinning the spinner and writing the numbers. Encourage the partners to work together to get the right answers. Give each pair 10 two-color counters and a number line. Observe children as they work.

Evaluating Student Work

As you observe children and read their work, look for the following:

- *Does the child use counters or a number line to model the addition sentences?*
- *Does the child write the addition sentences correctly?*
- *Does the child use strategies such as mental math, counting on, and counting the counters?*

You may wish to use the Holistic Scoring Guide and annotated samples of children's work to assess this task. See pages 29–32 and 37–61 in Teacher's Assessment Resources.

Follow-Up Interviews

Meet with children individually or in small groups to reflect on the Performance Assessment task. You can use the following questions to gain insight into children's thinking and evaluate their level of understanding:

- **How did you add to complete the addition sentences?**
- **How did you get this number? (Point to one of the sums.)**
- **What strategy did you use the most? Why?**
- **What does it mean to add?**
- **How would you explain to a friend how to complete one of the addition sentences?**

AT A GLANCE

OBJECTIVES Complete an addition table for facts to 10; use an addition table to find sums.

Using the Math Connection

Have children look for patterns in the table. Then have them complete the table by counting.

Demonstrate how to use the table to add. For example, to find the sum of 4 and 2, find the first addend, 4, in the first column and put a finger on it. Find the second addend, 2, in the top row and put a finger on it. Move the first finger across the row and the second finger down the column until they meet. The number where the fingers meet, 6, is the sum.

Some children may need to use a ruler to track the numbers in the rows and columns.

Developing Algebra Sense Some children may notice that they can use either the numeral down the side or the numeral across the top of the table to represent the first addend as long as the second addend is represented by the other part of the table (across the top or down the side). This is an example of the Order Property of Addition.

Name

Addition Tables

Complete the table. Use counting.

+	0	1	2	3	4	5	6	7	8	9
0	0	1	2	3	4	5	6	7	8	9
1	1	2	3	4	5	6	7	8	9	10
2	2	3	4	5	6	7	8	9	10	
3	3	4	5	6	7	8	9	10		
4	4	5	6	7	8	9	10			
5	5	6	7	8	9	10				
6	6	7	8	9	10					
7	7	8	9	10						
8	8	9	10							
9	9	10								

Use the table to add.

1. 4 + 2 = 6   5 + 3 = 8   2 + 2 = 4
2. 7 + 3 = 10   6 + 2 = 8   4 + 3 = 7

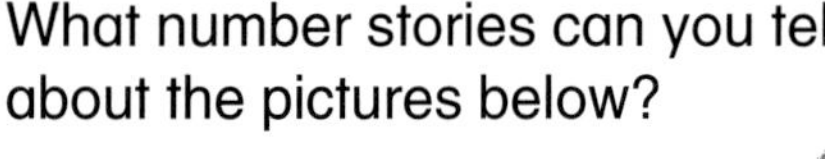

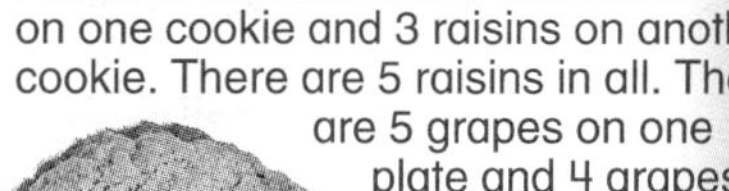

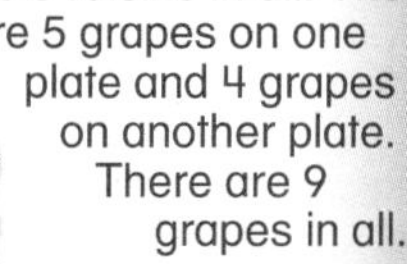

Curriculum Connection

Language Arts

Dot Stories

Talk What number stories can you tell about the pictures below?

Possible answer: There are 2 raisins on one cookie and 3 raisins on another cookie. There are 5 raisins in all. There are 5 grapes on one plate and 4 grapes on another plate. There are 9 grapes in all.

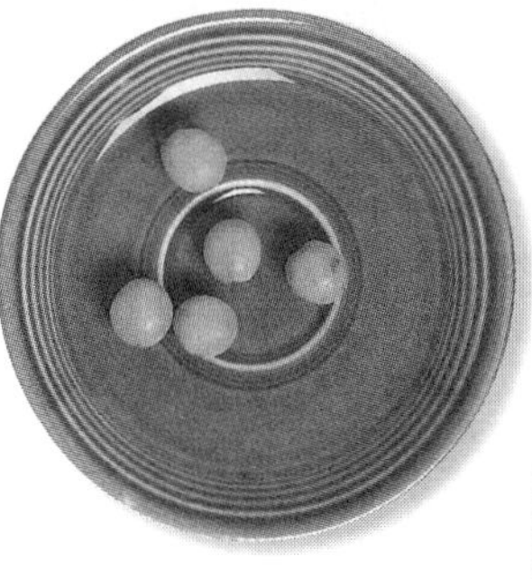

You need 10 dots. Pictures and number stories may vary.

- Draw a picture using some dots.
- Tell a number story about your dot picture.
- Trade pictures with a partner.
- Tell another number story.

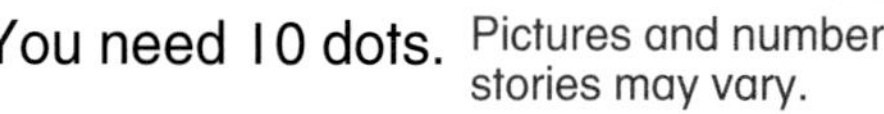

AT A GLANCE

OBJECTIVE Children use number stories to explore addition.

Materials per child: two-color counters

Using the Curriculum Connection

Have children look at the pictures at the top of the page. Ask volunteers to describe what they see. Encourage them to notice the amounts of things such as the raisins on the cookies and the grapes on the plates. You may wish to write the number sentences children describe on the chalkboard.

Invite pairs of children to create number stories about the remaining pictures on the page. Allow them to use counters to work out addition facts. Then have partners trade pictures and check each others' work.

Be sure children are creating accurate number stories that match the pictures. You can ask partners to write a number sentence to represent each story.

Extending the Activity Pairs of children can draw their own pictures, trade them with their partner, and write a number story.

CUMULATIVE REVIEW

PURPOSE Review and maintain the concepts, skills, and strategies that children have already learned.

Using the Cumulative Review

The **Cumulative Review** is presented in a multiple-choice format to provide practice in taking a standardized test. Discuss with children that in example 5, "not here" means the right answer may be different from the choices presented.

Assessment Resources

Test Masters

There are multiple-choice Cumulative Tests and a Year-End Test that provide additional opportunities for students to practice taking standardized tests.

Name ______________________

Cumulative Review

Choose the letter of the correct answer.

1 Find the missing part.

3	?
5	

● 2
ⓑ 3
ⓒ 4
ⓓ 5

4 Find the total.

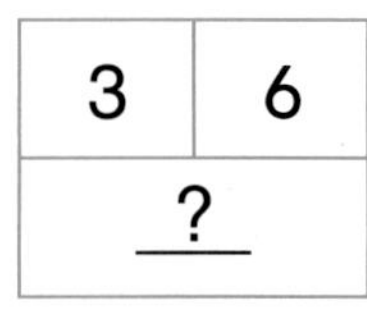

3	6
?	

ⓐ 3
ⓑ 7
ⓒ 8
● 9

2 Add.

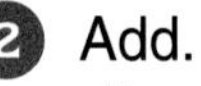
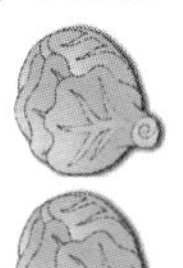
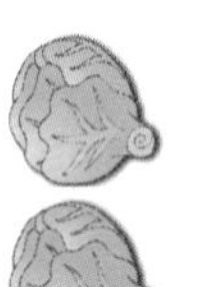
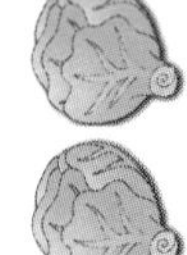
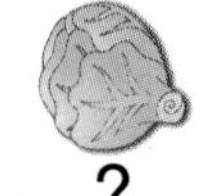

$3 + 3 =$?

ⓐ 3
ⓑ 5
● 6
ⓓ 7

5 Add.

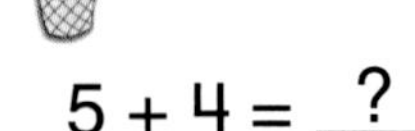
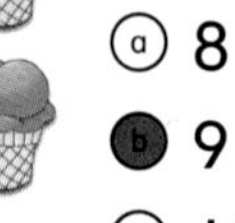

$5 + 4 =$?

ⓐ 8
● 9
ⓒ 10
ⓓ not here

3 How many cents?

● 3
ⓑ 4
ⓒ 5
ⓓ 6

6 How many?

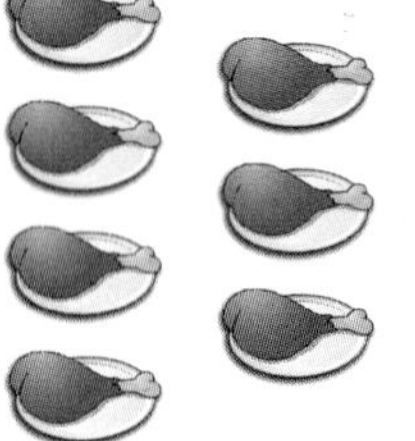

ⓐ 5
ⓑ 6
● 7
ⓓ 8

Cumulative Review Correlation

REVIEW ITEMS	TEXT PAGES
1	63
2	81
3	31
4	59
5	81
6	21
7	67
8	67
9	99
10	99

7 How many animals?

- (a) 3
- (b) 4
- (c) 5
- (d) 6

8 How many children?

- (a) 1
- (b) 2
- (c) 3
- (d) 4

9 How many in all?

- (a) 3
- (b) 4
- (c) 5
- (d) 6

10 How many in all?

- (a) 3
- (b) 4
- (c) 7
- (d) 8

Family Activities

PURPOSE Give family members an opportunity to help children maintain concepts and skills learned in the chapter.

Using the Wrap-Up

Page 109

Tell children that this side of the page will help them show their parents what they have been learning in this chapter.

Name

Food Totals

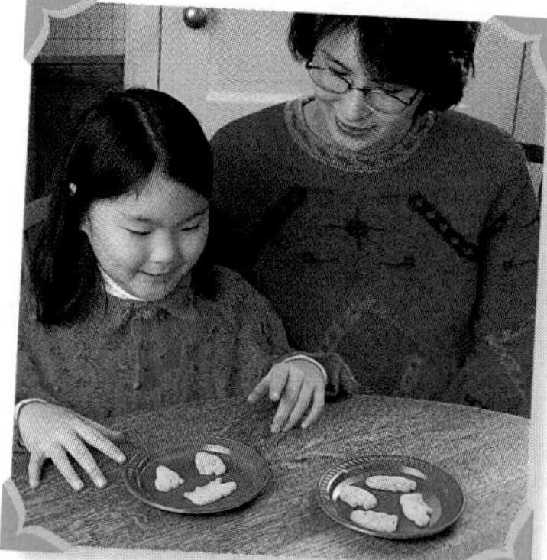

Draw. Write the addition.

___ + ___ = ___

___ + ___ = ___

___ + ___ = ___

___ + ___ = ___

___ + ___ = ___

Choose food items such as crackers, raisins, or dried macaroni to help your child practice addition. Use 2 plates to show 2 groups of a food item for a total of no more than 10. Your child draws to show the 2 groups, adds, and then writes the addition sentence.

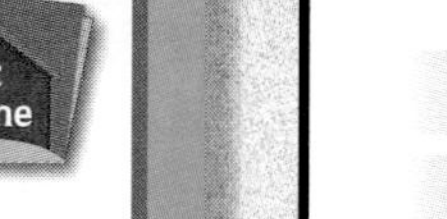

Dear Family,

At Home

We are starting a new chapter in our mathematics book. We are going to learn to subtract. We will use pictures and numbers to show subtraction.

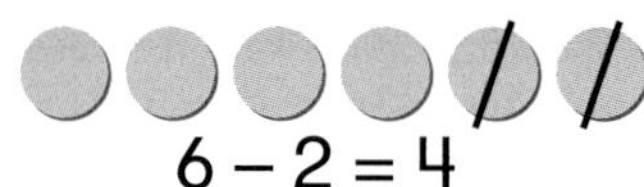

We will also be talking about folktales and favorite stories. Please help me complete this interview.

Your child,

____
Signature

Interview

What kind of stories do you like?
(You may check more than one.)

- ☐ Folktales
- ☐ True stories
- ☐ Mysteries
- ☐ Nursery rhymes
- ☐ Other ______________

Did you have a favorite story when you were a child? ______________

What was it? ______________

____

Family Activities

PURPOSE Give family members an opportunity to share in their child's mathematics learning.

Using the Preview

Page 110

Discuss the content of the page with children and have them sign the letter at the top. Be sure they understand how to conduct an interview with a family member, friend, or neighbor.

Explain to children that they may share what they learn during their next math lesson. You may wish to have children bring back the page.

BEGINNING TO SUBTRACT

Planning for Learning

Suggested Pacing : 10–12 days **Theme: Folk Tales and Rhymes**

Lesson Title/Description	Pages	Pacing	Real-life Connection	Chapter Objectives	Materials	Reteach/ Practice/Extend	Math Center Cards
Preview	110						
Introduction	111		acting out a story				
What Do You Know? (J) (P)	112						
▶ 1. Subtraction Stories Teaching with Technology	113–114	1-day lesson		4A	2-color counters, Workmat 3	29	22
▶ 2. Subtraction Sentences	115–118	2-day lesson		4A	2-color counters	30–31	23
▶ 3. Problem-Solving Strategy: Write a Subtraction Sentence	119–120	1-day lesson		4B	rhino counters, Workmat 1 (rhino environment)	32	24
Midchapter Review (J)	121		drawing a picture		rhino counters, 2-color counters		
Extra Practice Game: Collect Them All	122				number cubes (1–6); have available: rhino counters or 2-color counters		
Real-life Investigation: Applying Subtraction (P)	123–124		listing favorite stories				
▶ 4. Subtraction Fact Pairs	125–126	1-day lesson		4A	pennies	33	25
▶ 5. Count Back	127–130	2-day lesson	making up a tall tale	4A	2-color counters or beans, rhino counters	34–35	26
Extra Practice Game: Flying South	131–132				rhino counters, blank spinners (TA 7–8)		
▶ 6. Problem Solvers at Work	133–134	1-day lesson		4B	rhino counters or 2-color counters	36	27
ASSESSMENT OPTIONS (J) (P) Chapter Review Chapter Test Performance Assessment	 135–136 137 138		 visiting a public library				
CONNECTIONS MATH: Algebra TECHNOLOGY Home Connection	 139 140 141						

(J) = JOURNAL OPPORTUNITY

(P) = PORTFOLIO OPPORTUNITY

TA = TEACHER AID

Technology Links	NCTM Standards
Online Exploration, p. 112B Math Van: *Pig Tales*	4, 8
Math Van: Counters tool Math Forum, p. 114D	8
Math Van: Counters tool Math Forum, p. 118B	1, 2, 3, 4, 8
	1, 2, 3, 4, 8
Math Van: Money Models tool Math Forum, p. 124B	8, 13
Math Van: Counters tool Math Forum, p. 126B	8, 13
Math Van: Counters tool Math Forum, p. 132B	1, 2, 3, 4, 8
Math Van: Counters tool	1, 4, 6, 8

ASSESSMENT OPTIONS

INFORMAL

Ongoing Assessment

- Observation Checklist, pp. 115, 117, 119, 125, 129, 133
- Interview, p. 127

Portfolio Opportunities

- Chapter Project, p. 110F
- What Do You Know? p. 112
- Investigation, pp. 123–124
- Journal Writing, pp. 112, 121, 136
- Performance Assessment, p. 138

FORMAL

Chapter Tests

Student Book

- Midchapter Review, p. 121
- Chapter Review, pp. 135–136
- Chapter Test, p. 137

Test Masters

- Free-Response Test: Form C
- Multiple-Choice Test: Forms A and B

Performance Assessment

- What Do You Know? p. 112
- Performance Assessment, p. 138
- Self-Assessment: What Do You Think? p. 135
- Holistic Scoring Guide, Teacher's Assessment Resources, pp. 29–32
- Follow-Up Interviews, p. 138

Teacher's Assessment Resources

- Portfolio Guidelines and Forms, pp. 6–9, 27–36
- Holistic Scoring Guide, pp. 29–32
- Samples of Student Work, pp. 37–61

Chapter Objectives		Standardized Test Correlations
4A	Subtract, facts to 10	MAT, CAT, SAT, ITBS, CTBS
4B	Solve problems, including those that involve subtraction and writing a subtraction sentence	MAT, CAT, SAT, ITBS, CTBS

NCTM Standards Grades K–4

1 Problem Solving
2 Communication
3 Reasoning
4 Connections
5 Estimation
6 Number Sense and Numeration
7 Concepts of Whole Number Operations
8 Whole Number Computation
9 Geometry and Spatial Sense
10 Measurement
11 Statistics and Probability
12 Fractions and Decimals
13 Patterns and Relationships

Meeting Individual Needs

LEARNING STYLES

- AUDITORY/LINGUISTIC
- LOGICAL/ANALYTICAL
- VISUAL/SPATIAL
- MUSICAL
- KINESTHETIC
- SOCIAL
- INDIVIDUAL

Children who are talented in art, language, and physical activity may better understand mathematical concepts when these concepts are connected to their areas of interest. Use the following activity to stimulate the different learning styles of some of your children.

Individual Learners

Some children may enjoy working alone as they practice subtraction. Distribute a recording sheet with subtraction problems that begin with a total of 10. Have children toss a number cube and remove the number shown. They record their answers on the sheet.

10 – ___ = ___ 10 – ___ = ___

10 – ___ = ___ 10 – ___ = ___

See Lesson Resources, pp. 112A, 114C, 118A, 124A, 126A, 132A.

GIFTED AND TALENTED

Some children may begin to use addition facts to help them subtract. For example, if they have a good understanding of parts that make ten, then remove a part from ten to show subtraction. Encourage them to explain their thinking to other members of the class. Encourage the use of this strategy by having children work with addition and subtraction at the same time. Give them problems like these:

6 + 6 = ___ 12 – 6 = ___

8 + 4 = ___ ___ – 8 = 4

3 + ___ = 12 12 – ___ = 9

See also Meeting Individual Needs, p. 117.

EXTRA SUPPORT

Specific suggestions for ways to provide extra support to children appear in every lesson in this chapter.

See Meeting Individual Needs, pp. 113, 115, 119, 125, 129, 133.

EARLY FINISHERS

Children who finish their class work early may create and tape their own original tales that can be used for addition and subtraction problems. (See *Chapter Project,* p. 110F.)

See also Meeting Individual Needs, pp. 113, 115, 119, 125, 129, 133.

STUDENTS ACQUIRING ENGLISH

The concept of subtraction may not be as easy for children as addition. Create subtraction stories to model problems so children can develop an understanding of the subtraction process. Use the term subtract whenever possible. Help them to see that they are removing, rather than adding to.

See also Meeting Individual Needs, p. 117.

INCLUSION

- **For inclusion ideas, information, and suggestions, see pp. 127, T15.**
- **For gender fairness tips, see pp. T15.**

USING MANIPULATIVES

Building Understanding Use counters on a ten-frame mat to help children model the subtraction problems. Children can place the amount of counters for the total number on the ten-frame mat. They then take away the counters to show the number they are subtracting. This will help them count and see a relationship between ten and the numbers they are manipulating.

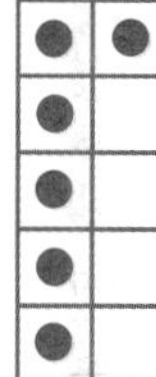

Easy-to-Make Manipulatives You can use beans, buttons, or paper clips if counters are not available.

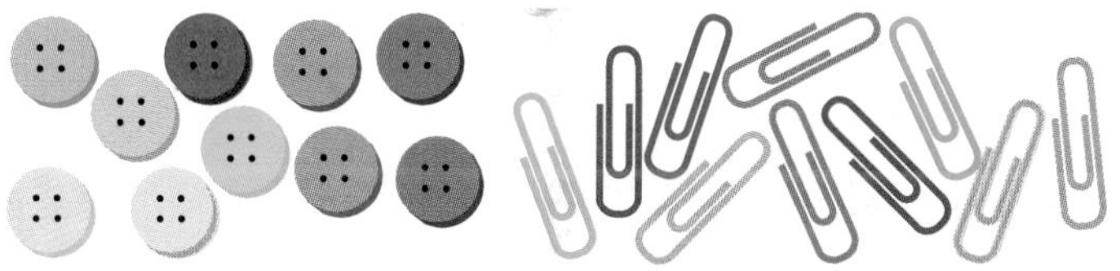

USING COOPERATIVE LEARNING

Partners Check This strategy develops simple teamwork by bringing children together to compare methods of learning and check for understanding.

- **Partners record each other's work.**
- **Partners compare two different methods.**
- **Partners check each other's understanding of a procedure or concept.**

USING LITERATURE

Use the selection *The Great Ball Game* to introduce the chapter theme, Folktales and Rhymes. This story is reprinted on pages 4–6 of the Read-Aloud Anthology.

Also available in the Read-Aloud Anthology are the poems "Two Birds," page 27; "Ten in a Bed," page 45; and "Five Little Ducks," page 47.

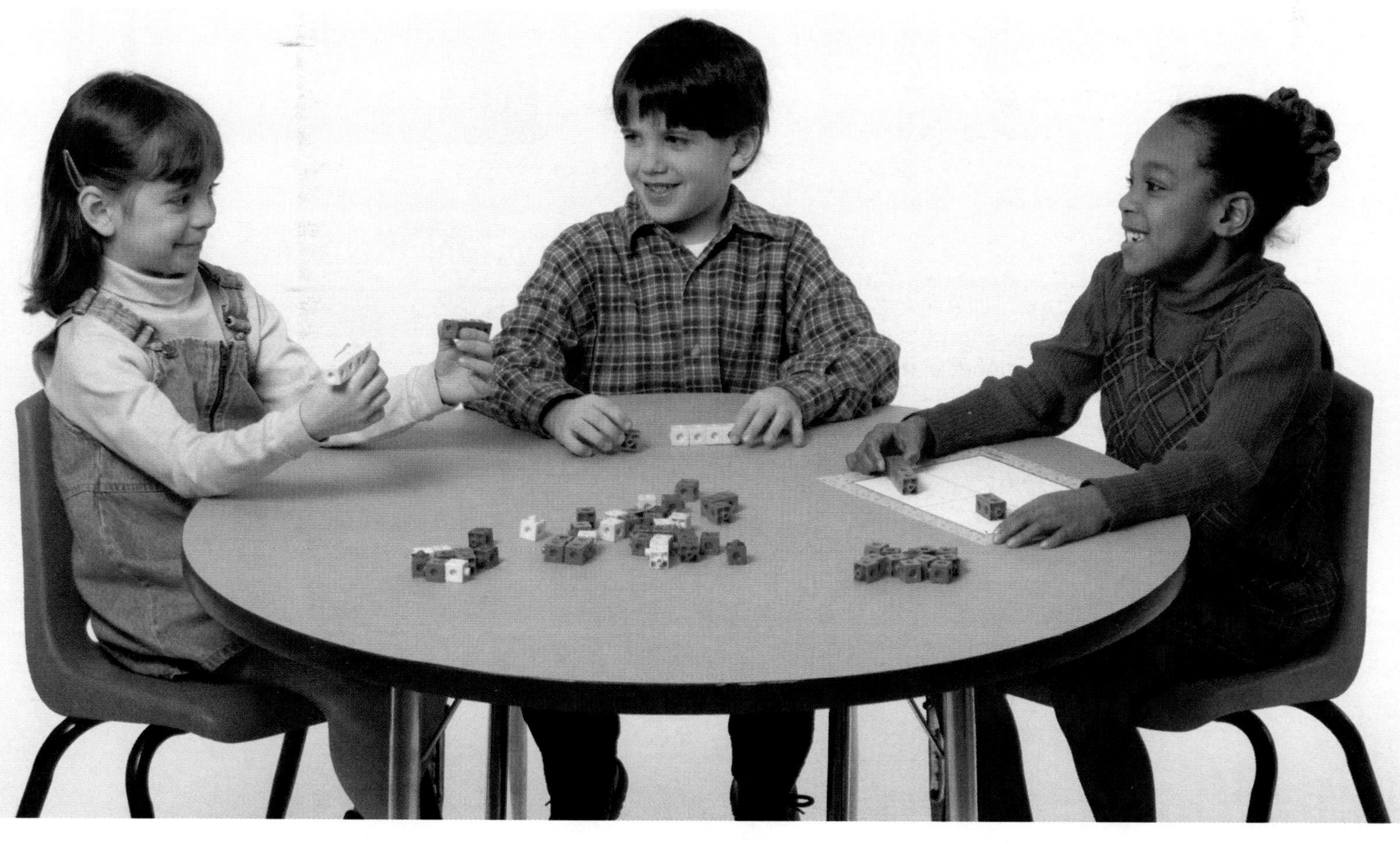

Linking Technology

This integrated package of programs and services allows students to explore, develop, and practice concepts; solve problems; build portfolios; and assess their own progress. Teachers can enhance instruction, provide remediation, and share ideas with other educational professionals.

MATH VAN ACTIVITY

In *Pig Tales,* students use counters to determine how many pigs are left after some of them run away. Students can use the online notebook to write about subtraction. To extend the activity, students use the Math Van tools to make up their own subtraction stories. *Available on CD-ROM.*

MATH VAN TOOLS

Students can use Math Van's counters to explore the concept of subtraction. The Tech Links on the Lesson Resources pages highlight opportunities for students to use this and other tools such as money models, online notes, and calculator to provide additional practice, reteaching, or extension. *Available on CD-ROM.*

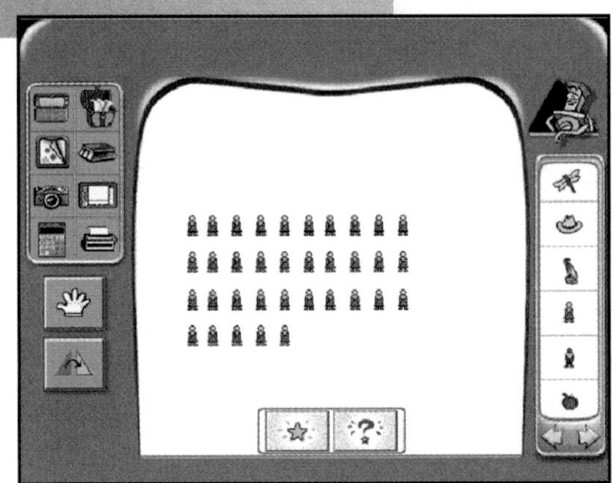

WEB SITE http://www.mhschool.com

Teachers can access the McGraw-Hill School Division World Wide Web site for additional curriculum support at http://www.mhschool.com. Click on our Resource Village for specially designed activities linking Web sites to subtraction. Motivate children by inviting them to explore Web sites that develop the chapter theme of "Folktales and Rhymes." Exchange ideas on classroom management, cultural diversity, and other areas in the Math Forum.

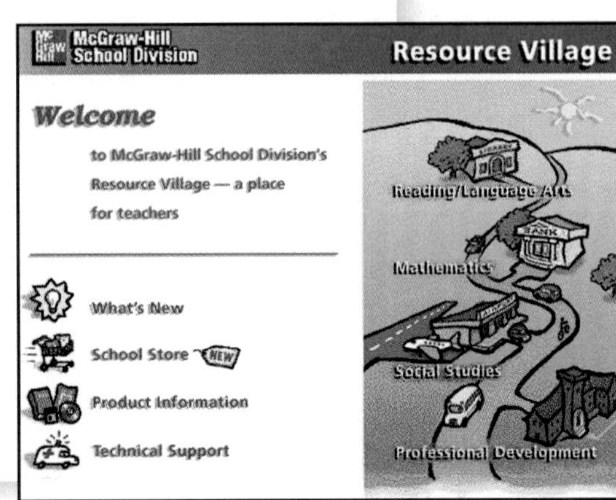

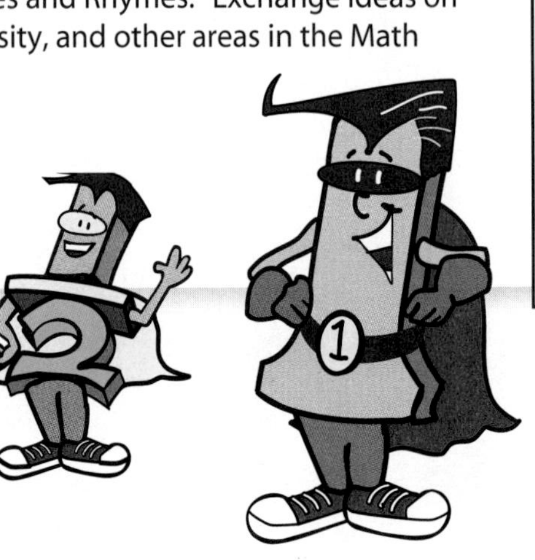

Chapter Project A CLASS FOLK TALE BOOK

Highlighting the Math

- count number of pages
- subtract or add items in stories

1 Starting the Project

Invite the class to make a book of folk tales. Begin by discussing possible tales that children might retell. List these on the chalkboard as they are suggested. Have children work with partners to decide on a folk tale. Consider ways in which family and community members can participate.

2 Continuing the Project

- Children work together to dictate their folk tale to you or an assistant.
- Have children illustrate their folk tales. Children may use plain white paper or construction paper and crayons.
- Children make up and write subtraction stories based on the folk tales. For example: "There were 3 Billy Goats Gruff grazing on the hillside. One went to the bridge. How many were left?"

3 Finishing the Project

- Compile the finished tales and story problems into a class book. Two children prepare a contents page for the book and another pair create a cover.
- Each group shares its folk tale and accompanying illustrations. You may wish to have a volunteer from each group read their story aloud into a tape recorder.

Community Involvement

Parent volunteers assist with the taping of the children reading their stories aloud. Children share the book with another class or on tape.

BUILDING A PORTFOLIO

Have children draw a picture showing their involvement with the folk tale book. Have them dictate or write a caption for the picture.

Each child's portfolio should include the picture and caption and any notes you made about the child's work. If photographs of the book are available, include them.

To assess work, refer to the Holistic Scoring Guide on page 27 in the Teacher's Assessment Resources.

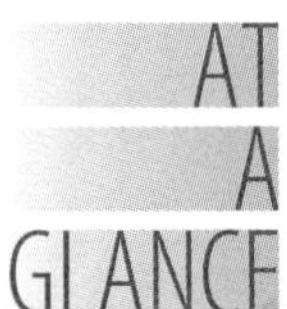

PURPOSE Introduce the theme of the chapter.

Resource Read-Aloud Anthology, pages 4–6.

Using Literature

Page 111

Synopsis of the Book

In "The Great Ball Game, A Muskogee Story," those with teeth (the Animals) and those with wings (the Birds) settle an argument about who is better by playing a ball game. At first, Bat is rejected by each side because he has both teeth and wings. Finally, the Animals allow him to play on their side.

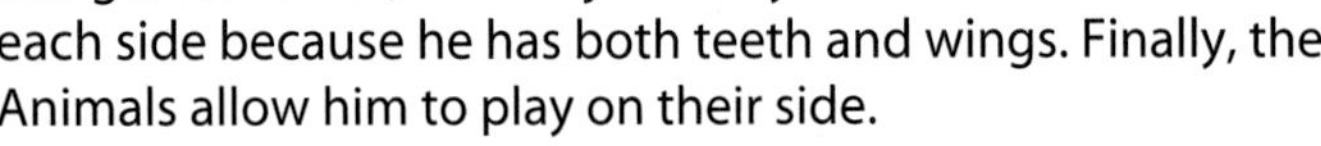

Bat wins the game for the Animals. He declares that the Birds must leave the land for part of every year as a penalty for losing, and this is why birds fly south each winter.

After reading the story through once, talk with children about how this story explains an event in nature—the migration of birds. Invite children to mime the story as you read it again. Children might also enjoy making masks to represent the Birds and Animals.

Developing the Theme

The theme of the chapter is "Folk Tales and Rhymes." Read aloud the rhyme, "Ten In a Bed," found in the Read-Aloud Anthology on pages 45–46. Point out that rhymes such as "Ten In a Bed" are long-time favorites.

Mention that many stories are also told and retold by families and groups. Some of these stories are folk tales such as "The Great Ball Game" and are passed down from one generation to the next.

Invite children to share other traditional stories or rhymes that they know. The theme will be revisited throughout the chapter on pages 116 and 117.

Making Cultural Connections

Every culture has a rich collection of folk tales. Many of these have been retold for young children. Start with the bibliography found on this page and consult your school librarian for other titles that reflect the math concepts in this chapter and the cultural heritages of your students.

After children have been exposed to several folk tales, take time to discuss how the stories are alike and different.

Folktales and Rhymes

Beginning to Subtract

CHAPTER 4

11

CHAPTER BIBLIOGRAPHY

Counting Rhymes selected by Shona McKellar. New York: Dorling Kindersley, Inc. 1993. ISBN: 1-56458-309-0

The First Strawberries: A Cherokee Story by Joseph Bruchac. New York: Dial Books for Young Readers, 1993. ISBN: 0-8037-1331-2

Lon PoPo: A Red Riding Hood Story from China translated by Ed Young. New York: Putnam Publishing Group, 1989. ISBN: 0-399-21619-7

COMMUNITY INVOLVEMENT

You may wish to contact a local library to find out whether they have a multicultural story-telling program. If possible, take the class to one of these sessions, or ask the library to send a story-teller to the class.

Name

You need 10 rhinos.

Find the missing part.

1

5	2
7	

4	1
5	

4	4
8	

2

4	6
10	

4	2
6	

3	1
4	

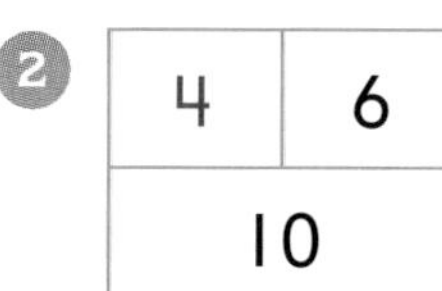

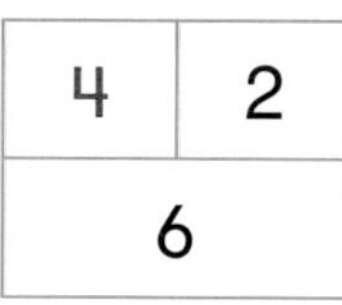

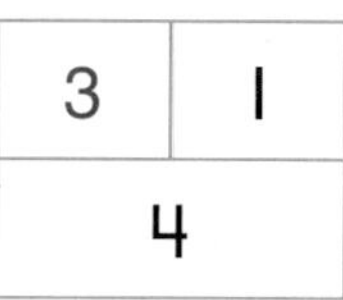

 Show how you find the missing part.

VOCABULARY

These math words will be used in this chapter.

- **subtract** (p. 115)
- **subtraction sentence** (p. 115)
- **minus sign** (p. 115)
- **minus** (p. 115)
- **equal sign** (p. 115)
- **equals** (p. 115)
- **difference** (p. 117)
- **none** (p. 124A)
- **all** (p. 124A)

JOURNAL Children may record new words in their math journals. Encourage them to show examples and draw pictures to help tell what the words mean.

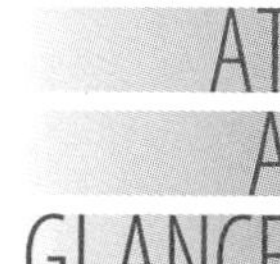

AT A GLANCE

PURPOSE Assess children's ability to apply prior knowledge of part-part-whole relationships.

Materials have available: rhino counters

Assessing Prior Knowledge

Draw a mat like the one at the top of the Student Book page on an overhead projector or the board.

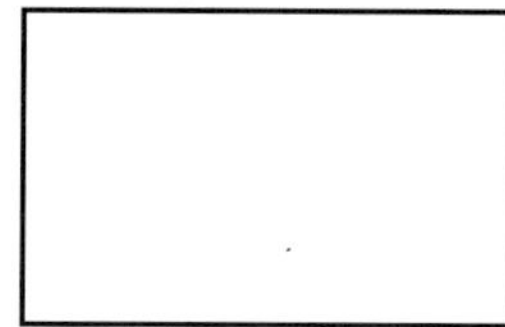

Have children look at the first item in row 1 on the Student Book page. Copy it on the overhead. Tell children you want to use rhino counters to show the total on the mat and find the missing part.

Use counters to model what the children are to do. Begin by asking how many counters they should put on the mat. When children agree there should be 7, place 7 counters on the mat on the overhead. Have children put 7 counters on the mat on their Student Book page. Ask children how they could find the missing part. *[Answers may vary.]*

Page 112

Tell children that you want them to do the rest of the problems in rows 1–2. They are to use counters to show the total on the mat and find the missing part. Observe children as they work.

Give positive feedback to children on what they already know about parts and totals. Tell them that in chapter 4 they will be learning more about parts and totals and about subtracting.

Prerequisite Skills

- *Can children count?*
- *Can children write the numbers?*
- *Can children find the missing part given the total and one of the parts?*

After children have solved the problems in rows 1 and 2, ask volunteers to share their solutions and methods. Ask children what they think of the methods that are different from the ones they used.

BUILDING A PORTFOLIO

Assign the problem at the bottom of the page. This piece provides an indicator of where children are in their understanding of the part-part-whole relationship.

A Portfolio Checklist for Students and a Checklist for Teachers are provided in Teacher's Assessment Resources, pp. 33–34.

Subtraction Stories

OBJECTIVE Explore the concept of subtraction through part-part-whole stories.

Day 1 Explore Activity Subtraction Stories

Teaching with Technology
See alternate computer lesson, pp. 114A–114B.

RESOURCE REMINDER
Math Center Cards 22
Practice 29, Reteach 29, Extend 29

SKILLS TRACE	
GRADE K	• Explore the concept of subtraction through part-part-whole stories. *(Chapter 11)*
GRADE 1	• Explore the concept of subtraction through part-part-whole stories.
GRADE 2	• Explore subtracting, facts to 12. *(Chapter 1)*

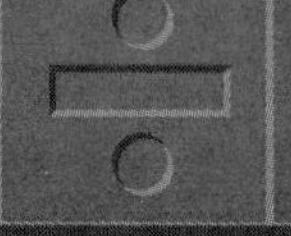

LESSON RESOURCES

WARM-UP

Whole Class — **Social**

OBJECTIVE Explore the concept of subtraction by acting out stories.

▶ Have small groups act out part-part-total stories, such as:
5 children are at the chalkboard.
3 children go back to their desks.
How many children are still at the chalkboard? *[2]*

▶ Talk about how many children were at the chalkboard (total), how many went back to their desks (part), and how many are still at the chalkboard (part). Discuss how children solved the problem.

▶ Encourage children to make up other part-part-total stories.

CONNECTION ACTIVITY

Whole Class — **Auditory/Linguistic**

OBJECTIVE Connect the concept of subtraction with music.

Resource Read-Aloud Anthology, pages 47–48

▶ Read the poem "Five Little Ducks," found in the Read-Aloud Anthology.

▶ Ask five volunteers to pretend they are the ducks as children help you reread or sing the poem. After each verse, pause to ask how many ducks went out one day, how many ducks came back, and how many ducks did not come back.

DAILY MATH

PREVIOUS DAY QUICK REVIEW

Count on to add.

1. 4 + 1 *[5]*
2. 4 + 2 *[6]*
3. 4 + 3 *[7]*
4. 4 + 0 *[4]*

FAST FACTS

1. 1 + 2 *[3]*
2. 3 + 2 *[5]*
3. 2 + 2 *[4]*
4. 7 + 2 *[9]*

Problem of the Day • 22

Read aloud to children:

The Animals have 6 sticks for playing ball.
Bear breaks a stick.
Then Fox breaks a stick.
How many sticks are not broken? *[4]*

TECH LINK

ONLINE EXPLORATION

Use our Web-linked activites and lesson plans to connect your students to the real world of folk tales and rhymes.

MATH VAN

Activity You may wish to use *Pig Tales* to teach this lesson.

Visit our Resource Village at http://www.mhschool.com to access the Online Exploration.

MATH CENTER

Practice

OBJECTIVE Use part-part-whole to subtract.

Materials per pair: bag, 10 counters; per child: Math Center Recording Sheet (TA 38 optional)

Children take turns determining the number of counters remaining in a bag. One child puts a known number of counters in a bag and the other child takes out a known number. *[Check that the part-part-whole answers are correct.]*

PRACTICE ACTIVITY 22 MATH CENTER Partners

Manipulatives • How Many Counters?

YOU NEED: bag, 10 counters

Take turns.

- Count some counters.
  Put them in a bag.
  Draw a picture of them, and write the total number.
- Your partner takes out some counters.
  Put each one on a counter that you drew.
  Write the number taken out.
- Write how many counters are left in the bag.
  Your partner checks your answer.

Total	Part	Part
8	5	3

Grade Level 1 · McGraw-Hill School Division

Chapter 4, Lesson 1 · Subtraction

NCTM Standards
- Problem Solving
- ✓ Communication
- ✓ Reasoning
- ✓ Connections

Problem Solving

OBJECTIVE Explore subtraction through part-part-whole stories.

Materials per pair: number cards for 1–6 (TA 9), 7 counters; per child: Math Center Recording Sheet (TA 38 optional)

Children complete a subtraction problem. They take turns using a number card to get a number they subtract, show the subtraction with models, and record the results. *[Check that children's work is correct.]*

PROBLEM-SOLVING ACTIVITY 22 MATH CENTER Partners

Formulating Problems • Fly Away

YOU NEED: number cards, 7 counters

There are 7 birds.

____ fly away.

____ birds are left.

Take turns.

- Pick a card to get a number.
  The number tells how many birds fly away.
- Your partner uses counters to show the story.
- Write the total and parts.

Total	Part	Part
7	5	2

Grade Level 1 · McGraw-Hill School Division

Chapter 4, Lesson 1 · Subtraction

NCTM Standards
- ✓ Problem Solving
- ✓ Communication
- ✓ Reasoning
- Connections

Lesson 4.1

EXPLORE ACTIVITY

Subtraction Stories

OBJECTIVE Children explore the concept of subtraction through part-part-total stories.

Materials per pair: 10 two-color counters, Workmat 3 (part-part-whole mat)

1 Motivate — Whole Class

Resource Read-Aloud Anthology, pages 4–6

Reread the story "The Great Ball Game," found in the Read-Aloud Anthology, to children. Talk about the Animals (Bear, Deer, Squirrel, Fox, Rabbit), Birds (Crane, Hawk), and Bat. Have children find the playing sticks and ball on selected pages and talk about a ball game they may have played. This review will help children understand the context for the problems they will hear on page 113.

2 Develop

Page 113

Working Together Read aloud to children each word problem found on the reduced student book page in this Teacher's Edition. Demonstrate the first problem as children show it with counters on Workmat 3.

Have children point to the total. *[5]* Remind children that there are two parts—tired bats and flying bats. Tell children that the two tired bats are drawn in the first box, the flying bats are drawn in the second box, and the numeral to show how many flying bats is written in the second box. Children may draw Xs or circles.

Critical Thinking

After children answer the question on the page, ask:

- **How can you find what part is left?** *[Possible answer: I can start with the total and take away the part I know.]*

Page 114

Try These Assign practice exercises 1–4.

Working together in pairs, children can tell each other stories about the total and the parts.

3 Close

Check for Understanding by having children explain how they found the unknown part.

- **When you know the total and one part, how do you find the part that is missing?** *[Possible answer: I take away the part that I know from the total.]*

Name ______

Explore Activity

Subtraction Stories

Working Together

You need 10 .

Listen to the story.

- Show the total.
- Draw the parts.
- Write the number for the part that is left.

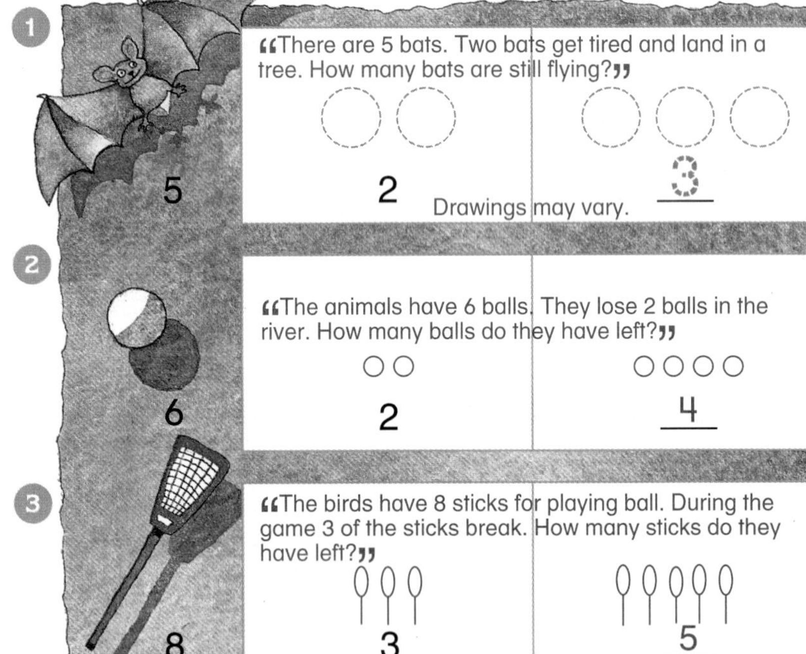

Critical Thinking: How can you check that the part you write is correct?

Possible answer: You can add the two parts, or count the two parts, to see if they equal the total.

MEETING INDIVIDUAL NEEDS

EARLY FINISHERS

Children can make up part-part-total subtraction stories and record them in their journals.

EXTRA SUPPORT

Have children make up several different stories for the same subtraction fact.

ONGOING ASSESSMENT

Anecdotal Report Observe whether children are drawing the correct number of objects as parts and writing the correct numeral. You may wish to keep this sample in their portfolio.

Follow Up For children who are having difficulty, practice subtracting on Workmat 3 and using counters before assigning **Reteach 29.**

For children who are recording correctly, assign **Extend 29.**

Try These!

Take turns.

- You show the total.
- Your partner takes part away and draws it.
- You draw and write the part that is left.

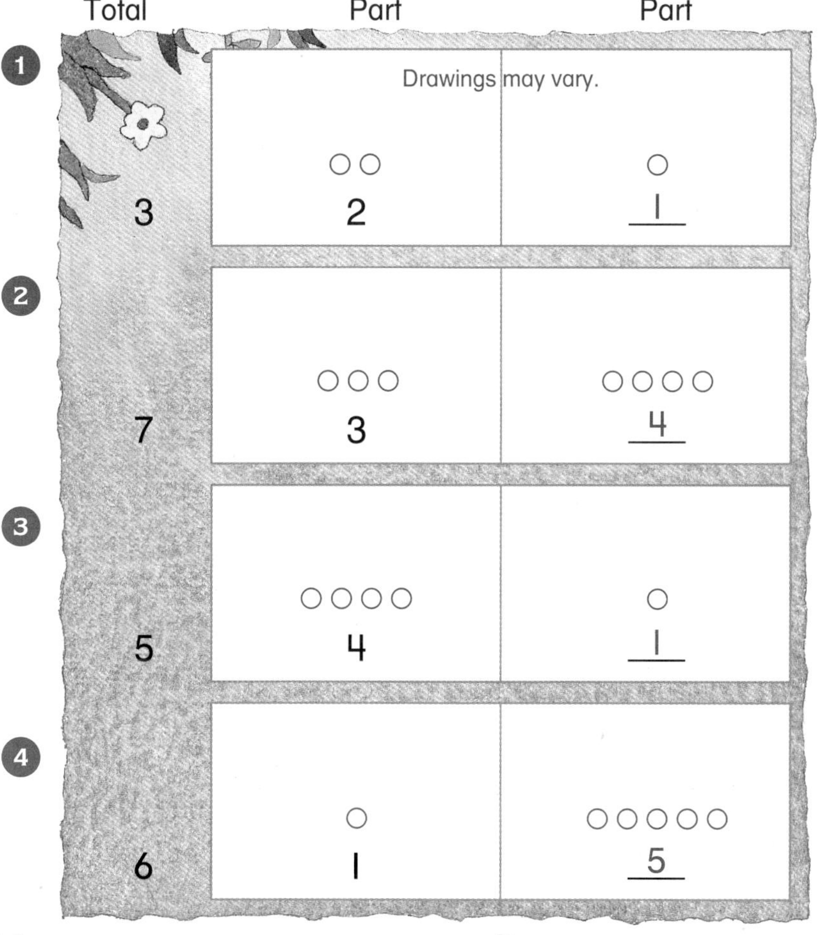

	Total	Part	Part
1	3	2	1
2	7	3	4
3	5	4	1
4	6	1	5

Drawings may vary.

At Home Have your child tell you a story about exercise 1 above.

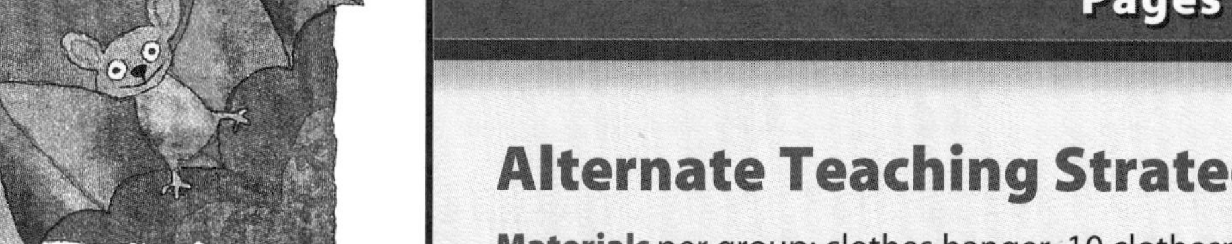

Alternate Teaching Strategy

Materials per group: clothes hanger, 10 clothespins

Have children write the numeral 6 on a sheet of paper. Clip 6 clothespins on the bottom of a clothes hanger, push them all to the left, and say:

There are 6 bats on the branch.
Two bats move to the other side of the branch.
How many bats do not move? *[4]*

Ask a child to move 2 clothespins to the right side and to tell the part that is left. *[4]* Children can then draw Xs or circles to show the two parts for 6 on their papers.

Continue writing other parts for 6. Then repeat, using other numbers less than 10.

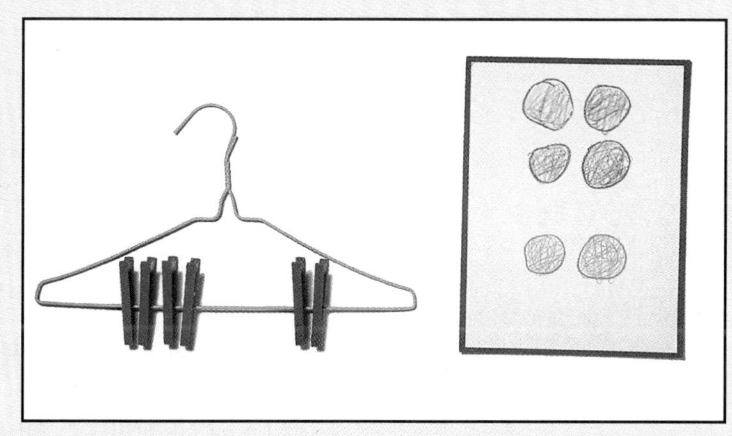

PRACTICE • 29

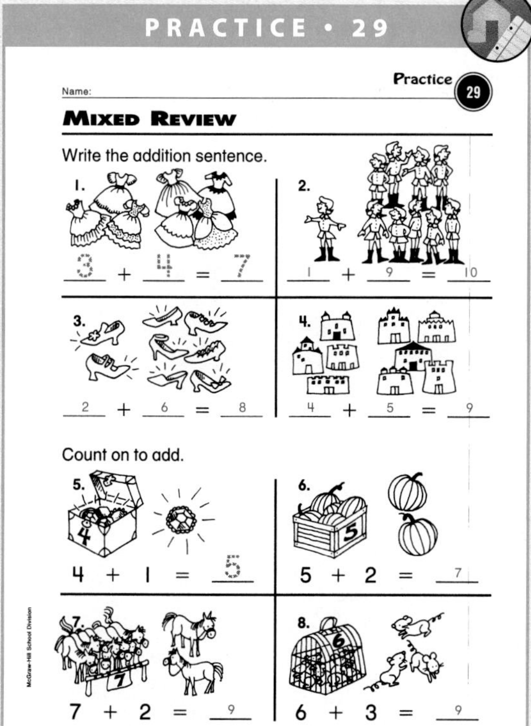

Practice 29

Name:

MIXED REVIEW

Write the addition sentence.

1. 3 + 4 = 7
2. 1 + 9 = 10
3. 2 + 6 = 8
4. 4 + 5 = 9

Count on to add.

5. 4 + 1 = 5
6. 5 + 2 = 7
7. 7 + 2 = 9
8. 6 + 3 = 9

RETEACH • 29

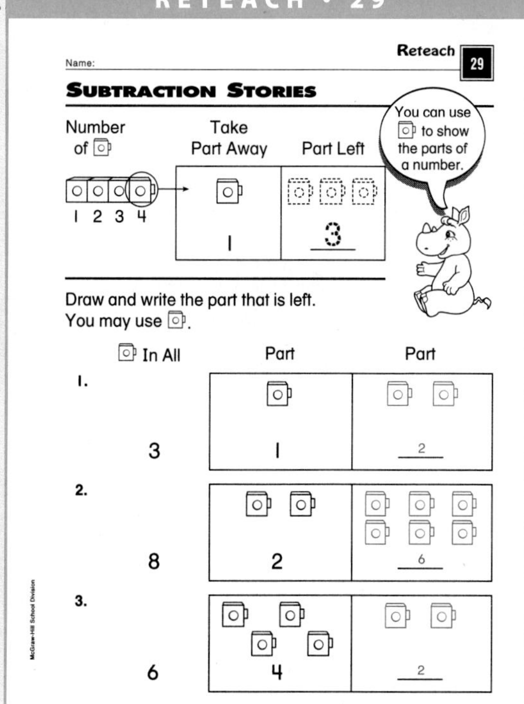

Reteach 29

Name:

SUBTRACTION STORIES

You can use [cube] to show the parts of a number.

Number of [cube]	Take Part Away	Part Left
1 2 3 4	1	3

Draw and write the part that is left. You may use [cube].

	[cube] In All	Part	Part
1.	3	1	2
2.	8	2	6
3.	6	4	2

EXTEND • 29

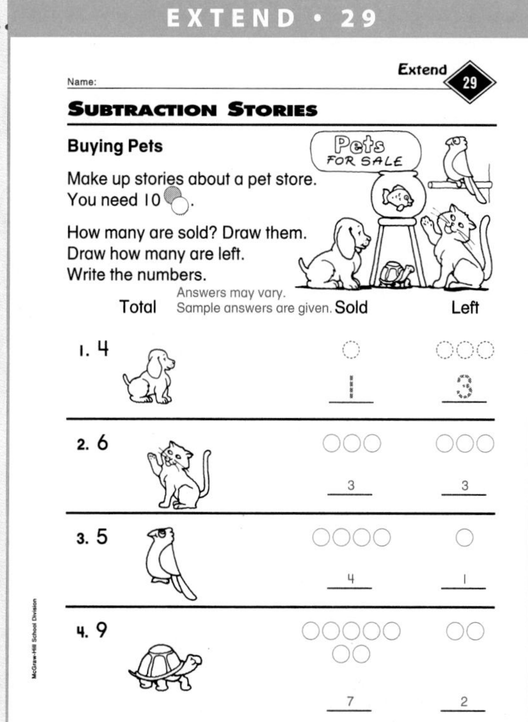

Extend 29

Name:

SUBTRACTION STORIES

Buying Pets

Make up stories about a pet store. You need 10 [counters].

How many are sold? Draw them. Draw how many are left. Write the numbers.

Answers may vary. Sample answers are given.

	Total	Sold	Left
1.	4	1	3
2.	6	3	3
3.	5	4	1
4.	9	7	2

Teaching With Technology

Subtraction Stories

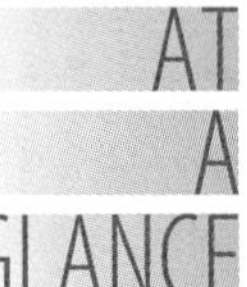

AT A GLANCE

OBJECTIVE Children use counters to explore the concept of subtraction through part-part-whole stories.

Resource Math Van Activity: *Pig Tales*

SET UP

Launch the ***Math Van*** program. Click the right arrow to locate Activity 4, *Pig Tales*. After listening to the activity's description, click *Start*.

Using the Math Van Activity

1 **Getting Started** Allow children to review stamping and moving counters on the Part-Part-Total Mat within the Counters tool.

2 **Practice and Apply** Using Counters to model the story, children determine how many pigs are left after three little pigs run away. Afterwards they take pictures of their work for their Math Journals and explain what they did.

3 **Close** Have children show the pictures from their Math Journal and discuss their work with you, each other, or the class.

Extend Children can create their own subtraction stories involving a total and a part that is removed. Have them work with partners and take turns.

TIPS FOR TOOLS

If children are having difficulty moving counters, remind them that they first need to click the *Move* button, which looks like a hand. Then they can drag each counter to its new position.

SCREEN 1

Children listen to the *Pig Tales* problem, which asks them to find out how many little pigs are left after three of them run away.

SCREEN 2

When the activity opens, children see a Part-Part-Total Mat with a group of pigs on the left side of the mat.

SCREEN 3

Children move three pigs to the right side of the mat. They then find out how many little pigs remain on the left side.

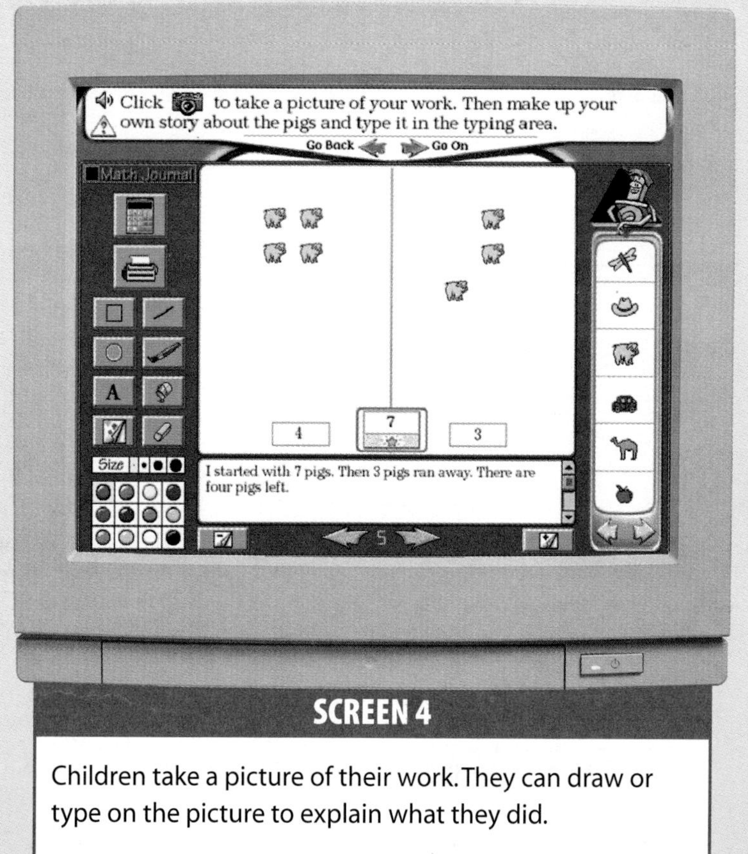

SCREEN 4

Children take a picture of their work. They can draw or type on the picture to explain what they did.

LESSON 4.2

Subtraction Sentences

OBJECTIVE Complete or write subtraction sentences.

Day 1 Subtraction Sentences

Day 2 More Subtraction Sentences

RESOURCE REMINDER
Math Center Cards 23
Practice 30–31, Reteach 30–31, Extend 30–31

SKILLS TRACE	
GRADE K	• Explore completing or writing a subtraction sentence. *(Chapter 11)*
GRADE 1	• Complete or write a subtraction sentence.
GRADE 2	• Complete or write a subtraction sentence. *(Chapter 1)*

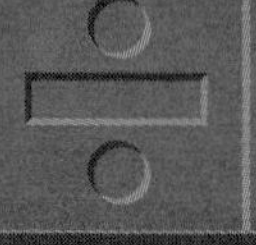

LESSON RESOURCES

MANIPULATIVES

MANIPULATIVE WARM-UP

Whole Group — Social

OBJECTIVE Explore the concept of subtraction.

Materials 10 rhino counters or other classroom objects; paper bag

▶ Place up to 10 rhino counters in a bag. One volunteer counts them. A second volunteer takes some out of the bag and counts those. A third volunteer counts how many rhino counters are left in the bag.

▶ Call on other volunteers to tell a story about the rhinos. *[Possible story: Chris had 7 rhinos. Rosa took away 5 rhinos. Ray counted 2 rhinos left in the bag.]*

▶ If a child needs prompting, ask intermediate questions such as:
- **Who counted the rhino counters in the bag? How many were there?**
- **Who took some rhino counters? How many?**
- **How many were left in the bag?**

▶ Repeat, using different numbers and different groups of children.

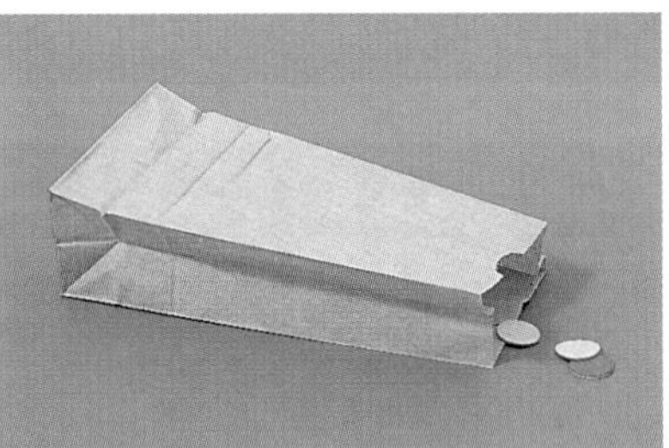

ART

CONNECTION ACTIVITY

Whole Class — Auditory/Linguistic

OBJECTIVE Connect the concept of subtraction with literature.

Resource Math Songs audiocassette, Side 2, Selection 3

Materials 5 stuffed teddy bears, or 5 counters

▶ Play "Five Brown Teddies" twice, encouraging children to join in. Have children use counters to illustrate the story told in the poem. They can slide one counter from the paper to the table to simulate the falling action. After the first verse, ask:
- **How many brown teddies are left sitting on a wall?** *[4]*

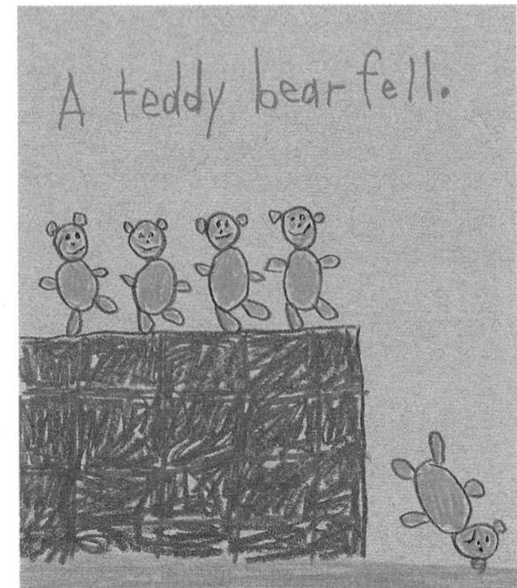

▶ Continue until the poem is finished. Then have children choose a verse to illustrate. Children should write a sentence about the illustration and record the appropriate number sentence on their papers. Illustrations may then be hung in the classroom or put into a class book.

DAILY MATH

PREVIOUS DAY QUICK REVIEW

Take away the part from the total. Use counters. Write the part that is left.

1. Total 4, Part 2 *[2]*
2. Total 6, Part 3 *[3]*
3. Total 3, Part 1 *[2]*

FAST FACTS

1. 3 +1 = *[4]*
2. 4 +1 = *[5]*
3. 5 +1 = *[6]*
4. 6 +1 = *[7]*

Problem of the Day • 23

Read aloud to children:

Mr. Boyle has 8 shells.
He gave 1 shell to a boy and 1 shell to a girl.
How many shells does he have left? *[6]*

TECH LINK

MATH VAN

Tool You may wish to use the Counters tool with this lesson.

MATH FORUM

Cultural Diversity I have children of various ethnic backgrounds describe traditional food or clothing.

Visit our Resource Village at http://www.mhschool.com to access the Math Forum.

MATH CENTER

Practice

OBJECTIVE Solve subtraction problems that use randomly selected data.

Materials per child: 2 blank spinners (TA 7), Math Center Recording Sheet (TA 38 optional)

Prepare Label one spinner 5–9 and one 1–4. Provide recording sheets with grids and numbers.

Children spin two numbers, find the difference, and circle the difference on the grid. They play until they have 3 circled numbers in a row, across, down, or in a diagonal.

PRACTICE ACTIVITY 23 — MATH CENTER On Your Own

Game • Double Spin

YOU NEED: 2 spinners, 9 counters

- Spin both spinners. Write the numbers.
- Use counters to find the difference.
- Find the difference in the box. Circle it.
- Play until you have 3 circles in a row.

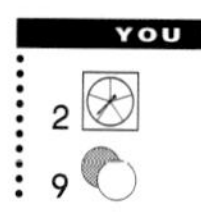

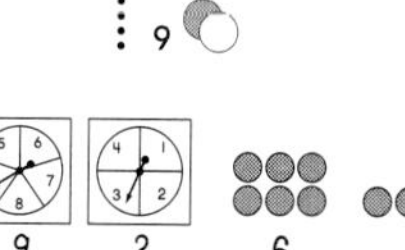

4	3	(6)
2	5	1
4	8	7

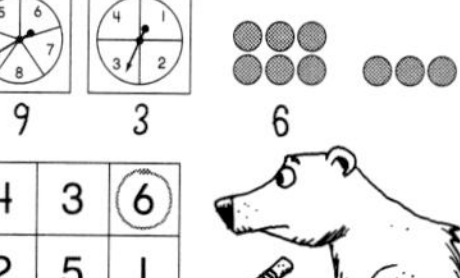

Grade Level 1 — McGraw-Hill School Division

Chapter 4, Lesson 2 — Subtraction

NCTM Standards
- Problem Solving
- Communication
- ✓ Reasoning
- ✓ Connections

Problem Solving

OBJECTIVE Show and write subtraction sentences.

Materials per child: 10 counters, number cards 0–10 (TA 1, 2), Math Center Recording Sheet (TA 38 optional)

Children show and write subtraction sentences to find the number left on various days. Children also discover the pattern in which dog treats are eaten. *[**1.** 10 – 1 = 9, 9 – 2 = 7, 7 – 1 = 6, 6 – 2 = 4. **2.** 2, 4 – 1 = 3, 3 – 2 = 1.]*

PROBLEM-SOLVING ACTIVITY 23 — MATH CENTER On Your Own

Patterning • How Many Treats Are Left?

YOU NEED: 10 counters

Nancy gets 10 dog treats for Spot.
He eats 1 on Monday and 2 on Tuesday.
He eats 1 on Wednesday and 2 on Thursday.
On Friday he eats 1 dog treat.

1. How many treats are left for Tuesday?
How many treats are left for Wednesday?
How many treats are left for Thursday?
How many treats are left for Friday?
2. How many treats can Spot eat on Saturday?

10 – 1 = 9

Grade Level 1 — McGraw-Hill School Division

Chapter 4, Lesson 2 — Subtraction

NCTM Standards
- ✓ Problem Solving
- ✓ Communication
- ✓ Reasoning
- Connections

Lesson 4.2

DAY 1

Subtraction Sentences

OBJECTIVE Children complete a subtraction sentence.

Materials per child: 10 two-color counters

1 Motivate — Whole Class

Materials various classroom objects or counters; a box with a cover

Use the poem "Old Mother Hubbard" as the basis for subtraction story problems. Place a few objects or counters in a box to act as the cupboard. Tell a story such as:

Old Mother Hubbard found 6 cookies in the cupboard. She gave her nephew 2 cookies. How many cookies were left? *[4]*

Write 6 – 2 = 4 on the chalkboard and tell children that this is a *subtraction sentence.* Explain that when you take something away from something, you *subtract.*

Point out the sign between the 6 and the 2 and tell children that this is a *minus sign.* Read the sentence with children. *[6 minus 2 equals 4.]* Review the word *equals,* which means "the same as," and point out the *equal sign.*

You may wish to tell other "Old Mother Hubbard" stories about other materials.

2 Develop

Page 115

Help children relate crossing out pictures to taking away objects. Draw 5 circles on the chalkboard. Say:

Old Mother Hubbard has 5 cookies in her cupboard. She gives her friend 2 of the cookies.

Cross out 2 circles. Then ask:

- **Why did I cross out 2 circles?** *[to show that Mother Hubbard gave away 2 cookies]*
- **How many cookies are still in the cupboard?** *[3]*

Children use two-color counters to do each problem on the workmat at the top of page 115 before drawing, crossing out objects and writing the answer.

CRITICAL THINKING

After children complete the page, ask:

- **Can the parts be the same? Give an example.** *[Possible answer: Yes; 8 – 4 = 4.]*

Name ______________________

Subtraction Sentences

You need 10 counters.
Subtract.

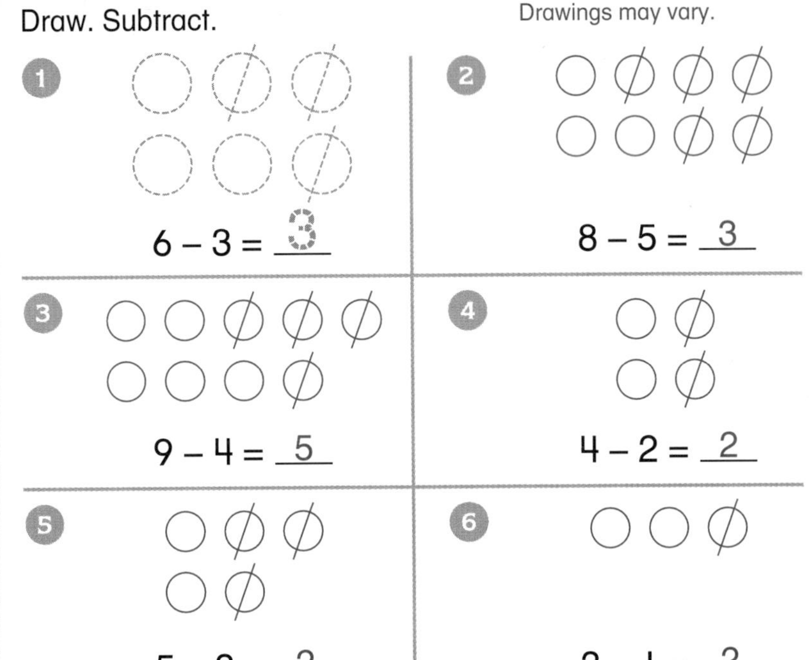

Draw. Subtract. — Drawings may vary.

1. 6 – 3 = 3
2. 8 – 5 = 3
3. 9 – 4 = 5
4. 4 – 2 = 2
5. 5 – 3 = 2
6. 3 – 1 = 2

MEETING INDIVIDUAL NEEDS

EARLY FINISHERS

Have children draw up to 9 objects, cross out some, and write the subtraction sentence.

EXTRA SUPPORT

Some children may record the number of crossed-out objects as the answer. Have them cover the crossed-out objects with one hand, then count and record the number of objects left over.

ONGOING ASSESSMENT

Observation Checklist
Observe children as they complete an exercise on page 116. Did they cross out the correct objects? Did they know what number to write?

Follow Up For children who are having difficulty, assign **Reteach 30.** Allow them to use counters to complete the exercises.

Have children who are recording correctly make up problems for the subtraction sentences on page 116. Then assign **Extend 30.**

Try These!

Find what is left in Mother Hubbard's cupboard.

$2 - 1 =$ 1

2 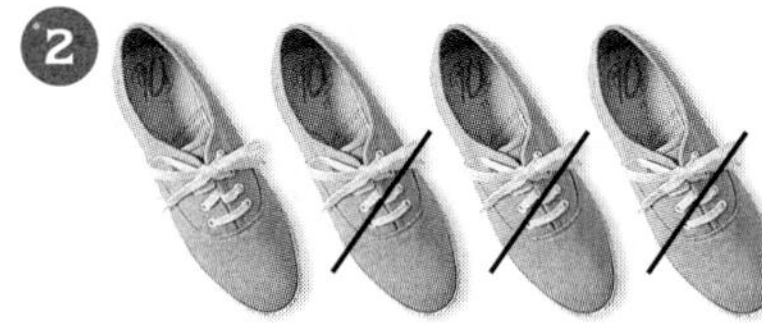

$4 - 3 =$ 1

3 

$6 - 2 =$ 4

4 

$7 - 5 =$ 2

5 

$8 - 4 =$ 4

6 

$9 - 3 =$ 6

Mixed Review

Add.

7 $5 + 1 =$ 6 $7 + 3 =$ 10 $6 + 2 =$ 8

8 $3 + 3 =$ 6 $8 + 2 =$ 10 $7 + 1 =$ 8

Your child has begun to subtract. Have your child tell you about the subtraction exercises on this page.

Page 116

Try These Discuss exercise 1, then assign practice exercises 2–6.

Mixed Review Children review addition facts from Chapter 3. Encourage children to count on to add.

3 Close

Check for Understanding Write 7 – 5 = ___ on the chalkboard. Draw a picture of 7 objects, and cross out 5 of them.

- **Tell how many are left. Then say the subtraction sentence with the answer.** *[2; 7– 5 = 2]*

Tomorrow children will write subtraction sentences.

PRACTICE • 30

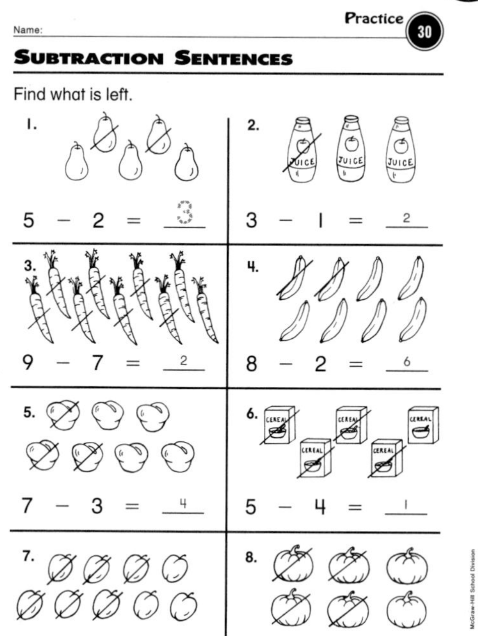

Name: Practice 30

SUBTRACTION SENTENCES

Find what is left.

1. 5 – 2 = 3
2. 3 – 1 = 2
3. 9 – 7 = 2
4. 8 – 2 = 6
5. 7 – 3 = 4
6. 5 – 4 = 1
7. 9 – 6 = 3
8. 6 – 4 = 2

RETEACH • 30

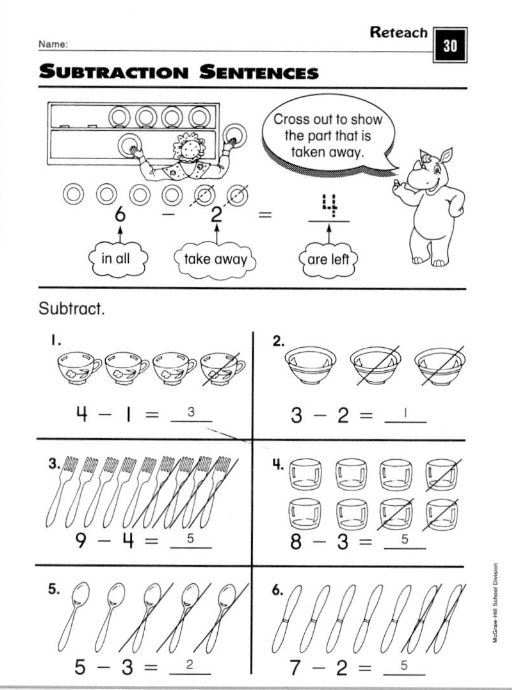

Name: Reteach 30

SUBTRACTION SENTENCES

Cross out to show the part that is taken away.

6 – 2 = 4

in all / take away / are left

Subtract.

1. 4 – 1 = 3
2. 3 – 2 = 1
3. 9 – 4 = 5
4. 8 – 3 = 5
5. 5 – 3 = 2
6. 7 – 2 = 5

EXTEND • 30

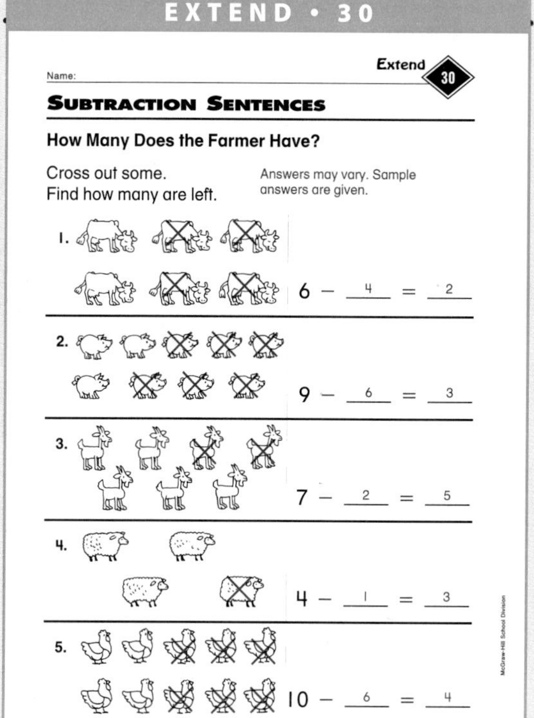

Name: Extend 30

SUBTRACTION SENTENCES

How Many Does the Farmer Have?

Cross out some. Find how many are left.

Answers may vary. Sample answers are given.

1. 6 – 4 = 2
2. 9 – 6 = 3
3. 7 – 2 = 5
4. 4 – 1 = 3
5. 10 – 6 = 4

More Subtraction Sentences

OBJECTIVE Children write a subtraction sentence.

Materials per child: have available 10 two-color counters

1 Motivate — Whole Class

Resources Jumbo Activity Book, page 6; Sticker sheet 4 (red counters); Sticker sheet 5 (numerals and symbols)

Use Jumbo Activity Book page 6 to demonstrate the following subtraction story:

There are 6 red beads in the jar. Billy Joe takes out 2 beads. How many beads are left in the jar? *[4]*

Then ask how a subtraction sentence is the same as an addition sentence and how it is different. *[Both sentences have an equal sign; a subtraction sentence starts with a total, has a minus sign, and I take away from the total; an addition sentence has a plus sign, and ends with a total because I add parts.]*

Have children help you fill in the blanks on Jumbo Activity Book page 6 to complete the subtraction sentence 6 – 2 = 4. Explain that 4 is the *difference,* or the amount that is left.

2 Develop

Page 117

Discuss the example at the top of the page, saying:

Old Mother Hubbard went to the cupboard and found 8 cups. She took out 2 cups. How many cups were left? *[6]*

Demonstrate writing a subtraction sentence for the models, if used, and then for the pictures. *[8 – 2 = 6]* Use the new vocabulary words throughout the lesson to reinforce the language of subtraction.

Critical Thinking

After children finish the page, ask:

- **Is it possible for the difference to be zero? Explain.** *[Possible answer: Yes; when you take away all the objects, like 4 – 4 = 0.]*

Page 118

Try These Assign practice exercises 1–8.

3 Close

Check for Understanding Draw 5 balloons on the chalkboard and cross out 4 of them. Tell children that there are 5 balloons, and 4 of them got away. Say:

- **Write a subtraction sentence about the balloons.** *[5 – 4 = 1]*

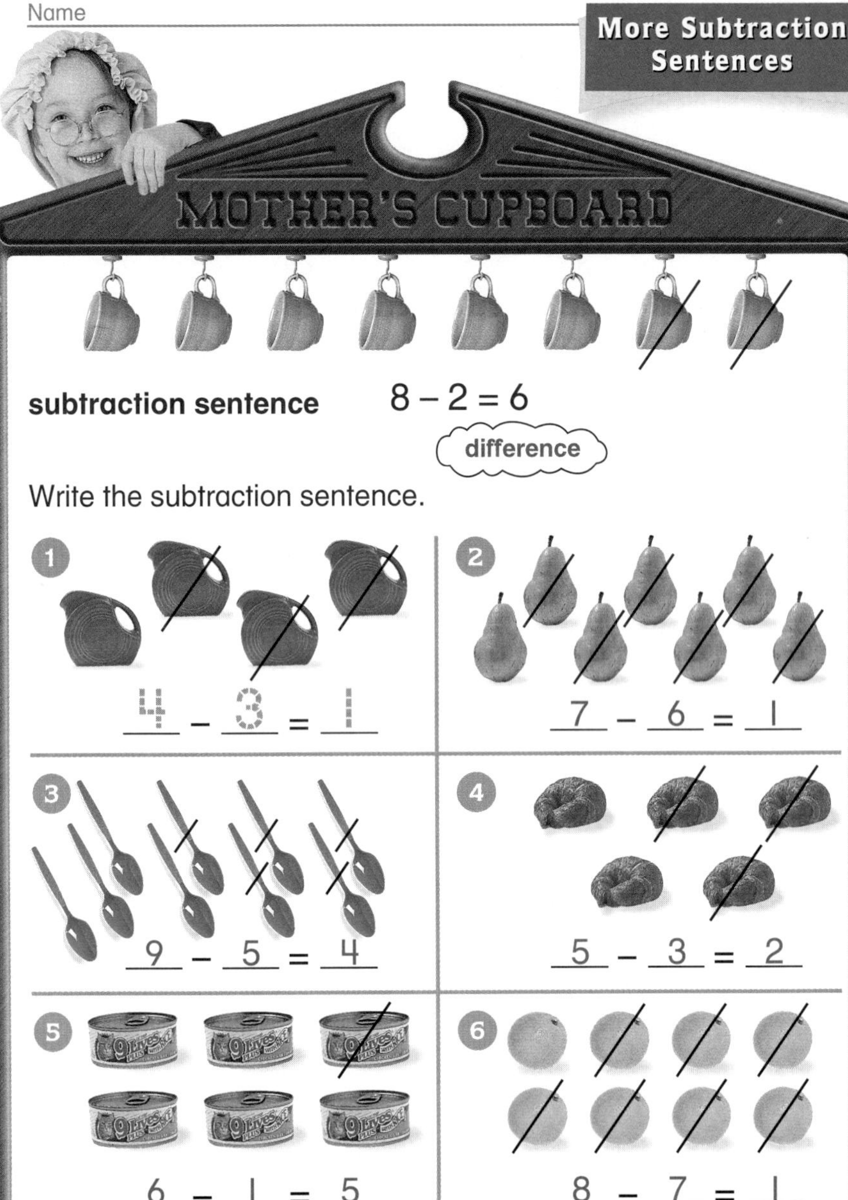

MEETING INDIVIDUAL NEEDS

STUDENTS ACQUIRING ENGLISH

Pair fluent English speakers with less-fluent children to help them do the page. Have pairs explain the words *subtract, minus,* and *equals* to each other.

GIFTED AND TALENTED

Have children write and illustrate subtraction sentences for the verses in the poem "Five Little Ducks."

ONGOING ASSESSMENT

Observation Checklist Observe how children write a subtraction sentence from page 117. The crossed-out objects should be the objects taken away.

Follow Up If children are having difficulty, pair them with partners who know how to write subtraction sentences before assigning **Reteach 31.**

For children who are writing correct subtraction sentences, assign **Extend 31.**

Try These!

Write the subtraction sentence.

1 

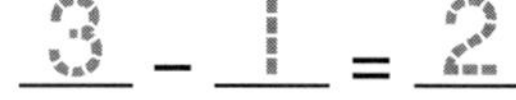

3 – 1 = 2

2 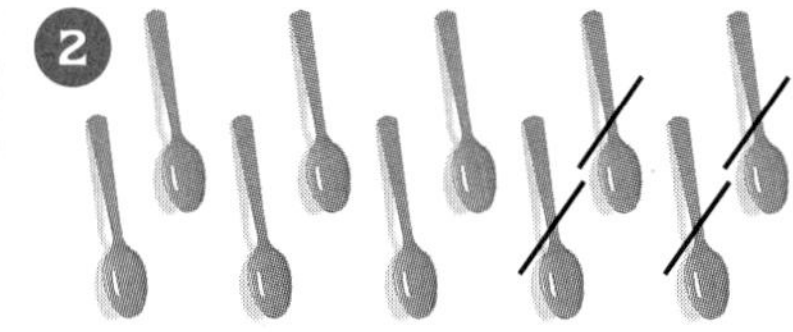

10 – 4 = 6

3 

6 – 2 = 4

4 

7 – 4 = 3

5 

2 – 1 = 1

6 

9 – 6 = 3

7 

5 – 4 = 1

8 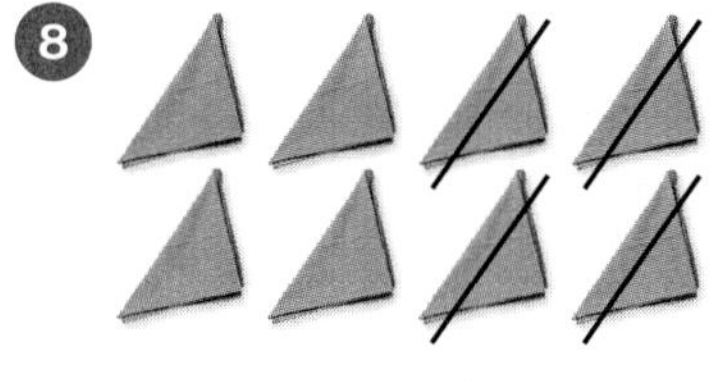

8 – 4 = 4

We are learning to write subtraction sentences. Have your child tell you about the exercises on this page.

Alternate Teaching Strategy

Materials per child: 8 connecting cubes in one color (red, blue, or yellow), 6 index cards

Prepare For each pair, make a set of subtraction cards for facts to 10, such as 5 – 2 = ___.

Have partners place subtraction fact cards facedown. One child turns over a card and makes a train showing the total number of cubes. The second child unsnaps the number of cubes to show which part is taken away.

Together, children write the other part and name the difference. Children switch roles and continue.

Cards may then be placed in a math center for all to use.

PRACTICE • 31

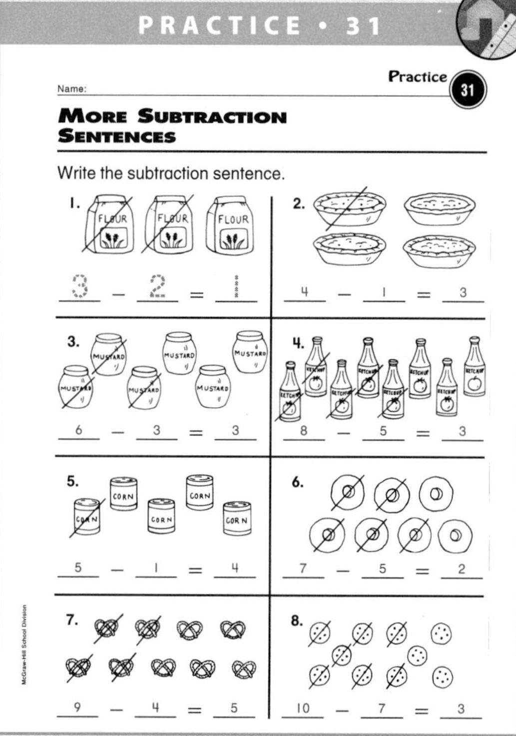

Practice 31

Name:

MORE SUBTRACTION SENTENCES

Write the subtraction sentence.

1. 3 – 2 = 1
2. 4 – 1 = 3
3. 6 – 3 = 3
4. 8 – 5 = 3
5. 5 – 1 = 4
6. 7 – 5 = 2
7. 9 – 4 = 5
8. 10 – 7 = 3

RETEACH • 31

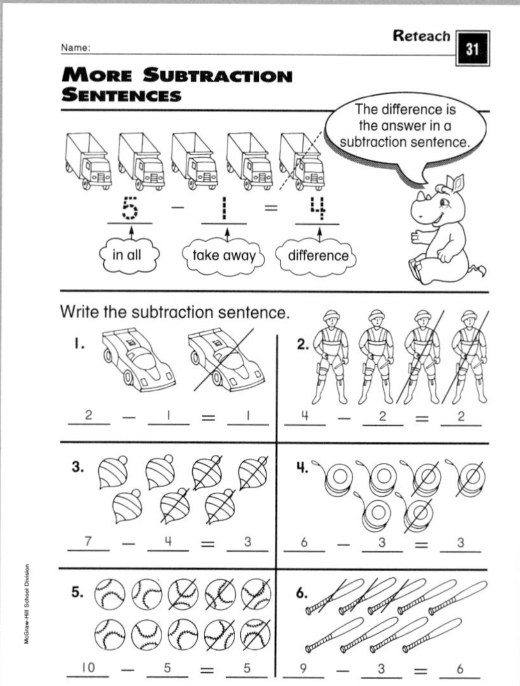

Reteach 31

Name:

MORE SUBTRACTION SENTENCES

5 – 1 = 4

in all / take away / difference

The difference is the answer in a subtraction sentence.

Write the subtraction sentence.

1. 2 – 1 = 1
2. 4 – 2 = 2
3. 7 – 4 = 3
4. 6 – 3 = 3
5. 10 – 5 = 5
6. 9 – 3 = 6

EXTEND • 31

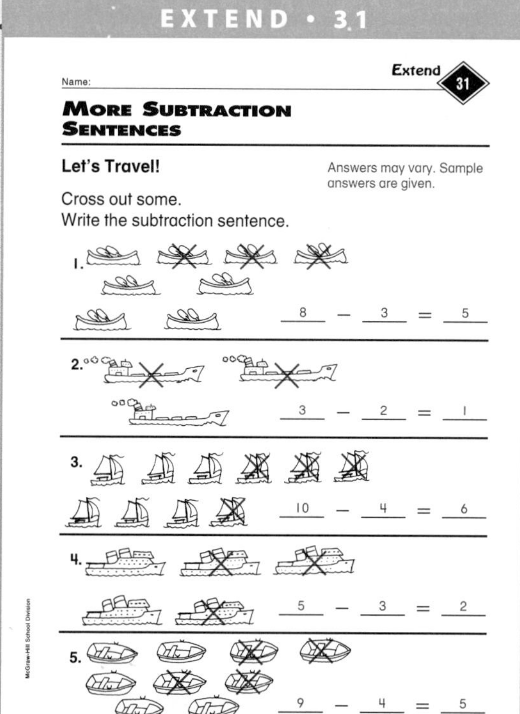

Extend 31

Name:

MORE SUBTRACTION SENTENCES

Let's Travel!

Answers may vary. Sample answers are given.

Cross out some.
Write the subtraction sentence.

1. 8 – 3 = 5
2. 3 – 2 = 1
3. 10 – 4 = 6
4. 5 – 3 = 2
5. 9 – 4 = 5

Problem-Solving Strategy: Write a Subtraction Sentence

OBJECTIVE Solve subtraction problems and write subtraction sentences to show the solutions.

Day 1 Problem-Solving Strategy: Write a Subtraction Sentence

RESOURCE REMINDER
Math Center Cards 24
Practice 32, Reteach 32, Extend 32

SKILLS TRACE

GRADE K	• Solve a subtraction problem by completing a subtraction sentence. *(Chapter 11)*
GRADE 1	• Solve a subtraction problem and write a subtraction sentence to show the solution.
GRADE 2	• Solve problems by writing a subtraction sentence. *(Chapter 1)*

LESSON RESOURCES

MANIPULATIVE WARM-UP

Cooperative Pairs **Auditory/Linguistic**

OBJECTIVE Explore using subtraction to solve problems.

Materials overhead projector; per pair: 10 counters

▶ Place 7 counters on the overhead projector and have children count them. Move 3 counters to one side. Write the number sentence 7 – 3 = 4 on the chalkboard.

▶ Ask a volunteer to tell a subtraction story about the display. If a child has difficulty interpreting the subtraction sentence, ask intermediate questions, such as:

- **What does the 7 tell you?** *[how many in all; total]*
- **What does the 3 tell you?** *[how many are taken away]*
- **What does the 4 tell you?** *[how many are left]*

▶ Give each pair of students 10 counters. Continue the activity, having partners use counters to show subtraction sentences and tell a subtraction story about each one.

7 - 3 = 4

CONNECTION ACTIVITY

Cooperative Pairs **Visual/Spatial**

OBJECTIVE Connect subtraction with art.

Resource Read-Aloud Anthology, pp. 1–3

Materials construction paper, crayons

▶ Read the story "How the Rhinoceros Got His Skin," found in the Read-Aloud Anthology. Discuss the situation that involves subtraction.

The Parsee made 1 cake. Strorks the rhino ate it. How many cakes were left? *[none, or zero]*

▶ Then make up other subtraction problems, such as:

The Parsee made 8 cakes. Strorks ate 2 of them. How many were left? *[6]*

▶ Have pairs of children work together to make up a subtraction story about the Parsee or Strorks, write the subtraction sentence, and illustrate it. Display childrens' pictures on a bulletin board decorated with palm trees.

DAILY MATH

PREVIOUS DAY QUICK REVIEW

Use counters. Subtract.

1. 4 – 1 *[3]*
2. 7 – 2 *[5]*
3. 6 – 3 *[3]*
4. 9 – 2 *[7]*

FAST FACTS

1. 5 + 2 *[7]*
2. 5 + 3 *[8]*
3. 6 + 2 *[9]*
4. 6 + 3 *[9]*

Problem of the Day • 24

Read aloud to children:

There are 10 ducks at the pond.
3 ducks swim away.
Then 1 duck comes back.
How many ducks are at the pond? *[8 ducks]*

TECH LINK

MATH VAN

Tool You may wish to use the Counters tool with this lesson.

MATH FORUM

Multi-Age Classes I have children who are ready to subtract larger numbers tell each other stories with numbers over 10. I encourage them to write subtraction sentences for the solutions.

Visit our Resource Village at http://www.mhschool.com to access the Math Forum.

MATH CENTER

Practice

OBJECTIVE Use part-part-whole to subtract and write a subtraction sentence.

Materials per child: box, 10 counters, Math Center Recording Sheet (TA 38 optional)

Children put 10 counters in a box and take a known number out. Since the whole and one part are known, they subtract to find the unknown part, the difference still in the bag. Then they write a subtraction sentence. *[Check that the number sentences are correct.]*

PRACTICE ACTIVITY 24 — MATH CENTER On Your Own

Logical Reasoning • How Many Were Taken Out?

YOU NEED: bag, 10 counters

- Put 10 counters in a bag. Take some out. How many did you take out?
- How many are left in the bag? Write a subtraction sentence to show what you did.
- Play 5 more times.

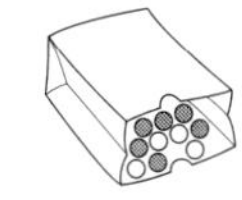

10 – ○○○○●● = 4

10 – 6 = 4

Grade Level 1 · McGraw-Hill School Division

Chapter 4, Lesson 3 — Subtraction

NCTM Standards
- Problem Solving
- ✓ Communication
- ✓ Reasoning
- ✓ Connections

Problem Solving

OBJECTIVE Write subtraction sentences to solve word problems.

Materials per child: 10 counters, Math Center Recording Sheet (TA 38 optional)

Children use counters to solve subtraction problems and write subtraction sentences to show the solutions. *[**1.** 7 – 2 = 5; **2.** 8 – 1 = 7; **3.** 10 – 3 = 7]*

PROBLEM-SOLVING ACTIVITY 24 — MATH CENTER On Your Own

Logical Reasoning • How Many Are Left?

YOU NEED: 10 counters

Solve. Use counters.
Write a subtraction sentence.

1. 7 children are at the lake. 2 leave. How many children are left?
2. 8 birds fly above the lake. 1 bird lands. How many birds are flying?
3. 10 boats are sailing. 3 stop. How many boats are sailing?

Grade Level 1 · McGraw-Hill School Division

Chapter 4, Lesson 3 — Subtraction

NCTM Standards
- ✓ Problem Solving
- Communication
- ✓ Reasoning
- Connections

Lesson 4.3

DAY 1

Problem-Solving Strategy: Write a Subtraction Sentence

OBJECTIVE Solve a subtraction problem and write a subtraction sentence to show the solution.

Materials per pair: 10 rhino counters; Workmat 1 (rhino environment)

1 Motivate — Cooperative Pairs

Materials per pair: 10 rhino counters; Workmat 1 (rhino environment)

Display 6 rhino counters on Workmat 1. Tell a rhino story:

There are 6 rhinos in a field. 2 rhinos walk away. How many rhinos are left? *[4]*

Write __ – __ = __ on the chalkboard. Retell the story as children act it out on their workmats. Ask a volunteer to write the subtraction sentence on the chalkboard. *[6 – 2 = 4]*

2 Develop

Page 119

Read aloud to children each word problem found on the reduced Student Book page in this Teacher's Edition. Children use the rhino counters in the workspace to solve each problem, and then write the answer in the blank. Have children write a subtraction sentence to show how they solved the problem.

Allow time to share the rhino stories. Have children take turns using rhino counters to act out their stories.

Critical Thinking

After children complete the first problem, ask:

- **What is another way to find the answers?** *[You can act out the problem or draw pictures.]*

Page 120

Try These Assign practice problems 1–3.

Suggest that children act out the subtraction situations.

More to Explore Discuss with children how these two problems are different from the subtraction stories above. *[You can't see how many are hiding.]* Ask how they found how many are hiding. *[Possible answer: I used counters and covered some until the number that showed matched the picture. Then I counted how many were covered.]*

3 Close

Check for Understanding by having children explain how they found the answer to one of the problems on page 120.

Name ____________

Problem-Solving Strategy

Read | Plan | Solve | Look Back

Write a Subtraction Sentence

You need 10 rhino counters.

"There are 9 rhinos at the river. Three rhinos walk away. How many rhinos are left?"

Listen to the problem.

1. At the river __6__ are left.

   __9__ – __3__ = __6__

Tell how you found the answer. I showed 9 counters and took 3 away—there are 6 left.

2. At the waterfall __3__ are left.

   "There are 8 rhinos at the waterfall. Five rhinos leave. How many rhinos are left?"

   __8__ – __5__ = __3__

3. At the game __8__ are left.

   "There are 10 rhinos watching the game. Two rhinos go home. How many rhinos are left at the game?"

   __10__ – __2__ = __8__

Make up a different problem about 10 rhinos. Possible problem: There are 10 rhinos on the team. Five rhinos quit. How many rhinos are left?

MEETING INDIVIDUAL NEEDS

EARLY FINISHERS

Working in pairs, children take turns telling a story and writing the subtraction sentence.

EXTRA SUPPORT

Some children may not write the answer in the correct blank in the number sentence. Remind them that the answer to the problem is the number that comes after the equal sign.

ONGOING ASSESSMENT

Observation Checklist Observe as children solve subtraction problems. Make notes on whether they can write the appropriate sentence.

Follow Up If children are having difficulty, have them use rhino counters on Jumbo Activity Book page 5 to solve new problems. Then assign **Reteach 32.**

For children who are recording correctly, assign **Extend 32.**

Try These!

Make up a problem for the picture.
Find how many are left.

1 

2 are left.

4 − 2 = 2

2 

5 are left.

6 − 1 = 5

3 

4 are left.

6 − 2 = 4

More to Explore — Number Sense

There are 5 sheep. How many are hiding? 3

There are 10 goats. How many are hiding? 4

Ask your child to tell you a subtraction story about the ballplayers in problem 3.

Alternate Teaching Strategy

Materials small box; per child: index card

Have each child write his or her name on an index card. Explain that children will use their name cards and the box to show subtraction stories. Tell this story:

4 children are in the park.
1 child leaves for school.
How many children are still in the park? *[3]*

Have children put their name cards into the box. To show that 1 child leaves for school, have a child take out one card. Ask another child to write the subtraction sentence on a sheet of paper.

Continue with other stories.

PRACTICE • 32

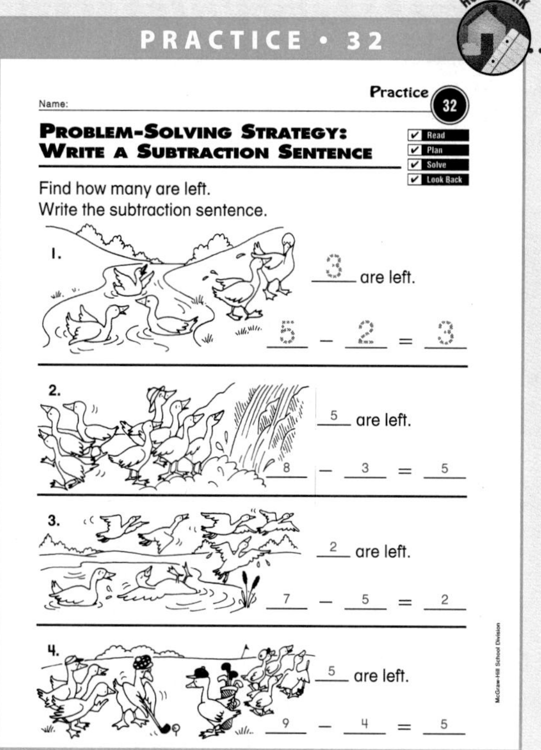

Name: Practice 32

PROBLEM-SOLVING STRATEGY: WRITE A SUBTRACTION SENTENCE Read / Plan / Solve / Look Back

Find how many are left.
Write the subtraction sentence.

1. 3 are left. 5 − 2 = 3
2. 5 are left. 8 − 3 = 5
3. 2 are left. 7 − 5 = 2
4. 5 are left. 9 − 4 = 5

McGraw-Hill School Division

RETEACH • 32

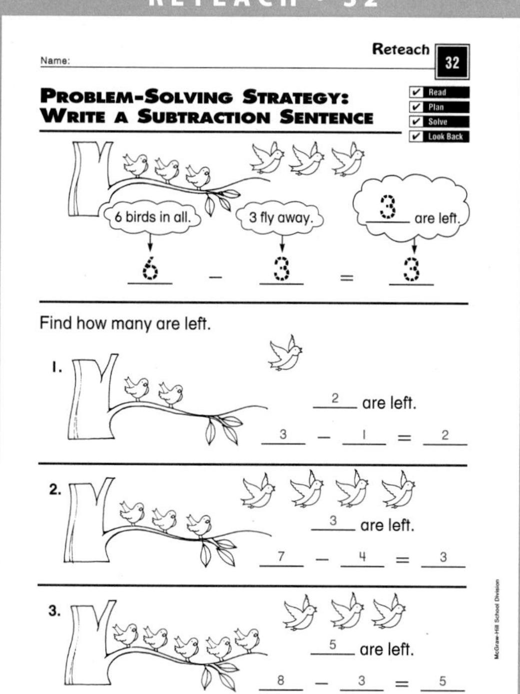

Name: Reteach 32

PROBLEM-SOLVING STRATEGY: WRITE A SUBTRACTION SENTENCE Read / Plan / Solve / Look Back

6 birds in all. 3 fly away. 3 are left.
6 − 3 = 3

Find how many are left.

1. 2 are left. 3 − 1 = 2
2. 3 are left. 7 − 4 = 3
3. 5 are left. 8 − 3 = 5

McGraw-Hill School Division

EXTEND • 32

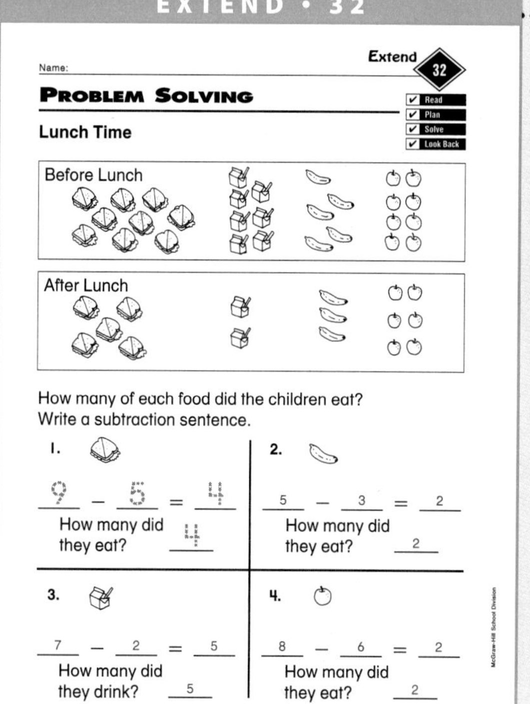

Name: Extend 32

PROBLEM SOLVING Read / Plan / Solve / Look Back

Lunch Time

Before Lunch

After Lunch

How many of each food did the children eat?
Write a subtraction sentence.

1. 9 − 5 = 4 How many did they eat? 4
2. 5 − 3 = 2 How many did they eat? 2
3. 7 − 2 = 5 How many did they drink? 5
4. 8 − 6 = 2 How many did they eat? 2

McGraw-Hill School Division

MIDCHAPTER REVIEW

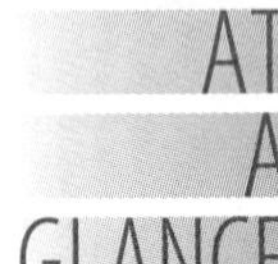

AT A GLANCE

PURPOSE Maintain and review the concepts, skills, and strategies that children have learned thus far in the chapter.

Materials rhino counters, two-color counters

Using the Midchapter Review

Page 121

Read aloud and explain the directions for the first problem on the page. Then read aloud the word problem found on the reduced student page in this Teacher's Edition. The Midchapter Review may be completed independently or by the class as a whole. Children may use rhino counters to help them solve the problems.

Have children draw a picture or cut and paste pictures from a magazine to show any subtraction sentence.

Vocabulary Review

Write the following on the chalkboard:

difference	**subtract**
equal sign	**subtraction sentence**
minus sign	

Ask for volunteers to explain, show, or act out the meanings of these words.

Name

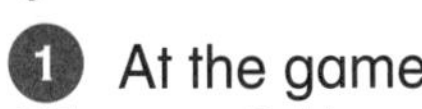

Find how many are left.

1 At the game 5 are left.

"There are 8 rhinos at the game. Three rhinos leave. How many rhinos are left?"

8 – 3 = 5

Subtract.

2 6 – 3 = 3

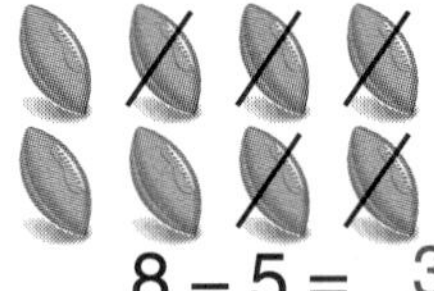

3 8 – 5 = 3

4 9 – 4 = 5

5 4 – 2 = 2

Write the subtraction sentence.

6 5 – 2 = 3

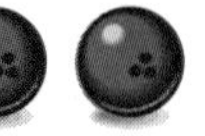

7 4 – 1 = 3

8 6 – 4 = 2

9 3 – 2 = 1

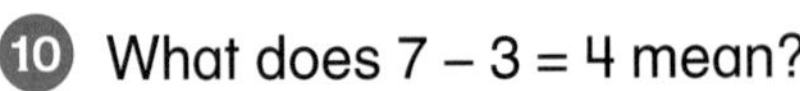

10 What does 7 – 3 = 4 mean?

Possible answer: There are 7 to start with, then 3 go away and 4 are left.

Draw a picture that shows subtraction. Children may draw pictures similar to those in the text.

Reinforcement and Remediation

CHAPTER OBJECTIVES	MIDCHAPTER REVIEW ITEMS	STUDENT BOOK PAGES	TEACHER'S EDITION PAGES		TEACHER RESOURCES
			Activities	Alternate Teaching Strategy	Reteach
*4A	1–10	113–118	112A, 114C	114, 118	29–31
*4B	1	119–120	118A	120	32

*4A Subtract, facts to 10

*4B Solve problems, including those that involve subtraction and writing a subtraction sentence

Extra Practice

Game !

Collect Them All

You need a 🎲.

Take turns.

- ▶ Roll the 🎲.
- ▶ Write the number you roll to show a difference.
- ▶ Fill the page.

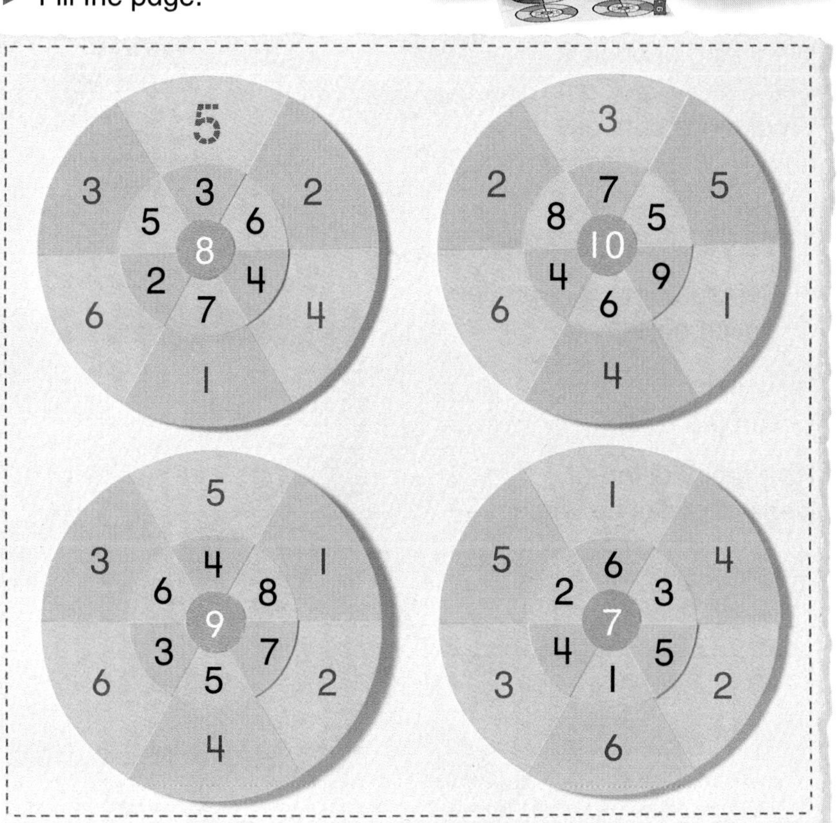

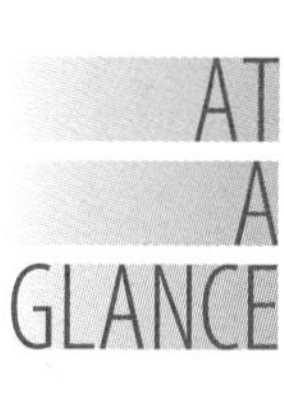

PURPOSE Provide an opportunity for review and practice.

Materials per pair: number cube (1-6); have available: rhino counters or two-color counters

Using the Extra Practice

Page 122

Two players play the game, but each player uses his or her own page. Point out that each subtraction wheel has a total in the middle and that one part is in the circle around the total. Tell children that they are to fill in the differences in the outside circles. Some children may need counters to find the differences between the total and that part at each turn.

Explain the rules: Roll the number cube. Write the number you rolled in any one of the subtraction wheels to show the correct difference. If you roll a number for which you cannot find a place, wait for your next turn.

After children finish playing, ask:

- **Do you think that you both had a chance to finish first? Explain.** *[The differences for each subtraction wheel are 1, 2, 3, 4, 5, and 6 to match the numbers on the cube; no one can roll a number that is not on the wheel.]*

Using the Additional Practice

The section below provides additional practice that you may want to write on the chalkboard or on a reproducible master.

ADDITIONAL PRACTICE

Subtract.

1. 6 – 5 = __ *[1]* 10 – 8 = __ *[2]*

2. 10 – 7 = __ *[3]* 9 – 5 = __ *[4]*

3. 10 – 5 = __ *[5]* 8 – 0 = __ *[8]*

4. 5 – 3 = __ *[2]* 7 – 2 = __ *[5]*

5. 9 – 3 = __ *[6]* 3 – 3 = __ *[0]*

6. 4 – 0 = __ *[4]* 6 – 6 = __ *[0]*

7. 8 – 7 = __ *[1]* 7 – 4 = __ *[3]*

8. 7 – 6 = __ *[1]* 8 – 4 = __ *[4]*

9. 10 – 8 = __ *[2]* 5 – 4 = __ *[1]*

10. 6 – 3 = __ *[3]* 8 – 6 = __ *[2]*

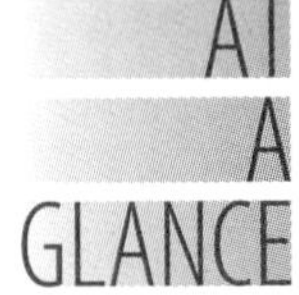

Applying Subtraction

OBJECTIVE Children use subtraction in a language arts context.

Resource Read-Aloud Anthology, pages 4–6: "The Great Ball Game"

Materials books from the classroom or school library

1 Engage

Discuss the theme of the chapter, "Folk Tales and Rhymes."

- **How are folk tales and other stories alike? How are they different?** *[Alike: Both are about make-believe things; different: folk tales are stories that were made up long ago by peoples around the world, and other stories are newer.]*

Discuss with children what they saw during trips to the school library and the town library. Talk about how the books were placed on the shelves.

- **Why do libraries sort the books into groups on the shelves?** *[Possible answer: to make it easier for people to find the kinds of books they want]*

2 Investigate — Cooperative Pairs

Page 123

Reread aloud to children "The Great Ball Game." Ask:

- **What other stories do you know about animals that talk and act like people?** *[Possible answers: stories about Peter Rabbit, Goldilocks and the Three Bears]*

Cultural Note Tell children that the story is a folk tale of the Muskogee, or Creek, Indian Nation, and that folk tales have always been very popular among Native Americans.

Working Together Using the Partners Check Strategy, have partners take turns putting books into categories. Partners correct or appreciate each other's work. You may want to give each pair a certain number of books to sort.

Pairs choose the categories for sorting. Discuss the methods of recording the sortings—drawings, tally charts, tables with pictures or words, and so on. Have children compare the numbers of books in each group. Ask questions such as:

- **Do you have more sports books or more animal books? How many more?**

3 Reflect and Share

Page 124

After pairs have sorted their books let them share their results with the class.

Write a Report Encourage children to report how many kinds of books were in each group and to compare the numbers.

Name ____________________

Books and More Books

Listen to *The Great Ball Game.*

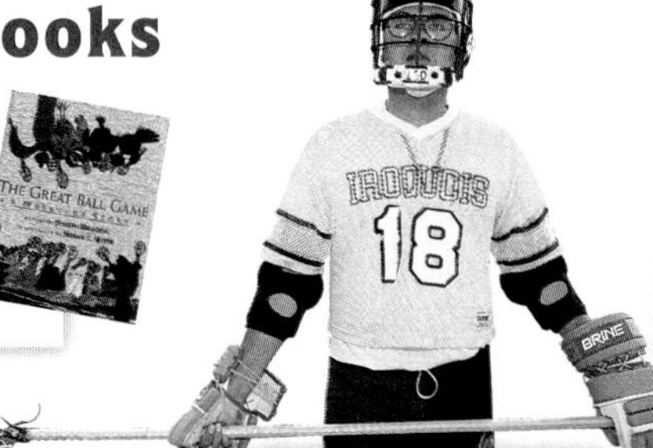

What kind of book is *The Great Ball Game*? a folktale

What kinds of books do you have in your classroom library?
Possible answers: sports books, animal books, picture books

Cultural Note
Ball games have been played by Native Americans for centuries.

Working Together

- Sort some books from the classroom library.
- Decide how you want to sort the books.

How many different kinds of books do you have?

Answers may vary.

Show how you sorted.

MORE TO INVESTIGATE

Predict Sample answer: Our classmates like books about animals best.

Explore To manage the survey, you may wish to have one member from each group survey five or six children.

Find After groups have shared what they found, combine the results in a tally chart on the chalkboard. Ask:

- **Which kind of book got the most votes?**
- **How many more votes did [sports] books get than [fairy tale] books?**

Bibliography Children may enjoy reading the following books:

Arthur Writes a Story by Marc Brown. Boston: Little Brown, 1996. ISBN 0-316-10916-9.

Check It Out: The Book About Libraries by Gail Gibbons. San Diego, CA: Harcourt Brace, & Company, 1985. ISBN 0-15-216400-6.

Decision Making

Answers may vary. See Teacher's Edition for sample of children's work.

Choose another way to sort the books.

Show how you sorted.

1. How many kinds of books do you have now?

___

2. Do you have more or fewer kinds of books?

___

Write a report.

3. Show what you found.

4. Tell how you sorted the books each time.

More to Investigate

See Teacher's Edition.

PREDICT What kinds of book do your classmates like best?

EXPLORE Take a survey.

FIND What kind of book is the most popular book on your survey?

BUILDING A PORTFOLIO

This assignment will provide information about children's ability to sort and re-sort objects and to use counting and subtraction to interpret results of sortings.

Allow children to revise their work for the portfolio. Each child's portfolio piece should consist of her or his written report and any notes you made about the child's work.

You may wish to use the Holistic Scoring Guide to assess this task. See page 27 in Teacher's Assessment Resources.

Children's Work

My table sorted books. We had a little bet trobbl decideing. We finley decided to sort by "I can read" books and not "I can read books. We had two sets. Then we had to sort agin! The next time we had to sort books but it had to be more then two sets. We decided to sort by Anumuls, peple, and peple and Anumuls. We had three sets. Peple had the least.

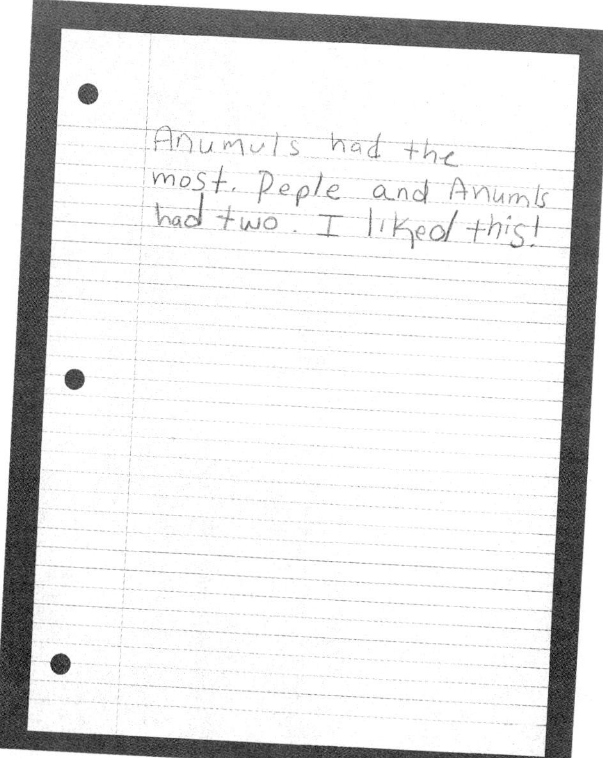

Anumuls had the most. Peple and Anumls had two. I liked this!

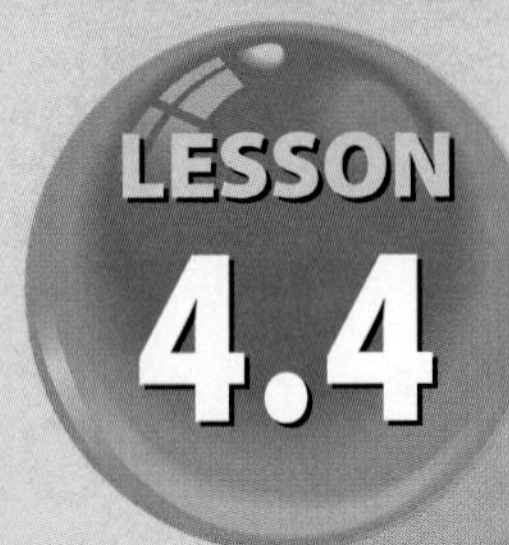

LESSON 4.4

Subtraction Fact Pairs

OBJECTIVES Subtract money amounts; subtract all or zero.

Day 1 Subtraction Fact Pairs

RESOURCE REMINDER
Math Center Cards 25
Practice 33, Reteach 33, Extend 33

SKILLS TRACE	
GRADE K	• Explore completing or writing a subtraction sentence. *(Chapter 9)*
GRADE 1	• Subtract money amounts. • Subtract all or zero.
GRADE 2	• Subtract money amounts. *(Chapter 8)*

LESSON RESOURCES

WARM-UP

Whole Class — **Social**

OBJECTIVE Explore the concept of subtracting all or none.

▶ Have 4 children stand at the front of the room. Then tell all of them to go to the door. Ask:

- **How many children are still at the front of the room?** *[none, or zero]*
- **How did you know how many were supposed to go to the door?** *[All means "the total number of children."]*

▶ Next, ask 4 children to stand at the front of the room. Say:
Four children are standing at the chalkboard. None of them sit down. How many children are still at the chalkboard? *[all, or 4]*

▶ Ask children how they knew how many didn't sit down even though you didn't say a number. *[None means "no children."]* Write the number sentences on the board. Have children tell other "all" or "none" stories and act them out.

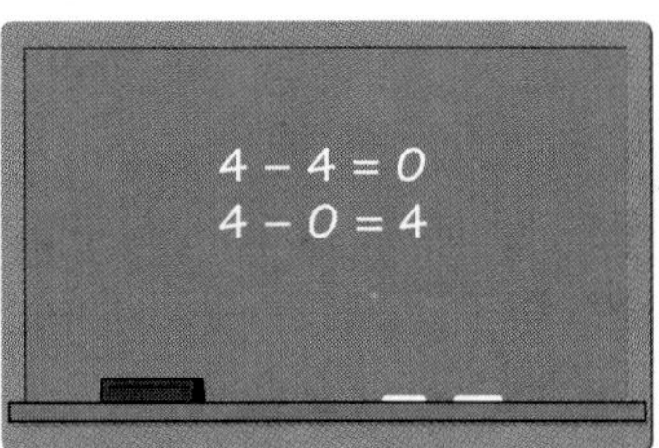

CONNECTION ACTIVITY

Cooperative Pairs — **Kinesthetic**

OBJECTIVE Connect the concept of subtraction with buying and selling.

Materials per pair: price tags (TA 12), 5 pennies, 5 small classroom objects, paper, pencil, tape

Prepare Label price tags 1¢, 2¢, 3¢, 4¢, 5¢. Tape one to each object.

▶ Pairs take turns being the buyer and the seller. The buyer chooses an object, gives its price to the seller, and tells how much is left.

▶ The seller writes a subtraction sentence on a piece of paper that shows what was just bought and gives it to the buyer. The buyer and seller must agree on the amount paid and the amount left over, as well as on the subtraction sentence.

▶ Pairs continue until all 5 objects have been "bought" and "sold."

DAILY MATH

PREVIOUS DAY QUICK REVIEW

Draw. Subtract.

1. 4 – 1 = ___ *[3]*
2. 5 – 2 = ___ *[3]*
3. 3 – 0 = ___ *[3]*
4. 8 – 5 = ___ *[3]*

FAST FACTS

1. 3 + 3 *[6]*
2. 4 + 3 *[7]*
3. 5 + 3 *[8]*
4. 6 + 3 *[9]*

Problem of the Day • 25

Read aloud to children.

Jill and Ben each have 4 crayons.
How many crayons do Jill and Ben have in all?
[8]

TECH LINK

MATH VAN

Tool You may wish to use the Money Models tool with this lesson.

MATH FORUM

Idea I reinforce subtraction vocabulary by asking children to read the subtraction sentences aloud to themselves after completing each problem.

Visit our Resource Village at http://www.mhschool.com to access the Math Forum.

MATH CENTER

Practice

OBJECTIVE Write related subtraction sentences.

Materials per child: ten 3" x 5" index cards, 10 pennies, blank spinner (TA 7), Math Center Recording Sheet (TA 38 optional)

Prepare Write 6¢ on each of 10 cards. Label the spinner 1¢, 2¢, 3¢, 4¢, 5¢.

Children spin for a number to subtract from a total on a card. They write the subtraction sentence. They can use pennies if they need help.

PRACTICE ACTIVITY 25 — MATH CENTER On Your Own

Game • Penny Sense

Take turns.

- Pick a number card.
- Spin for a number. Subtract that number.
- Use pennies to help you.
- Write the subtraction sentence.

Play until you use all the number cards.

YOU NEED: number cards; 10 (pennies)

8¢ – 2¢ = 6¢

Grade Level 1 · McGraw-Hill School Division

Chapter 4, Lesson 4 — Subtraction

NCTM Standards
- Problem Solving
- ✓ Communication
- ✓ Reasoning
- ✓ Connections

Problem Solving

OBJECTIVE Find and write subtraction fact pairs.

Materials per child: number cards (TA 9), 9 counters, Math Center Recording Sheet (TA 38 optional)

Prepare Cut out cards for 0, 0, 3, 3, 3, 3, 4, 5, and 9.

Through a process of elimination, children find and write possible subtraction sentences, using a given assortment of numerals. The sentences will be related subtraction sentences. *[Order of answers may vary. 9 – 5 = 4, 3 – 3 = 0, 3 – 0 = 3.]*

PROBLEM-SOLVING ACTIVITY 25 — MATH CENTER On Your Own

Logical Reasoning • Fix the Table

Sue made a subtraction table.
It shows subtraction sentences.
The table fell on the floor.
The numbers got mixed up.
Solve.
Write 4 different subtraction sentences.

YOU NEED: number cards; 9 (counters)

9	–	4	=	5
	–		=	
	–		=	
	–		=	

3 3 4 9 0 3 3 5 0

Grade Level 1 · McGraw-Hill School Division

Chapter 4, Lesson 4 — Subtraction

NCTM Standards
- ✓ Problem Solving
- Communication
- ✓ Reasoning
- Connections

DAY 1

Subtraction Fact Pairs

OBJECTIVE Children subtract money amounts; subtract with related fact pairs.

Materials per child: 10 pennies or play pennies

1 Motivate — Whole Class

Materials per child: 10 pennies or play pennies, 2 pieces of paper

On the chalkboard draw a piggy bank with 3 pennies in it. Have children place 3 pennies on one piece of paper. Tell children to move 2 pennies off the paper as you cross out 2 pennies on the chalkboard. Ask how many pennies are left. *[1]* Write the subtraction sentence 3¢ −2¢ = 1¢ under the piggy bank. Have children write the subtraction sentence on their papers.

Repeat with 3¢ − 1¢ = 2¢. Ask:

- **How are these two subtraction sentences alike? How are they different?** *[Possible answers: They have the same numbers; the numbers that stand for the parts are in different places.]*

2 Develop

Page 125

Discuss how the amounts in the piggy banks and the number sentences in exercises 1 and 2 are the same and how they are different. Then discuss the Talk question. Children should use pennies to find the answers to exercises 3–6.

Critical Thinking

After children answer the question on the page, ask:

- **Can you take 3 pennies away from 2 pennies? Explain.** *[No; I cannot take away more than I have.]*

Page 126

Try These Assign practice exercises 1–7.

Children may use pennies to find the answers.

Mixed Review Children review counting backward, learned in Chapter 1.

3 Close

Check for Understanding by writing 5 − 1 = 4 on the chalkboard and asking:

- **What is another subtraction sentence that uses the same numbers?** *[5 − 4 = 1]*

Name ____________________

Subtraction Fact Pairs

Find how many cents are left.

1. 4¢ − 3¢ = __1__ ¢
2. 4¢ − 1¢ = __3__ ¢

How are the parts different? When you take 3¢ away you have 1¢ left, but when you take away 1¢ you have 3¢ left.

3. 

5¢ − 0¢ = __5__ ¢

4. 

5¢ − 5¢ = __0__ ¢

5. 

7¢ − 2¢ = __5__ ¢

6. 

7¢ − 5¢ = __2__ ¢

What happens when you subtract 0¢? The number (part) left is the same as the number you started with.

MEETING INDIVIDUAL NEEDS

EARLY FINISHERS

Have children use pennies to show all the related facts for 10¢. Have them record the facts in their journals.

EXTRA SUPPORT

Children may confuse subtracting all and subtracting none. Have them use counters to act out each subtraction problem and then describe the process orally.

ONGOING ASSESSMENT

Observation Checklist
Observe if children understand subtracting zero as they do page 126.

Follow Up Allow children who are having difficulty to work more problems with pennies before assigning **Reteach 33.**

Have children who understand the lesson work in pairs to play store and subtract with pennies. Then assign **Extend 33.**

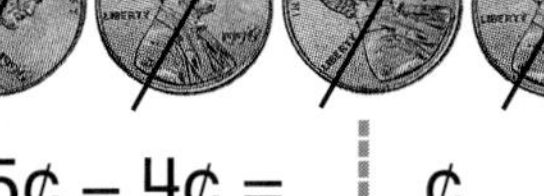
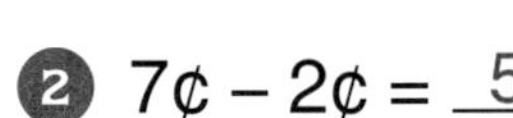

Try These!

Subtract.

1. 5¢ – 4¢ = 1 ¢

2. 7¢ – 2¢ = 5 ¢ 7¢ – 5¢ = 2 ¢	3. 3¢ – 0¢ = 3 ¢ 3¢ – 3¢ = 0 ¢
4. 9¢ – 8¢ = 1 ¢ 9¢ – 1¢ = 8 ¢	5. 6¢ – 2¢ = 4 ¢ 6¢ – 4¢ = 2 ¢
6. 8¢ – 8¢ = 0 ¢ 8¢ – 0¢ = 8 ¢	7. 10¢ – 9¢ = 1 ¢ 10¢ – 1¢ = 9 ¢

Mixed Review

Count backward.

8. 7, 6, 5, 4
9. 9, 8, 7, 6
10. 5, 4, 3, 2
11. 6, 5, 4, 3
12. 3, 2, 1, 0
13. 8, 7, 6, 5

At Home: Ask your child to show you how to subtract zero pennies.

Alternate Teaching Strategy

Materials per child: 8 counters

Have a volunteer show 5 counters, and another volunteer take away 2 counters. Discuss how many counters there were, how many counters were taken away, and how many are left.

Write the subtraction sentence, 5 – 2 = 3, on the chalkboard.

Repeat the procedure for 5 – 3 = 2. Compare the examples and the subtraction sentences. Ask:

- **How are the subtraction sentences the same?** *[Possible answer: They have the same total and parts.]*
- **How are the subtraction sentences different?** *[Possible answer: The part you take away and the part that is left change places.]*

Have each child use counters to act out a pair of related subtraction facts for 6, 7, and 8. Then have children write the related subtraction sentences in their journals.

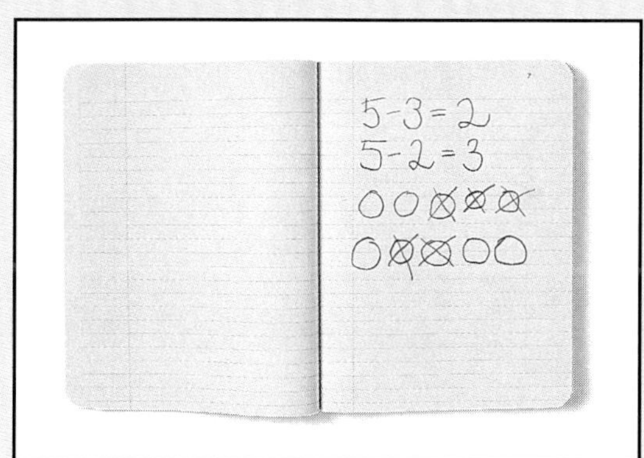

PRACTICE • 33

Practice 33

Name:

SUBTRACTION FACT PAIRS

Subtract.

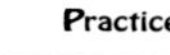

1. 6¢ – 5¢ = 1 ¢

2. 3¢ – 2¢ = 1 ¢ 3¢ – 1¢ = 2 ¢	3. 5¢ – 0¢ = 5 ¢ 5¢ – 5¢ = 0 ¢
4. 9¢ – 7¢ = 2 ¢ 9¢ – 2¢ = 7 ¢	5. 7¢ – 4¢ = 3 ¢ 7¢ – 3¢ = 4 ¢
6. 8¢ – 7¢ = 1 ¢ 8¢ – 1¢ = 7 ¢	7. 4¢ – 3¢ = 1 ¢ 4¢ – 1¢ = 3 ¢
8. 9¢ – 3¢ = 6 ¢ 9¢ – 6¢ = 3 ¢	9. 8¢ – 6¢ = 2 ¢ 8¢ – 2¢ = 6 ¢

RETEACH • 33

Reteach 33

Name:

SUBTRACTION FACT PAIRS

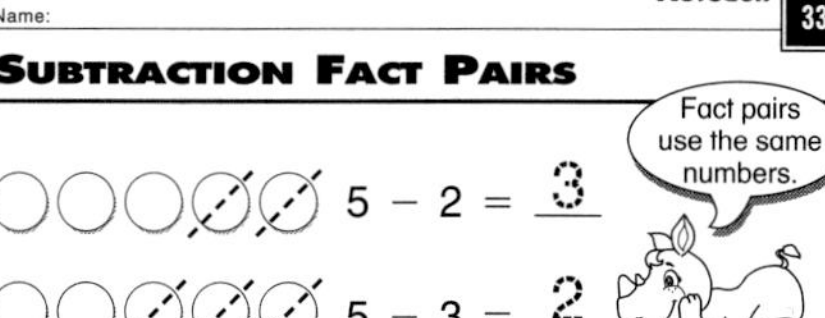

Subtract.

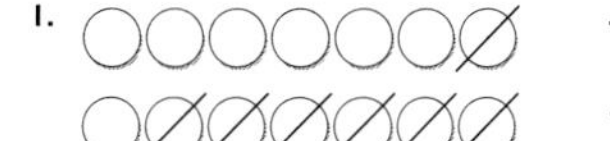

1. 7 – 1 = 6
7 – 6 = 1

2. 8 – 3 = 5
8 – 5 = 3

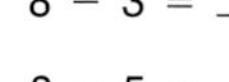

3. 4 – 4 = 0
4 – 0 = 4

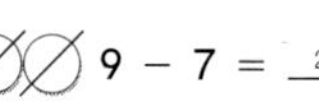

4. 9 – 7 = 2
9 – 2 = 7

EXTEND • 33

Extend 33

Name:

SUBTRACTION FACT PAIRS

Shopping Patterns

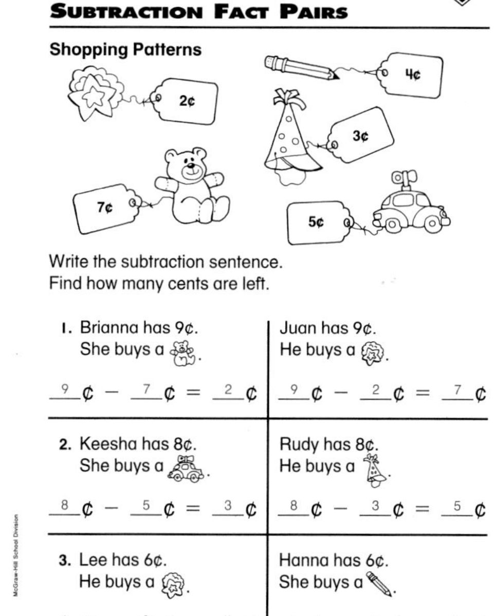

Write the subtraction sentence.
Find how many cents are left.

1. Brianna has 9¢. She buys a [bear]. 9 ¢ – 7 ¢ = 2 ¢	Juan has 9¢. He buys a [flower]. 9 ¢ – 2 ¢ = 7 ¢
2. Keesha has 8¢. She buys a [car]. 8 ¢ – 5 ¢ = 3 ¢	Rudy has 8¢. He buys a [hat]. 8 ¢ – 3 ¢ = 5 ¢
3. Lee has 6¢. He buys a [flower]. 6 ¢ – 2 ¢ = 4 ¢	Hanna has 6¢. She buys a [pencil]. 6 ¢ – 4 ¢ = 2 ¢

Count Back

OBJECTIVE Using a counting-back strategy to subtract.

Day 1 Counting Back

Day 2 More Counting Back

RESOURCE REMINDER
Math Center Cards 26
Practice 34–35, Reteach 34–35, Extend 34–35

SKILLS TRACE	
GRADE K	• Introduced at Grade 1.
GRADE 1	• Use a counting-back strategy to subtract.
GRADE 2	• Use counting-back and related facts to find differences to 12. *(Chapter 1)*

LESSON RESOURCES

MANIPULATIVE WARM-UP

Cooperative Pairs — **Kinesthetic**

OBJECTIVE Explore the counting-back strategy to subtract.

Materials per pair: blank number cube, 10 connecting cubes

Prepare Label the sides of each number cube 1, 2, and 3.

▶ Display 10 connecting cubes. Demonstrate tossing the number cube and counting back while you remove that number of cubes. Ask:

- **How would I count back 2?** *[10, then 9, 8]*
- **How many cubes are left?** *[8]*

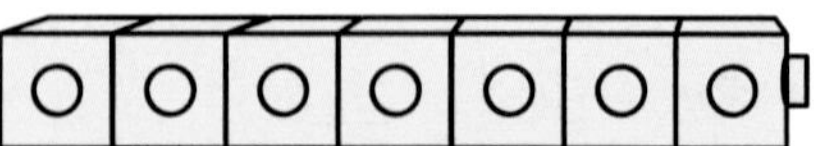

▶ Have partners make a train of 10 cubes. Children take turns rolling the number cube and counting back until they have no cubes left. Remind children to say the number of cubes they start with, count back, and say the number of remaining cubes.

CONNECTION ACTIVITY

Cooperative Pairs — **Logical/Analytical**

OBJECTIVE Connect the counting-back strategy to subtracting with mental math.

Materials per child: 10 pennies, paper cup; per pair: blank spinner (TA 8), pictures of items for sale.

Prepare Label a six-part spinner 1¢, 1¢, 2¢, 2¢, 3¢, 3¢. Cut out a selection of items from a magazine or catalog, and label them 1¢, 2¢, or 3¢.

▶ The first child spins the spinner and buys any item for that amount by taking that number of pennies from his or her cup. The child counts back while removing the pennies and then says the appropriate subtraction fact.

▶ The second child does the same. If a player spins a number but doesn't have that many pennies left, play passes to the other player. Partners continue until one child has no pennies left.

DAILY MATH

PREVIOUS DAY QUICK REVIEW

Use counters. Subtract.

1. 6 − 1 *[5]*
2. 5 − 1 *[4]*
3. 4 − 1 *[3]*
4. 3 − 1 *[2]*

FAST FACTS

1. 5 + 2 *[7]*
2. 6 + 2 *[8]*
3. 7 + 2 *[9]*
4. 8 + 2 *[10]*

Problem of the Day • 26

Read aloud to children:

There are 4 children and 5 oranges. How many more oranges are there than children? *[1 more]*

TECH LINK

MATH VAN

Tool You may wish to use the Counters tool with this lesson.

MATH FORUM

Multi-Age Class I have children who are able use the counting-back strategy to count back by 10s.

Visit our Resource Village at http://www.mhschool.com to access the Math Forum.

MATH CENTER

Practice

OBJECTIVE Count back to subtract.

Materials per child: blank number cube (TA 31), 10 counters, Math Center Recording Sheet (TA 38 optional)

Prepare Make a number cube and label it 1, 1, 2, 2, 3, 3.

Children put counters in a bag and count back as they subtract the numbers they rolled by removing counters from the bag. Then they write the subtraction sentences.

PRACTICE ACTIVITY 26 — MATH CENTER On Your Own

Number Sense • Cubes Away!

YOU NEED: 10 counters, number cube

- Take 4 or more counters and make a line. Count the counters.
- Roll the number cube.
- Take that many counters away from the line. Count back to subtract.
- Write the subtraction sentence.

Play 4 more times.

6 − 2 = 4

Chapter 4, Lesson 5 — Subtraction

NCTM Standards
- Problem Solving
- Communication
- ✓ Reasoning
- Connections

Problem Solving

OBJECTIVE Subtract by counting back 1, 2, or 3.

Materials 3–7 spinner (TA 7), blank number cube (TA 31), Math Center Recording Sheet (TA 38 optional)

Prepare Label a blank number cube 1, 1, 2, 2, 3, 3. On a blank spinner, write 3, 4, 5, 6, 7.

Children spin to move up and roll to move down on a ladder used as a number line. *[Answers may vary.]*

PROBLEM-SOLVING ACTIVITY 26 — MATH CENTER On Your Own

Logical Reasoning • Clem the Clown

YOU NEED: spinner, number cube, counter

Help Clem get to 10 at the top of the ladder.

- Write a subtraction sentence for each move.
- Put your counter on 0. Spin for a number. Move your counter up the ladder that many steps.
- Roll the number cube. Move down the ladder that many steps.

Play until you get to 10.

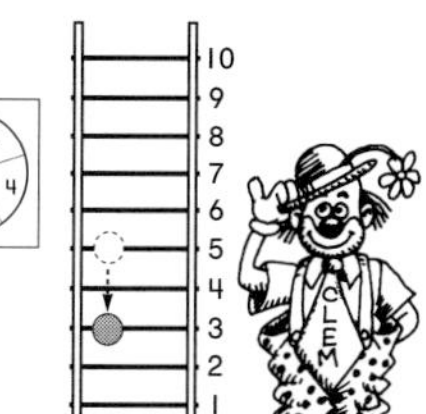

5 − 2 = 3

Chapter 4, Lesson 5 — Subtraction

NCTM Standards
- ✓ Problem Solving
- ✓ Communication
- ✓ Reasoning
- ✓ Connections

Lesson 4.5

DAY 1

Counting Back

OBJECTIVE Children use models to count back 1, 2, or 3 to subtract.

Materials per child: 10 two-color counters or beans

1 Motivate — Whole Class

Materials number cards for 5–10 (TA 9)

Show children a number card and count back with them from the number by ones.

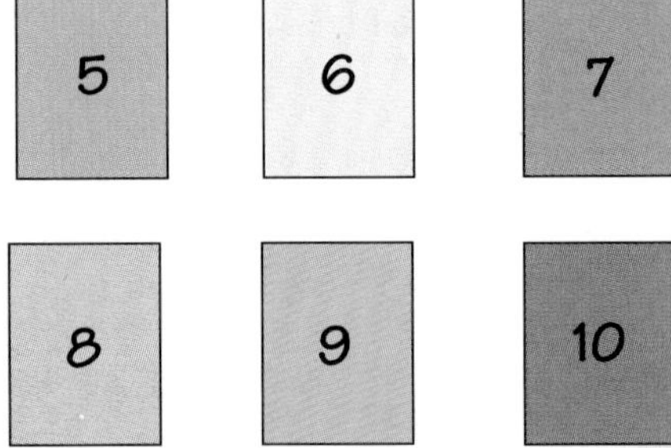

Choose another card and ask a volunteer to count back from that number. If the child counts back correctly, he or she then chooses a card and the next person to count back.

2 Develop

Page 127

Demonstrate the example at the top of the page, putting 7 counters (or beans) in a bag. Have children count back as you remove the counters (or beans). Have volunteers do several sample exercises, such as 7 − 1 and 9 − 3. Ask:

- **How do you know how many beans are left in the bag?** *[When I count back, the last number that I count is the same as the number of beans left in the bag.]*

CRITICAL THINKING
After children answer the question on the page, ask:

- **How can you check your answer when you count back to subtract?** *[Possible answer: Count up from the difference—for 6 − 2 = 4, start at 4, and count on 5, 6.]*

Page 128

Try These Assign practice exercises 1–7.

Children may use counters to show the problem and to help them count back.

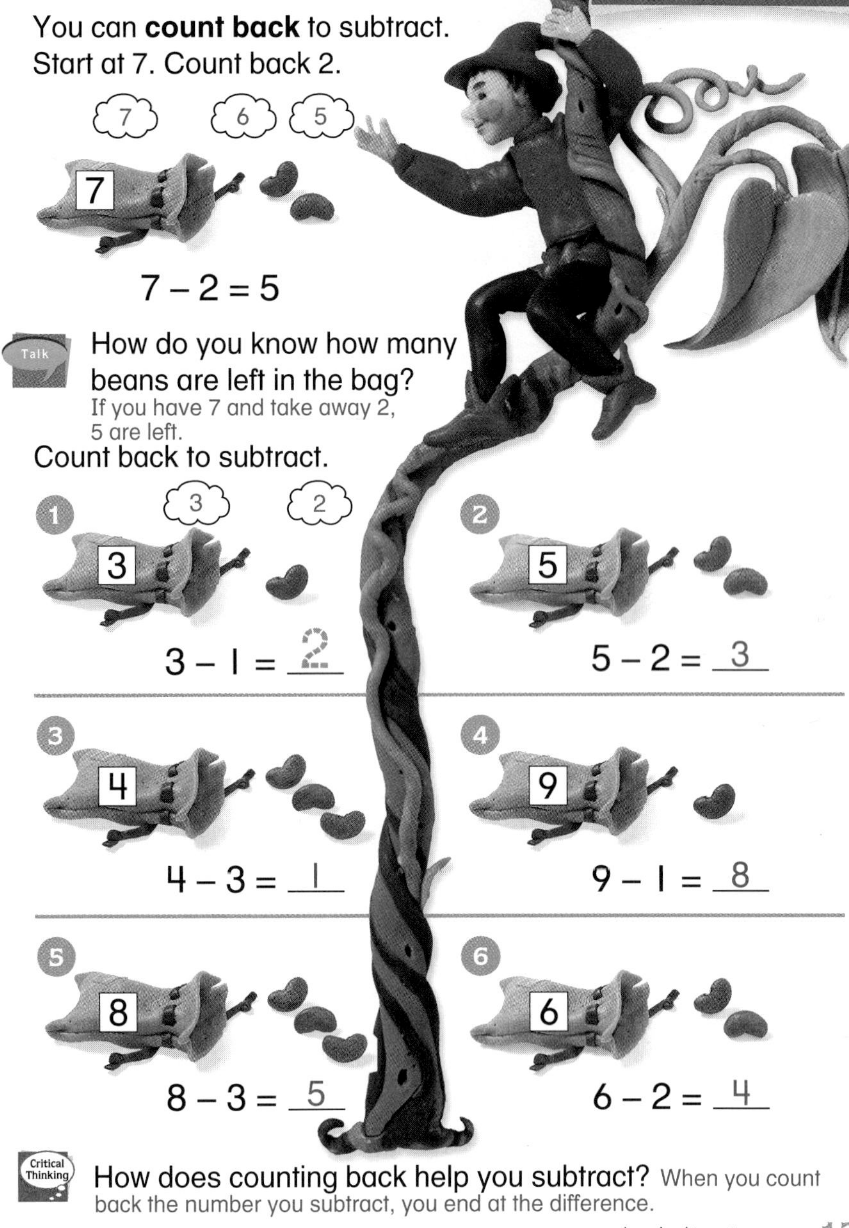

Name

Counting Back

You can **count back** to subtract.
Start at 7. Count back 2.

7 6 5

7

7 − 2 = 5

Talk: How do you know how many beans are left in the bag? If you have 7 and take away 2, 5 are left.

Count back to subtract.

1. 3 (3, 2) 3 − 1 = 2
2. 5 — 5 − 2 = 3
3. 4 — 4 − 3 = 1
4. 9 — 9 − 1 = 8
5. 8 — 8 − 3 = 5
6. 6 — 6 − 2 = 4

Critical Thinking: How does counting back help you subtract? When you count back the number you subtract, you end at the difference.

CHAPTER 4 *Lesson 5* — one hundred twenty-seven • 127

MEETING INDIVIDUAL NEEDS

COMMON ERROR

Some children may start counting back from the total amount. For example, for 5 − 2 = ___, the child may count back "5, 4" instead of "4, 3." Have the child say, "5; count back, 4, 3."

INCLUSION

Have children line up counters in a row and then count aloud to find each difference. These visual and auditory cues may help children internalize the concept.

ONGOING ASSESSMENT

Interview Determine if children can count back to subtract. Say:

- **How do you count back for 8 minus 3?** *[Start with 8, then count back three numbers: 7, 6, 5—5 is the difference.]*

Follow Up For children who are having difficulty counting back to subtract, assign **Reteach 34.**

For children who demonstrate understanding, provide patterned exercises such as 10 − 2, 9 − 2, 8 − 2, 7 − 2, and 6 − 2. Have children count back to find the differences and then explain the pattern. Assign **Extend 34.**

Try These!

Count back to subtract.

1 

2 − 1 = 1

2 

5 − 3 = 2

3 6 − 1 = 5 　 7 − 2 = 5 　 10 − 2 = 8

4 8 − 2 = 6 　 4 − 1 = 3 　 9 − 2 = 7

5 10 − 3 = 7 　 3 − 2 = 1 　 5 − 1 = 4

6 9 − 1 = 8 　 7 − 3 = 4 　 8 − 3 = 5

7 5 − 2 = 3 　 10 − 2 = 8 　 6 − 3 = 3

More to Explore — Patterns

Look for a pattern. Complete.

9 − 1 = 8 　 5 − 1 = 4

8 − 1 = 7 　 4 − 1 = 3

7 − 1 = 6 　 3 − 1 = 2

6 − 1 = 5 　 2 − 1 = 1

Ask your child to tell you about counting back to subtract.

More to Explore Children practice subtraction facts dealing with one fewer. Ask:

- **What rule could you make about subtracting 1?** *[Possible answer: The difference is 1 less than the number I'm subtracting from.]*

3 Close

Check for Understanding Write 7 − 2 = ___ on the chalkboard. Say:

- **Tell how to count back to find the difference.** *[Start with 7, then count back two numbers—-6, 5. The difference is 5.]*

Tomorrow children will count back using a number line.

PRACTICE • 34

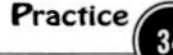

Name: 　 Practice 34

COUNTING BACK

Count back to subtract.

1.

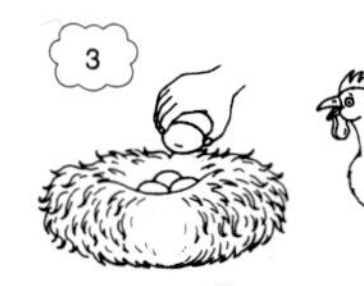

4 − 1 = 3

2. 3 − 2 = 1 　 3. 8 − 2 = 6

4. 9 − 1 = 8 　 5. 4 − 3 = 1

6. 6 − 2 = 4 　 7. 5 − 1 = 4

8. 5 − 2 = 3 　 9. 9 − 2 = 7

10. 6 − 1 = 5 　 11. 4 − 2 = 2

Look for a pattern. Complete.

12. 10 − 3 = 7 　 13. 7 − 3 = 4

9 − 3 = 6 　 6 − 3 = 3

8 − 3 = 5 　 5 − 3 = 2

RETEACH • 34

Name: 　 Reteach 34

COUNTING BACK

4¢ − 2¢ = 2 ¢

1.

3¢ − 2¢ = 1 ¢

2.

4¢ − 3¢ = 1 ¢

3.

6¢ − 3¢ = 3 ¢

4.

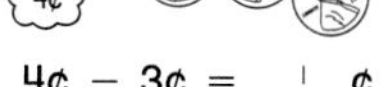

8¢ − 2¢ = 6 ¢

5.

7¢ − 2¢ = 5 ¢

6.

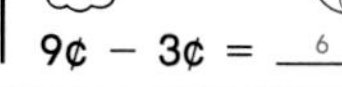

9¢ − 3¢ = 6 ¢

EXTEND • 34

Name: 　 Extend 34

COUNTING BACK

Find the Hidden Word

Count back to solve.
Color red.

9 − 3 = 6 　 8 − 2 = 6 　 5 − 2 = 3

7 − 2 = 5 　 6 − 3 = 3 　 6 − 1 = 5

Color yellow.

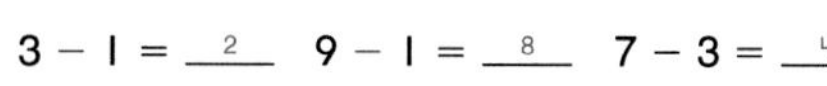

9 − 2 = 7 　 6 − 2 = 4 　 4 − 2 = 2

3 − 1 = 2 　 9 − 1 = 8 　 7 − 3 = 4

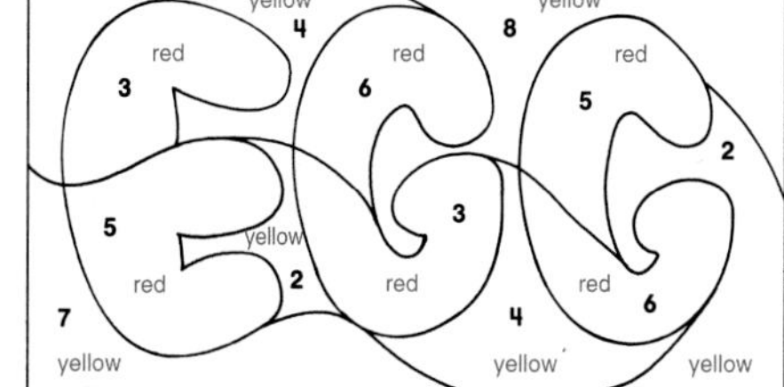

What was Humpty Dumpty? EGG

Lesson 4.5

DAY 2

More Counting Back

OBJECTIVE Children count back 1, 2, or 3 on a number line.

Materials per child: rhino counter

1 Motivate — Whole Class

Resources Jumbo Activity Book, page 7; Sticker sheet 5 (numerals and symbols)

Record the subtraction sentence 7 – 3 = 4 on Jumbo Activity Book page 7 with number and symbol stickers.

Demonstrate the subtraction on the number line. Place your finger on the 7. Then move it to the left along the number line to the 4 to show the counting-back strategy and to find the answer. Ask children to tell you where the counting stops and what the answer is. Children should relate that the number you counted back to and the answer are the same.

Then have children use the number line to demonstrate solving problems such as 8 – 3 = __, 9 – 2 = __, or 10 – 3 = __.

2 Develop

Page 129

Discuss the example at the top of the page. Have children use a rhino counter to keep track as they count back.

Critical Thinking
After children complete the exercises on the page, ask:

- **Can you write a subtraction sentence where you count back 1, 2, or 3 and get an answer of zero?** *[Yes—1 – 1 = 0, 2 – 2 = 0, 3 – 3 = 0]*

Page 130

Try These Assign practice exercises 1–5.

Allow children to use a counter or a finger to keep track of the counting process on the number line.

Cultural Connection Tell children that Egyptians used picture writing called *hieroglyphics* (hie ruh GLI´ fix) to write numerals, and that Egyptians formed numerals by putting different symbols together. Help children make a chart of the symbols for the numbers 1–10. Ask children how to figure out the differences for the first row of problems, and how to write the answers in hieroglyphics.

3 Close

Check for Understanding by asking:

- **How does a number line help you count back to subtract?** *[Possible answer: You can see the numbers and keep track of them as you count back.]*

Name ______________________

More Counting Back

Here is another way to count back to subtract.

Start at 9. Count back 3.

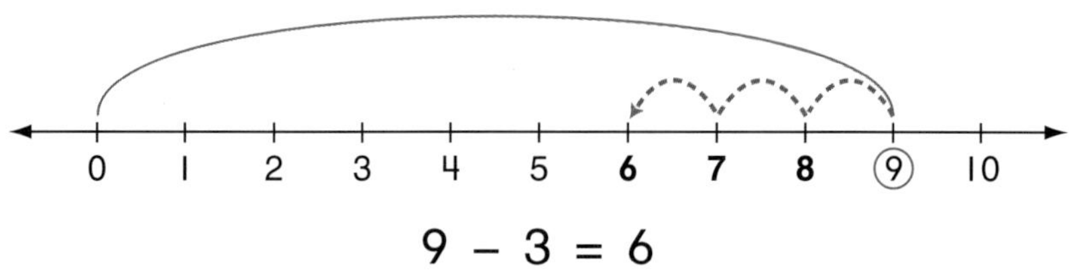

9 – 3 = 6

Count back to subtract.

1.
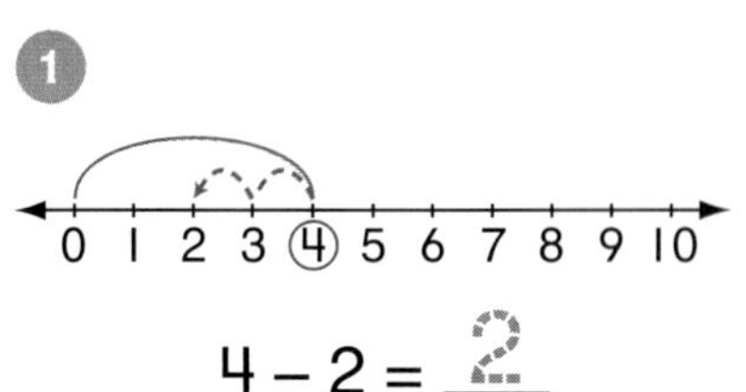

4 – 2 = 2

2.
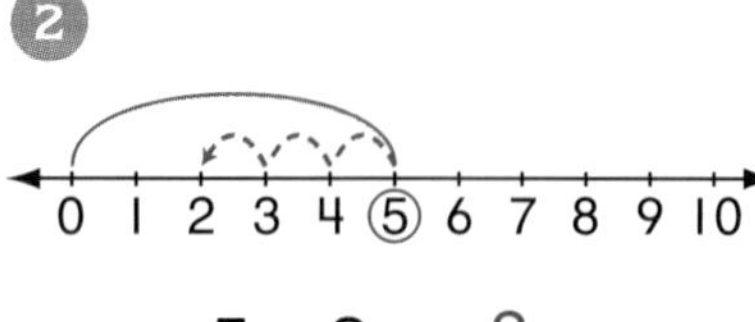

5 – 3 = 2

3.

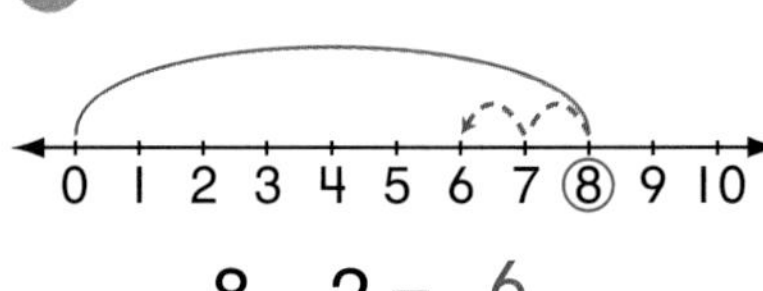

8 – 2 = 6

4.

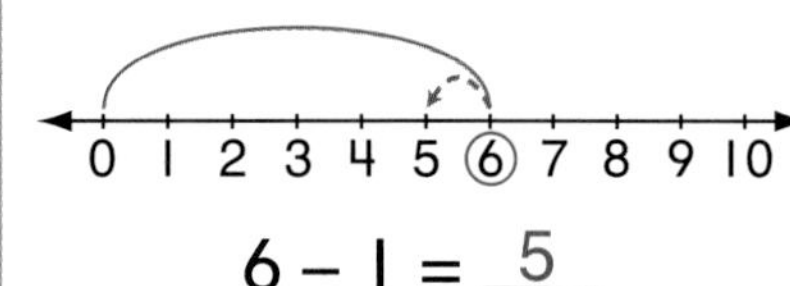

6 – 1 = 5

5.
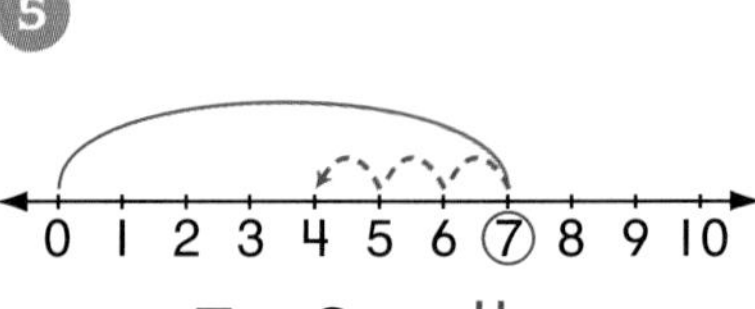

7 – 3 = 4

6.
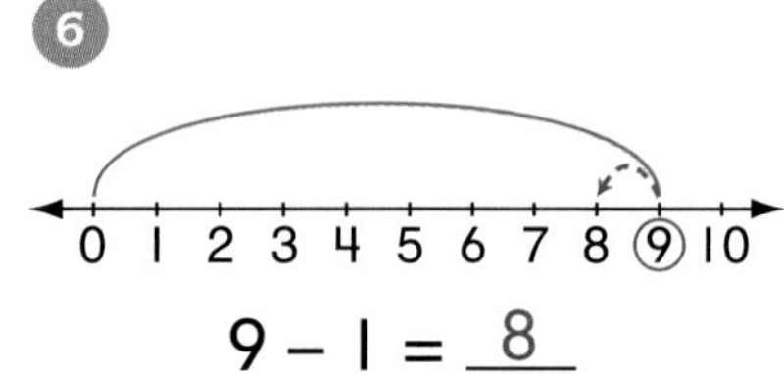

9 – 1 = 8

MEETING INDIVIDUAL NEEDS

EARLY FINISHERS

Ask pairs of children to draw a number line in their journals. One child gives a starting number between 5 and 10 and the number 1, 2, or 3. The second child uses it to write the subtraction sentence.

EXTRA SUPPORT

If children need additional support, have them say the total, and walk the number of steps backwards as they count aloud.

ONGOING ASSESSMENT

Observation Checklist Determine if children understand how to use a number line to solve a subtraction problem by observing how they count back on the number line with a counter.

Follow Up For children who are having difficulty, assign **Reteach 35.**

Have children who understand the lesson work in pairs to make up and solve problems about rhinos, using the number line. Then assign **Extend 35.**

Try These!

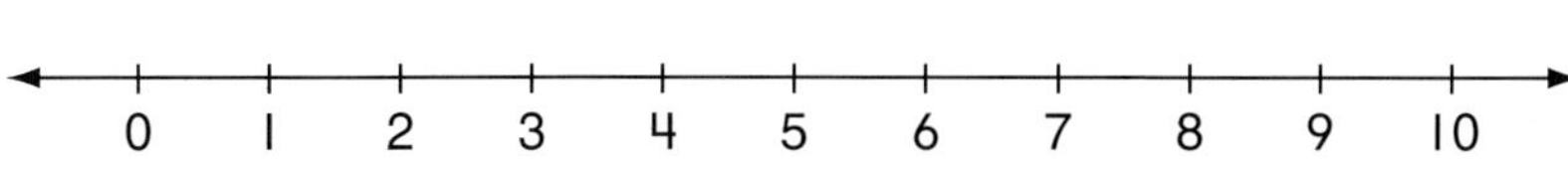

1	10 − 1 = 9	4 − 3 = 1	2 − 2 = 0
2	6 − 3 = 3	8 − 1 = 7	7 − 2 = 5
3	5 − 1 = 4	3 − 3 = 0	9 − 3 = 6
4	8 − 2 = 6	10 − 3 = 7	2 − 1 = 1
5	3 − 1 = 2	4 − 2 = 2	6 − 2 = 4

Cultural Connection — Egyptian Numbers

These numbers were used a long time ago.

| = 1 ∩ = 10

You can subtract with Egyptian numbers.

(10) ∩ − (1)	= (9) |||||||||	(6) |||||| − (2) || = (4) ||||
||||| − |||| =		∩ − ||||| = |||||

At Home Ask your child to show you how to count back to subtract on a number line.

Alternate Teaching Strategy

Materials 11 large sheets of colored construction paper

Prepare Number the sheets of paper 0 to 10 and tape them to the floor to form a number line.

Tell children they are going to play a game called "Stepping Back on the Number Line."

Write 8 − 2 = __ on the chalkboard. Ask:

- **How many numbers do you step back to subtract 2 from 8?** *[2]*

Ask children to count back aloud as a volunteer demonstrates the fact by walking on the number line. Then that child writes the answer in the subtraction sentence.

Repeat the activity with different facts until every child has had a turn to use the number line to subtract.

PRACTICE • 35 (HOMEWORK)

Name: Practice 35

More Counting Back

Count back to subtract.

1. 3 − 1 = 2	5 − 3 = 2	7 − 3 = 4
2. 8 − 2 = 6	8 − 3 = 5	7 − 2 = 5
3. 3 − 2 = 1	1 − 1 = 0	4 − 3 = 1
4. 6 − 3 = 3	5 − 1 = 4	4 − 1 = 3
5. 8 − 1 = 7	4 − 2 = 2	2 − 2 = 0
6. 10 − 2 = 8	6 − 1 = 5	9 − 2 = 7

RETEACH • 35

Name: Reteach 35

More Counting Back

8 − 3 = 5

Start at 8.

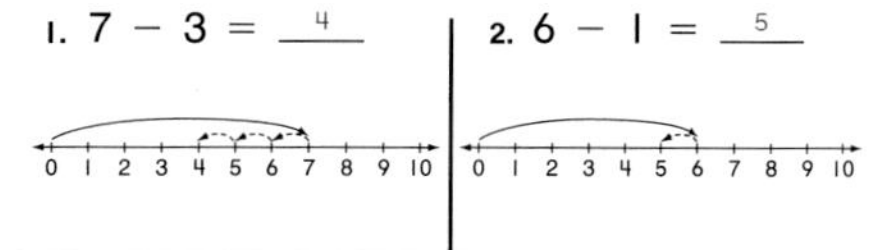

Count back to subtract.

1. 7 − 3 = 4
2. 6 − 1 = 5

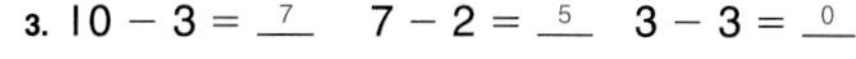

3. 10 − 3 = 7	7 − 2 = 5	3 − 3 = 0
4. 8 − 3 = 5	4 − 1 = 3	9 − 2 = 7
5. 5 − 2 = 3	6 − 3 = 3	5 − 3 = 2
6. 2 − 2 = 0	10 − 2 = 8	9 − 1 = 8

EXTEND • 35

Name: Extend 35

More Counting Back

Where Did the Beanstalk Come From?

Count back to subtract. Write the letter.

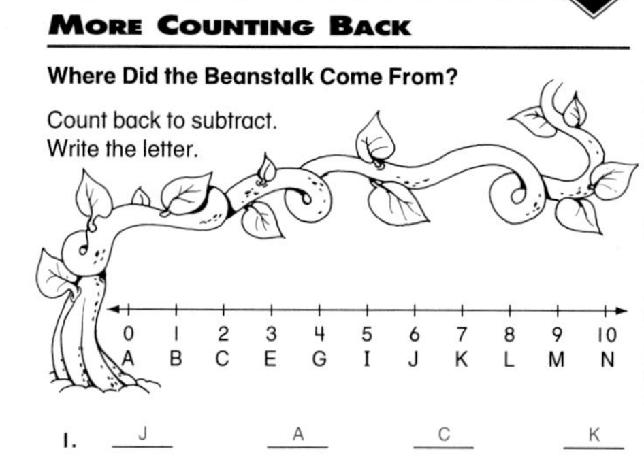

1. J A C K

9 − 3 = 6 1 − 1 = 0 3 − 1 = 2 8 − 1 = 7

planted a

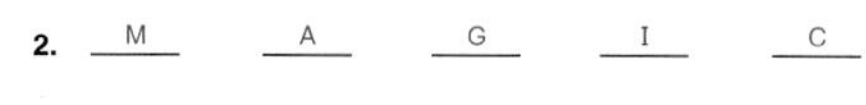

2. M A G I C

10 − 1 = 9 3 − 3 = 0 7 − 3 = 4 8 − 3 = 5 4 − 2 = 2

3. B E A N

3 − 2 = 1 6 − 3 = 3 2 − 2 = 0 10 − 0 = 10

EXTRA PRACTICE

AT A GLANCE

PURPOSE Provide an opportunity for review and practice.

Materials per pair: 2 rhino counters; blank spinner (TA 8)

Using the Extra Practice

Page 131

The spinner for this game should be marked with the numbers 0 to 3. Each partner uses his or her own game board. The game continues until a player gets to the south space.

After children finish playing, ask:

- **Which number on the spinner may help you get to south fastest? Why?** *[Possible answer: 3; you can count back more if you spin a 3 instead of a 2, 1, or 0.]*

Page 132

Have children complete the exercises independently or in pairs. They can use cubes to keep track of their moves on the number line and to do exercises 9 and 10.

Using the Additional Practice

The section below provides additional practice that you may want to write on the chalkboard or on a reproducible master.

Name

Extra Practice Game!

Flying South

You need 2 rhino counters and a spinner.

- ▶ Put your rhino counter on 10.
- ▶ Take turns. Spin.
- ▶ Subtract. Move your rhino counter to the difference.

The first player to get to **South** wins.

10 9 8 7 6 5 4 3 2 1 SOUTH

ADDITIONAL PRACTICE

Subtract.

1. 10 − 6 = __ *[4]* 10 − 4 = __ *[6]*

2. 8 − 1 = __ *[7]* 8 − 7 = __ *[1]*

3. 7 − 4 = __ *[3]* 7 − 3 = __ *[4]*

4. 9 − 0 = __ *[9]* 9 − 9 = __ *[0]*

5. 6 − 2 = __ *[4]* 6 − 4 = __ *[2]*

6. 7 − 0 = __ *[7]* 7 − 7 = __ *[0]*

7. 6 − 5 = __ *[1]* 6 − 1 = __ *[5]*

8. 5 − 3 = __ *[2]* 5 − 2 = __ *[3]*

9. 8 − 5 = __ *[3]* 8 − 3 = __ *[5]*

10. 7 − 2 = __ *[5]* 7 − 5 = __ *[2]*

Subtract.

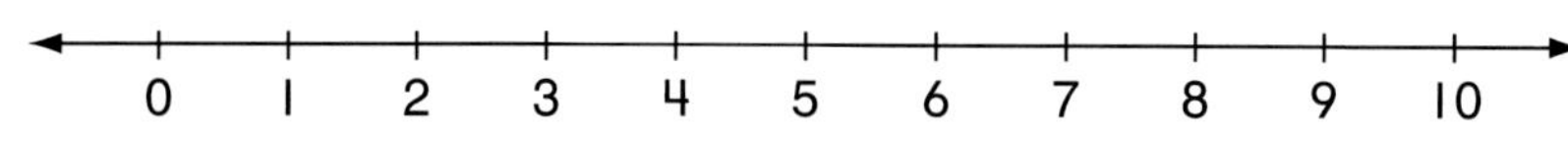

1. $8 - 2 =$ 6 $\quad 2 - 1 =$ 1 $\quad 5 - 0 =$ 5
2. $9 - 3 =$ 6 $\quad 7 - 2 =$ 5 $\quad 6 - 2 =$ 4
3. $10 - 2 =$ 8 $\quad 1 - 1 =$ 0 $\quad 3 - 2 =$ 1
4. $4 - 2 =$ 2 $\quad 10 - 3 =$ 7 $\quad 9 - 0 =$ 9
5. $8 - 1 =$ 7 $\quad 7 - 1 =$ 6 $\quad 5 - 2 =$ 3
6. $6 - 3 =$ 3 $\quad 2 - 0 =$ 2 $\quad 8 - 3 =$ 5
7. $4 - 1 =$ 3 $\quad 9 - 2 =$ 7 $\quad 8 - 0 =$ 8
8. $7 - 3 =$ 4 $\quad 10 - 1 =$ 9 $\quad 9 - 1 =$ 8

Find out how many are left.

9. 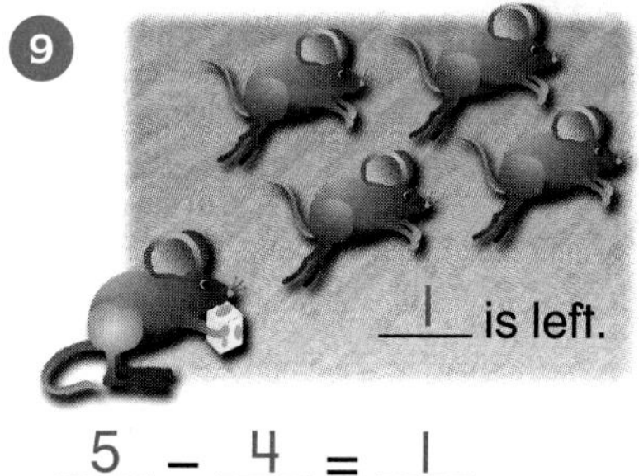

1 is left.

5 − 4 = 1

10. 

2 are left.

6 − 4 = 2

Developing Algebra Sense

This section provides an opportunity to reinforce algebraic ideas.

Complete.

1.

	−1
6	*[5]*
7	*[6]*
8	*[7]*
9	*[8]*
10	*[9]*

2.

	−2
2	*[0]*
4	*[2]*
6	*[4]*
8	*[6]*
10	*[8]*

3.

	−0
3	*[3]*
4	*[4]*
5	*[5]*
6	*[6]*
7	*[7]*

Mixed Applications/Problem Solving

Solve.

1. Old Mother Hubbard has 9 cakes in her cupboard.
She takes out 3 cakes.
How many cakes does she have left? *[6]*

2. Franklin has 8¢.
He buys an apple for 5¢.
How much money does he have left? *[3¢]*

3. There are 9 ball players on the field.
9 go home.
How many ball players are left? *[0]*

4. 8 birds are in the tree.
3 birds are red.
5 birds are yellow.
How many more yellow birds are there than red birds? *[2]*

5. Scott puts 9 shells in a basket.
4 shells fall out.
How many shells are left? *[5]*

6. 6 bikes are in the bike rack.
2 of them are red.
The rest are black.
How many bikes are black? *[4]*

Problem-Solvers at Work: Can You Subtract to Solve?

OBJECTIVE Write and solve problems, including those involving subtraction.

Day 1 Problem Solvers at Work: Can You Subtract to Solve?

RESOURCE REMINDER
Math Center Cards 27
Practice 36, Reteach 36, Extend 36

SKILLS TRACE	
GRADE K	• Solve problems, including those that involve subtraction. *(Chapter 11)*
GRADE 1	• Formulate and solve problems, including those that involve subtraction.
GRADE 2	• Formulate and solve problems, including those that involve subtraction. *(Chapter 1)*

MANIPULATIVE WARM-UP

Cooperative Pairs — **Kinesthetic**

OBJECTIVE Create problems for number sentences.

Materials per pair: Workmat 3 (part-part-whole mat), 10 rhino counters

▶ Write the subtraction sentence 6 – 4 = 2 on the chalkboard. Have volunteers make up a problem that matches the sentence. Provide this example to get children started:

6 rhinos go into a lake.
Later, 4 of them come out.
How many rhinos are still in the lake?

▶ Have pairs use rhino counters to act out the subtraction sentence on the workmat.

▶ Then display the addition sentence 1 + 6 = 7. Have children make up a problem for it and act it out on the workmat. Continue the activity, having children make up and act out addition and subtraction sentences.

CONNECTION ACTIVITY

Whole Class — **Logical/Analytical**

OBJECTIVE Connect missing number problems and algebra.

Resources Jumbo Activity Book, page 6; Stickers, sheet 1 (rhino counters), sheet 5 (numerals and symbols)

▶ Display Jumbo Activity Book page 6. Use numerals and symbol stickers to record the number sentence 7 – __ = 5 on the page. Tell a story such as, "There were 7 rhinos at the watering hole, but now there are only 5. How many rhinos have left the watering hole?" Ask:

- **How can you solve the problem?** *[Think 7 and count back to 5.]*
- **How many rhinos have already left?** *[2]*

▶ Encourage children to tell other stories using stickers and the counting-back strategy to find the missing numbers.

DAILY MATH

PREVIOUS DAY QUICK REVIEW

Count back to subtract.

1. 6 – 2 *[4]*
2. 8 – 1 *[7]*
3. 7 – 3 *[4]*
4. 2 – 2 *[0]*

FAST FACTS

1. 6 + 3 *[9]*
2. 5 + 3 *[8]*
3. 4 + 3 *[7]*
4. 3 + 3 *[6]*

Problem of the Day • 27

Read aloud to children:

10 children are playing ball.
2 children go home.
1 child comes back to play.
How many children are playing now? *[9]*

TECH LINK

MATH VAN

Tool You may wish to use the Counters tool with this lesson.

MATH FORUM

Idea I give children the raw data for a problem without asking a question. After children think through the possible choices of operations they have, they can write and solve the problem.

Visit our Resource Village at http://www.mhschool.com to access the Math Forum.

MATH CENTER

Practice

OBJECTIVE Make up and solve subtraction and addition problems.

Materials per pair: crayons, number cards, two Math Center Recording Sheets (TA 38 optional)

Prepare Write the numbers 0–5 in blue on one set of cards and in red on the other set.

Children use number cards to draw and tell stories. Children then write number sentences for the stories. *[Check children's work for accuracy.]*

PRACTICE ACTIVITY 27 — MATH CENTER, Partners

Formulating Problems • Turn About

YOU NEED: crayons, number cards

Take turns.

- Pick a card from each pile. Draw an addition story.
- Your partner writes the addition sentence.
- Use the numbers from the addition sentence. Draw a subtraction story.
- Your partner writes the subtraction sentence.

Play 3 more times.

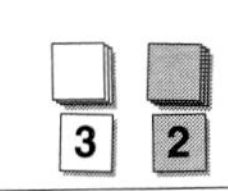

3 + 2 = 5
5 – 3 = 2

Chapter 4, Lesson 6 — Subtraction

McGraw-Hill School Division — Grade Level 1

NCTM Standards

- ✓ Problem Solving
- ✓ Communication
- ✓ Reasoning
- Connections

Problem Solving

OBJECTIVE Use addition and subtraction sentences to solve problems.

Materials per pair: blank spinner, blank number cube, 10 counters, Math Center Recording Sheet (TA 38 optional)

Children spin to have passengers get on the bus and roll a number cube to have them get off. *[Answers may vary. 4 + 2 = 6, 6 – 1 = 5, 5 + 3 = 8, 8 – 2 = 6, 6 + 3 = 9, 9 – 1 = 8]*

PROBLEM-SOLVING ACTIVITY 27 — MATH CENTER, On Your Own

Decision Making • Bus Stops

YOU NEED: spinner, number cube, 10 counters

Cat, Dog, Bear, and Mouse are on the bus.

- Spin for a number. That many get on the bus. Write the number sentence.
- Roll the number cube. That many get off the bus. Write the number sentence.

Play again.
You may want to use counters.

BUS STOP

4 + 3 = 7
7 – 2 = 5

Chapter 4, Lesson 6 — Subtraction

McGraw-Hill School Division — Grade Level 1

NCTM Standards

- ✓ Problem Solving
- ✓ Communication
- ✓ Reasoning
- ✓ Connections

Lesson 4.6

Problem Solvers at Work: Can You Subtract to Solve?

OBJECTIVE Solve problems including those involving subtraction.

Materials have available: rhino counters or 2-color counters

1 Motivate — Whole Class

On the chalkboard, draw 3 stick figures standing and 2 stick figures walking toward them.

- **If I asked you how many children in all, would you add or subtract to find the answer?** *[Add.]*

Call on a volunteer to write the number sentence on the chalkboard. *[3 + 2 = 5]* Next, draw 2 stick figures and say that there are 5 children, but some are hiding, so you only see 2.

- **If I asked you how many children are hiding, would you add or subtract to find the answer?** *[Subtract.]*

Ask a child to write the number sentence. *[5 – 2 = 3]*

2 Develop

Page 133

Read aloud to children the directions and the first word problem found on the reduced Student Book page in this Teacher's Edition. Discuss the Talk question. Then read aloud problems 2 and 3. Ask questions, focusing on whether each problem can be solved by subtracting or adding.

CRITICAL THINKING
After children answer the question on the page, ask:

- **When do you add to solve a problem?** *[Possible answer: when I need to find how many in all]*

Page 134

Try These Assign practice problems 1–4.

Read aloud to children word problems 1 and 2, found on the reduced student book page. Discuss how to solve problem 3. Monitor problem 4 to observe whether children can correctly write and solve an addition or subtraction problem.

3 Close

Check for Understanding by asking:

- **How can you solve a problem that asks how many are left?** *[Possible answer: I have to find a part, so I subtract the part I know from the total.]*

Name ____________________

Problem Solvers at Work

Can You Subtract to Solve?

Read · Plan · Solve · Look Back

Listen to the problem.

1 "There are 8 animals in the woods. Three of the animals are raccoons. The rest are foxes. How many foxes are in the woods?"

What do you need to find? How many foxes there are in the woods.
Can you subtract to find the answer? Yes.

Animals

8 – 3 = 5

2 How many are left?

"There are 4 deer. Three deer run away. How many deer are left?" 1 left

4 – 3 = 1

3 How many in all?

"There are 2 rabbits. There are 3 birds. How many animals in all?" 5 in all

2 + 3 = 5

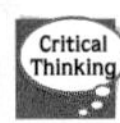

When do you subtract to solve a problem? Possible answer: Subtract when you need to find how many are left or to find a missing part.

MEETING INDIVIDUAL NEEDS

EARLY FINISHERS

If children wrote an addition problem for exercise 4 on page 134, have them write a subtraction problem in their journals, and vice versa.

EXTRA SUPPORT

If children are having difficulty in choosing the correct operation, encourage them to listen carefully and think about whether they need to find a total or a part before deciding whether to add or subtract.

ONGOING ASSESSMENT

Observation Checklist Make notes on how children figure out whether to add or subtract to solve problems. Note the strategies children use to find the answers.

Follow Up For children who are having difficulty, have them act out problems on Workmat 3 with counters before assigning **Reteach 36.**

For children who understand the work, assign **Extend 36.**

Talk Listen to the problem.

1 “There were 6 bats in the cave. Three bats flew in. How many bats are in the cave in all?” 9 in all

6 + 3 = 9

2 “What if the 3 bats flew out again. How many bats are left in the cave?” 6 are left.

9 − 3 = 6

Jamal McKenzie
Snowden School
Memphis, Tennessee

3 Solve Jamal's problem. 10 − 5 = 5, 5 are left.

Talk How did you solve Jamal's problem? Possible answers:

Subtracted, counted how many are in the tree.

4 Write a problem. Have a partner solve it. Use your own paper. Problems may vary.

Your partner's answer: ______

At Home: Ask your child to tell you about the problem he or she wrote.

Alternate Teaching Strategy

Materials small classroom objects such as pencils or crayons

Show pencils or other small objects to children. Make up an oral subtraction problem for them. Then ask:

- **Will you add or subtract to find the answer?** *[Subtract.]*

Discuss with children why they chose that operation and then have children write the subtraction sentence for the problem.

Repeat the procedure, telling an addition story.

PRACTICE • 36

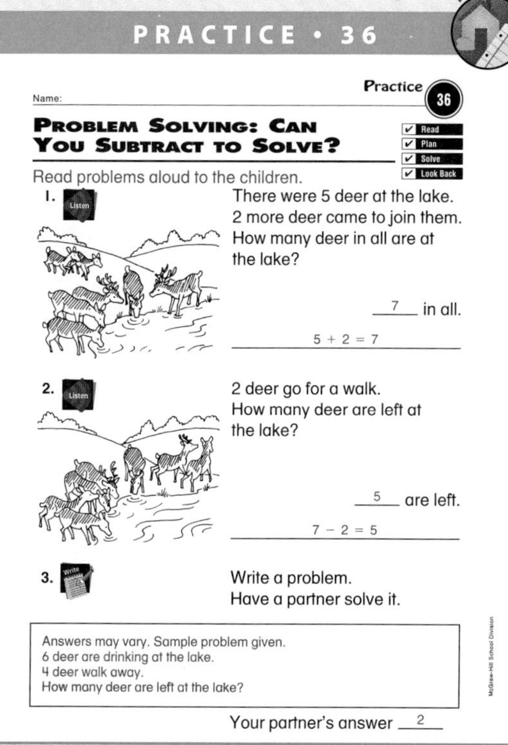
Practice 36

Name:

PROBLEM SOLVING: CAN YOU SUBTRACT TO SOLVE?

Read · Plan · Solve · Look Back

Read problems aloud to the children.

1. There were 5 deer at the lake. 2 more deer came to join them. How many deer in all are at the lake? 7 in all.
5 + 2 = 7

2. 2 deer go for a walk. How many deer are left at the lake? 5 are left.
7 − 2 = 5

3. Write a problem. Have a partner solve it.

Answers may vary. Sample problem given.
6 deer are drinking at the lake.
4 deer walk away.
How many deer are left at the lake?

Your partner's answer 2

RETEACH • 36

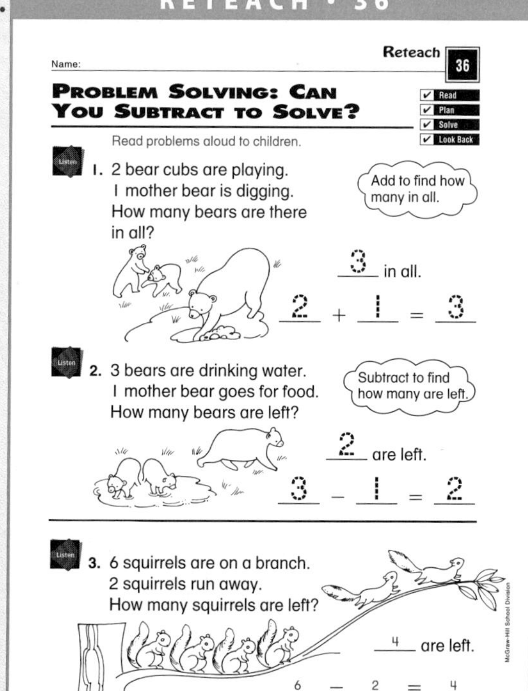
Reteach 36

Name:

PROBLEM SOLVING: CAN YOU SUBTRACT TO SOLVE?

Read · Plan · Solve · Look Back

Read problems aloud to children.

1. 2 bear cubs are playing. 1 mother bear is digging. How many bears are there in all? (Add to find how many in all.) 3 in all.
2 + 1 = 3

2. 3 bears are drinking water. 1 mother bear goes for food. How many bears are left? (Subtract to find how many are left.) 2 are left.
3 − 1 = 2

3. 6 squirrels are on a branch. 2 squirrels run away. How many squirrels are left? 4 are left.
6 − 2 = 4

EXTEND • 36

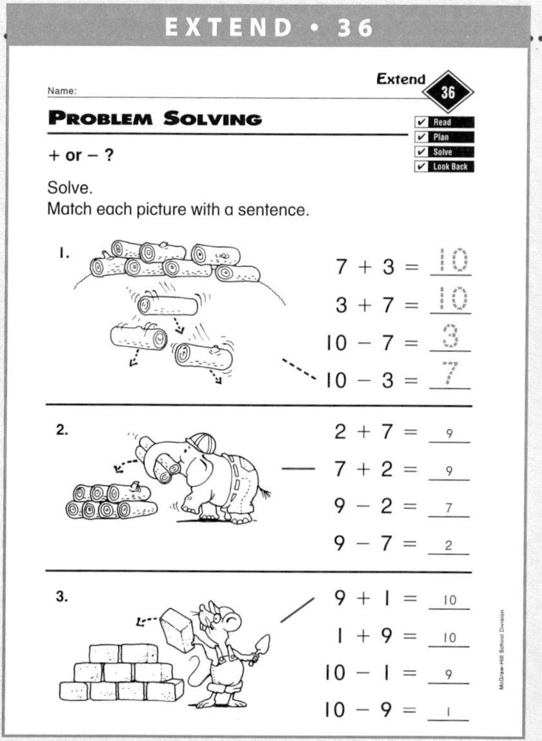
Extend 36

Name:

PROBLEM SOLVING

Read · Plan · Solve · Look Back

+ or − ?

Solve.
Match each picture with a sentence.

1. 7 + 3 = 10
3 + 7 = 10
10 − 7 = 3
10 − 3 = 7

2. 2 + 7 = 9
7 + 2 = 9
9 − 2 = 7
9 − 7 = 2

3. 9 + 1 = 10
1 + 9 = 10
10 − 1 = 9
10 − 9 = 1

CHAPTER REVIEW

PURPOSE Review and assess the concepts, skills, and strategies that children have learned in this chapter.

Chapter Objectives

4A Subtract, facts to 10

4B Solve problems including those that involve subtraction and writing a subtraction sentence

Using the Chapter Review

The **Chapter Review** can be used as a review, practice test, or chapter test. Read the directions for each section of problems on the page. Children may use counters to help them complete the problems.

What Do You Think? This feature gives children an opportunity for self-assessment. Assure children that there are no right or wrong answers. The emphasis is on what they think and how they justify their answers.

Have children choose a subtraction sentence to illustrate. Illustrating a subtraction sentence provides the opportunity to show understanding of subtraction and the symbols associated with it.

Name

Chapter Review

Write the subtraction sentence.

1 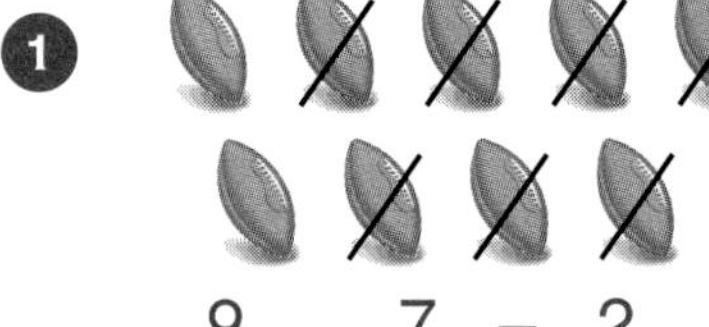

9 − 7 = 2

2 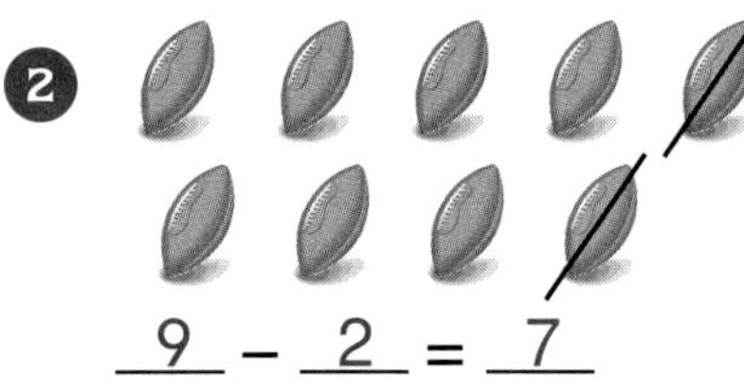

9 − 2 = 7

Subtract.

3 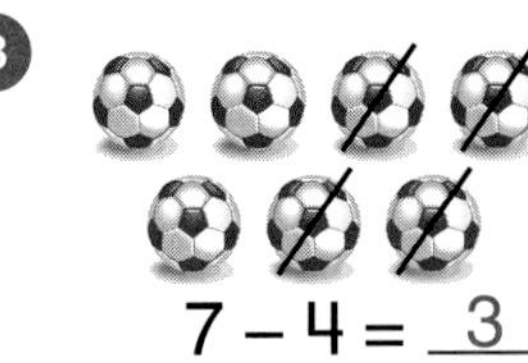

7 − 4 = 3

4 

8 − 6 = 2

5 6 − 1 = 5

6 3 − 2 = 1

7 5 − 5 = 0

8 9 − 1 = 8

9 9 − 3 = 6

10 8 − 3 = 5

11 4 − 2 = 2

12 6 − 2 = 4

13 7 − 3 = 4

14 5 − 0 = 5

15 2¢ − 2¢ = 0 ¢

16 4¢ − 1¢ = 3 ¢

Reinforcement and Remediation

CHAPTER OBJECTIVES	REVIEW ITEMS	STUDENT BOOK PAGES		TEACHER'S EDITION PAGES		TEACHER RESOURCES
		Lessons	Midchapter Review	Activities	Alternate Teaching Strategy	Reteach
4A	3–6	113–118, 125–130	121	112A, 114C, 124A, 126A	114, 118, 126, 130	29–31, 33–35
4B	1–2, 17–20	119–120, 133–134	121	118A, 132A	120, 134	32, 36

Listen to the problem.

17  

"There are 6 ballplayers. One player walks away. How many players are left?"

5 are left.

6 – 1 = 5

18 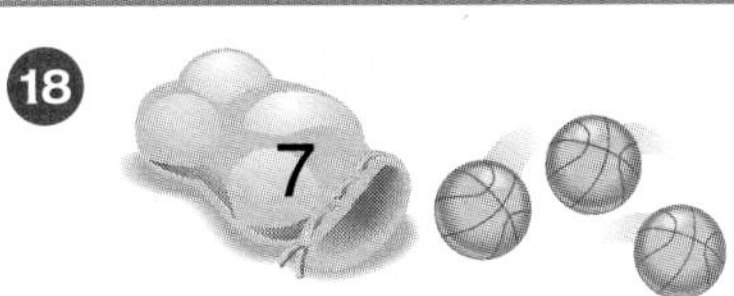

"There are 7 balls in a bag. Three balls fall out. How many balls are left in the bag?"

4 are left.

7 – 3 = 4

19 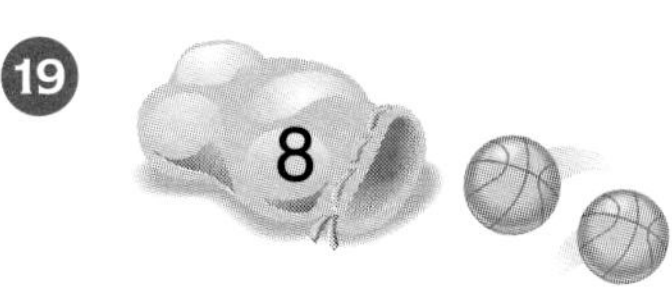

"There are 8 balls in a bag. Two balls fall out. How many balls are left in the bag?"

6 are left.

8 – 2 = 6

20 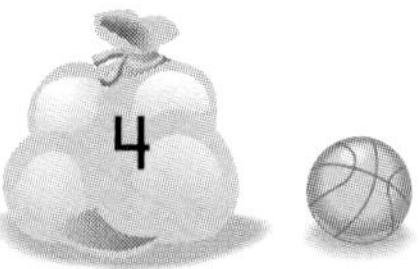

"There are 4 balls in a bag. There is 1 ball on the table. How many balls in all?"

5 in all

4 + 1 = 5

What Do You Think?

How do you subtract 7 – 2? This self-assessment should not be graded. All explanations are acceptable.

Check one.

☐ With  ☐ With 4 5 6 7 8 ☐ In my head

Why? ______________________________

Draw a subtraction picture.

Write the subtraction sentence. Children may draw pictures similar to those in the text; sentences should reflect the numbers in the pictures.

AT A GLANCE

PURPOSE Assess the concepts, skills, and strategies that children have learned in this chapter.

Chapter Objectives

4A Subtract, facts to 10

4B Solve problems including those that involve subtraction and writing a subtraction sentence

Using the Chapter Test

The **Chapter Test** can be used as a practice test, a chapter test, or as an additional review. The **Performance Assessment** on Student Book page 138 provides an alternate means of assessing children's understanding of subtraction.

The table below correlates the test items to the chapter objectives and to the Student Book pages on which the skills are taught.

Assessment Resources

Test Masters

The Testing Program Blackline Masters provides three forms of the Chapter Test. Form C uses a free-response format. Forms A and B use a multiple-choice format.

Teacher's Assessment Resources

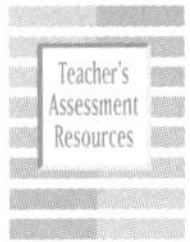

Teacher's Assessment Resources provides resources for alternate assessment. It includes guidelines for Building a Portfolio, page 6, and the Holistic Scoring Guide, page 27.

Name

Chapter Test

Write the subtraction sentence.

1. 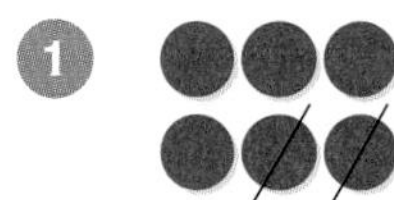
6 − 2 = 4

2. 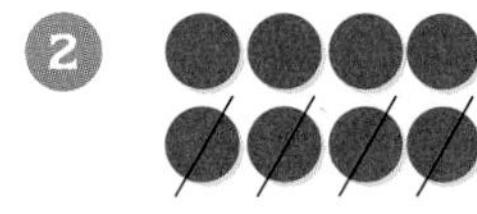
8 − 4 = 4

Subtract.

3. 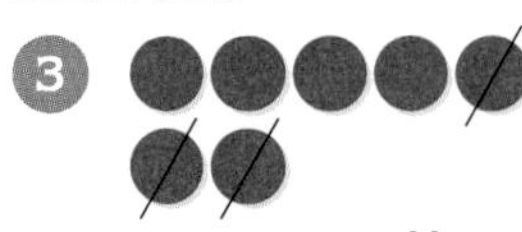
7 − 3 = 4

4. 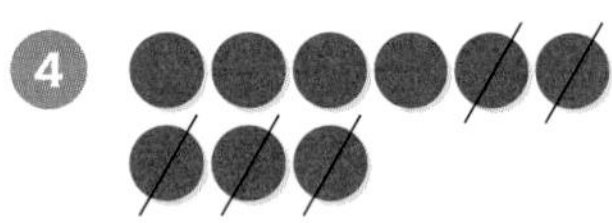
9 − 5 = 4

5. 5 − 0 = 5

6. 8 − 3 = 5

7. 5¢ − 5¢ = 0 ¢

8. 6¢ − 1¢ = 5 ¢

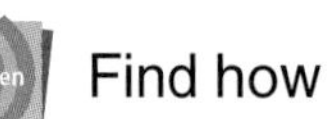

Find how many are left.

"There are 9 blackbirds on a wire. Three fly away. How many blackbirds are left on the wire?"

9. 
6 are left.
9 − 3 = 6

10. 
4 are left.
"There are 6 cats in the yard. Two run away. How many cats are left?"
6 − 2 = 4

Test Correlation		
CHAPTER OBJECTIVES	TEST ITEMS	TEXT PAGES
4A	1–8	113–118, 125–130
4B	9–10	119–120, 133–134

Performance Assessment

What Did You Learn?

You need 10 counters.

Make up a subtraction problem for each picture.

Write a subtraction sentence for each problem.

Sample problems are given.

1 

There were 10 books standing on a shelf. Four books fell down. How many books are still standing?

10 − 4 = 6

2 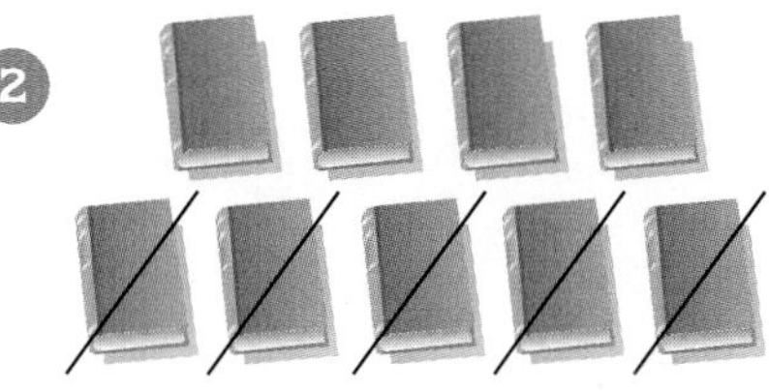

I have 9 books. I give 5 away. How many books do I have left?

9 − 5 = 4

3  

There are 7 children reading. Three children go home. How many children are still reading?

7 − 3 = 4

You may want to put this page in your portfolio.

REVIEWING A PORTFOLIO

Have children review their portfolios. Consider including the following items:
- Finished work on a project, page 110F.
- Selected math journal entries, pages 121 and 136.
- Products from investigations, pages 123–124.
- Children's self-selected "best piece" drawn from the work completed during the chapter. Have them attach a note explaining why they chose that piece.
- Any work that you or individual children wish to keep for future reference.

You may wish to take this opportunity to conduct conferences with children.

The Portfolio Analysis Form can help you in the reporting of children's progress. See Teacher's Assessment Resources, page 33.

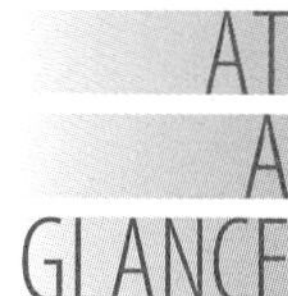

AT A GLANCE

PURPOSE Review and assess the concepts, skills, and strategies that children have learned in this chapter.

Materials per child: 10 counters

Using the Performance Assessment

Discuss the directions next to the word *Talk*. Then read the sentences next to each picture. Make sure children understand what they are to do. Give each child 10 counters. Assign the tasks. Observe children as they work.

Evaluating Student Work

As you read children's papers, look for the following:
- *Do the subtraction problems fit the pictures?*
- *Do the subtraction sentences fit the problems?*
- *Are the subtraction sentences correct?*

You may wish to use the Holistic Scoring Guide and annotated samples of children's work to assess this task. See pages 29–32 and 37–61 in Teacher's Assessment Resources.

Follow-Up Interviews

Meet with children individually or in small groups to reflect on the Performance Assessment task. You can use the following questions to gain insight into children's thinking and evaluate their level of understanding:
- **How did you make up your subtraction problem for this picture? (Point to one of the pictures.)**
- **Explain this problem to me. (Point to one of the problems.)**
- **What strategy did you use to write this subtraction sentence? (Point to one of the subtraction sentences.)**
- **How would you explain to a friend how to solve this problem? (Point to one of the problems.)**
- **What does it mean to subtract?**

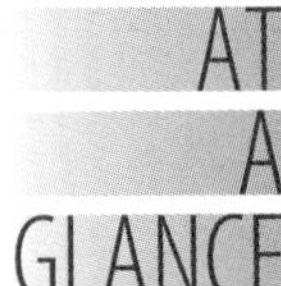

AT A GLANCE **OBJECTIVE** Find missing addends.

Using the Math Connection

Work through the first two exercises with children, discussing strategies for finding the missing addend. Some children may remember doing the "Finding the Missing Part" lesson with parts and total (Lesson 2.5, pages 63–64). Other children may think of addition facts (Chapter 3) or the subtraction facts in this chapter.

Developing Algebra Sense Working with addition sentences to find a missing addend provides an opportunity for children to extend their understanding of using a variable.

Extending the Activity Children can use a bowl and counters, such as nuts and beans, to act out the problems on the page.

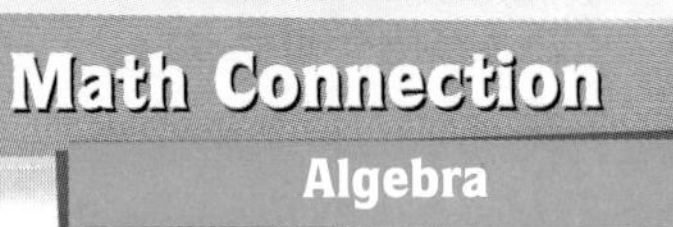

Math Connection

Algebra

Name

Missing Addend

Find how many beans are hidden.

1. 5 in all

2 + 3 = 5

2. 4 in all

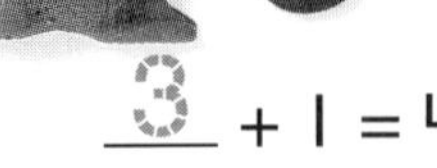

3 + 1 = 4

3. 7 in all

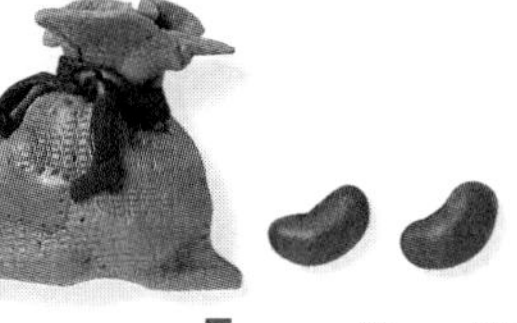

5 + 2 = 7

4. 6 in all

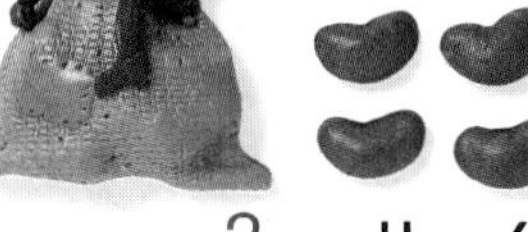

2 + 4 = 6

5. 3 in all

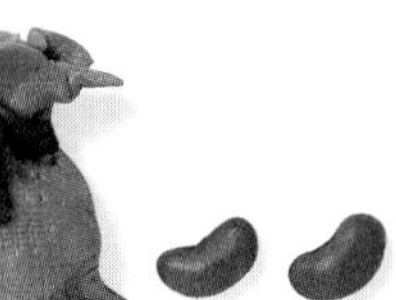

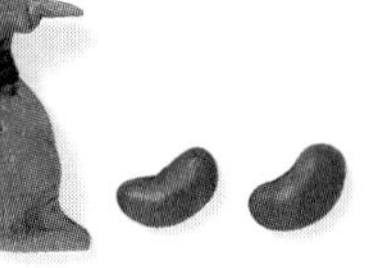

1 + 2 = 3

6. 8 in all

1 + 7 = 8

Technology Connection

Computer

Subtract Pennies

How does using counters help you subtract? Possible answer: I can show the total with counters, take away the number to subtract, and count how many are left.

You have 8 pennies.
You spend 5 pennies.
How many pennies are left?

3 pennies

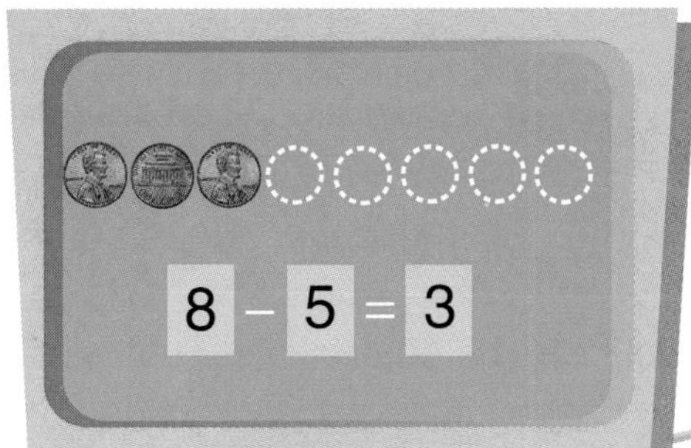

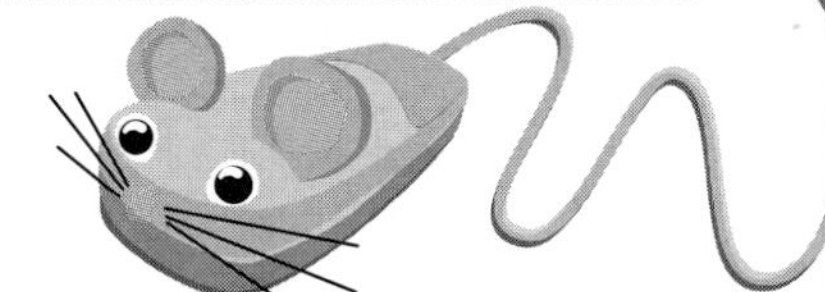

At the Computer

Use penny models to solve.

1. You have 6 pennies
   You spend 2 pennies.
   How many pennies are left? 4 pennies
2. You spend 3 pennies.
   You have 5 pennies left.
   How many pennies did you start with? 8 pennies
3. Write a problem.
   Show how to solve it with penny models.
   Problems and solutions may vary.

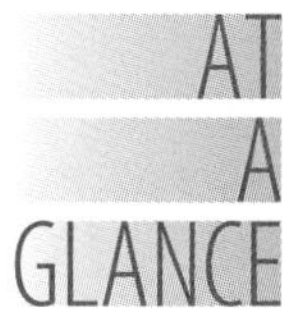

AT A GLANCE

OBJECTIVE Use pennies as counters to explore subtracting.

Resources Software program with money models, or Math Van Tools

Using the Technology Connection

Have children stamp out the pennies needed to act out the problem and find the number of pennies that are left. Ask them to talk about how using the counters helps them subtract.

Children then use pennies to solve other subtraction problems and to formulate their own problems.

If computers and software are not available, allow children to use play money.

Extending the Activity Have children work with partners to write and solve subtraction problems.

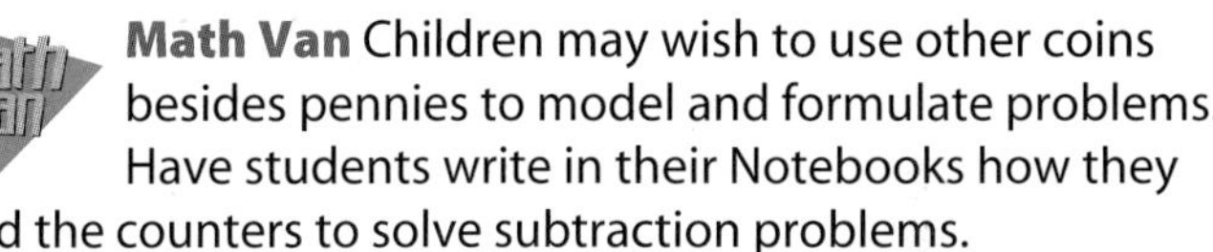

Math Van Children may wish to use other coins besides pennies to model and formulate problems. Have students write in their Notebooks how they used the counters to solve subtraction problems.

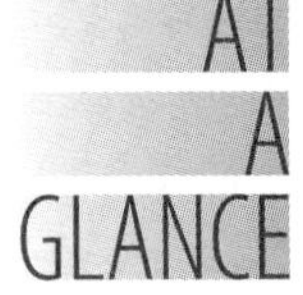

Family Activities

PURPOSE Give family members an opportunity to help children maintain concepts and skills learned in the chapter.

Using the Wrap-Up

Page 141

Tell children that this side of the page will help them show their parents what they have been learning in this chapter.

You may wish to practice with children by drawing the grid on the chalkboard and playing the game as a whole class activity prior to children taking the activity home.

Name

Penny Subtraction

PLAYERS 2

MATERIALS 10 pennies, 2 colors of crayons

DIRECTIONS One player shows some of the pennies and tells an amount to subtract. The other player subtracts and colors to show how many cents are left.

Play until all the boxes are colored.

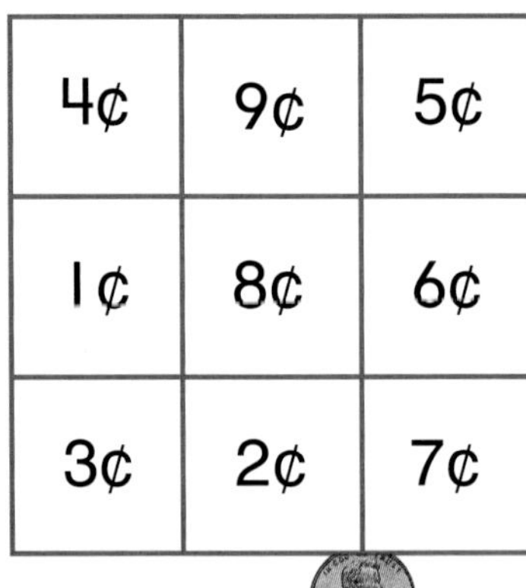

4¢	9¢	5¢
1¢	8¢	6¢
3¢	2¢	7¢

At Home: Play this game with your child. Your child can count the pennies before you say the amount to subtract. Vary the starting amount. Your child uses the pennies to subtract.

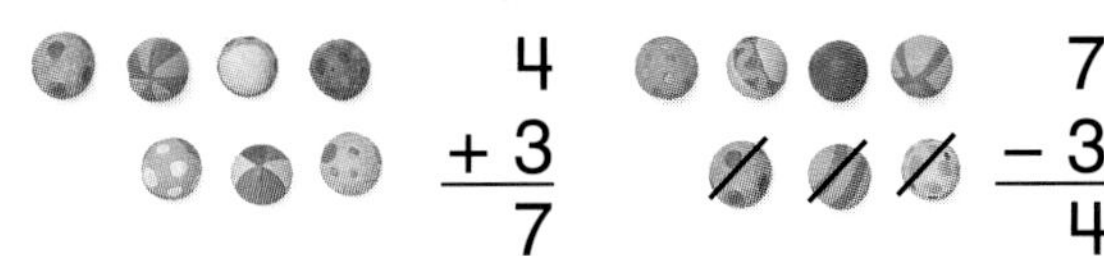

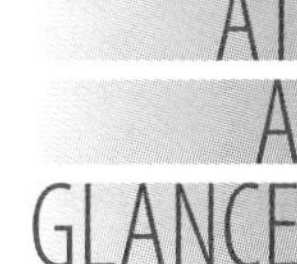

Dear Family,

We are beginning a new chapter in mathematics. We will be learning more about addition and subtraction.

$$\begin{array}{r} 4 \\ +3 \\ \hline 7 \end{array} \qquad \begin{array}{r} 7 \\ -3 \\ \hline 4 \end{array}$$

We will also be talking about the circus and ways to have fun with numbers. Please help me complete this interview.

Your child,

____
Signature

Interview

What kind of circus acts do you like?
(You may check more than one.)

- ❑ Animals
- ❑ Trapeze artists
- ❑ Acrobats
- ❑ Clowns
- ❑ Other ________________

What is the most fun at a circus?

____

AT A GLANCE

Family Activities

PURPOSE Give family members an opportunity to share in their child's mathematics learning.

Using the Preview

Page 142

Discuss the contents of the page with children, and have them sign the letter at the top. Be sure they understand how to conduct an interview with a family member, friend, or neighbor.

Explain to children that they may share what they learn during their next math lesson. You may wish to have children bring back the page.

ADDING AND SUBTRACTING TO 10

Planning for Learning

Suggested Pacing : 13–15 days **Theme: Number Fun**

Lesson Title/Description	Pages	Pacing	Real-life Connection	Chapter Objectives	Materials	Reteach/ Practice/Extend	Math Center Cards
Preview	142						
Introduction	143		going to the circus				
What Do You Know? (J) (P)	144						
▶ 1. Another Way to Add	145–148	2-day lesson		5A	red and blue connecting cubes	37–38	28
▶ 2. Related Addition Facts	149–150	1-day lesson		5A	have available: 2-color counters	39	29
Extra Practice Activity: Rhino Riddle	151–152						
▶ 3. Add Money (J)	153–154	1-day lesson		5A	play pennies, 2-color counters	40	30
Midchapter Review (J)	155						
Extra Practice Game: Cover the Circus Wagon	156				number cubes, rhino counters		
Real-life Investigation: Applying Addition (P)	157–158		choosing a favorite circus act				
▶ 4. Another Way to Subtract	159–162	2-day lesson			connecting cubes	41–42	31
▶ 5. Related Subtraction Facts	163–164	1-day lesson			have available: 2-color counters	43	32
Extra Practice Activity: Number Fun House	165–166				crayons (6 colors)		
▶ 6. Subtract Money	167–168	1-day lesson			penny models, 2-color counters, pennies	44	33
▶ 7. Addition and Subtraction (J) Math Van Teaching with Technology	169–170	1-day lesson	drawing a map		red and blue connecting cubes	45	34
▶ 8. Problem-Solving Strategy: Choose the Operation	171–172	1-day lesson			have available: 2-color counters	46	35
▶ 9. Problem Solvers at Work	173–174	1-day lesson			classroom items, price tags (TA 12), play pennies	47	36
ASSESSMENT OPTIONS (J) (P) Chapter Review Chapter Test Performance Assessment	 175–176 177 178						
CONNECTIONS MATH: Patterns and Functions MUSIC Home Connection	 179 180 181		 listing circus animals				

= JOURNAL OPPORTUNITY

= PORTFOLIO OPPORTUNITY TA = TEACHER AID

Technology Links	NCTM Standards
Online Exploration, p. 144B Math Forum, p. 144B	4, 8
Math Van: Counters tool Math Forum, p. 148B	8, 13
Math Van: Money Models tool Math Forum, p. 152B	8
	1, 2, 3, 4, 8
Math Forum, p. 158B	4, 8
Math Forum, p. 162B	8, 13
Math Forum, p. 166B	8
Math Van: *Dancing Cows* Math Forum, p. 168B	4, 8
Math Van: Counters tool Math Forum, p. 170D	1, 2, 3, 4, 8
Math Van: Money Models tool Math Forum, p. 172B	1, 2, 3, 4, 8
	1, 4, 8, 13

ASSESSMENT OPTIONS

INFORMAL

Ongoing Assessment

- Observation Checklist, pp. 147, 163
- Interview, pp. 145, 149, 153, 159, 161, 167, 173
- Anecdotal Report, pp. 169, 171

Portfolio Opportunities

- Chapter Project, p. 142F
- What Do You Know? p. 144
- Investigation, pp. 157–158
- Journal Writing, pp. 144, 154, 155, 170, 176
- Performance Assessment, p. 178

FORMAL

Chapter Tests

Student Book

- Midchapter Review, p. 155
- Chapter Review, pp. 175–176
- Chapter Test, p. 177

Test Masters

- Free-Response Test: Form C
- Multiple-Choice Test: Forms A and B

Performance Assessment

- What Do You Know? p. 144
- Performance Assessment, p. 178
- Self-Assessment: What Do You Think? p. 175
- Holistic Scoring Guide, Teacher's Assessment Resources, pp. 29–32
- Follow-Up Interviews, p. 178

Teacher's Assessment Resources

- Portfolio Guidelines and Forms, pp. 6–9, 27–36
- Holistic Scoring Guide, pp. 29–32
- Samples of Student Work, pp. 37–61

Chapter Objectives		Standardized Test Correlations
5A	Add, facts to 10	MAT, CAT, SAT, ITBS, CTBS
5B	Subtract, facts to 10	MAT, CAT, SAT, ITBS, CTBS
5C	Solve problems, including those that involve addition, subtraction, and choosing the operation	MAT, CAT, SAT, ITBS, CTBS

NCTM Standards Grades K–4

1 Problem Solving
2 Communication
3 Reasoning
4 Connections
5 Estimation
6 Number Sense and Numeration
7 Concepts of Whole Number Operations
8 Whole Number Computation
9 Geometry and Spatial Sense
10 Measurement
11 Statistics and Probability
12 Fractions and Decimals
13 Patterns and Relationships

Meeting Individual Needs

LEARNING STYLES

- AUDITORY/LINGUISTIC
- LOGICAL/ANALYTICAL
- VISUAL/SPATIAL
- MUSICAL
- KINESTHETIC
- SOCIAL
- INDIVIDUAL

Children who are talented in art, language, and physical activity may better understand mathematical concepts when these concepts are connected to their areas of interest. Use the following activity to stimulate the different learning styles of some of your children.

Social Learners

Have two children work together to solve problems. Assign a job to each child. One child can be the creator. Another child can be the writer. The creator thinks of the problem, while the writer records it. You may wish to select a third child to explain the problem and the solution to the class. Have the members of each group switch roles and create additional problems.

See Lesson Resources, pp. 144A, 148A, 152A, 158A, 162A, 166A, 168A, 170C, 172A.

GIFTED AND TALENTED

Introduce problems in which the beginning information is unknown. Vary the problems so children may have to add or subtract to find the answer.

I had some apples in a basket.
A rhino ate 4.
Now I have 3 apples left in the basket.
How many apples did I have to start with?

The zookeeper has some keys on her chain.
Another zookeeper gave her 5 more keys.
Now the zookeeper has 7 keys.
How many keys did she have to begin with?

See also Meeting Individual Needs, p. 161.

EXTRA SUPPORT

Specific suggestions for ways to provide extra support to children appear in every lesson in this chapter.

See Meeting Individual Needs, pp. 145, 149, 153, 159, 163, 167, 169, 171, 173.

EARLY FINISHERS

Children who finish their class work early may make invitations in the shape of tickets asking another class to attend a performance of the Great Number Circus. (See *Chapter Project*, p. 142F.)

See also Meeting Individual Needs, pp. 145, 149, 153, 159, 163, 167, 169, 171, 173.

STUDENTS ACQUIRING ENGLISH

Children may confuse addition and subtraction when solving problems. Telling children stories and then having them discuss what operation is needed will help them choose the correct operation as well as improving comprehension and thinking skills.

See also Meeting Individual Needs, pp. TK.

INCLUSION

- **For inclusion ideas, information, and suggestions, see pp. 147, T15.**
- **For gender fairness tips, see pp. 147, T15.**

USING MANIPULATIVES

Building Understanding Some children miscount or recount objects that are randomly placed. Encourage children to organize their materials in order to help them count. Connecting cubes are very useful because they are "self-organizing." Children who build a cube train for a total and snap off the part being subtracted are left with the difference.

Easy-to-Make Manipulatives If connecting cubes are not available, coated paper clips, pop-beads, or other items that connect are a good substitute. Cut-paper squares or beans can also be used. Store sets in zipper bags.

USING COOPERATIVE LEARNING

Partners Practice This strategy develops simple teamwork by bringing children together for support and to practice concepts, methods, or operations.

- **Partners work side by side, discussing and sharing ideas along the way.**
- **Partners show each other their own work, and may add to their partner's work.**

USING LITERATURE

Use the Literature Big Book *Number One, Number Fun* to introduce the chapter theme, Number Fun.

Also available in the Read-Aloud Anthology are the poems "Ten Little Candles," page 28 and "Snowflake Souffle," page 29.

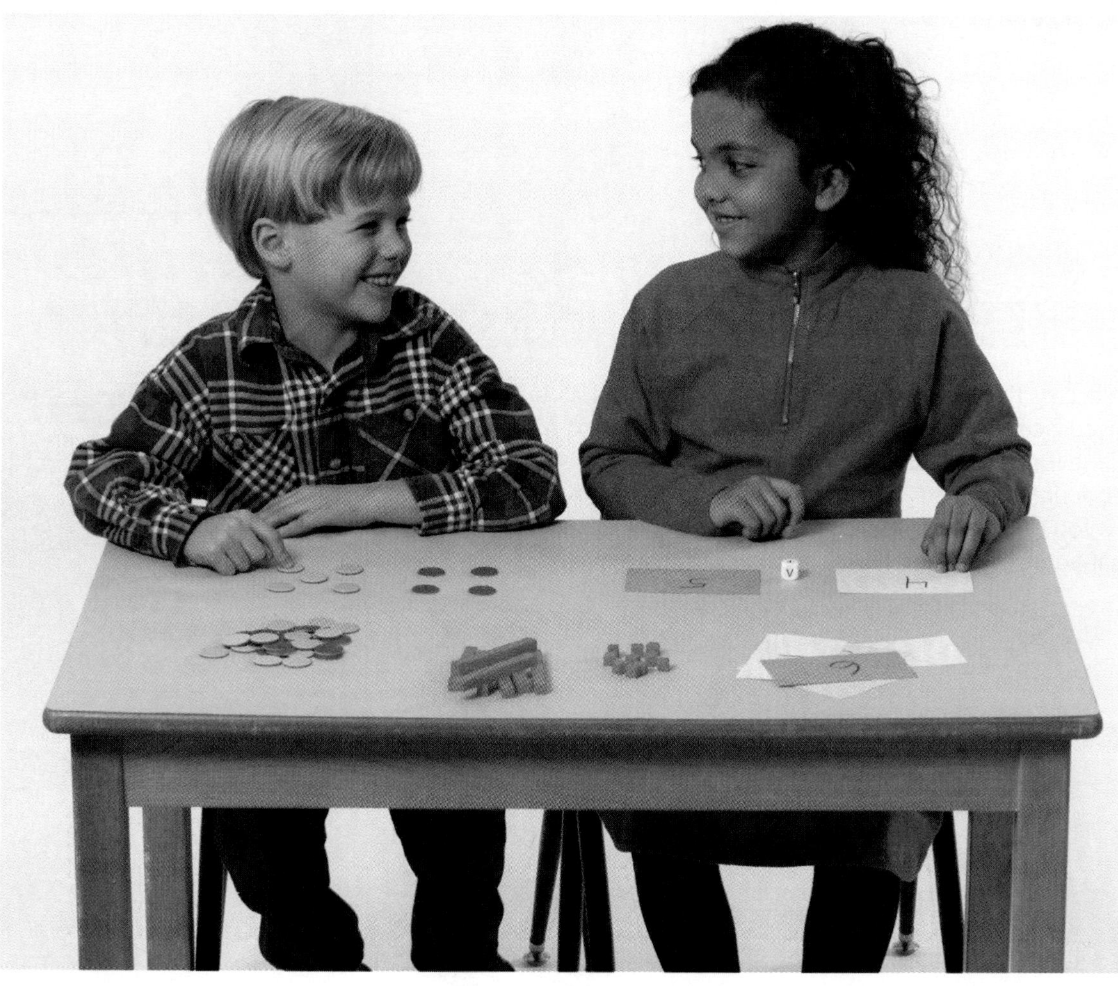

Linking Technology

This integrated package of programs and services allows students to explore, develop, and practice concepts; solve problems; build portfolios; and assess their own progress. Teachers can enhance instruction, provide remediation, and share ideas with other educational professionals.

MATH VAN ACTIVITY

In *Dancing Cows,* students use counters to figure out the total number of cows on a stage. Students can use the online notebook to write addition and subtraction number sentences. To extend the activity, students use the Math Van tools to create pictures that show how addition and subtraction are related. *Available on CD-ROM.*

MATH VAN TOOLS

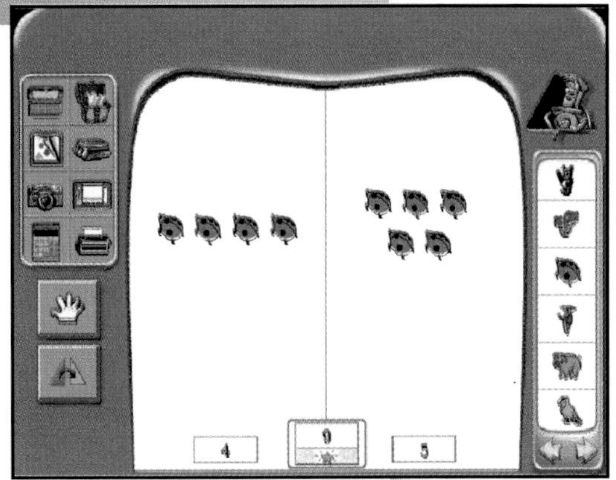

Students can use Math Van's counters to explore adding and subtracting to 10. The Tech Links on the Lesson Resources pages highlight opportunities for students to use this and other tools such as money models, drawing, online notes, and calculator to provide additional practice, reteaching, or extension. *Available on CD-ROM.*

WEB SITE http://www.mhschool.com

Teachers can access the McGraw-Hill School Division World Wide Web site for additional curriculum support at http://www.mhschool.com. Click on our Resource Village for specially designed activities linking Web sites to addition and subtraction. Motivate children by inviting them to explore Web sites that develop the chapter theme of "Number Fun." Exchange ideas on classroom management, cultural diversity, and other areas in the Math Forum.

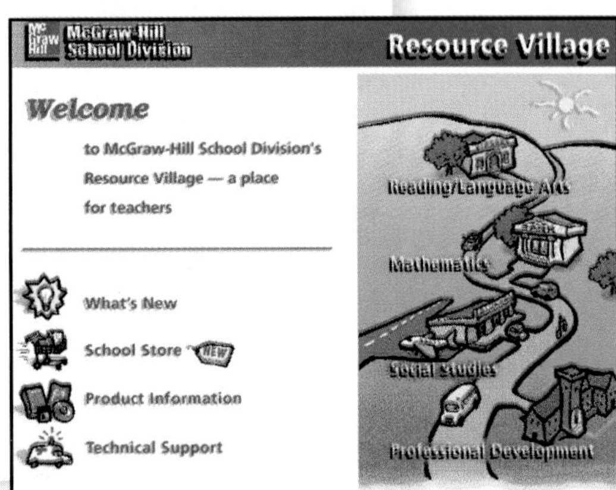

Chapter Project THE GREAT NUMBER CIRCUS

Highlighting the Math

- add to find the number in all
- subtract to find how many are left

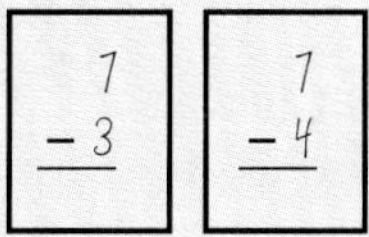

1 Starting the Project

Introduce the idea of a Great Number Circus. Guide a discussion about circuses the children have attended or have seen on TV. Children will wear costumes representing a circus act, and make up and illustrate addition and subtraction facts based on their acts.

Have children suggest acts to include in the "circus." Have children choose partners to work on the acts. Consider ways in which family and community members can participate.

2 Continuing the Project

- Pairs of children agree on two addition and two subtraction facts to present, and writes each on a card.
- Assign one child to be the ringmaster. He or she will introduce each act and read the math-fact cards aloud.
- Children make simple costumes and props.
- As groups rehearse their acts, the ringmaster practices announcing each act and reading the facts from the cards.

3 Finishing the Project

Plan a time for children to present their acts and facts. You might want to invite other classes to attend.

Community Involvement

You may wish to videotape the Great Number Circus and share it at Parents' Night.

BUILDING A PORTFOLIO

Have children write or dictate a sentence or two about the circus act they like best. Ask them to write the addition and subtraction facts used in their favorite act, and to illustrate each of the facts.

Each child's portfolio should include the writing, the addition or subtraction facts, the illustration, and any notes you make about their work.

To assess the work, refer to the Holistic Scoring Guide on page 27 in the Teacher's Assessment Resources.

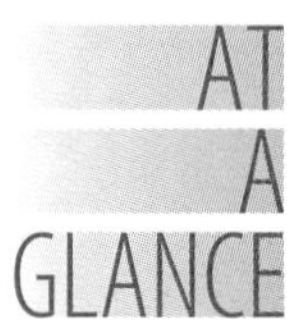

PURPOSE Introduce the theme of the chapter.

Resource Literature Big Book: *Number One Number Fun*

Using Literature

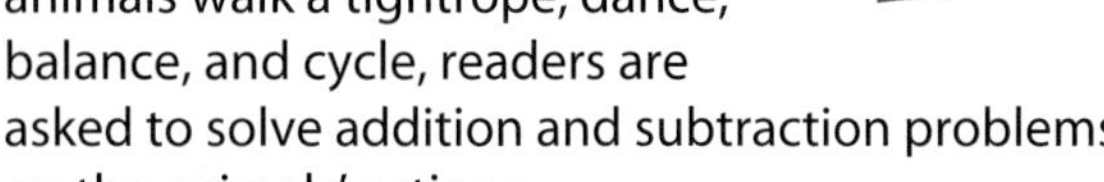

Page 143

Synopsis of the Book

In *Number One Number Fun,* Ringmaster Rat leads a lively group of barnyard animals in a circus. As the animals walk a tightrope, dance, balance, and cycle, readers are asked to solve addition and subtraction problems based on the animals' actions.

After reading the story, talk about the different animals mentioned. Ask children to think of other animals they might find on a farm. *[Possible answers: sheep, ducks, rabbits, chicks]* Ask which of the farm animals in the story they might see in a circus. *[horses]*

Developing the Theme

The theme of this chapter is "Number Fun." Lead a discussion about fun with numbers at the circus. Have children use numbers to describe what they might see at a circus.

Begin two class lists entitled "Circus Animals" and "Circus Performers." The lists should include what children learned from listening to and discussing the story, as well as information from their own experiences at the circus.

The theme will be revisited throughout the chapter on pages 145, 149, 151, 153, 156, 165, 167, 171–173.

Making Cultural Connections

Different cultures have different types of circus entertainment. In China, acrobats who perform complicated balancing acts are popular. The Moscow Circus in Russia is famous for its performing bears. Ask if any children in your class have gone to a circus other than the traditional American kind. What culture was represented? What did they see there? *[Answers may vary.]*

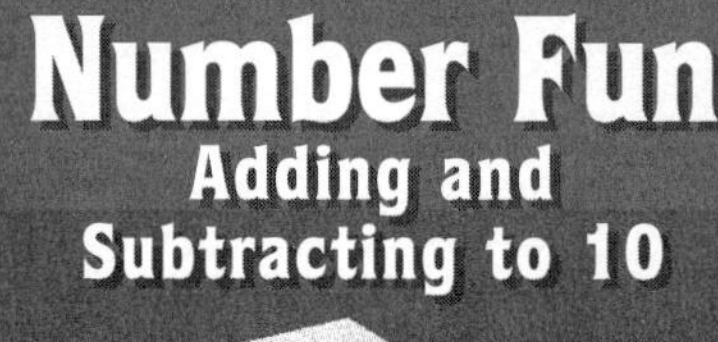

Number Fun
Adding and Subtracting to 10

Listen to the story *Number One Number Fun.*

Talk about how you have fun with numbers.

CHAPTER BIBLIOGRAPHY

How Many Feet in the Bed by Diane J. Hamm. New York: Simon & Schuster Books for Young Readers, 1991. ISBN 0-671-72638-2.

I Had a Hippopotamus by Hector Viveros Lee. New York: Lee & Low Books, 1996. ISBN 1-880000-28-8.

The Right Number of Elephants by Jeff Sheppard. New York: HarperCollins Children's Books, 1990. ISBN 0-06-025616-8.

COMMUNITY INVOLVEMENT

You may wish to invite a local gymnast to demonstrate samples of the kinds of acrobatics children would see at a circus. Get an itinerary in advance and look for addition or subtraction patterns of certain tricks to point out to children, such as juggling (adding 1 to a number). Invite other classes to attend.

Name

What Do You Know?

Mike has 9¢ to buy balloons.
He buys a balloon and a balloon.

1. How much money does Mike spend? 7 ¢

   5¢ + 2¢ = 7 ¢

2. How much money does Mike have left? 2 ¢

   Write the subtraction sentence. 9¢ − 7¢ = 2¢

You have 9¢.
Show which balloon you would buy.
Write the addition sentence.

VOCABULARY

These math words will be used in this chapter:

part (p. 145)	**order** (p. 149)
total (p. 145)	**diagonal** (p. 156)
sum (p. 147)	**difference** (p. 161)
fact (p. 149)	**operation** (p. 171)
related facts (p. 149)	

JOURNAL Children may record new words in their math journals. Encourage them to show examples and draw pictures to help tell what the words mean.

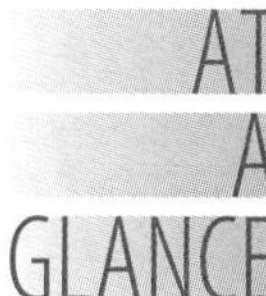

AT A GLANCE

PURPOSE Assess children's ability to apply prior knowledge of adding and subtracting to solve problems.

Materials have available: counters

Assessing Prior Knowledge

Draw a picture of two stickers, one with a 4¢ price tag and one with a 3¢ price tag.

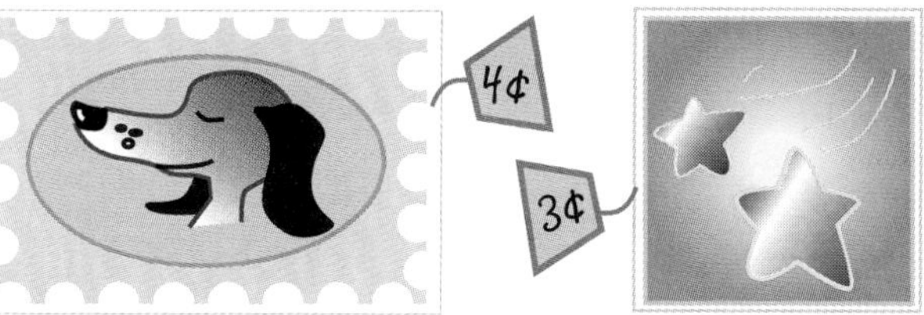

Ask children how much it costs to buy both stickers. *[7¢]* Allow them to use counters to find the answer.

Give positive feedback to children on what they already know about adding and subtracting. Tell them that in chapter 5 they will be learning more about adding and subtracting and different ways to write addition and subtraction sentences.

Page 144

Discuss the picture at the top of the page. Ask children how much a green balloon costs.

Assign problems 1–2. Make sure children understand that they get the prices from the picture. Have counters available for children who want to use them. Observe children as they work.

Prerequisite Skills

- *Can children identify when to use addition and when to use subtraction to solve problems?*
- *Can children add and subtract to solve problems?*

After children have solved the first two problems, ask volunteers to share their solutions and methods. Get children to discuss each others' methods.

Building a Portfolio

Assign the problem at the bottom of the page. This piece provides an indicator of where children are in their understanding of using addition to solve problems.

A Portfolio Checklist for Students and a Checklist for Teachers are provided in Teacher's Assessment Resources, pp. 33–34.

LESSON 5.1

Vertical Addition

OBJECTIVE Explore adding in vertical form.

Day 1 Explore Activity: Another Way to Add
Day 2 Vertical Addition

RESOURCE REMINDER
Math Center Cards 28
Practice 37–38, Reteach 37–38, Extend 37–38

SKILLS TRACE	
GRADE K	• Explore adding facts to 10. *(Chapter 11)*
GRADE 1	• Explore adding in vertical form, facts to 10.
GRADE 2	• Explore adding, facts to 12. *(Chapter 1)*

LESSON RESOURCES

MANIPULATIVES

MANIPULATIVE WARM-UP

Cooperative Pairs — **Social**

OBJECTIVE Explore adding, facts to 10.

Resources Jumbo Activity Book, page 9; Stickers, sheet 1 (rhino counters)

▶ Display 3 red and 4 blue rhino counters on Jumbo Activity Book page 9. Ask children how many there are in each part. Then have a volunteer combine the counters and tell how many there are in all. Repeat with 2 yellow and 5 red rhino counters.

▶ Have children work in pairs. One child shows some counters and writes the number. The partner does the same. Children take turns finding and writing the total.

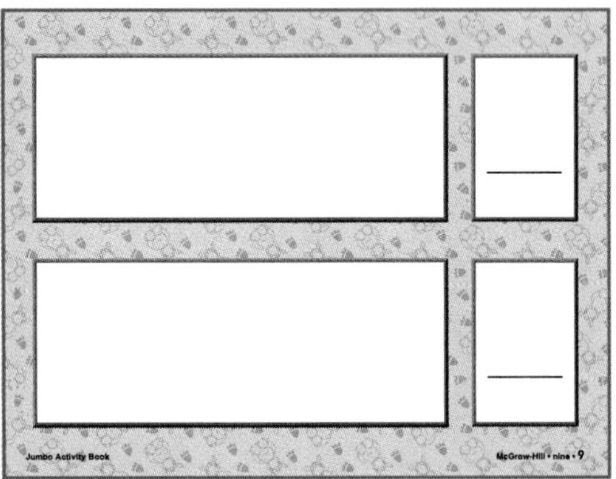

ART

CONNECTION ACTIVITY

Cooperative Pairs — **Visual/Spatial**

OBJECTIVE Connect addition facts with art.

Materials per pair: 1–5 spinner (TA 7), crayons

▶ Have each child in a pair draw a large circus ring on one sheet of paper. One child spins the spinner to find the first part of an addition fact and draws simple animal faces in one ring to show the number. The second child spins for the second part of the fact and draws faces in the other ring to show that number.

▶ Together, the partners add the parts and write the total number of animals in the circus rings.

▶ Ask volunteers to tell the parts and the total in their addition facts and to talk about the animal faces they drew.

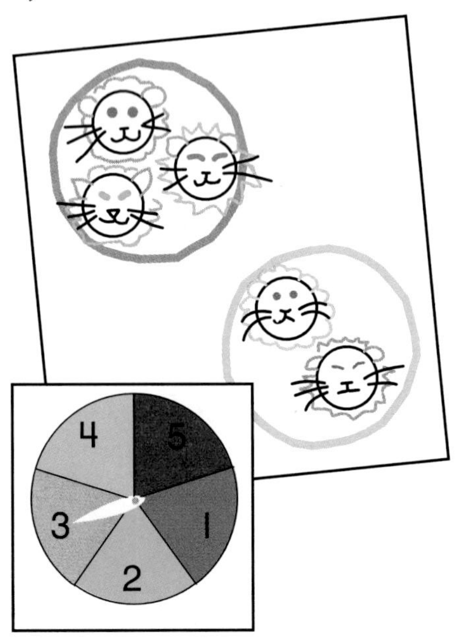

DAILY MATH

PREVIOUS DAY QUICK REVIEW

What number is 2 more

1. than 2? *[4]*
2. than 4? *[6]*
3. than 3? *[5]*
4. than 5? *[7]*

FAST FACTS

1. 2 + 2 *[4]*
2. 3 + 2 *[5]*
3. 4 + 3 *[7]*
4. 5 + 1 *[6]*

Problem of the Day • 28

Read aloud to children:

There are 6 clowns inside a car.
The car can hold 10 clowns.
How many more clowns can fit in the car? *[4]*

TECH LINK

ONLINE EXPLORATION

Use our Web-linked activities and lesson plans to connect your students to the real world of the circus.

MATH FORUM

Idea To reinforce the concepts of across and down, I have volunteers write their names on the chalkboard going across and then going down.

Visit our Resource Village at http://www.mhschool.com to access the Online Exploration and the Math Forum.

MATH CENTER

Practice

OBJECTIVE Find sums to 10.

Materials per child: 2 spinners (1-5), 10 connecting cubes (5 red, 5 blue), Math Center Recording Sheet (TA 38 optional)

Children will spin two spinners, find the sum using connecting cubes, and write the addition two ways. If children spin the same two numbers again in the same order, encourage them to check their previous addition. If the order is different, encourage them to add in the new order.

Problem Solving

OBJECTIVE Match parts and their total.

Materials Four addend/sum cards, Math Center Recording Sheet (TA 38 optional)

Prepare Make the four cards shown on the Math Center Card. A total is drawn in a circle at the bottom. Parts are in a box at the top.

Children will match addends and their sums. The cards will form a square. You may guide them to match a "box" on one card with a "circle" or ring on another card.

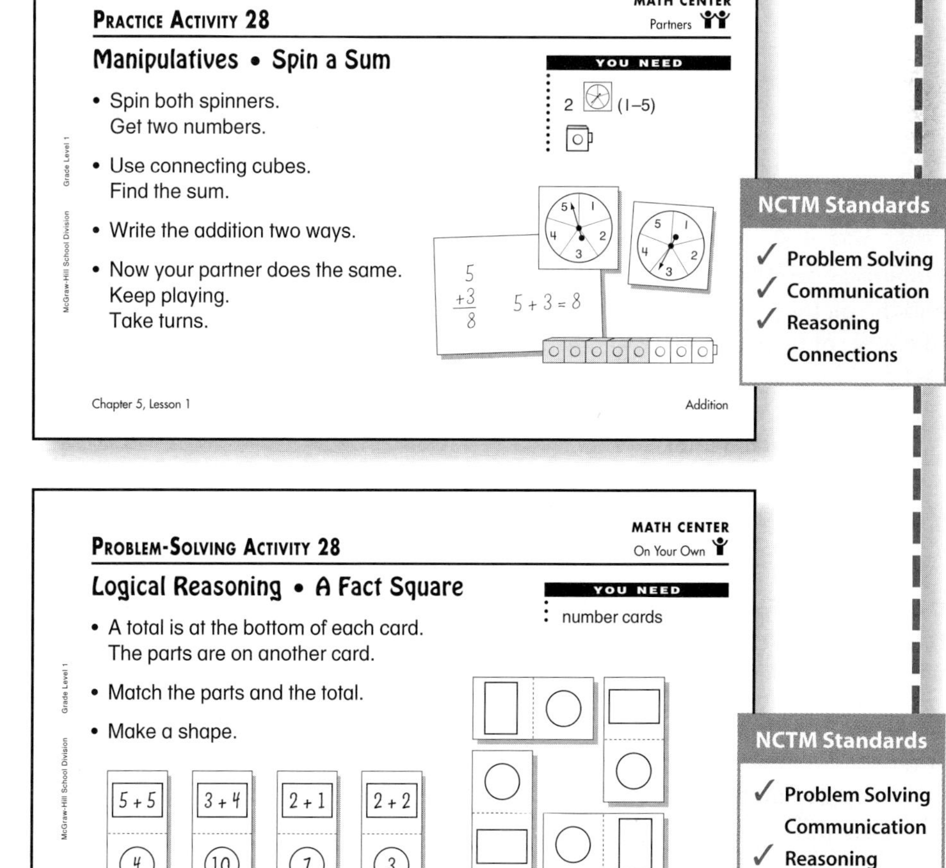

PRACTICE ACTIVITY 28 — MATH CENTER, Partners

Manipulatives • Spin a Sum

YOU NEED: 2 spinners (1–5); connecting cubes

- Spin both spinners. Get two numbers.
- Use connecting cubes. Find the sum.
- Write the addition two ways.
- Now your partner does the same. Keep playing. Take turns.

Chapter 5, Lesson 1 — Addition

NCTM Standards
✓ Problem Solving
✓ Communication
✓ Reasoning
Connections

PROBLEM-SOLVING ACTIVITY 28 — MATH CENTER, On Your Own

Logical Reasoning • A Fact Square

YOU NEED: number cards

- A total is at the bottom of each card. The parts are on another card.
- Match the parts and the total.
- Make a shape.

Chapter 5, Lesson 1 — Addition

NCTM Standards
✓ Problem Solving
Communication
✓ Reasoning
Connections

Lesson 5.1

EXPLORE ACTIVITY

Another Way to Add

OBJECTIVE Children explore the relationship between horizontal and vertical notation for addition.

Materials per pair: 5 red and 5 blue connecting cubes

1 Motivate — Cooperative Pairs

Materials per pair: 5 red and 5 blue connecting cubes

Begin by having one child in each pair make a cube train of 4 red cubes and the other make a train of 3 blue cubes.

- **How could you show the total?** *[Possible answer: Join the cube trains to show 7 in all.]*

Have a volunteer write the numbers for the parts and the total on the chalkboard. Then have children unsnap their cubes.

- **How could you arrange your cubes and write the parts and the total in a different way?**

Have volunteers draw their solutions on the chalkboard. *[Possible answers: Children may make vertical cube trains or may display one color horizontally and the other vertically, or they may write the numbers vertically.]*

2 Develop

Page 145

Working Together Have children tell stories about the seals and the pictured models at the top of the page. Point out the two ways of recording parts and totals—horizontal form and vertical form.

- **What is different about the ways the parts and the totals are recorded?** *[Possible answer: One is written across and the other is written down.]*

Have pairs make cube trains of two colors and write the numbers for the parts and total horizontally and vertically.

Developing Algebra Sense Ask children if switching the order of the parts changes the total. Have them explain their answers. *[No; the size of the parts stays the same.]*

CRITICAL THINKING

After children complete the page, ask:

- **Why do you get the same total going across as going down?** *[The parts are the same in both.]*

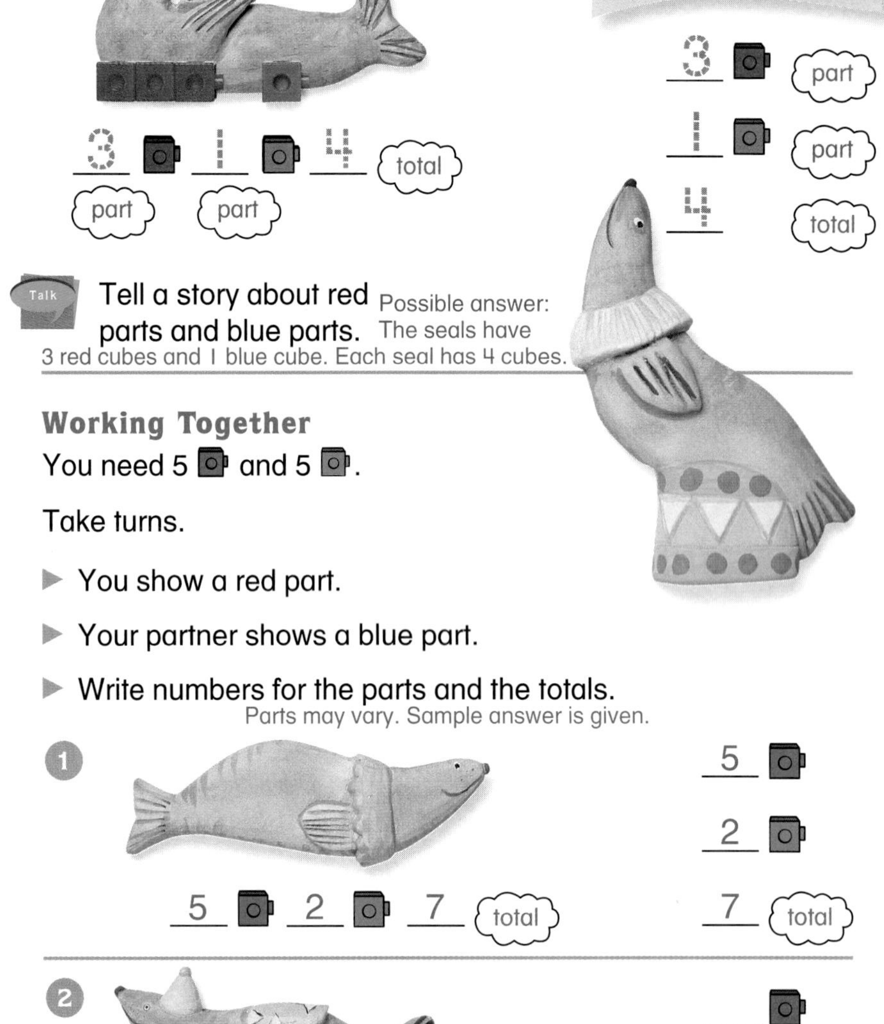

Name ________

Explore Activity

Another Way to Add

3 ▪ 1 ▪ 4 (total)
(part) (part)

3 ▪ (part)
1 ▪ (part)
4 (total)

Talk: Tell a story about red parts and blue parts. Possible answer: The seals have 3 red cubes and 1 blue cube. Each seal has 4 cubes.

Working Together

You need 5 ▪ and 5 ▪.

Take turns.

- You show a red part.
- Your partner shows a blue part.
- Write numbers for the parts and the totals.

Parts may vary. Sample answer is given.

1. 5 ▪ 2 ▪ 7 (total) — 5 ▪ / 2 ▪ / 7 (total)

2. ___ ▪ ___ ▪ ___ (total) — ___ ▪ / ___ ▪ / ___ (total)

CHAPTER 5 *Lesson 1* — one hundred forty-five • 145

MEETING INDIVIDUAL NEEDS

EARLY FINISHERS

Have children make up and illustrate an addition story about a circus animal other than seals. Then have them write the numbers for the parts and the total in both horizontal and vertical forms.

EXTRA SUPPORT

Use cards with the words *part* and *total* as children create cube trains in two colors. Ask them to place the cubes on the cards as they work.

ONGOING ASSESSMENT

Interview Determine if children understand that the horizontal and vertical forms are two ways of writing the same thing by having them make a cube train for 2 and 3 and then having them write the parts and total in both forms.

- **What are the parts?** *[2 and 3]* **What is the total?** *[5]*
- **Why are both totals the same?** *[The parts are the same.]*

Follow Up For children having difficulty, assign **Reteach 37.**

For children who demonstrate understanding, assign **Extend 37.**

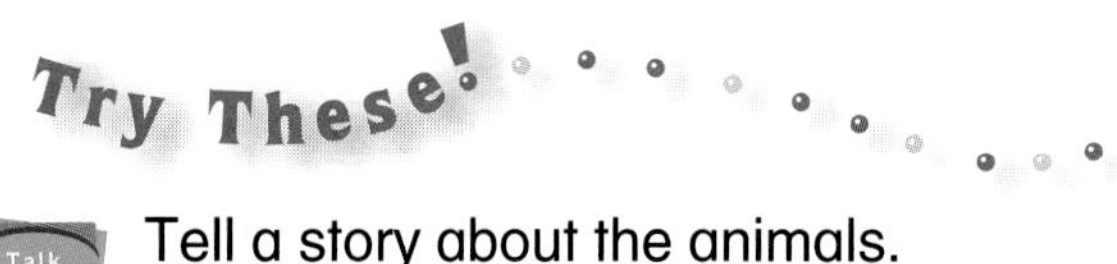

Tell a story about the animals.
Write numbers for the parts and the totals.

Possible story for exercise
There are 4 dogs with gree
hats and 1 dog with a purp
hat. There are 5 dogs with

We explored parts and totals going across and going down.
Ask your child to tell you a story about one of the pictures.

Page 146

Try These Assign practice exercises 1–4.

Have children tell their partners a story about each picture before they write the numbers.

3 Close

Check for Understanding by having children make a cube train with 4 red and 5 blue cubes, and then write the parts and total horizontally and vertically.

Tomorrow children will record sums vertically.

PRACTICE • 37

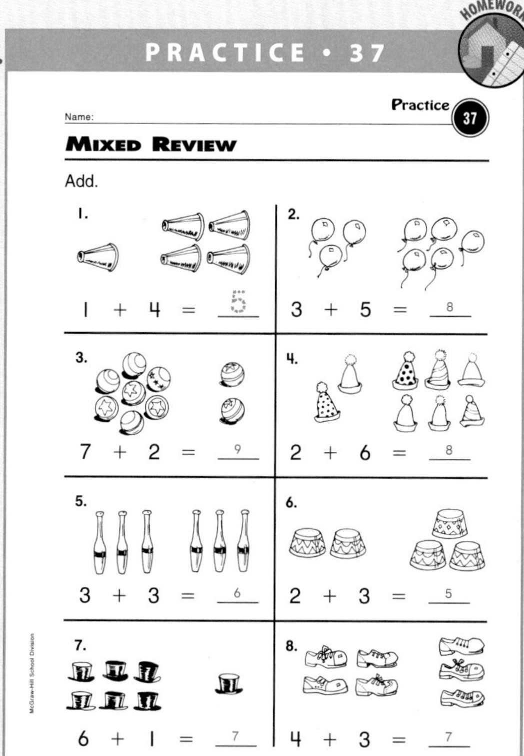

RETEACH • 37

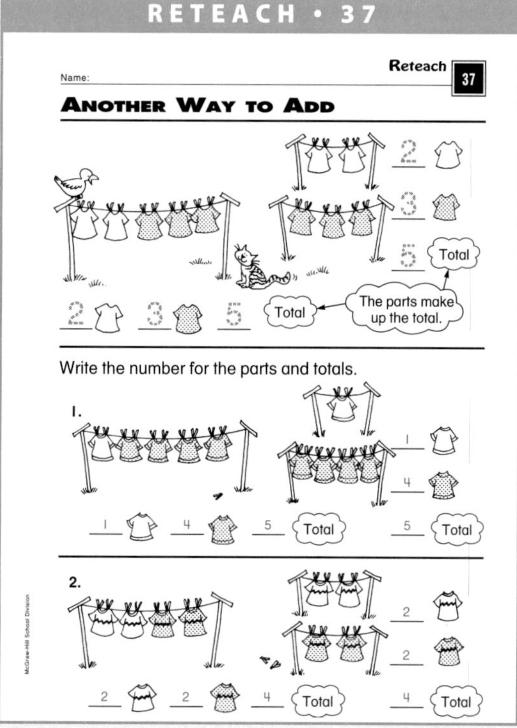

EXTEND • 37

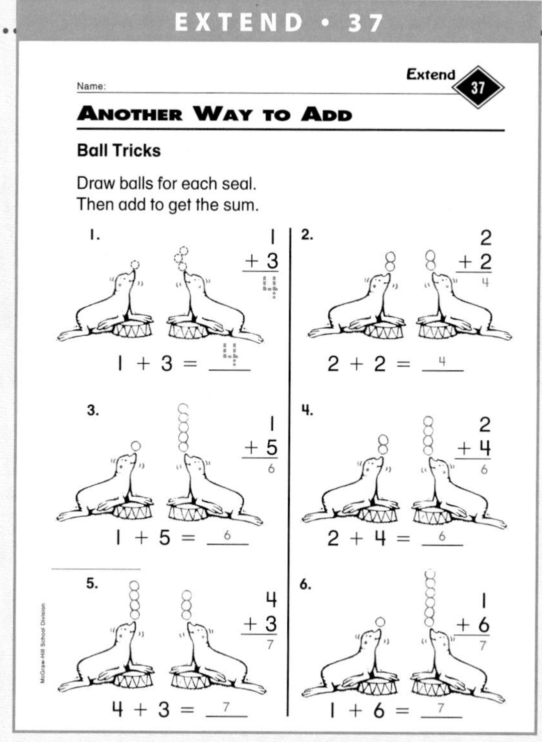

DAY 2

Vertical Addition

OBJECTIVE Children add in vertical form.

Materials per child: 9 red and 9 blue connecting cubes

1 Motivate — Whole Class

Materials per child: 9 red and 9 blue connecting cubes

Display a train of 6 red cubes and 3 blue cubes. Have a volunteer say the numbers for the parts and the total. *[6, 3, 9]* Write the addition sentence on the chalkboard and ask the class to read it aloud with you. *[6 + 3 = 9]* Then write the addition fact in vertical form, and read it aloud from top to bottom. Point to the numbers:

$6 + 3 = 9$ $\begin{array}{r} 6 \\ +\ 3 \\ \hline 9 \end{array}$

- **What is the same about these two addition facts?** *[parts and total]* **What is different?** *[the way they are written]*

Show a train of 2 blue cubes and 5 red cubes. Have a child write the addition sentence on the chalkboard and read it aloud. Have another child write the addition vertically and read it aloud. Point to the addition sentence and the vertical addition.

- **Which number do you say first in each fact?** *[2]*

Ask children to make two cube trains with some of their red and blue cubes. Then have them write the addition in vertical form. Have several volunteers display their trains and read their facts aloud.

2 Develop

Page 147

Discuss the example. Point out that the total in an addition fact is called the *sum.* Assign exercises 1–6.

Critical Thinking
After children answer the question on the page, ask:

- **Is the sum the same for 2 yellow and 2 green cubes as for 2 red and 2 blue cubes? Why?** *[Yes. You add the numbers, not the colors.]*

Page 148

Try These Assign practice exercises 1–6.

Mixed Review Children review subtraction sentences.

3 Close

Check for Understanding by displaying a train of 5 red cubes and 3 blue cubes. Have children write the addition in the two forms. *[5 + 3 = 8 and* $\begin{array}{r} 5 \\ +\ 3 \\ \hline 8 \end{array}$ *]*

Name ____________________

Vertical Addition

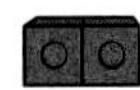

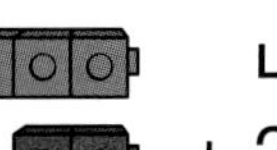

$4 + 2 = 6$ (sum)

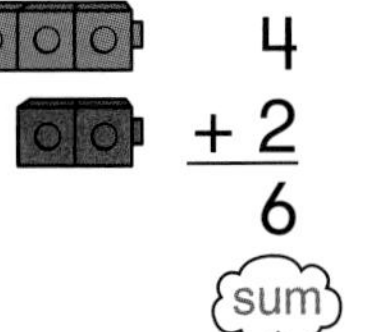

$\begin{array}{r} 4 \\ +\ 2 \\ \hline 6 \end{array}$ (sum)

two ways to write addition

You need 9 red and 9 blue cubes.

- Show parts with cubes.
- Color to show the parts.
- Find the sum.

Colors and positions of colors may vary.

1. 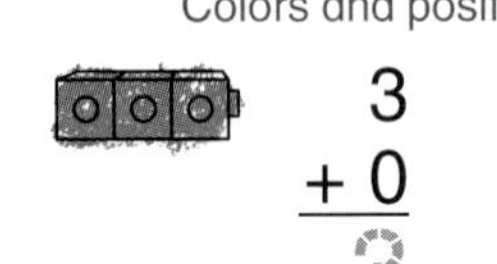 $\begin{array}{r} 3 \\ +\ 0 \\ \hline 3 \end{array}$

2. 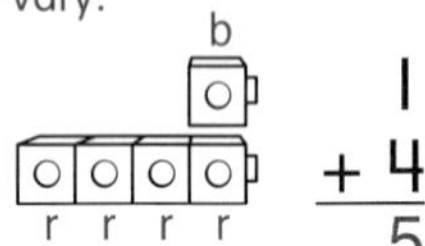 $\begin{array}{r} 1 \\ +\ 4 \\ \hline 5 \end{array}$

3. 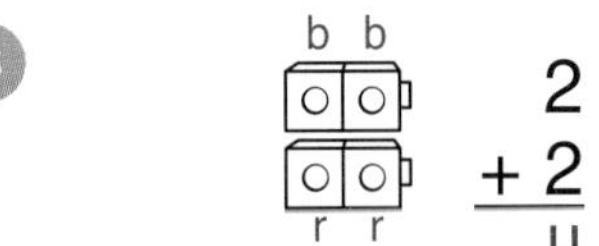 $\begin{array}{r} 2 \\ +\ 2 \\ \hline 4 \end{array}$

4. 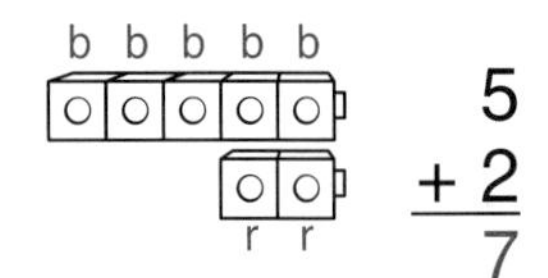 $\begin{array}{r} 5 \\ +\ 2 \\ \hline 7 \end{array}$

5. 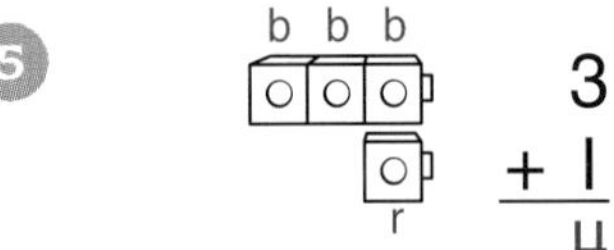 $\begin{array}{r} 3 \\ +\ 1 \\ \hline 4 \end{array}$

6. 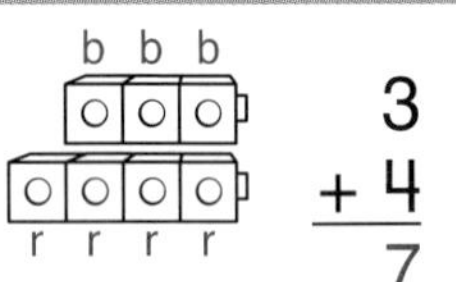 $\begin{array}{r} 3 \\ +\ 4 \\ \hline 7 \end{array}$

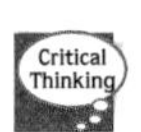

How could you use counters to show addition?

Possible answer: Show each part with the counters, then count to find the sum.

MEETING INDIVIDUAL NEEDS

GENDER FAIRNESS

A class list, alphabetized by name, can help you ask Critical Thinking questions in an impartial way. Encourage all answers, especially from reticent children.

INCLUSION

Encourage children who are having difficulty to use pictures or manipulatives to demonstrate the relationship between horizontal and vertical forms of addition.

ONGOING ASSESSMENT

Observation Checklist Determine if children understand how to record addition vertically by observing if they write the fact directly or need to write the horizontal addition sentence first.

Follow Up Children who have difficulty can make models of the numbers and write the addition horizontally, then rearrange their models and write the addition vertically. Then assign **Reteach 38.**

For children who demonstrate understanding, assign **Extend 38.**

Try These!

Add.

1. $\begin{array}{r} 4 \\ +\ 3 \\ \hline 7 \end{array}$

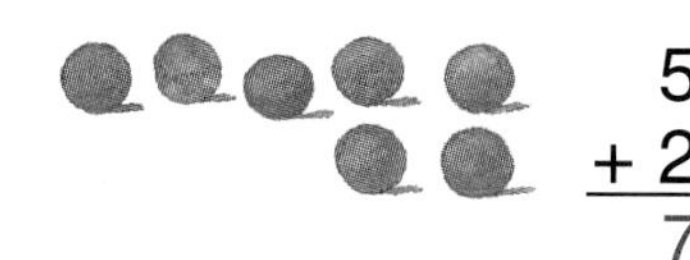

2. $\begin{array}{r} 5 \\ +\ 2 \\ \hline 7 \end{array}$

3. $\begin{array}{r} 8 \\ +\ 2 \\ \hline 10 \end{array}$

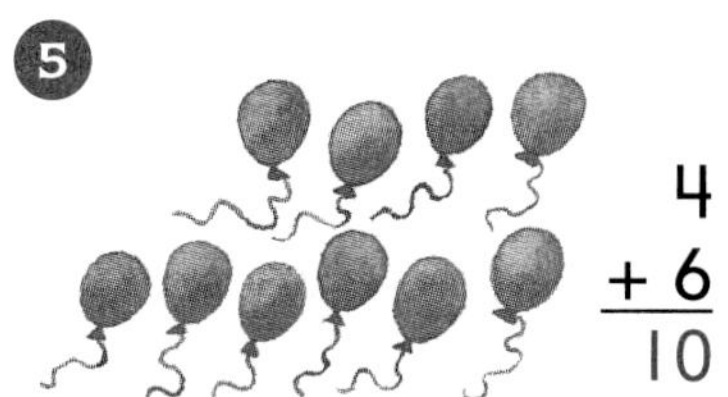

4. $\begin{array}{r} 6 \\ +\ 3 \\ \hline 9 \end{array}$

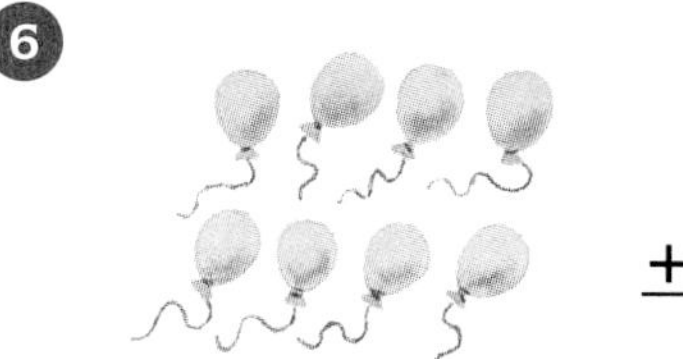

5. $\begin{array}{r} 4 \\ +\ 6 \\ \hline 10 \end{array}$

6. $\begin{array}{r} 4 \\ +\ 4 \\ \hline 8 \end{array}$

Mixed Review

7. 5 − 1 = 4 5 − 2 = 3 5 − 3 = 2

8. 6 − 1 = 5 6 − 2 = 4 6 − 3 = 3

At Home: We learned another way to show addition. Ask your child to explain the 4 + 2 example on page 147.

Alternate Teaching Strategy

Have children draw pictures or objects to illustrate this story.

- **Six big elephants lead the circus parade. Three baby elephants follow them. How many elephants are there?** *[9]*

Then have children write the horizontal addition sentence.

- **What is another way to write the addition fact 6 + 3 = 9?** *[from top to bottom]*

Write both forms of the addition fact on the chalkboard and draw arrows to match the parts.

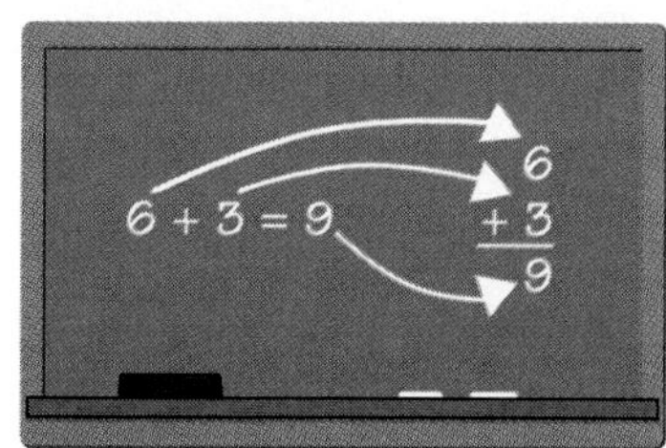

- **Does it matter which way you add? Why?** *[Possible answer: No; you get the same total because the parts are the same.]*

Continue with other stories involving circus animals.

PRACTICE • 38

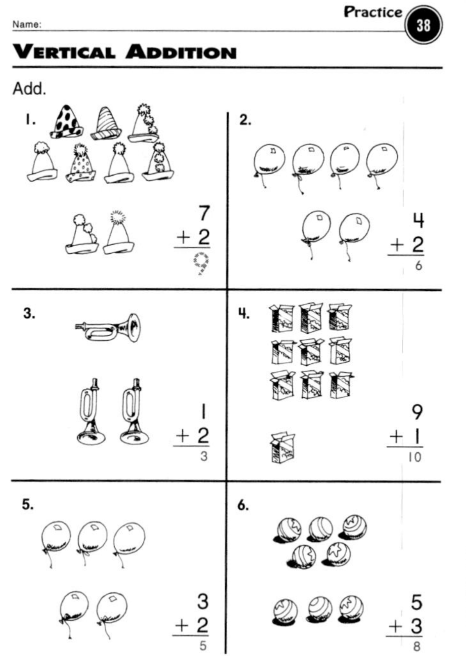

Practice 38

Name:

VERTICAL ADDITION

Add.

1. 7 + 2 = 9
2. 4 + 2 = 6
3. 1 + 2 = 3
4. 9 + 1 = 10
5. 3 + 2 = 5
6. 5 + 3 = 8

RETEACH • 38

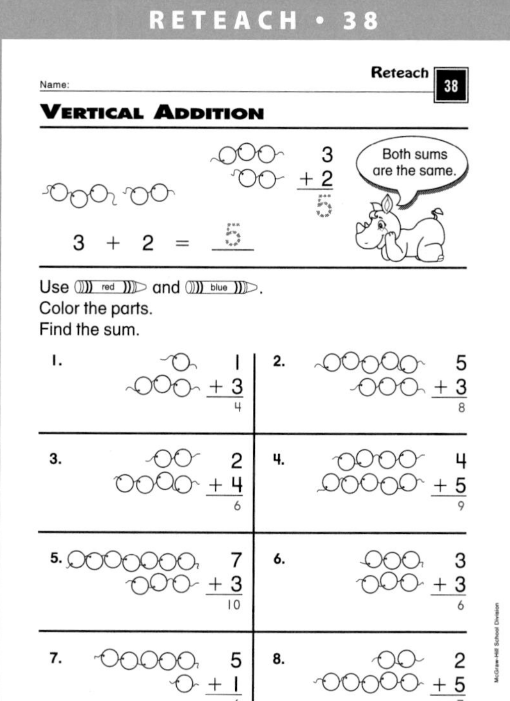

Reteach 38

Name:

VERTICAL ADDITION

3 + 2 = 5 (3 + 2 = 5 vertically). Both sums are the same.

Use red and blue. Color the parts. Find the sum.

1. 1 + 3 = 4
2. 5 + 3 = 8
3. 2 + 4 = 6
4. 4 + 5 = 9
5. 7 + 3 = 10
6. 3 + 3 = 6
7. 5 + 1 = 6
8. 2 + 5 = 7

EXTEND • 38

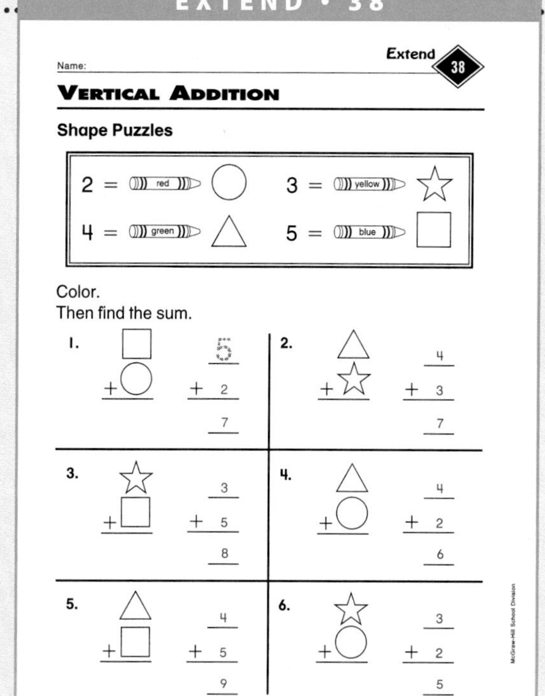

Extend 38

Name:

VERTICAL ADDITION

Shape Puzzles

2 = red ○ 3 = yellow ☆
4 = green △ 5 = blue □

Color. Then find the sum.

1. 5 + 2 = 7
2. 4 + 3 = 7
3. 3 + 5 = 8
4. 4 + 2 = 6
5. 4 + 5 = 9
6. 3 + 2 = 5

LESSON 5.2

Related Addition Facts

OBJECTIVES Use the Order Property to find sums; recognize related facts.

Day 1 Related Addition Facts

RESOURCE REMINDER
Math Center Cards 29
Practice 39, Reteach 39, Extend 39

SKILLS TRACE

GRADE K	• Explore adding facts to 10. *(Chapter 11)*
GRADE 1	• Use the Order Property to find sums to 10. • Recognize related facts.
GRADE 2	• Use the Order Property and related facts to find sums to 12. *(Chapter 1)*

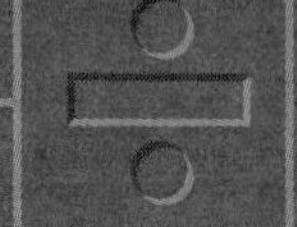

LESSON RESOURCES

WARM-UP

Cooperative Pairs — **Visual/Spatial**

OBJECTIVE Make domino cards and use them to write addition facts.

Materials per child: a sheet of $8\frac{1}{2}$" x 11" art paper

▶ Assign each pair 5 different addition combinations, such as 3 + 4, 1 + 4, 2 + 2, 6 + 1, 5 + 5. Have children make domino cards by drawing circus animals or balls, balloons, and pennants.

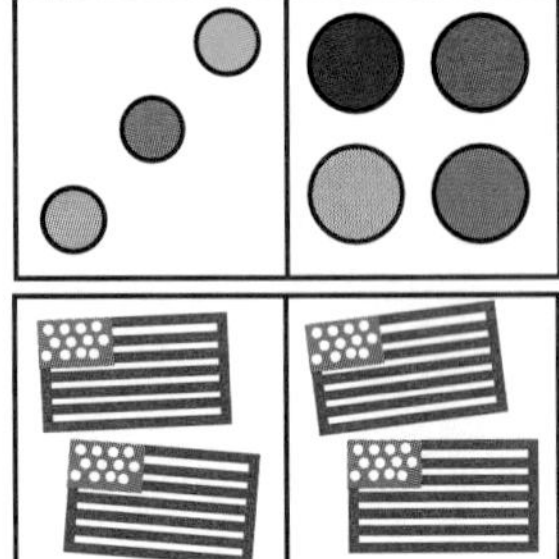
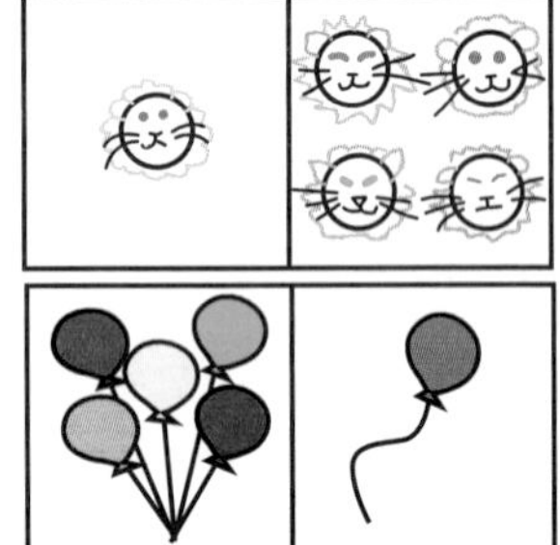

▶ Have children write an addition fact for each domino card in horizontal or vertical form. Children exchange cards until all have written a sentence for each card.

CONNECTION ACTIVITY

Cooperative Pairs — **Kinesthetic**

OBJECTIVE Connect related addition facts with physical education.

▶ Write this addition fact on the chalkboard:

$$\begin{array}{r} 4 \\ +3 \\ \hline 7 \end{array}$$

▶ Have one child in each pair jump in place four times, while the partner counts to 4. Then have the second child jump three times, while the first child counts on to 7. Have children say the addition fact.

▶ Have partners trade places. The first child jumps three times, and the second child jumps four times. This time, children count to 3, and then count on to 7. Have children say the addition fact.

▶ Repeat with other addition facts to 10.

DAILY MATH

PREVIOUS DAY QUICK REVIEW

Add.

1. 1 +3 [4]
2. 6 +0 [6]
3. 1 + 3 [4]
4. 6 + 0 [6]

FAST FACTS

1. 2 + 3 [5]
2. 3 + 3 [6]
3. 4 + 3 [7]
4. 5 + 3 [8]

Problem of the Day • 29

Read aloud to children:

There are 4 bareback riders on a horse. Two riders fall off and 3 more get on. How many riders are on the horse now? *[5]*

TECH LINK

MATH VAN

Tools You may wish to use the Counters tool with this lesson.

MATH FORUM

Idea Children soon make the connection between related addition facts and related subtraction facts. I encourage them to draw pictures in their journals or tell oral stories to share what they have discovered.

Visit our Resource Village at http://www.mhschool.com to see more of the Math Forum.

MATH CENTER

Practice

OBJECTIVE Find related addition facts for 7.

Materials per child: 2 colors of connecting cubes (7 of each); Math Center Recording Sheet (TA 38 optional)

Children use connecting cubes to show related addition facts for 7. They can draw a picture to show the addition and write the addition facts.
[1 + 6 = 7, 6 + 1 = 7
2 + 5 = 7, 5 + 2 = 7
3 + 4 = 7, 4 + 3 = 7]

PRACTICE ACTIVITY 29 — MATH CENTER On Your Own

Algebra Sense • Make Seven

YOU NEED: 7 cubes, 7 cubes

- Make 7 in as many ways as you can. Use these numbers:

  0 1 2 3 4 5 6 7

- Use cubes to show the parts.
- Draw a picture to show the addition.
- Write the addition.

Build as many sums of seven as you can. Show your work.

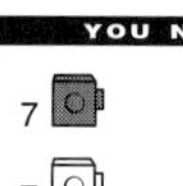

Grade Level 1 · McGraw-Hill School Division

Chapter 5, Lesson 2 — Addition

NCTM Standards
✓ Problem Solving
Communication
✓ Reasoning
Connections

Problem Solving

OBJECTIVE Use addition facts to complete a puzzle.

Materials per child: inch graph paper (TA 1) or Math Center Recording Sheet (TA 38 optional)

You may want to ask students which sums are the same and why.

Answer:

	6	6	
8	5	3	8
4	1	3	4
	6	6	

PROBLEM-SOLVING ACTIVITY 29 — MATH CENTER On Your Own

Spatial Reasoning • Add All Ways

YOU NEED: graph paper

Copy and complete.
Write sums in the empty boxes.

- Add up and down. ↕
- Add across. ↔

Make your own puzzle.
Use 1, 2, 3, 4, or 5.

	↕	↕	
↔	5	3	↔
↔	1	3	↔
	↕	↕	

Grade Level 1 · McGraw-Hill School Division

Chapter 5, Lesson 2 — Addition

NCTM Standards
✓ Problem Solving
Communication
✓ Reasoning
Connections

Related Addition Facts

OBJECTIVES Children use the Order Property to find sums; recognize related facts.

Materials have available per child: 10 two-color counters

1 Motivate — Whole Class

Draw groups of 2 and 5 counters on the chalkboard. Have children tell the sum. Ask a volunteer to write the addition sentence. *[2 + 5 = 7]* Draw the two groups of counters again, reversing the order. Have children tell the sum and ask a volunteer to write the new addition sentence. *[5 + 2 = 7]*

- **How are these addition facts the same?** *[Possible answer: They have the same parts and the same sum.]*
- **How are they different?** *[Possible answer: The parts are turned around.]*

2 Develop

Page 149

Read the addition facts at the top of the page with children and discuss the Talk question. Tell children that the order of the numbers being added has been changed.

- **Why do you think 5 + 4 = 9 and 4 + 5 = 9 are called related facts?** *[Possible answer: Because some things about them are the same—they show adding the same numbers.]*

CRITICAL THINKING
After children answer the question on the page, ask:

- **If you know an addition fact, how can you find its related fact?** *[You can change the order of the numbers you add.]*

Page 150

Try These Assign practice exercises 1–6. Ask:

- **Why are there no related facts for exercises 1–3?** *[Possible answer: The two parts are the same, so the related fact would be exactly the same.]*

More to Explore Children find the missing part in addition facts. They begin to understand the algebraic concept that any number in a sentence could be the unknown number.

3 Close

Check for Understanding by having children find the sums and write the related facts for the following exercises.

5	2	8	0
+ 2	+ 5	+ 0	+ 8
[7]	*[7]*	*[8]*	*[8]*

Name

Related Addition Facts

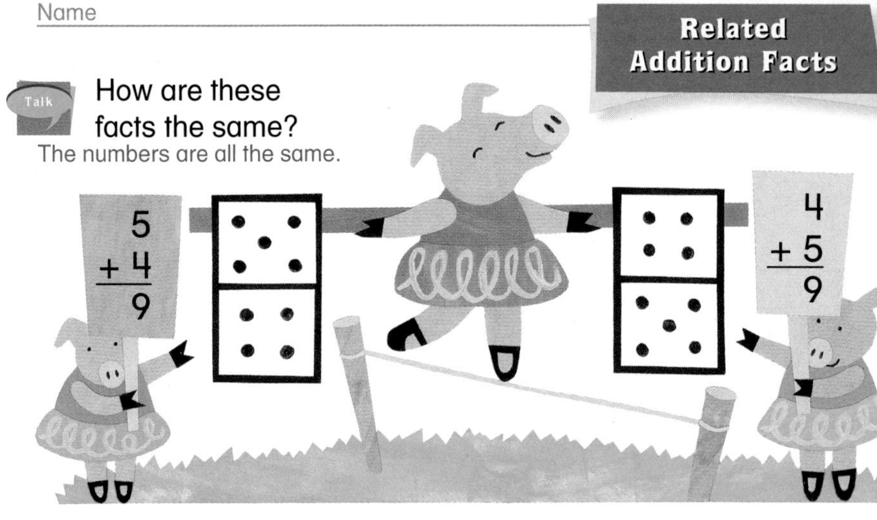

Draw the other part. Add.
Arrangements of dots may vary.

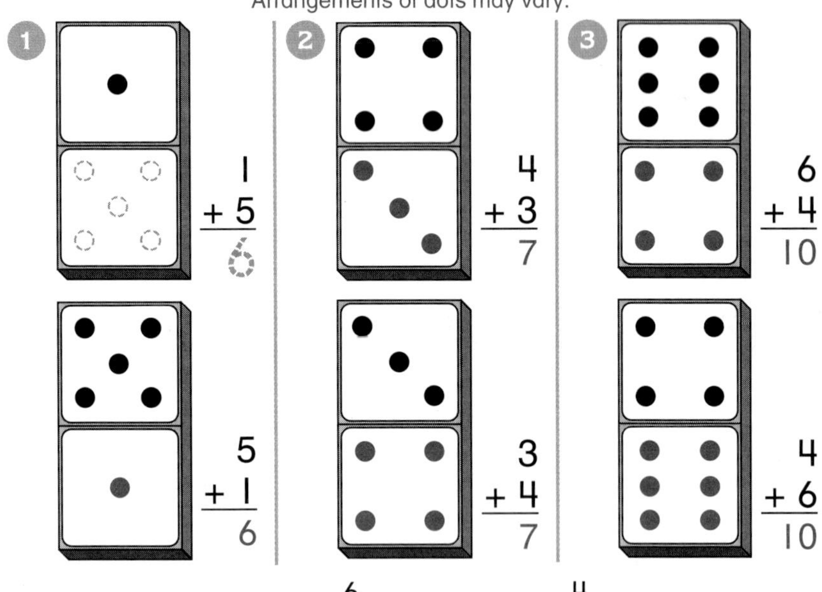

Critical Thinking: Why is the sum for 6 + 4 the same as 4 + 6? The sums are the same because the parts are the same.

MEETING INDIVIDUAL NEEDS

EARLY FINISHERS

Have children draw a picture and write the addition sentence and the related fact.

EXTRA SUPPORT

Pair children and have them use two-color counters to show the related facts for 3 + 5, 5 + 4, 2 + 7, and 7 + 0.

ONGOING ASSESSMENT

Interview Determine if children understand the Order Property by asking:

- **How are 6 + 3 = 9 and 3 + 6 = 9 alike? different?** *[The parts and the sums are the same; the order of the parts is different.]*
- **What happens to the sum when you change the order of the parts?** *[The sum stays the same.]*

Follow Up Have children use dominoes to show related facts. Then assign **Reteach 39.**

For children who demonstrate understanding, assign **Extend 39.**

Try These!

Add.

1. $3 + 3 = 6$
2. $4 + 4 = 8$

3. $5 + 5 = 10$

4. $7 + 2 = 9$ | $2 + 7 = 9$ | $1 + 6 = 7$ | $6 + 1 = 7$ | $9 + 0 = 9$ | $0 + 9 = 9$

5. $5 + 3 = 8$ | $3 + 5 = 8$ | $4 + 2 = 6$ | $2 + 4 = 6$ | $3 + 7 = 10$ | $7 + 3 = 10$

6. $2 + 8 = 10$ | $8 + 2 = 10$ | $6 + 3 = 9$ | $3 + 6 = 9$ | $8 + 1 = 9$ | $1 + 8 = 9$

Tell about each pair of sums. The sums in each pair are the same.

More to Explore — Algebra Sense

Find the missing number.

$5 + \boxed{2} = 7$ | $2 + \boxed{5} = 7$ | $1 + \boxed{7} = 8$ | $7 + \boxed{1} = 8$ | $2 + \boxed{2} = 4$

We learned about related addition facts. Ask your child to tell you how the pairs of execises are the same.

Alternate Teaching Strategy

Materials per pair: 9 blue and 9 red connecting cubes; number cards 0–10 (TA 9)

Have one child make two cube trains of different colors to show this addition fact: 7 + 2 = 9. The partner shows the fact with number cards. Ask the first child to write the fact on a sheet of paper.

- **How could you show the same sum using the same cubes and number cards?** *[Possible answer: by changing the order of the parts]*

Have one child change the order of the cube trains and the number cards, and ask the partner to write the new addition fact on the paper. Ask children to explain how the two facts are the same and different.

PRACTICE • 39

HOMEWORK

Practice 39

Name:

Related Addition Facts

Add.

1. $2 + 3 = 5$ | $3 + 2 = 5$

2. $4 + 2 = 6$ | $2 + 4 = 6$ | $2 + 5 = 7$ | $5 + 2 = 7$ | $1 + 9 = 10$ | $9 + 1 = 10$

3. $3 + 5 = 8$ | $5 + 3 = 8$ | $0 + 7 = 7$ | $7 + 0 = 7$ | $6 + 2 = 8$ | $2 + 6 = 8$

4. $5 + 4 = 9$ | $4 + 5 = 9$ | $1 + 2 = 3$ | $2 + 1 = 3$ | $2 + 3 = 5$ | $3 + 2 = 5$

McGraw-Hill School Division

RETEACH • 39

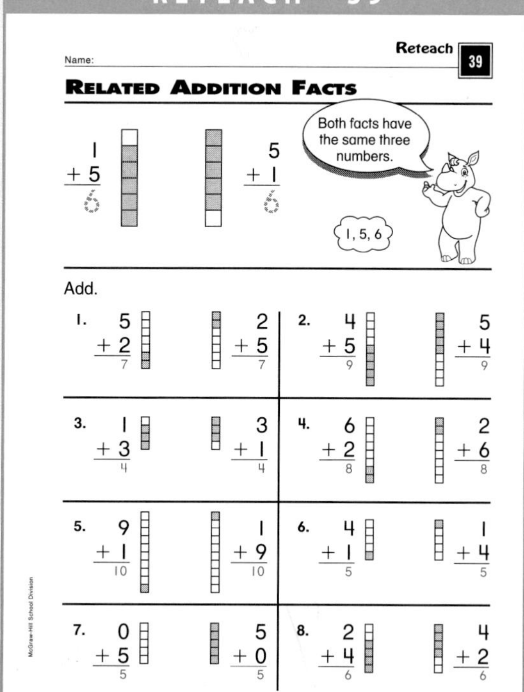
Reteach 39

Name:

Related Addition Facts

$1 + 5 = 6$ | $5 + 1 = 6$

Add.

1. $5 + 2 = 7$ | $2 + 5 = 7$
2. $4 + 5 = 9$ | $5 + 4 = 9$
3. $1 + 3 = 4$ | $3 + 1 = 4$
4. $6 + 2 = 8$ | $2 + 6 = 8$
5. $9 + 1 = 10$ | $1 + 9 = 10$
6. $4 + 1 = 5$ | $1 + 4 = 5$
7. $0 + 5 = 5$ | $5 + 0 = 5$
8. $2 + 4 = 6$ | $4 + 2 = 6$

McGraw-Hill School Division

EXTEND • 39

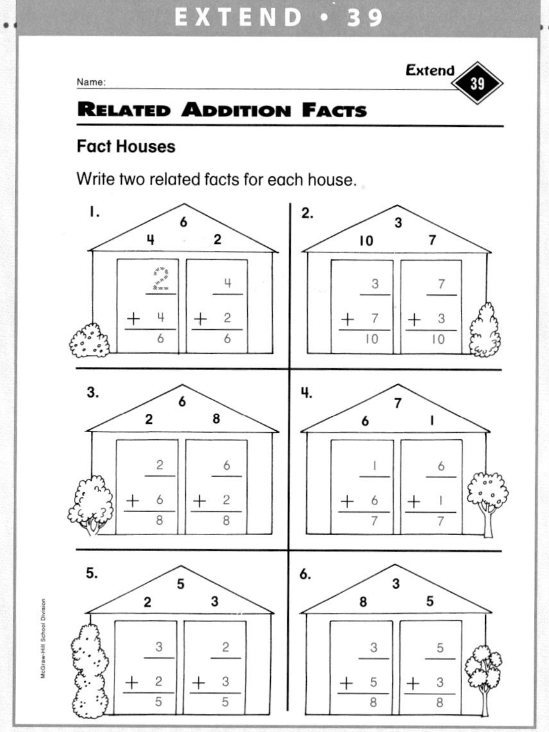
Extend 39

Name:

Related Addition Facts

Fact Houses

Write two related facts for each house.

1. 6; 4, 2: $2 + 4 = 6$ | $4 + 2 = 6$
2. 3; 10, 7: $3 + 7 = 10$ | $7 + 3 = 10$
3. 6; 2, 8: $2 + 6 = 8$ | $6 + 2 = 8$
4. 7; 6, 1: $1 + 6 = 7$ | $6 + 1 = 7$
5. 5; 2, 3: $3 + 2 = 5$ | $2 + 3 = 5$
6. 3; 8, 5: $3 + 5 = 8$ | $5 + 3 = 8$

McGraw-Hill School Division

EXTRA PRACTICE

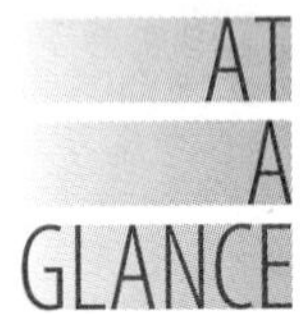

PURPOSE Provide an opportunity for review and practice.

Using the Extra Practice

Page 151

Explain that the answer to the Rhino Riddle is written in code. Use the example to demonstrate how to solve the code. Children should solve each addition fact first, then find the letter in the flag above each example and write it in the correct space within the answer to the riddle at the bottom of the page.

Page 152

Have children complete the exercises independently or in pairs.

Using the Additional Practice

The section below provides additional practice that you may want to write on the chalkboard or put on a reproducible master.

Name

Extra Practice Activity !

Rhino Riddle

Add.

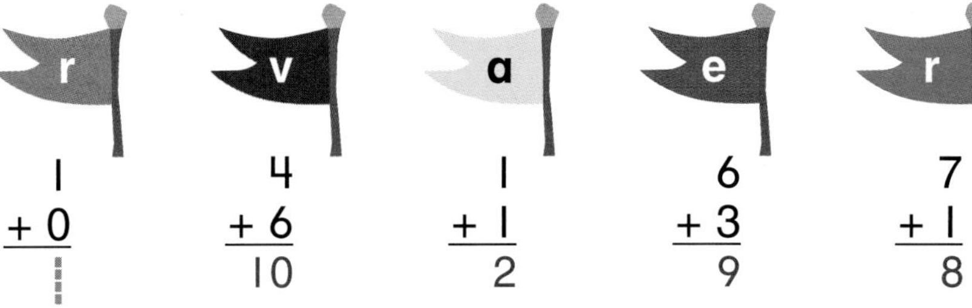

1	4	1	6	7
+ 0	+ 6	+ 1	+ 3	+ 1
1	10	2	9	8

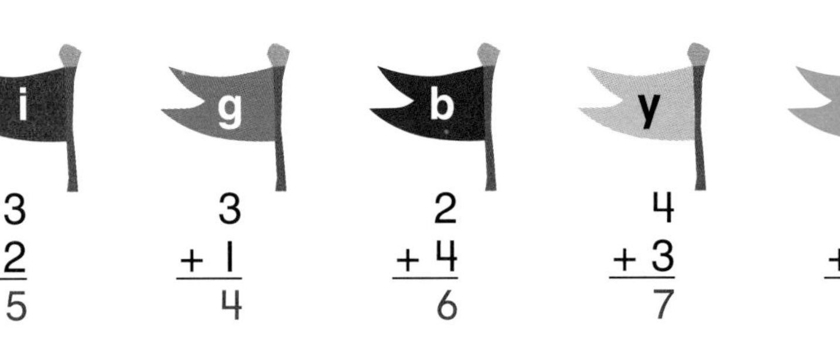

3	3	2	4	1
+ 2	+ 1	+ 4	+ 3	+ 2
5	4	6	7	3

Match sums to answer the riddle.

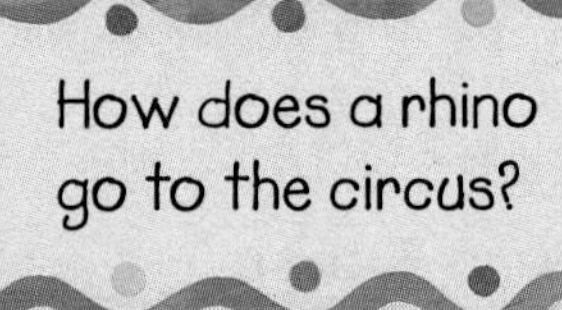

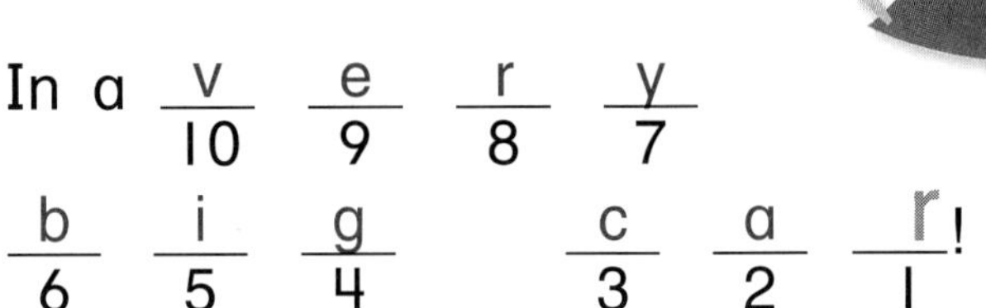

In a v(10) e(9) r(8) y(7) b(6) i(5) g(4) c(3) a(2) r(1)!

ADDITIONAL PRACTICE

Add.

1. 3 + 1 *[4]* 3 + 3 *[6]* 5 + 2 *[7]*

2. 1 + 8 *[9]* 6 + 2 *[8]* 4 + 5 *[9]*

3. 1 + 0 *[1]* 9 + 1 *[10]* 2 + 1 *[3]*

4. 7 + 2 *[9]* 0 + 4 *[4]* 3 + 6 *[9]*

5. 5 + 3 *[8]* 1 + 6 *[7]* 4 + 4 *[8]*

6. 3 + 7 *[10]* 9 + 0 *[9]* 5 + 5 *[10]*

7. 2 + 3 *[5]* 3 + 2 *[5]* 1 + 7 *[8]* 7 + 1 *[8]*

8. 5 + 4 *[9]* 4 + 5 *[9]* 6 + 3 *[9]* 3 + 6 *[9]*

9. 3 + 3 *[6]* 8 + 0 *[8]* 4 + 3 *[7]* 1 + 3 *[4]*

Use counters if you want to.

Add.

1	4	5	3	7	4	9
	+ 6	+ 2	+ 3	+ 2	+ 4	+ 1
	10	7	6	9	8	10
2	3	5	2	4	9	1
	+ 7	+ 4	+ 2	+ 1	+ 0	+ 6
	10	9	4	5	9	7
3	5	3	7	6	5	6
	+ 3	+ 1	+ 0	+ 4	+ 5	+ 0
	8	4	7	10	10	6
4	8	6	0	5	0	4
	+ 1	+ 2	+ 8	+ 1	+ 5	+ 5
	9	8	8	6	5	9

Draw lines to match.

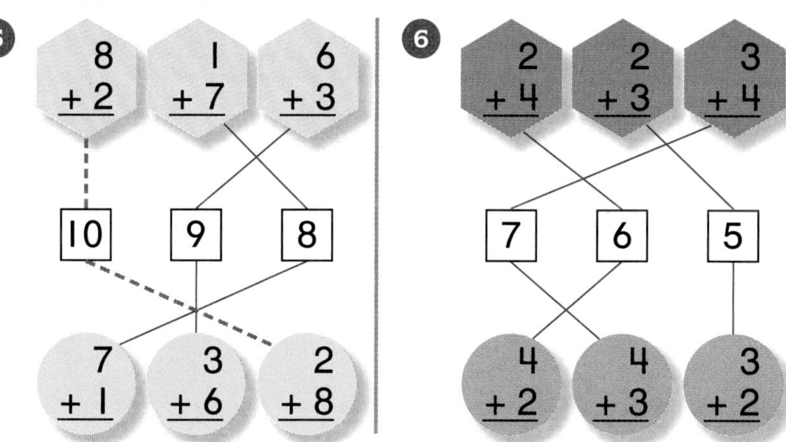

Developing Number Sense

This section provides another opportunity for children to apply number-sense concepts. You may wish to copy these exercises onto the chalkboard or a reproducible master.

Find the pattern. Add.

1.	0	0	0	0
	+ 1	+ 2	+ 3	+ 4
	[1]	*[2]*	*[3]*	*[4]*
2.	1	2	3	4
	+ 1	+ 1	+ 1	+ 1
	[2]	*[3]*	*[4]*	*[5]*
3.	2	2	2	2
	+ 3	+ 4	+ 5	+ 6
	[5]	*[6]*	*[7]*	*[8]*
4.	2	3	4	5
	+ 2	+ 3	+ 4	+ 5
	[4]	*[6]*	*[8]*	*[10]*
5.	1	1	2	2
	+ 1	+2	+ 2	+ 3
	[2]	*[3]*	*[4]*	*[5]*
6.	3	3	4	4
	+ 3	+ 4	+ 4	+ 5
	[6]	*[7]*	*[8]*	*[9]*

Mixed Applications/Problem Solving

Listen. Solve.

1. 2 clowns rode bicycles.
2 clowns rollerskated.
How many clowns are there in all? *[4]*

2. One acrobat swung on a rope.
She caught another acrobat by the hands.
How many acrobats are on the rope now? *[2]*

3. A juggler juggled 7 balls.
He dropped 1 ball.
How many balls did he have left? *[6]*

4. 8 riders rode on horses.
4 riders jumped off.
How many riders were still on horses? *[4]*

5. 1 seal ate 3 fish.
The zoo keeper fed it 7 more fish.
How many fish did the seal eat? *[10]*

6. 3 dogs jumped through hoops.
6 dogs ran in a circle.
How many dogs are there in all? *[9]*

Add Money

OBJECTIVE Add money amounts, facts to 10.

Day 1 Add Money

RESOURCE REMINDER
Math Center Cards 30
Practice 40, Reteach 40, Extend 40

SKILLS TRACE	
GRADE K	• Explore adding facts to 10. *(Chapter 11)*
GRADE 1	• Add money amounts, facts to 10.
GRADE 2	• Explore adding money amounts, including 3 addends. *(Chapter 7)*

LESSON RESOURCES

MANIPULATIVE WARM-UP

Whole Class — **Logical/Analytical**

OBJECTIVE Review matching money amounts and pennies.

Materials clear plastic change purse or container; per child: 10 play pennies

▶ Write various amounts of money, from 1¢ to 10¢, on the chalkboard. Have volunteers put pennies in the change purse to show the amount.

▶ Next, put various numbers of pennies in the purse. Have volunteers count them and write the amounts of money on the chalkboard.

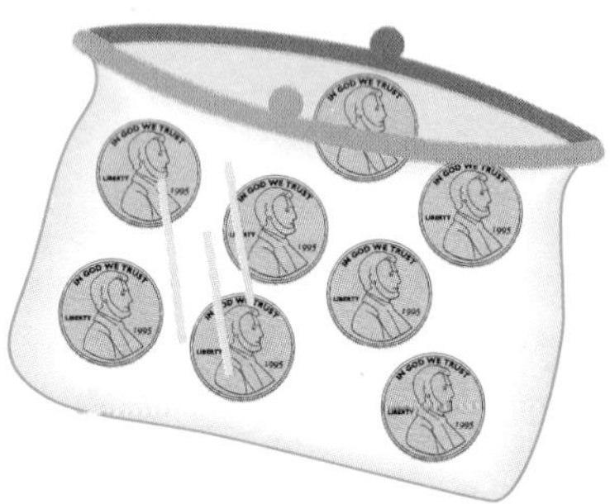

CONNECTION ACTIVITY

Whole Class — **Individual**

OBJECTIVE Connect money amounts and the value of objects.

Materials classroom items, price tags (TA 12)

Prepare Write prices from 1¢ to 10¢ on price tags and attach them to classroom objects.

▶ Display classroom items with price tags. Ask questions such as:
- **Which things could you buy for 2¢? For 4¢? For 5¢? For 7¢? For 10¢?**
- **If two children each had 4¢, what could they buy together?**
- **Which costs the most?** *[Answers may vary.]*

DAILY MATH

PREVIOUS DAY QUICK REVIEW

Add.

1. 2 + 7 = [9]; 7 + 2 = [9]
2. 5 + 3 = [8]; 3 + 5 = [8]

FAST FACTS

1. 7 − 4 = [3]
2. 9 − 8 = [1]
3. 8 − 5 = [3]
4. 5 − 2 = [3]

Problem of the Day • 30

Read aloud to children:

Carla wants to buy 3 circus stickers.
One costs 5¢.
The second costs 4¢.
The third costs 1¢.
How much money does she need? *[10¢]*

TECH LINK

MATH VAN

Tools You may wish to use the Money Models tool with this lesson.

MATH FORUM

Idea I lead a discussion with children about the real prices of items they might like to buy. We list items and prices, using newspaper ads as a guide. Then we try to name something that costs exactly 10¢.

Visit our Resource Village at http://www.mhschool.com to see more of the Math Forum.

MATH CENTER

Practice

OBJECTIVE Add pennies to 10.

Materials per pair: 10 pennies, per child: Math Center Recording Sheet (TA 38 optional)

Students will take 1 to 5 pennies in each hand and ask their partner to tell how many in all. They record their work. You may want to assess whether students use number facts or counting on to find the totals.

PRACTICE ACTIVITY 30 — MATH CENTER — Partners

Number Sense • Penny Sums

YOU NEED: 10 pennies

Take turns.

- Take 1, 2, 3, 4, or 5 pennies in each hand.
- Show your partner.
- Ask your partner to tell how many in all.
- Draw a picture of the pennies.
- Write the addition.
- Do this six times.

5 + 4 = 9

Chapter 5, Lesson 3 — Addition

NCTM Standards

- ✓ Problem Solving
- ✓ Communication
- ✓ Reasoning
- ✓ Connections

Problem Solving

OBJECTIVE Find addends for a given sum.

Materials per child: 10 pennies, Math Center Recording Sheet (TA 38 optional)

Children will select two animals that cost a given number of pennies. They will then write the addition sentence.

Then they will write their own problems. *[A whale and a monkey cost 5¢. An elephant and a monkey cost 8¢. An elephant and a whale cost 7¢. A tiger and a monkey cost 4¢. Children's problems will vary.]*

PROBLEM-SOLVING ACTIVITY 30 — MATH CENTER — On Your Own

Logical Reasoning • Buy a Toy!

YOU NEED: 10 pennies

Use pennies.

- Buy 2 animals for 5¢. Draw what you can buy. Write the addition.
- Buy 2 animals for 8¢.
- Buy 2 animals for 7¢.
- Buy 2 animals for 4¢.
- Write your own problem.

TIGER 1¢ · WHALE 2¢ · ELEPHANT 5¢ · MONKEY 3¢

Chapter 5, Lesson 3 — Addition

NCTM Standards

- ✓ Problem Solving
- ✓ Communication
- Reasoning
- Connections

DAY 1

Add Money

OBJECTIVE Children add money amounts, facts to 10.

Materials per child: 10 play pennies

1 Motivate — Whole Class

Materials 10 two-color counters, 10 play pennies

Display 2 red and 7 yellow counters. Ask a volunteer to combine the counters and tell how many there are in all. *[9]* Have another child write the addition sentence on the chalkboard. *[2 + 7 = 9]*

- **How could you write this addition fact another way?** *[You can write it vertically.]*

Have the child write the addition in vertical form, then ask the class to read the two exercises aloud with you.

Display 2 pennies and 7 pennies and have a volunteer combine them and tell how many in all. Ask another volunteer to write the addition in two ways on the chalkboard. *[2¢ + 7¢ = 9¢, horizontally and vertically]* Ask:

- **How are these facts the same as the ones we wrote for the counters? How are they different?** *[Possible answers: The numbers and the sums are the same; they can both be written in two ways; the exercise with pennies has cents signs; it is about money instead of counters.]*

2 Develop

Page 153

Talk about what Kim is buying at the top of the page.

- **What do you need to find out?** *[how much money Kim needs to buy a toy seal and a toy elephant]*
- **What do you need to remember when you write an addition fact about money?** *[to write the cents sign]*

Have children complete exercises 1–6.

CRITICAL THINKING
Before children answer the question on the page, ask:

- **Suppose you had 3¢. Which toys could you buy?** *[Possible answers: 1 panda ;1 seal; 1 dog;1 mouse; 3 mice]*

Page 154

Try These Discuss the example, assign exercises 1–7.

Encourage children to give examples as they write their journal entries. They can use exercises from the lesson if they wish.

3 Close

Check for Understanding by having children use pennies to show two money amounts and then tell the sum.

Name ______

Find how much money Kim needs.

3¢
+ 5¢
8¢

You need 10 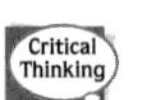.
Add to find how much money.

1 

6¢ + 1¢ = 7¢

2 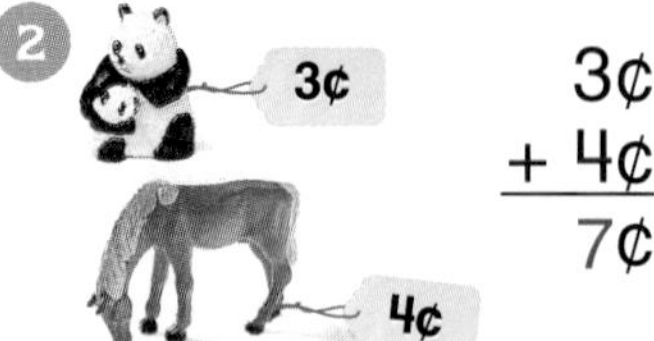

3¢ + 4¢ = 7¢

3 

8¢ + 2¢ = 10¢

4 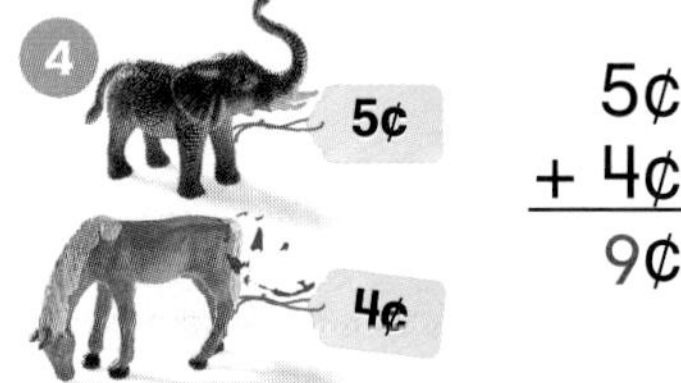

5¢ + 4¢ = 9¢

5 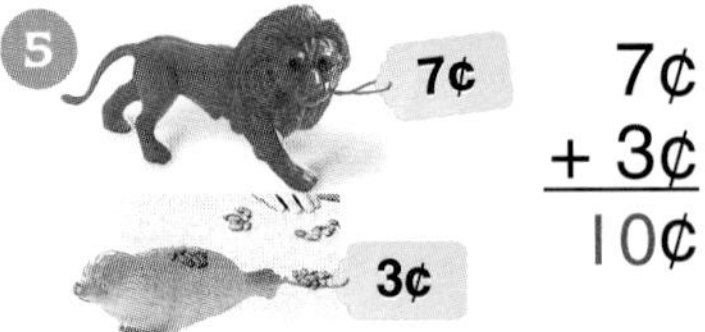

7¢ + 3¢ = 10¢

6 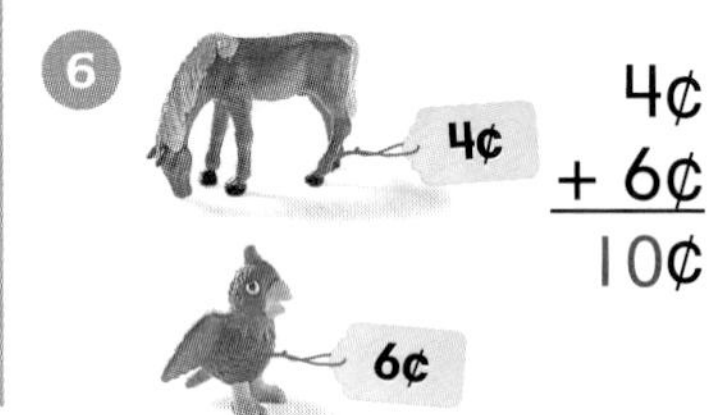

4¢ + 6¢ = 10¢

Critical Thinking: Which of the toys could you buy for 6¢? Possible answers: 1 macaw, 2 seals, 1 seal and 1 dog and 1 mouse, 3 dogs, 6 mice

MEETING INDIVIDUAL NEEDS

EARLY FINISHERS

Figure out all combinations of toys shown on page 153 for 6¢. *[1 macaw; 1 elephant, 1 mouse; 1 horse, 1 dog; 1 horse, 2 mice; 2 pandas; 2 seals; 1 panda, 1 dog, 1 mouse; 1 seal, 1 dog, 1 mouse; 2 dogs, 2 mice; 3 dogs; 6 mice]*

EXTRA SUPPORT

Have children use pennies to show the addends for some of the lesson exercises. They can combine and count to find the sums.

ONGOING ASSESSMENT

Interview Present 6 + 3 and 6¢ + 3¢. Ask:

- **How is adding money the same as adding numbers?** *[You add the same way for both.]*
- **How is it different?** *[You use the cents signs.]*

Follow Up For children having difficulty, use pennies and counters in one to one correspondence. Then assign **Reteach 40.**

For children who demonstrate understanding, assign **Extend 40.**

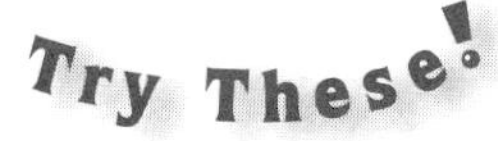

Add.

1

	2¢
+	4¢
	6¢

2
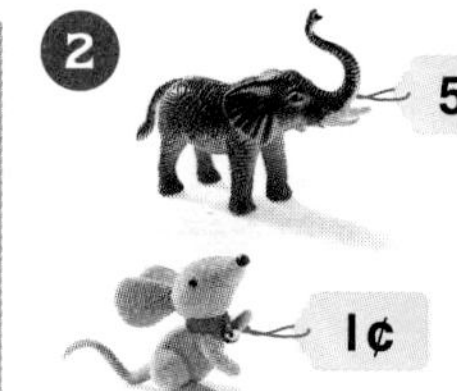

	5¢
+	1¢
	6¢

3

	9¢
+	1¢
	10¢

4

	3¢
+	6¢
	9¢

5

1¢	7¢	2¢	4¢	1¢	3¢
+ 3¢	+ 2¢	+ 5¢	+ 4¢	+ 8¢	+ 3¢
4¢	9¢	7¢	8¢	9¢	6¢

6

5¢	4¢	3¢	9¢	6¢	8¢
+ 4¢	+ 3¢	+ 5¢	+ 1¢	+ 2¢	+ 2¢
9¢	7¢	8¢	10¢	8¢	10¢

7

3¢	5¢	4¢	8¢	4¢	5¢
+ 7¢	+ 5¢	+ 4¢	+ 1¢	+ 6¢	+ 3¢
10¢	10¢	8¢	9¢	10¢	8¢

Journal Draw and write about adding money. Children may draw pennies, show prices, or compare adding money to adding with whole numbers.

Show your child 2 pennies in one hand and 4 pennies in the other. Ask how much money you have in both hands.

Alternate Teaching Strategy

Materials 8–10 pictures of food items, index cards (5" x 8"); per child: 10 play pennies

Prepare Paste the pictures of food items on the cards and mark them with prices from 1¢ to 8¢.

Give each child 10 pennies. Display pictures of food items and have children take turns choosing two that they could buy with their money. Have children show the amounts for the items with their pennies and tell you the total cost.

Call on a volunteer to write on the chalkboard the addition fact in horizontal and vertical forms that tells the total cost. Then draw arrows to match the parts and totals.

- **Why do you get the same total?** *[because the parts are the same]*
- **How is adding money different from adding other numbers?** *[Possible answer: Addition sentences about money have cents signs.]*

PRACTICE • 40

HOMEWORK

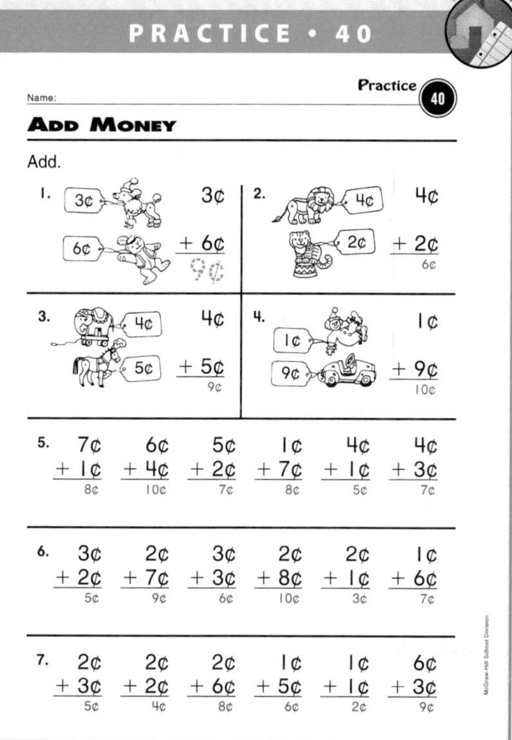

Name:　　　　　　Practice 40

ADD MONEY

Add.

1. 3¢ + 6¢ = 9¢
2. 4¢ + 2¢ = 6¢
3. 4¢ + 5¢ = 9¢
4. 1¢ + 9¢ = 10¢

5.

7¢	6¢	5¢	1¢	4¢	4¢
+ 1¢	+ 4¢	+ 2¢	+ 7¢	+ 1¢	+ 3¢
8¢	10¢	7¢	8¢	5¢	7¢

6.

3¢	2¢	3¢	2¢	2¢	1¢
+ 2¢	+ 7¢	+ 3¢	+ 8¢	+ 1¢	+ 6¢
5¢	9¢	6¢	10¢	3¢	7¢

7.

2¢	2¢	2¢	1¢	1¢	6¢
+ 3¢	+ 2¢	+ 6¢	+ 5¢	+ 1¢	+ 3¢
5¢	4¢	8¢	6¢	2¢	9¢

McGraw-Hill School Division

RETEACH • 40

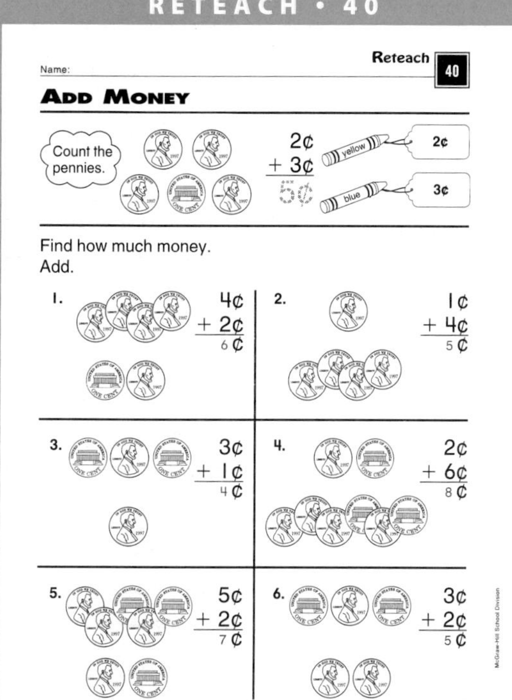

Name:　　　　　　Reteach 40

ADD MONEY

Count the pennies.

2¢ + 3¢ = 5¢ (yellow 2¢, blue 3¢)

Find how much money.
Add.

1. 4¢ + 2¢ = 6¢
2. 1¢ + 4¢ = 5¢
3. 3¢ + 1¢ = 4¢
4. 2¢ + 6¢ = 8¢
5. 5¢ + 2¢ = 7¢
6. 3¢ + 2¢ = 5¢

McGraw-Hill School Division

EXTEND • 40

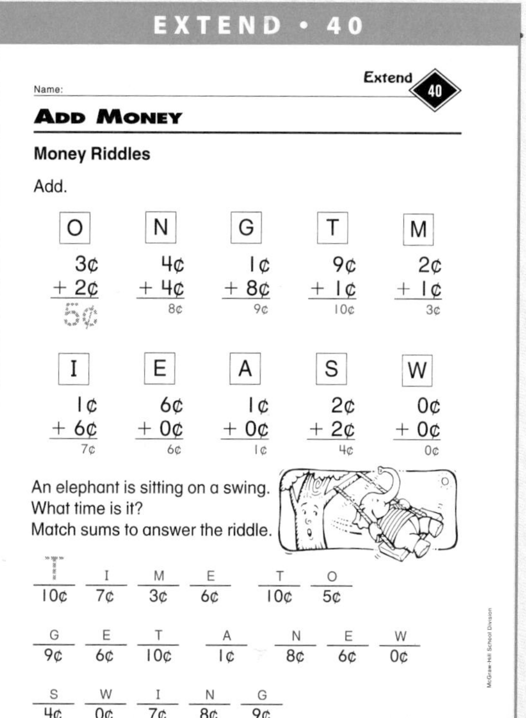

Name:　　　　　　Extend 40

ADD MONEY

Money Riddles

Add.

O	N	G	T	M
3¢ + 2¢ = 5¢	4¢ + 4¢ = 8¢	1¢ + 8¢ = 9¢	9¢ + 1¢ = 10¢	2¢ + 1¢ = 3¢

I	E	A	S	W
1¢ + 6¢ = 7¢	6¢ + 0¢ = 6¢	1¢ + 0¢ = 1¢	2¢ + 2¢ = 4¢	0¢ + 0¢ = 0¢

An elephant is sitting on a swing.
What time is it?
Match sums to answer the riddle.

T I M E　T O
10¢ 7¢ 3¢ 6¢　10¢ 5¢

G E T　A　N E W
9¢ 6¢ 10¢　1¢　8¢ 6¢ 0¢

S W I N G
4¢ 0¢ 7¢ 8¢ 9¢

McGraw-Hill School Division

AT A GLANCE

PURPOSE Maintain and review the concepts, skills, and strategies that children have learned thus far in the chapter.

Using the Midchapter Review

Page 155

The **Midchapter Review** may be completed independently or by the class as a whole. Explain to children that they may draw a picture to help them solve Item 20.

JOURNAL Children write or draw about ways to add. They may show horizontal or vertical form, and use pictures or counting on. Use children's writing or drawings to help you evaluate their understanding of the different ways to add.

Vocabulary Review

Write the following words on the chalkboard:

part	**sum**	**related facts**
total	**fact**	**order**

Ask for volunteers to explain, show, and/or act out the meanings of these words.

Name

Midchapter Review

Do your best!

Add.

1. 4 + 3 = 7
2. 6 + 4 = 10
3. 3 + 5 = 8
4. 1 + 8 = 9
5. 5 + 5 = 10
6. 8 + 2 = 10
7. 1 + 9 = 10
8. 3 + 6 = 9
9. 3 + 7 = 10
10. 2 + 4 = 6
11. 5 + 4 = 9
12. 3 + 3 = 6
13. 4 + 6 = 10
14. 4¢ + 4¢ = 8¢
15. 2¢ + 5¢ = 7¢
16. 4¢ + 1¢ = 5¢
17. 7¢ + 2¢ = 9¢
18. 2¢ + 3¢ = 5¢
19. 4¢ + 5¢ = 9¢
20. Why are 3 + 1 and $\begin{array}{r}3\\+1\\\hline\end{array}$ the same?

Possible answers: The same parts are added, the numbers are the same.

Journal Write or draw about ways to add. Children may describe counting on and how to use pictures, and they may show horizontal or vertical form.

Reinforcement and Remediation

CHAPTER OBJECTIVES	MIDCHAPTER REVIEW ITEMS	STUDENT BOOK PAGES	TEACHER'S EDITION PAGES		TEACHER RESOURCES
			Activities	Alternate Teaching Strategy	Reteach
*5A	1–20	145–150, 153–154	84A, 148A, 152A	148, 150, 154	37–40

*5A Add, facts to 10

Extra Practice
Game!

Cover the Circus Wagon

You need 2 [number cube] and 9 [rhino counter].

Take turns.

- ▶ Roll the 2 [number cube].
- ▶ Add. Put a [rhino counter] on the sum.
- ▶ Get 3 [rhino counter] in a row.

AT A GLANCE

PURPOSE Provide an opportunity for review and practice.

Materials per pair: 2 number cubes (labeled 0–5); 9 rhino counters

Using the Extra Practice

Page 156

Draw horizontal, vertical, and diagonal lines on the chalkboard. Discuss the terms with the class. Have children draw corresponding lines in the air.

Explain the rules of the game. Each person in the pair works on his or her own game board. Pairs share the number cubes. The winner is the first player to get 3 in a row horizontally, vertically, or diagonally.

Using the Additional Practice

The section below provides additional practice that you may want to write on the chalkboard or put on a reproducible master.

ADDITIONAL PRACTICE

Add.

1. 4 + 3 = *[7]*   6 + 2 = *[8]*   3 + 7 = *[10]*   5 + 1 = *[6]*
2. 5 + 5 = *[10]*   3 + 5 = *[8]*   6 + 3 = *[9]*   4 + 4 = *[8]*
3. 2 + 7 = *[9]*   4 + 6 = *[10]*   0 + 5 = *[5]*   8 + 0 = *[8]*
4. 1¢ + 4¢ = *[5¢]*   3¢ + 2¢ = *[5¢]*   6¢ + 1¢ = *[7¢]*   2¢ + 5¢ = *[7¢]*
5. 4¢ + 6¢ = *[10¢]*   5¢ + 1¢ = *[6¢]*   7¢ + 2¢ = *[9¢]*   0¢ + 6¢ = *[6¢]*
6. 8¢ + 1¢ = *[9¢]*   9¢ + 0¢ = *[9¢]*   3¢ + 1¢ = *[4¢]*   7¢ + 3¢ = *[10¢]*

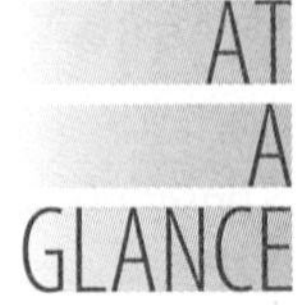

Applying Addition

OBJECTIVE Children use addition and subtraction in a social studies context.

Resource Literature Big Book, *Number One Number Fun*

Materials per child: 2 index cards, 2 sheets of drawing paper; 2 large sheets of posterboard

1 Engage

Review with children why people take surveys. Talk about the surveys the class has taken. Discuss the questions they asked in the surveys and how they presented the results.

2 Investigate — Whole Class

Page 157

Reread *Number One Number Fun* aloud to children. Relate the story to the chapter theme, "At the Circus." Have children look at the different circus acts shown in the book. Point out the goats and donkeys on a trapeze.

Cultural Note The Moscow Circus School, located in Russia, prepares children to perform in the circus. Have children name specialized schools in the United States. *[Possible answers: gymnastics school, ballet school]*

Read with children the survey question on the Student Book page 157. Distribute the index cards. In the survey, children will vote *yes* or *no* by drawing a picture of their feet on the index cards, either on a trapeze or on the ground.

Make a Class Graph To make the class graph, let children take turns attaching their drawings to the poster paper in the appropriate row.

3 Reflect and Share

Page 158

Discuss questions to ask for the survey about the circus. You may wish to suggest ideas such as:

- **What is our favorite circus act?**
- **What is our favorite circus snack?**
- **Would you be brave enough to perform with lions?**

Write a Report After taking the survey and making the class graph, children begin their portfolio reports. Using the Partners Practice Strategy, have partners show each other their own work, and add to their partner's work. Encourage them to include comparisons of numbers in the data, for example, "The lion act got 3 more votes than the elephant act."

Name ______________________

Circus Fun

Listen to *Number One Number Fun.*

Take a survey. Ask this question:

"Would you be brave enough to swing on a trapeze?"

Make a class graph.

1. How many children said *yes*? ______ Data may vary.
2. How many children said *no*? ______
3. Did more children say *yes* or *no*? ______

   How many more? ______

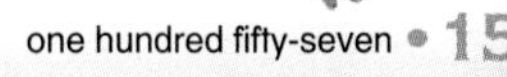

MORE TO INVESTIGATE

Predict Possible answer: The children in another class are different, so you probably would get different numbers.

Explore Arrange for the children to meet with another class. Provide more index cards for children to distribute. Make another class graph on poster paper.

Find Display the two graphs side by side. Ask questions such as:

- **Did more children in [Ms. Green's] class answer "yes" or did more in our class answer "yes"? How many more? How many children voted "yes"in both classes together?**

Bibliography Children may enjoy reading the following books:

How to Weigh an Elephant by Bob Barner. New York: Bantam Doubleday Dell Books for Young Readers, 1995. ISBN 0–553–37569–5.

Mirette on the High Wire by Emily Arnold McCully. New York: The Putnam Berkley Group, Inc., 1992. ISBN 0–399–22130–1.

Decision Making

Answers may vary. See Teacher's Edition for sample of children's work.

1. Write a question to ask. Take another survey.

____

____

2. Make a class graph.

Write a report.

3. Tell what you found out.
4. Use numbers to show what you learned.

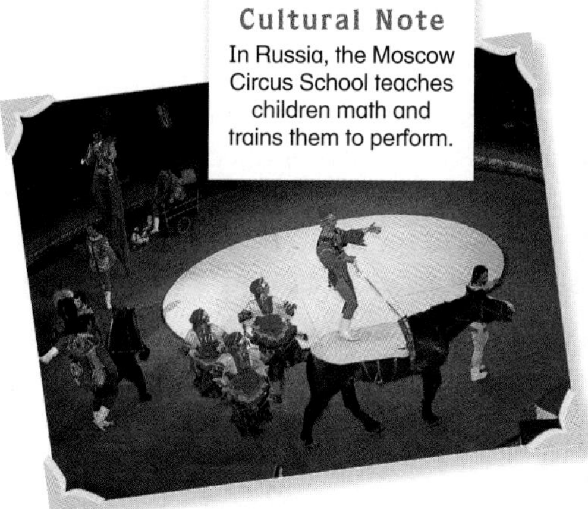

Cultural Note
In Russia, the Moscow Circus School teaches children math and trains them to perform.

More to Investigate

See Teacher's Edition.

PREDICT What if you ask another class. Will you get the same numbers?

EXPLORE Try it. Then make another graph.

FIND Compare the two graphs. How are they alike? How are they different?

BUILDING A PORTFOLIO

This assignment will provide insight into children's ability to use various methods of recording in a survey and to use addition, and subtraction in interpreting the results.

Allow children to revise their work for the portfolio. Each child's portfolio piece should consist of her or his written report and any notes you made about the child's work.

You may wish to use the Holistic Scoring Guide and the annotated samples of children's work to assess this task. See page 27 in Teacher's Assessment Resources.

Children's Work

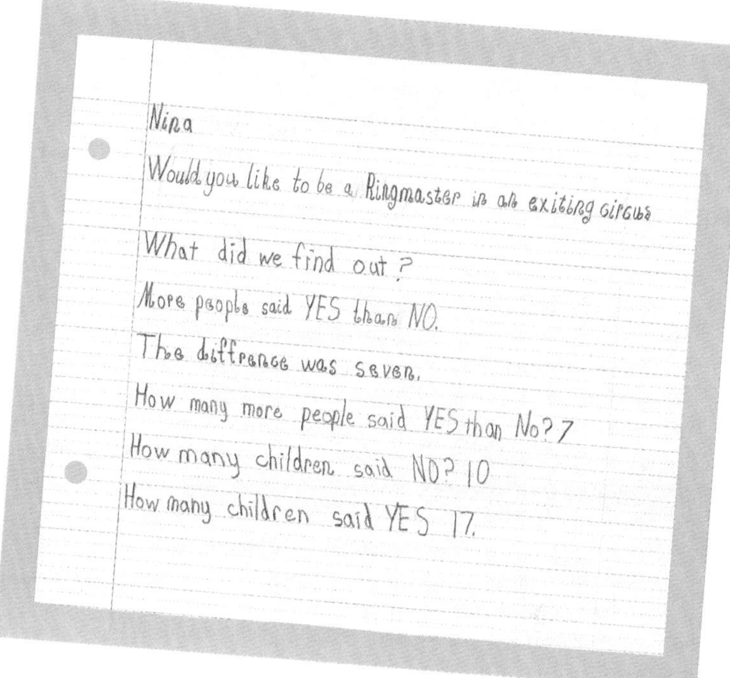

Nina
Would you like to be a Ringmaster in an exciting circus
What did we find out?
More people said YES than NO.
The difference was seven.
How many more people said YES than No? 7
How many children said NO? 10
How many children said YES 17.

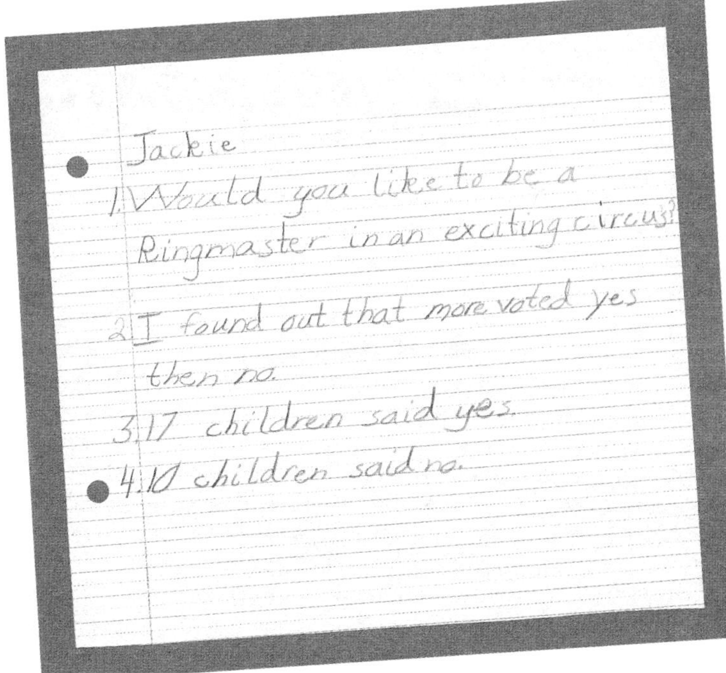

Jackie
1. Would you like to be a Ringmaster in an exciting circus?
2. I found out that more voted yes then no.
3. 17 children said yes.
4. 10 children said no.

Vertical Subtraction

OBJECTIVE Subtract in vertical form.

Day 1 Explore Activity: Another Way to Subtract
Day 2 Vertical Subtraction

RESOURCE REMINDER
Math Center Cards 31
Practice 41–42, Reteach 41–42, Extend 41–42

SKILLS TRACE	
GRADE K	• Explore subtracting facts to 6. *(Chapter 11)*
GRADE 1	• Explore subtraction in vertical form, facts to 10.
GRADE 2	• Explore subtracting, facts to 12. *(Chapter 1)*

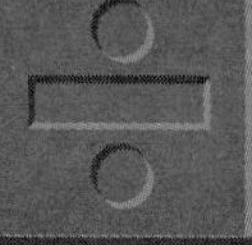

LESSON RESOURCES

MANIPULATIVE WARM-UP

Cooperative Pairs Social

OBJECTIVE Explore subtracting continuously from 10.

Materials per pair: 10 counters; number cube

▶ Each pair begins with a set of 10 counters. One child tosses the number cube and removes that number of counters from the set. The child then writes the subtraction sentence for what he or she has done. The next child tosses the cube, subtracts from the number of counters that remain, and writes the subtraction sentence.

▶ Players continue until someone tosses a number that results in an answer of 0. That child gets 1 point.

▶ Repeat the activity, starting again with 10 counters. Play continues until each child gets 3 points.

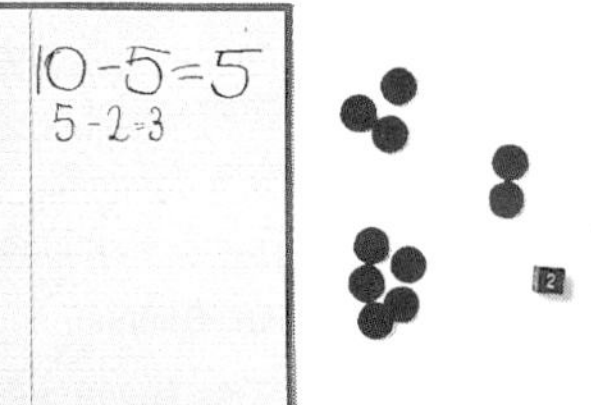

CONNECTION ACTIVITY

Whole Class Auditory/Linguistic

OBJECTIVE Connect subtraction to storytelling.

▶ Have two children each pick a number from 1 to 10. Write the numbers on the chalkboard. Start with the greater number. Have a volunteer begin a story about that number of circus animals. *[Possible answer: Six elephants stood on balls.]*

▶ Have a second child use the lesser number to continue the story. *[Possible answer: Two of the elephants went to get a drink of water.]* Have a third child tell how many animals are left. *[Four elephants are left.]*

▶ Repeat the activity with other numbers.

DAILY MATH

PREVIOUS DAY QUICK REVIEW

Add.

1. 3¢ + 5¢ *[8¢]*   5¢ + 4¢ *[9¢]*
2. 2¢ + 8¢ *[10¢]*   6¢ + 2¢ *[8¢]*

FAST FACTS

1. 5 – 1 = *[4]*
2. 4 – 2 = *[2]*
3. 3 – 0 = *[3]*
4. 6 – 2 = *[4]*

Problem of the Day • 31

Read aloud to children:

At the circus, Jed spent 3¢.
Sal spent 2¢.
Tom spent 4¢.
Did the children spend more than 10¢ in all?
How do you know?
[No; 3¢ + 2¢ + 4¢ = 9¢]

TECH LINK

MATH FORUM

Idea I have children write the horizontal and vertical forms of subtraction facts on index cards. They can use the cards to play Subtraction Concentration.

Visit our Resource Village at http://www.mhschool.com to see more of the Math Forum.

MATH CENTER

Practice

OBJECTIVE Show subtraction with cubes and write subtraction vertically and horizontally.

Materials per pair: 10 connecting cubes; per child: Math Center Recording Sheet (TA 38 optional)

One partner makes a cube train, and the other partner draws it. On the drawing, the second partner crosses off one or more cubes. Both partners write the subtraction in two ways.

PRACTICE ACTIVITY 31 — MATH CENTER, Partners

Algebra Sense • Snap Three

YOU NEED

Take turns.

- Your partner makes a cube train.
- You draw it.
  Cross out some cubes.
  How many are left?
- Each of you writes the subtraction fact.
  Write it in two different ways.

9 – 3 = 6

$$\begin{array}{r} 9 \\ -3 \\ \hline 6 \end{array}$$

Grade Level 1 · McGraw-Hill School Division

Chapter 5, Lesson 4 — Subtraction

NCTM Standards
- ✓ Problem Solving
- Communication
- ✓ Reasoning
- Connections

Problem Solving

OBJECTIVE Use cube trains to write subtraction facts and problems.

Materials per child: 10 connecting cubes, Math Center Recording Sheet (TA 38 optional)

Children use cubes to show the subtraction facts needed to solve the problem. Then children write a similar problem with different numbers. *[10 – 3 = 7; 7 – 4 = 3; the mouse has 3 kernels left. Children's problems may vary.]*

PROBLEM-SOLVING ACTIVITY 31 — MATH CENTER, On Your Own

Formulating Problems • Picture Subtraction

YOU NEED

10

The mouse has 10 kernels of corn to eat.
Two crows pay a visit.
One crow eats 3 kernels.
Then another eats 4 kernels.
What is left for the mouse?

- Use cubes to solve.
  Write your work.
- Write a problem like this one.
  Change the numbers.

Grade Level 1 · McGraw-Hill School Division

Chapter 5, Lesson 4 — Subtraction

NCTM Standards
- ✓ Problem Solving
- Communication
- ✓ Reasoning
- ✓ Connections

Lesson 5.4

EXPLORE ACTIVITY
Another Way to Subtract

OBJECTIVE Children explore the relationship between horizontal and vertical notation for subtraction.

Materials per pair: 10 connecting cubes of one color

1 Motivate — Cooperative Pairs

Materials per pair: 10 connecting cubes of one color

Have one child in each pair make a train of 8 cubes. Then have the partners snap off 3 cubes.

- **How many cubes were in the whole train?** *[8]* **How many cubes are in the part you snapped off?** *[3]*
- **How many cubes are left?** *[5]*

Have a child write the numbers to show the subtraction on the chalkboard.

- **How could you arrange your cubes and write the total and the parts in a different way?** *[Possible answer: Children may write the number for the total, then show the cubes in two groups below. They may write the numbers for the subtraction vertically.]*

Have volunteers draw and write their solutions on the chalkboard. Explain that there are two ways to write subtraction facts, just as there are two ways to write addition facts—across and down.

2 Develop

Page 159

Working Together Have several volunteers tell a story about the bears and the cube train. Then have pairs make cube trains, snap off a part, and write the total and the parts horizontally and vertically.

CRITICAL THINKING
Focus attention on the bears. Ask:

- **What if the bear snapped off all 6 cubes? How many would the other bear have left? Why?** *[0; If you have 6 and take away 6, none are left.]*

Name ____________

Explore Activity
Another Way to Subtract

6 total   2 part   4 part

6 total
2 part
4 part

Tell a story about taking away 2 cubes.
Possible problem: The bears have 6 cubes. One bear snaps off 2 cubes. The other bear has 4 cubes left.

Working Together

You need 10 cubes.

Take turns.

▶ You make a train.

▶ Your partner snaps off a part.

▶ Write numbers for the totals and parts.
Totals and parts may vary. Sample answer is given.

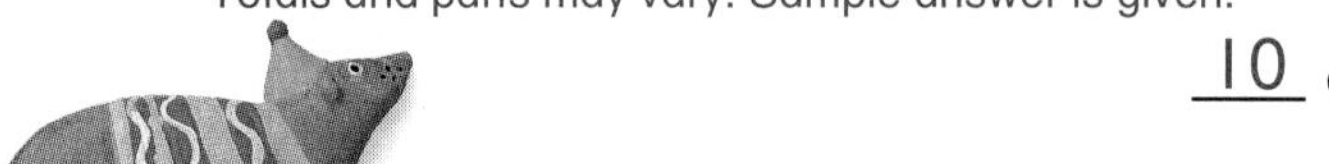

1. 10 total   3   7

10 total
3
7

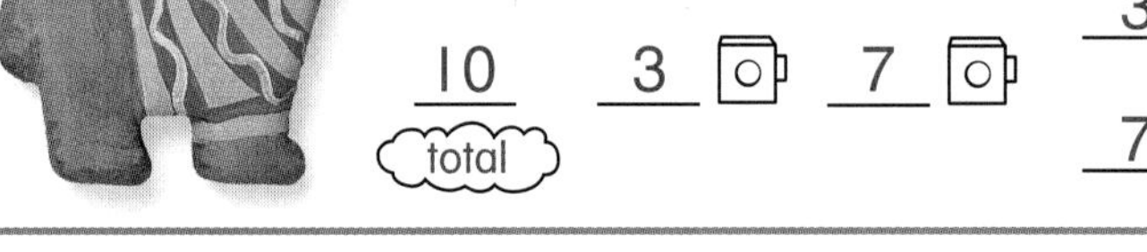

2. ___ total   ___   ___

___ total
___
___

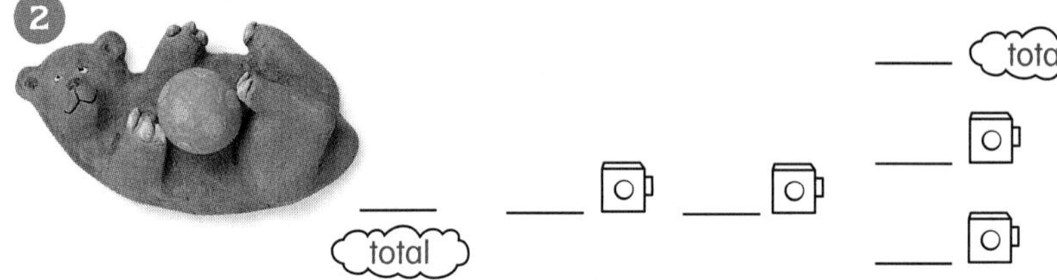

MEETING INDIVIDUAL NEEDS

EARLY FINISHERS

Have children draw a picture to illustrate another subtraction story about one of the animals on page 160. Have them write the subtraction fact horizontally and vertically.

EXTRA SUPPORT

You may wish to pair children having difficulty with others who have internalized the concepts of *total, part,* and *difference.* Have them work together using cubes or drawings to solve the exercises.

ONGOING ASSESSMENT

Interview Determine if children understand the relationship between the horizontal and vertical forms of subtraction by having them make a cube train for 6, take off 1, and write the total and the parts in both forms. *[6 – 1 = 5]*

- **Why are both differences the same?** *[The whole and the part removed are the same.]*

Follow Up For children having difficulty, assign **Reteach 41.**

For children who demonstrate understanding, assign **Extend 41.**

Try These!

Talk

Tell a story about the animals.
Write numbers for the totals and parts.

1 

2 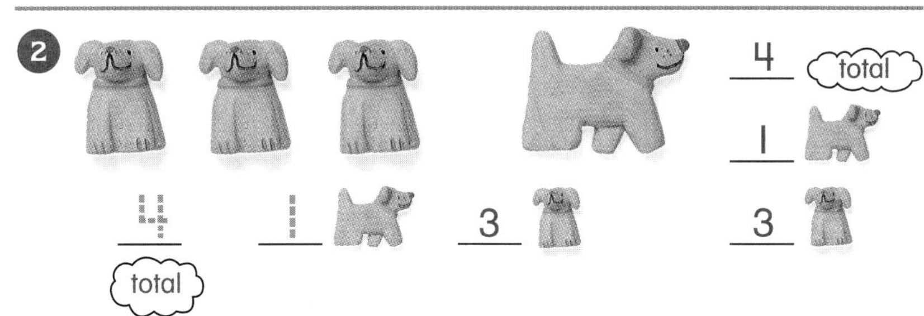

3 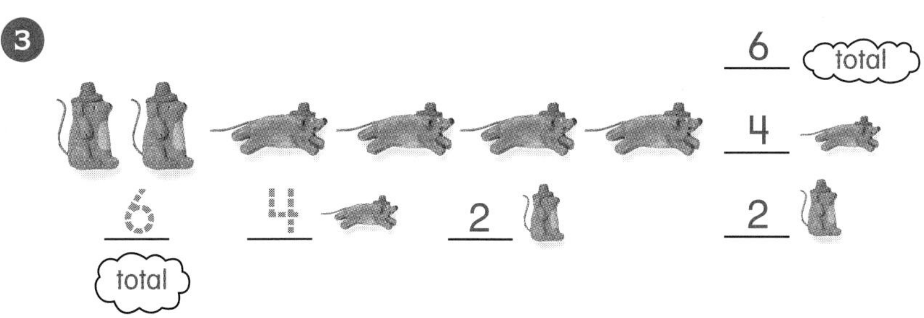

4 

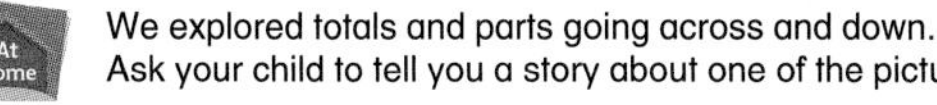

At Home: We explored totals and parts going across and down. Ask your child to tell you a story about one of the pictures.

Page 160

Try These Assign practice exercises 1–4.

Have children tell their partners a story about each picture before they record. Talk about how they can tell which part is being subtracted. *[It is the part that is shown going away.]*

3 Close

Check for Understanding by having children make a train of 9 cubes, snap off 5, and write the numbers for the total and the parts horizontally and vertically. *[9 − 5 = 4 and the same fact vertically]*

Tomorrow children will subtract vertically.

PRACTICE • 41

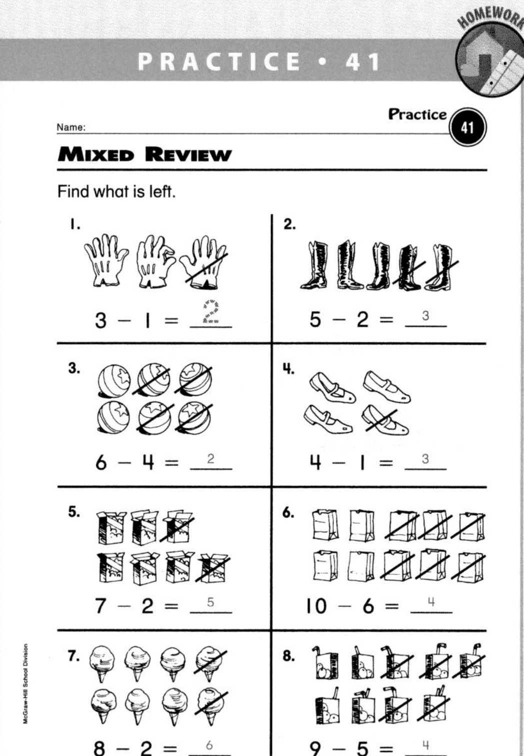

Name: Practice 41

Mixed Review

Find what is left.

1. 3 − 1 = 2
2. 5 − 2 = 3
3. 6 − 4 = 2
4. 4 − 1 = 3
5. 7 − 2 = 5
6. 10 − 6 = 4
7. 8 − 2 = 6
8. 9 − 5 = 4

McGraw-Hill School Division

RETEACH • 41

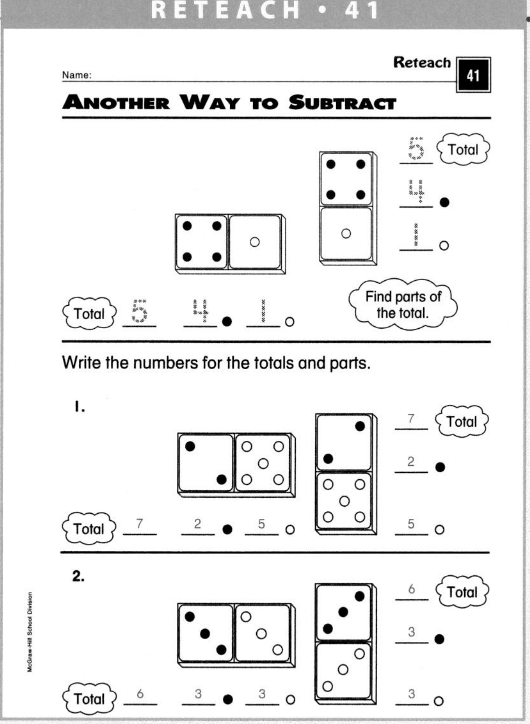

Name: Reteach 41

Another Way to Subtract

5 Total
4 •
1 ○

Total 5 4 • 1 ○

Find parts of the total.

Write the numbers for the totals and parts.

1. 7 Total, 2 •, 5 ○ — Total 7, 2 •, 5 ○
2. 6 Total, 3 •, 3 ○ — Total 6, 3 •, 3 ○

McGraw-Hill School Division

EXTEND • 41

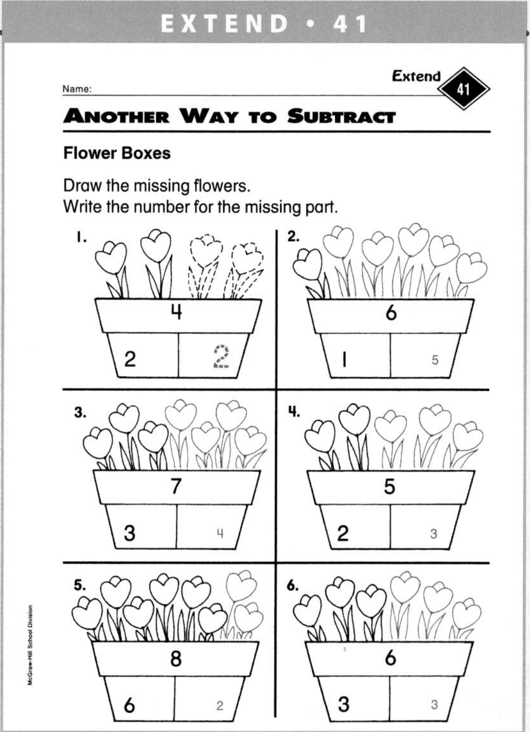

Name: Extend 41

Another Way to Subtract

Flower Boxes

Draw the missing flowers.
Write the number for the missing part.

1. 4: 2, 2
2. 6: 1, 5
3. 7: 3, 4
4. 5: 2, 3
5. 8: 6, 2
6. 6: 3, 3

McGraw-Hill School Division

DAY 2

Vertical Subtraction

OBJECTIVE Children subtract facts to 10 in vertical form.

Materials per child: 10 connecting cubes

1 Motivate — Whole Class

Materials per child: 10 connecting cubes

Display a train of 10 connecting cubes, and ask children how many there are in all. Draw the 10 cubes on the chalkboard. Snap off 6 cubes from the train.

- **How could I show in the picture that I snapped off 6 cubes?** *[Possible answer: Cross out 6 cubes.]*

10 – 6 = 4

Cross out 6 cubes and have a volunteer write the subtraction sentence that shows what you did. *[10 – 6 = 4]* Ask the class to read it aloud with you as you point to the total and each part. Then write the subtraction in vertical form and read it aloud from top to bottom, pointing to the numbers.

- **What is the same about these two subtraction facts?** *[Possible answer: They have the same total and parts].* **What is different?** *[The way they are written.]*

2 Develop

Page 161

Discuss the worked-out example. Explain that the part that remains after the subtraction is called the *difference*.

Assign exercises 1–6. Have children use conecting cubes.

CRITICAL THINKING
After children answer the question on the page, ask:

- **Why do you get the same answer across or down?** *[The total and the part taken away are the same.]*

Page 162

Try These Assign practice exercises 1–6.

Mixed Review Children review finding the missing part.

3 Close

Check for Understanding by writing exercises such as the following on the chalkboard. Have children read the exercises aloud and solve. They may draw pictures or use cubes.

$$\begin{array}{r}10\\-\ 8\\\hline[2]\end{array}\qquad\begin{array}{r}8\\-\ 4\\\hline[4]\end{array}\qquad\begin{array}{r}6\\-\ 5\\\hline[1]\end{array}\qquad\begin{array}{r}9\\-\ 2\\\hline[7]\end{array}$$

Name

Vertical Subtraction

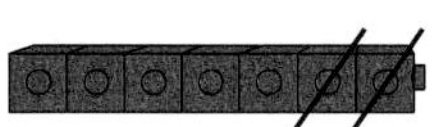

7 – 2 = 5

difference

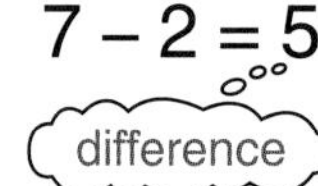

$$\begin{array}{r}7\\-\ 2\\\hline 5\end{array}$$

difference

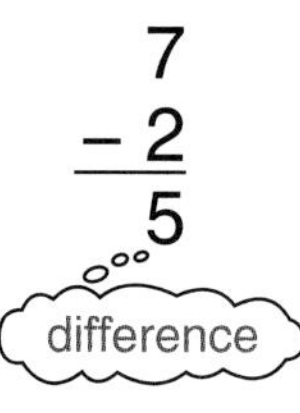

You need 10 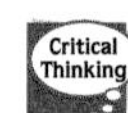.

- Show the total. Take away part.
- Cross out that part.
- Find the difference. Position of slashes may vary.

1. 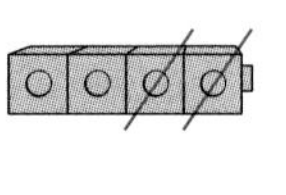 $\begin{array}{r}5\\-\ 5\\\hline 0\end{array}$
2. 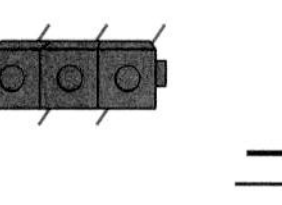 $\begin{array}{r}4\\-\ 3\\\hline 1\end{array}$
3. 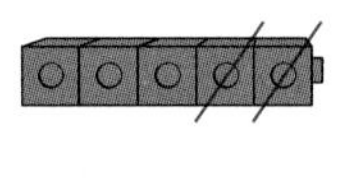 $\begin{array}{r}4\\-\ 2\\\hline 2\end{array}$
4. 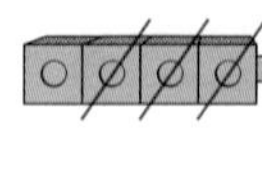 $\begin{array}{r}3\\-\ 3\\\hline 0\end{array}$
5. 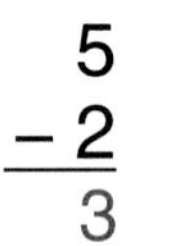 $\begin{array}{r}5\\-\ 2\\\hline 3\end{array}$
6. 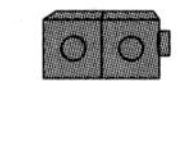 $\begin{array}{r}2\\-\ 0\\\hline 2\end{array}$

Critical Thinking: What if there are 6 red and 2 blue cubes. What subtraction could you show? Most likely answers are 8 – 2 and 8 – 6, but any fact for 8 or less could be shown.

MEETING INDIVIDUAL NEEDS

COMMON ERROR

Some children may reverse the part taken away and the part that remains. Have them record each step as they show subtraction with cubes.

GIFTED AND TALENTED

Challenge children to write as many addition and subtraction facts as they can using the numbers 7, 3, 4, and 6, 2, 8. Note if any patterns emerge, and have the child explain them to you or to classmates.

ONGOING ASSESSMENT

Interview Determine if children understand the distinction between *part* and *difference*.

- **In 8 – 6 = 2, which number is the part subtracted?** *[6]* **Which number is the difference?** *[2]* **How do you know?** *[The part subtracted comes after the minus sign; the difference comes after the equal sign.]*

Follow Up For children who have difficulty, assign **Reteach 42.**

For children who demonstrate understanding, assign **Extend 42.**

Subtract.

1. 10 − 2 = 8
2. 6 − 3 = 3
3. 9 − 3 = 6
4. 8 − 2 = 6
5. 6 − 4 = 2
6. 9 − 5 = 4

Mixed Review

Find the missing part.

7.

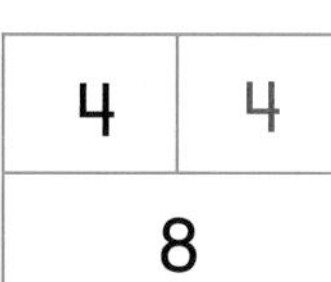

5	1	2	5	4	4	6	3
6		7		8		9	

We learned another way to show subtraction. Ask your child to explain the 7 − 2 example on 161.

Alternate Teaching Strategy

Materials per child: 10 counters

Write 8 − 5 on the chalkboard, and have children show the subtraction with counters. Complete the subtraction sentence: 8 − 5 = 3. Then write the same subtraction fact in vertical form, and have children show it with counters.

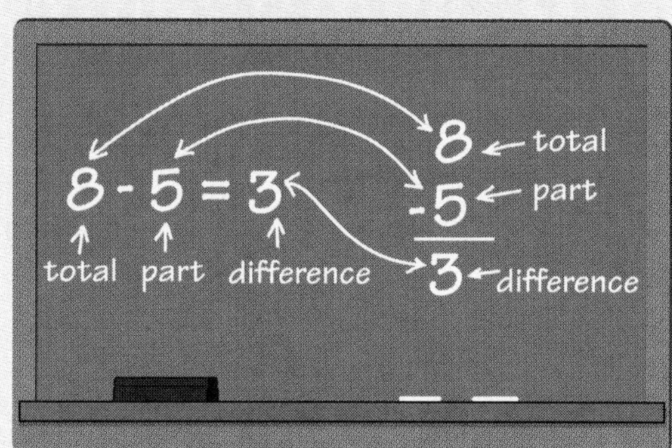

Use the horizontal and vertical forms of the fact to demonstrate the relationship between the numbers in the two formats. Draw arrows between the corresponding numbers in the facts as you say the names for them aloud—*total, part,* and *difference.*

Continue with other facts.

PRACTICE • 42

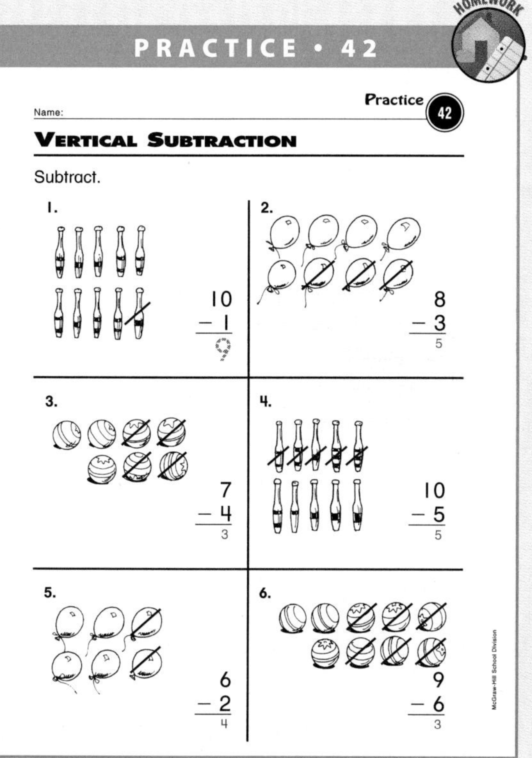

Practice 42

Name:

VERTICAL SUBTRACTION

Subtract.

1. 10 − 1 = 9
2. 8 − 3 = 5
3. 7 − 4 = 3
4. 10 − 5 = 5
5. 6 − 2 = 4
6. 9 − 6 = 3

RETEACH • 42

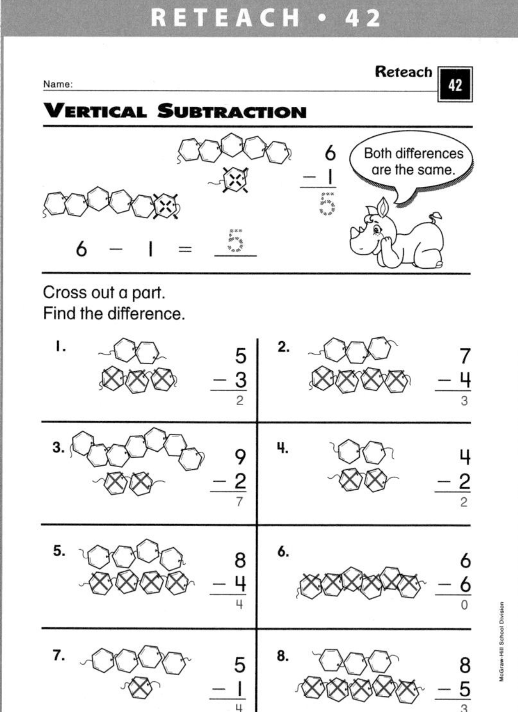

Reteach 42

Name:

VERTICAL SUBTRACTION

6 − 1 = 5

Both differences are the same.

6 − 1 = 5

Cross out a part.
Find the difference.

1. 5 − 3 = 2
2. 7 − 4 = 3
3. 9 − 2 = 7
4. 4 − 2 = 2
5. 8 − 4 = 4
6. 6 − 6 = 0
7. 5 − 1 = 4
8. 8 − 5 = 3

EXTEND • 42

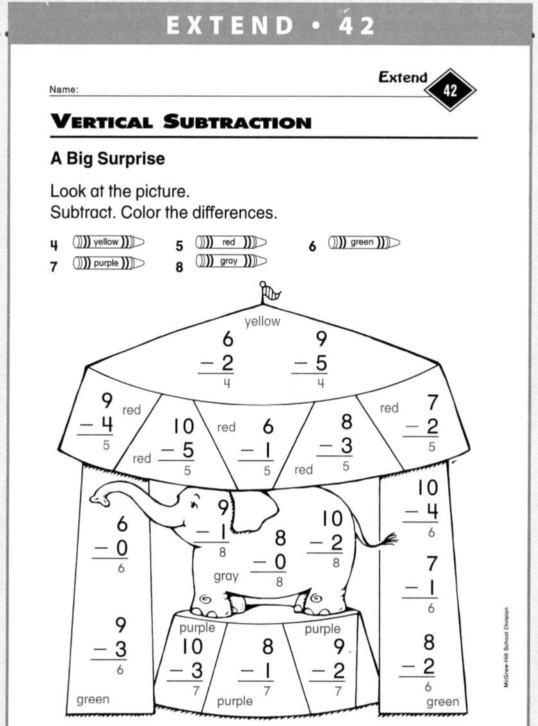

Extend 42

Name:

VERTICAL SUBTRACTION

A Big Surprise

Look at the picture.
Subtract. Color the differences.

4 yellow 5 red 6 green
7 purple 8 gray

6 − 2 = 4, 9 − 5 = 4 (yellow); 9 − 4 = 5, 10 − 5 = 5, 6 − 1 = 5, 8 − 3 = 5, 7 − 2 = 5 (red); 9 − 1 = 8, 8 − 0 = 8, 10 − 2 = 8 (gray); 6 − 0 = 6, 10 − 4 = 6, 7 − 1 = 6, 9 − 3 = 6, 8 − 2 = 6 (green); 10 − 3 = 7, 8 − 1 = 7, 9 − 2 = 7 (purple)

Related Subtraction Facts

OBJECTIVE Recognize related facts.

Day 1 Related Subtraction Facts

RESOURCE REMINDER
Math Center Cards 32
Practice 43, Reteach 43, Extend 43

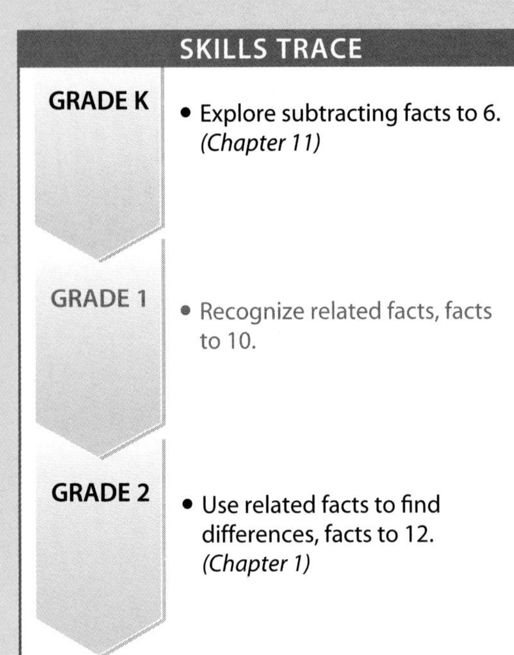

SKILLS TRACE	
GRADE K	• Explore subtracting facts to 6. *(Chapter 11)*
GRADE 1	• Recognize related facts, facts to 10.
GRADE 2	• Use related facts to find differences, facts to 12. *(Chapter 1)*

LESSON RESOURCES

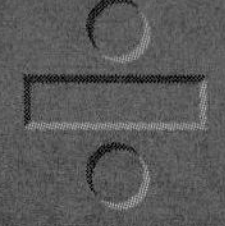

WARM-UP

Whole Class — **Social**

OBJECTIVE Act out subtraction problems.

▶ Talk briefly with children about circus parades and ask them to describe what they think they would see in one. Then read this problem aloud:

Nine clowns are marching in a circus parade. Two of the clowns sit down. How many clowns are still marching? *[7]*

▶ Have children act out the problem and solve it. Then have them act out and solve:

Nine clowns are marching in a circus parade. Seven of them sit down. How many are still marching? *[2]*

▶ Continue with other circus subtraction problems.

CONNECTION ACTIVITY

Cooperative Pairs — **Logical/Analytical**

OBJECTIVE Solve subtraction facts in vertical form to move from "Start" to "End" on a game board.

Materials per pair: Game Board (TA 13), Subtraction Fact Cards (TA 18), 2 two-color counters

▶ Give each pair of children a game board. Children put their counters on "Start" and place the subtraction fact cards face down.

▶ Players take turns. They take a fact card, solve it, and move their counter as many spaces as the number of the difference.

▶ The winner is the first player to reach "End."

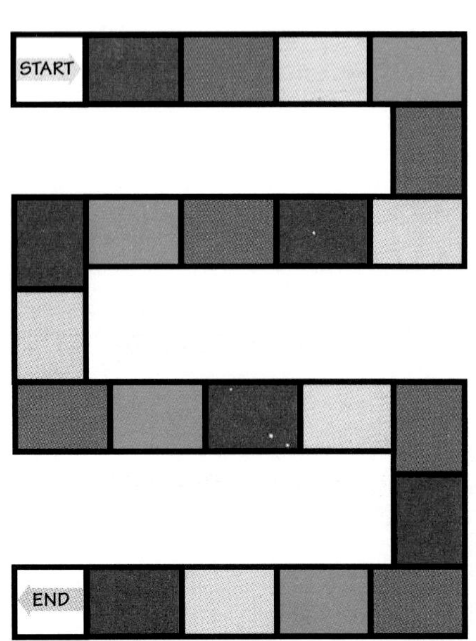

DAILY MATH

PREVIOUS DAY QUICK REVIEW

Subtract.

1. $8 - 3$ *[5]*   **2.** $6 - 4$ *[2]*   **3.** $5 - 1$ *[4]*

FAST FACTS

1. 6 + 4 *[10]*
2. 5 + 3 *[8]*
3. 7 + 0 *[7]*
4. 4 + 4 *[8]*

Problem of the Day • 32

Read aloud to children:

Joe has a bag of 10 peanuts.
He feeds 5 peanuts to an elephant.
He eats the rest himself.
How many peanuts does Joe eat? *[5]*

TECH LINK

MATH FORUM

Idea I have children write their ages in Chinese numerals, using the chart on page 164.

Visit our Resource Village at http://www.mhschool.com to see more of the Math Forum.

MATH CENTER

Practice

OBJECTIVE Recognize and write related subtraction facts.

Materials 18 connecting cubes; Math Center Recording Sheet (TA 38 optional)

Children use each row of numbers to build and write two related subtraction facts. *[7 – 6 = 1, 7 – 1 = 6; 9 – 4 = 5, 9 – 5 = 4; 5 – 3 = 2, 5 – 2 = 3]*

Problem Solving

OBJECTIVE Recognize related facts.

Materials per child: 10 connecting cubes, Math Center Recording Sheet (TA 38 optional)

Children make cube trains and then create related facts by snapping off cubes and recording two vertical subtraction facts. Guide them to start with 9, 8, 7, 6, and 5 cube trains.

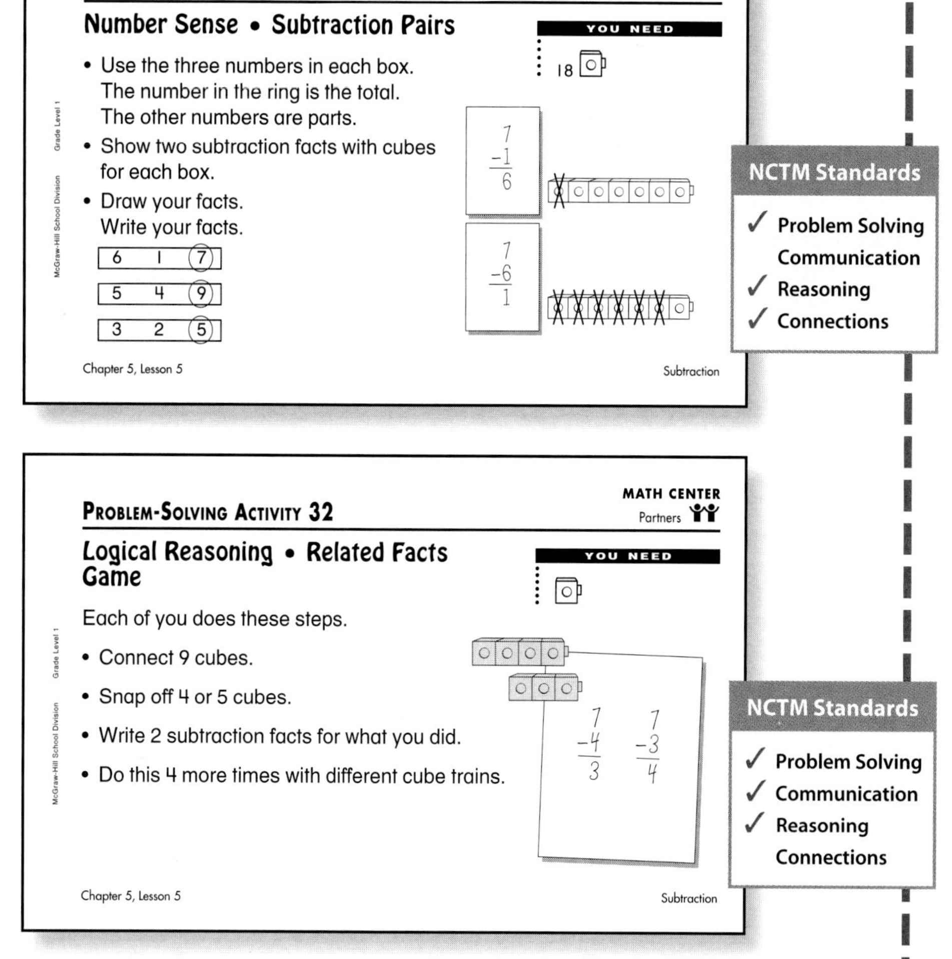

PRACTICE ACTIVITY 32 — MATH CENTER, On Your Own

Number Sense • Subtraction Pairs

YOU NEED: 18 cubes

- Use the three numbers in each box. The number in the ring is the total. The other numbers are parts.
- Show two subtraction facts with cubes for each box.
- Draw your facts. Write your facts.

6	1	(7)
5	4	(9)
3	2	(5)

7 − 1 = 6; 7 − 6 = 1

Chapter 5, Lesson 5 — Subtraction

NCTM Standards
✓ Problem Solving
Communication
✓ Reasoning
✓ Connections

PROBLEM-SOLVING ACTIVITY 32 — MATH CENTER, Partners

Logical Reasoning • Related Facts Game

YOU NEED: cubes

Each of you does these steps.

- Connect 9 cubes.
- Snap off 4 or 5 cubes.
- Write 2 subtraction facts for what you did.
- Do this 4 more times with different cube trains.

7 − 4 = 3; 7 − 3 = 4

Chapter 5, Lesson 5 — Subtraction

NCTM Standards
✓ Problem Solving
✓ Communication
✓ Reasoning
Connections

Lesson 5.5

DAY 1

Related Subtraction Facts

OBJECTIVE Children recognize related facts.

Materials have available per child: 10 two-color counters

1 Motivate — Whole Class

Resources Jumbo Activity Book, page 9; Stickers, sheet 1 (two-color counters)

Display 4 red and 5 yellow counters in the workspace on Jumbo Activity Book page 9. Write the vertical addition fact in the top box. Ask:

- **What is the related addition fact for 4 + 5 = 9?** *[5 + 4 = 9]*

Write the related fact in the same box. Ask a volunteer to use the counters to show a subtraction fact with the same numbers on the Jumbo Book page. *[9 − 4 = 5 or 9 − 5 = 4]* Write the vertical subtraction fact in the bottom box.

- **How could you show another subtraction fact with the same numbers?** *[Possible answer: You could change the places of the part you take away and the part that is left.]*

2 Develop

Page 163

Read the subtraction facts at the top of the page and discuss the Talk question.

- **How are the two facts the same?** *[They use the same numbers.]*

Point to the results of the related subtraction facts.

- **Why are the answers different?** *[Possible answer: because a different part is being subtracted from each total]*
- **What is the same about two related subtraction facts?** *[Possible answer: The total and the parts are the same.]*

CRITICAL THINKING

Before children answer the question on the page, ask:

- **If you know a subtraction fact, how can you find its related fact?** *[Possible answer: You can change the places of the part you subtract and the part that is left.]*

Page 164

Try These Assign practice exercises 1–6.

Cultural Connection Talk about the patterns children see in Chinese numbers.

3 Close

Check for Understanding by having children find the differences and then say the related subtraction facts for 8 − 3 and 5 − 0. *[8 − 3 = 5, 8 − 5 = 3; 5 − 0 = 5; 5 − 5 = 0]*

Name ____________________

Related Subtraction Facts

How are these facts different?
The part being subtracted and the difference are different.

$$\begin{array}{r} 9 \\ -\,3 \\ \hline 6 \end{array}$$

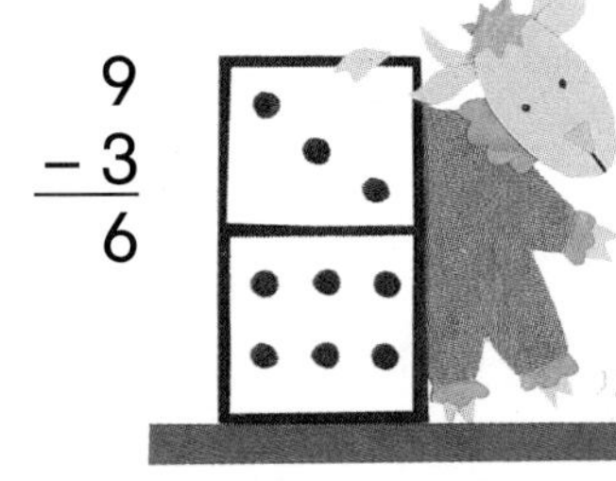

$$\begin{array}{r} 9 \\ -\,6 \\ \hline 3 \end{array}$$

Draw the missing part. Subtract. Arrangement of dots may vary.

1. 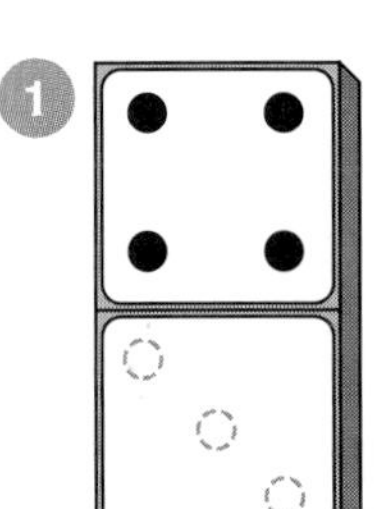
$\begin{array}{r} 7 \\ -\,4 \\ \hline 3 \end{array}$ $\begin{array}{r} 7 \\ -\,3 \\ \hline 4 \end{array}$

2. 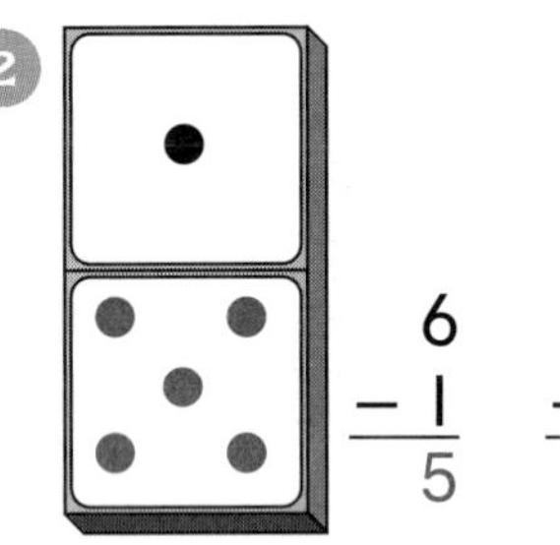
$\begin{array}{r} 6 \\ -\,1 \\ \hline 5 \end{array}$ $\begin{array}{r} 6 \\ -\,5 \\ \hline 1 \end{array}$

3. 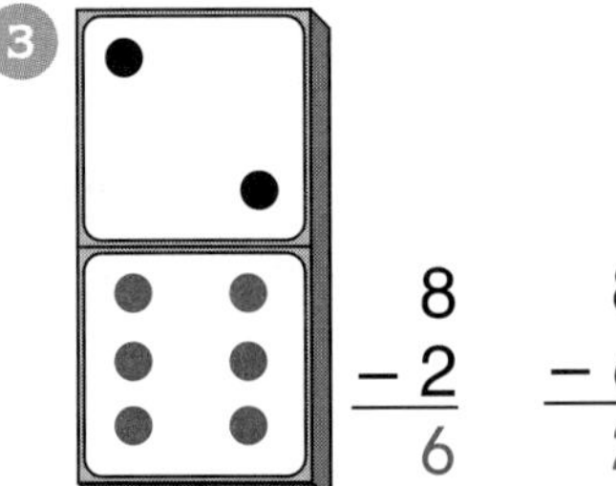
$\begin{array}{r} 8 \\ -\,2 \\ \hline 6 \end{array}$ $\begin{array}{r} 8 \\ -\,6 \\ \hline 2 \end{array}$

4. 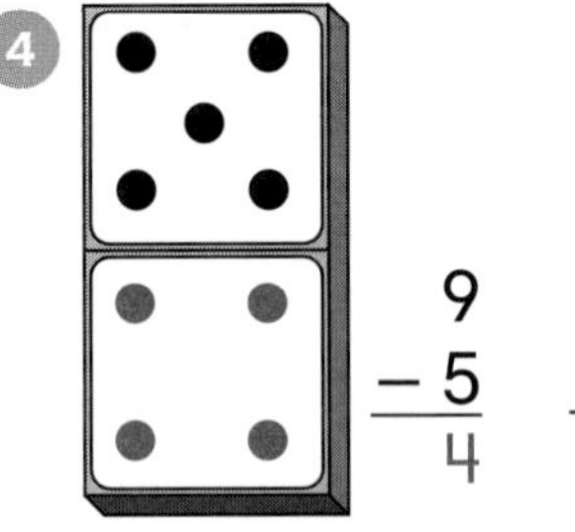
$\begin{array}{r} 9 \\ -\,5 \\ \hline 4 \end{array}$ $\begin{array}{r} 9 \\ -\,4 \\ \hline 5 \end{array}$

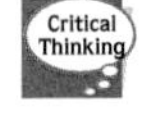

How could you show this subtraction with crossing out?

Possible answer: Draw dots for the total and cross out the dots in the part being subtracted.

MEETING INDIVIDUAL NEEDS

EARLY FINISHERS

Have pairs of children draw dominoes, using dots to show some of the subtraction facts presented on page 164. Children can take turns drawing a fact and its related fact.

EXTRA SUPPORT

Sort subtraction fact cards into two sets with a related fact in each set. Have children place the cards in each set face up and try to match the related facts. Talk about how the numbers in each fact are the same.

ONGOING ASSESSMENT

Observation Checklist Determine if children understand related subtraction facts by observing whether they can say the related facts in **Check for Understanding.**

Follow Up If children have difficulty, have them work with a partner and use two-color counters to show the related facts on p. 164. Then assign **Reteach 43.**

For children who demonstrate understanding, assign **Extend 43.**

Try These!

Subtract.

1. 6 − 3 = 3
2. 8 − 4 = 4
3. 10 − 5 = 5

4	7 − 2 = 5	7 − 5 = 2	9 − 2 = 7	9 − 7 = 2	8 − 5 = 3	8 − 3 = 5
5	6 − 4 = 2	6 − 2 = 4	10 − 7 = 3	10 − 3 = 7	7 − 1 = 6	7 − 6 = 1
6	9 − 9 = 0	9 − 0 = 9	10 − 2 = 8	10 − 8 = 2	9 − 1 = 8	9 − 8 = 1

Cultural Connection

Chinese Numbers

Chinese numbers are like pictures.

一	二	三	四	五
1	2	3	4	5

Write the Chinese number that is 1 less.

 二 三  四 五 一 二

At Home: We learned about related subtraction facts. Ask your child to tell you how the pairs of facts are alike.

Alternate Teaching Strategy

Materials per pair: 10 two-color counters

Have children use the red and yellow sides of the counters to show 6 and 4. Write the related addition facts for 6, 4, and 10 on the chalkboard, and ask a volunteer to show how the model can be used for both additions.

Then write the related subtraction facts next to each of the additions.

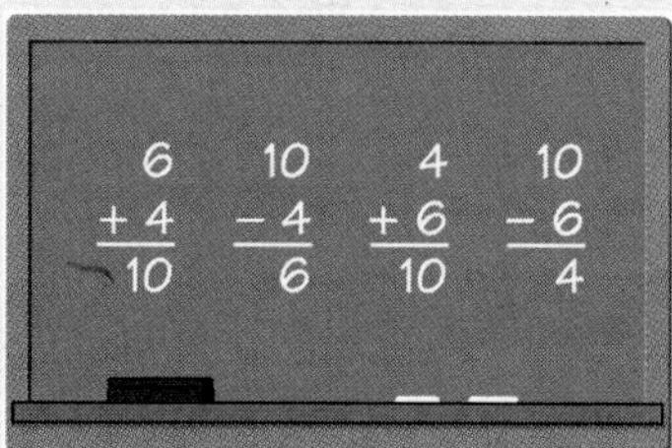

Help children see that the same 10 counters can also be used to show the subtraction fact. Ask them to point out the total and both parts in the model.

- **How are these two subtraction facts alike?** *[They have the same total and the same parts.]* **How are they different?** *[Possible answers: Different parts are being subtracted, the answers are different.]*

Repeat for related addition and subtraction facts for 3, 4, and 7.

PRACTICE • 43

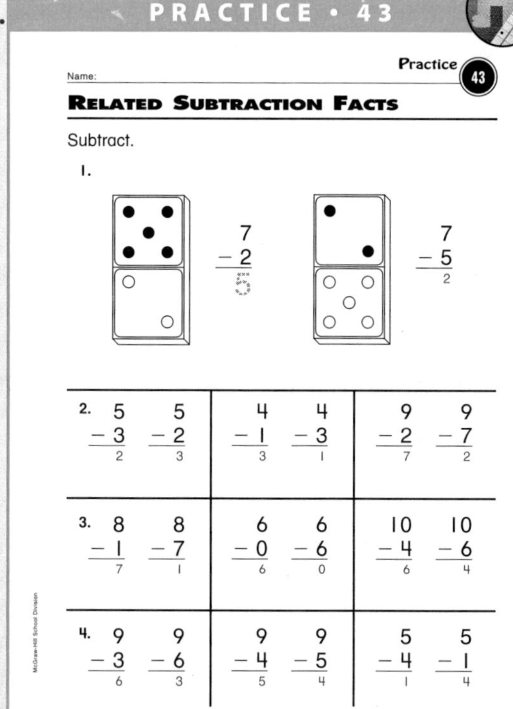

RETEACH • 43

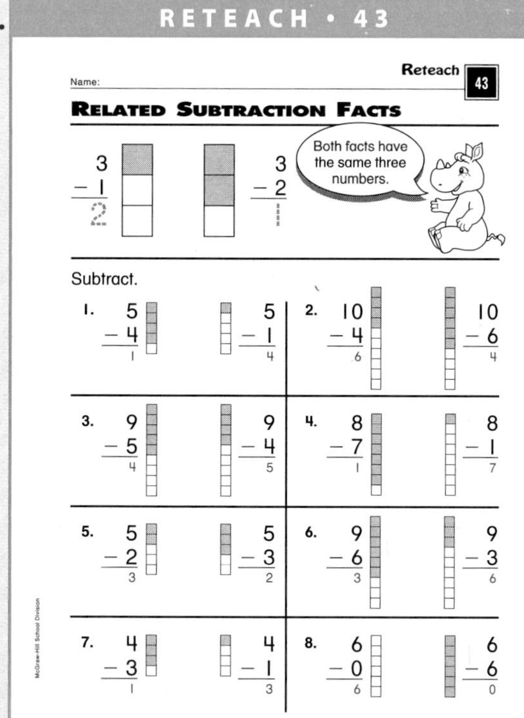

EXTEND • 43

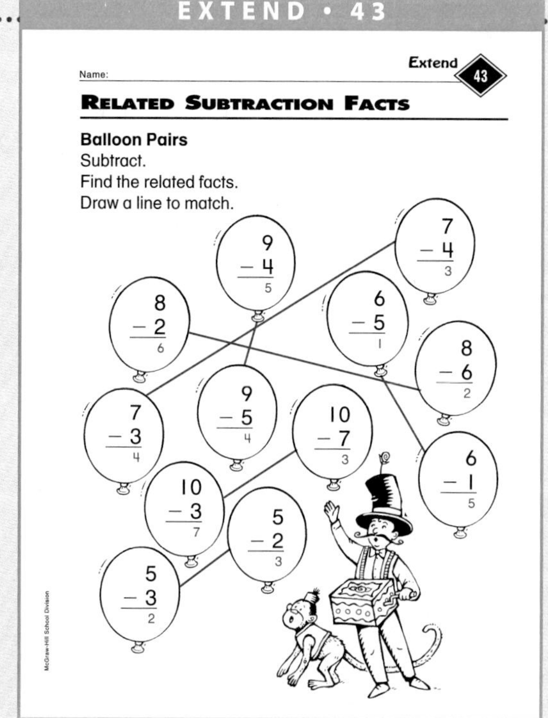

AT A GLANCE

PURPOSE Provide an opportunity for review and practice.

Materials crayons (blue, green, purple, orange, yellow, and red)

Using the Extra Practice

Page 165

Explain and demonstrate how to use the color key.

Tell children to solve all the subtraction facts first. Then they can match colors to differences and color the picture.

After children have finished coloring, ask:

- **What color patterns do you see in the picture?** *[Possible answers: red/yellow; green/orange; blue/purple]*

Page 166

Have children complete the exercises independently or in pairs.

For Items 5 and 6, you may want to remind children to look for facts with the same parts.

Using the Additional Practice

The section below provides additional practice that you may want to write on the chalkboard or put on a reproducible master.

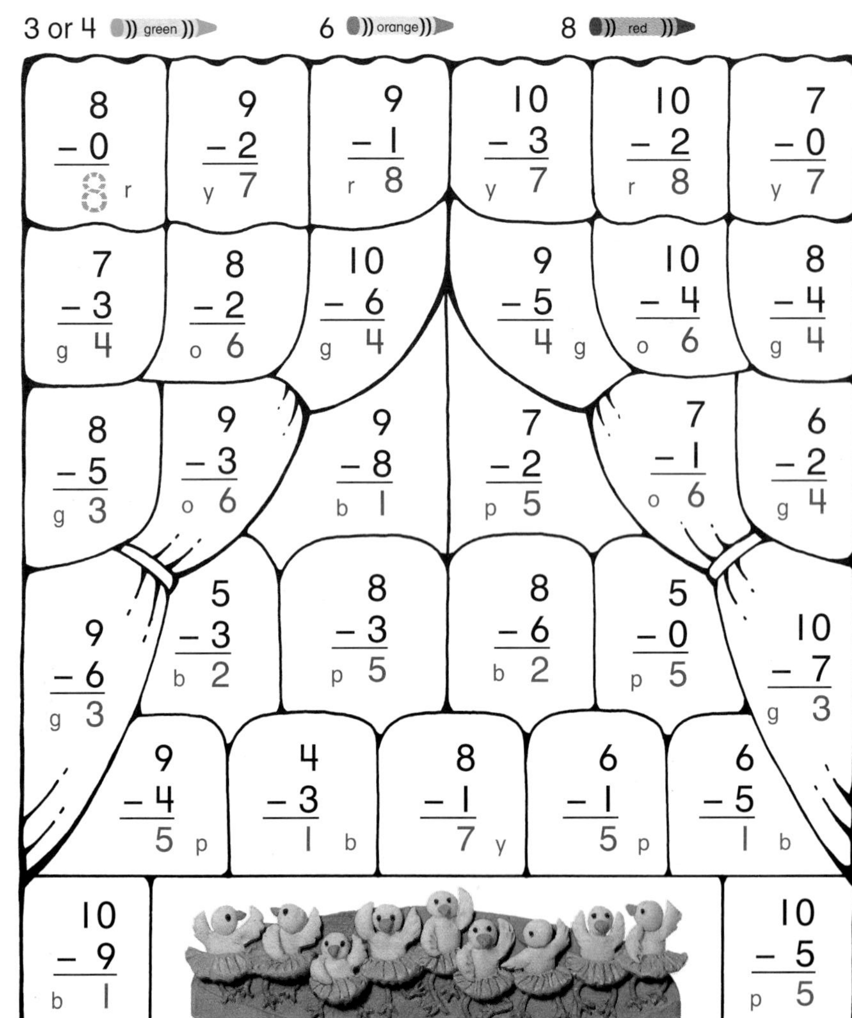

Name ______________________ Extra Practice Activity !

Number Fun House

Subtract. Color to match differences.

1 or 2 blue; 3 or 4 green; 5 purple; 6 orange; 7 yellow; 8 red

8 − 0 = 8 r	9 − 2 = 7 y	9 − 1 = 8 r	10 − 3 = 7 y	10 − 2 = 8 r	7 − 0 = 7 y
7 − 3 = 4 g	8 − 2 = 6 o	10 − 6 = 4 g	9 − 5 = 4 g	10 − 4 = 6 o	8 − 4 = 4 g
8 − 5 = 3 g	9 − 3 = 6 o	9 − 8 = 1 b	7 − 2 = 5 p	7 − 1 = 6 o	6 − 2 = 4 g
9 − 6 = 3 g	5 − 3 = 2 b	8 − 3 = 5 p	8 − 6 = 2 b	5 − 0 = 5 p	10 − 7 = 3 g
9 − 4 = 5 p	4 − 3 = 1 b	8 − 1 = 7 y	6 − 1 = 5 p	6 − 5 = 1 b	
10 − 9 = 1 b					10 − 5 = 5 p

CHAPTER 5 *Extra Practice* — one hundred sixty-five • 165

ADDITIONAL PRACTICE

Subtract.

1.	8 − 4 = [4]	3 − 2 = [1]	5 − 3 = [2]	6 − 1 = [5]
2.	6 − 5 = [1]	7 − 4 = [3]	4 − 3 = [1]	9 − 4 = [5]
3.	9 − 0 = [9]	6 − 2 = [4]	8 − 7 = [1]	7 − 0 = [7]
4.	5 − 3 = [2]	5 − 2 = [3]	3 − 2 = [1]	3 − 1 = [2]
5.	6 − 4 = [2]	6 − 2 = [4]	8 − 3 = [5]	8 − 5 = [3]
6.	9 − 8 = [1]	9 − 1 = [8]	7 − 2 = [5]	7 − 5 = [2]

Use counters if you want to.

Subtract.

1	10 − 9 = 1	6 − 6 = 0	9 − 8 = 1	7 − 6 = 1	9 − 0 = 9	
2	8 − 8 = 0	10 − 5 = 5	6 − 1 = 5	8 − 6 = 2	5 − 5 = 0	9 − 2 = 7
3	9 − 4 = 5	5 − 2 = 3	7 − 5 = 2	10 − 8 = 2	6 − 4 = 2	8 − 1 = 7
4	7 − 4 = 3	10 − 7 = 3	6 − 3 = 3	8 − 7 = 1	9 − 6 = 3	7 − 0 = 7

Match related facts. Subtract.

5

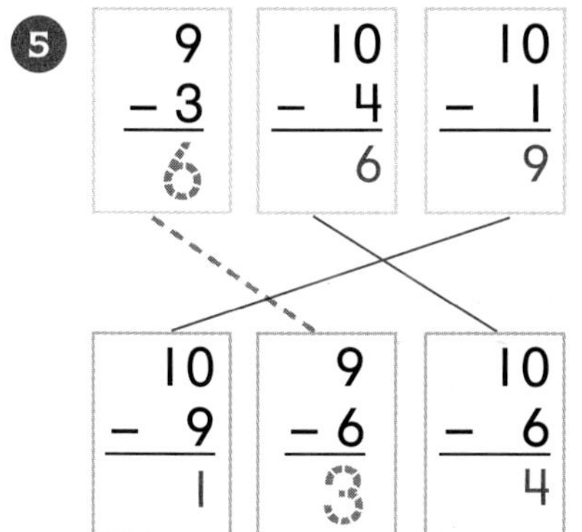

6

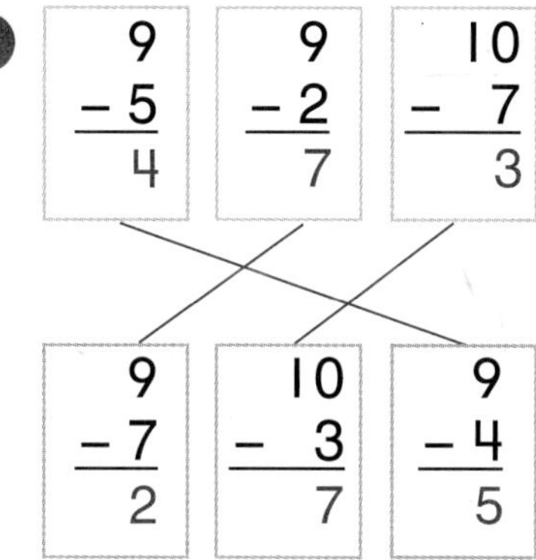

EXTRA PRACTICE

Developing Algebra Sense

This section provides another opportunity for children to reinforce algebraic ideas. You may wish to copy the exercises onto a chalkboard or onto a reproducible master.

Complete.

1. Subtract 3.	**2. Subtract 2.**	**3. Subtract 1.**
6 *[3]*	4 *[2]*	10 *[9]*
7 *[4]*	6 *[4]*	9 *[8]*
8 *[5]*	8 *[6]*	8 *[7]*
10 *[7]*	10 *[8]*	7 *[6]*

ADDITIONAL PRACTICE

Mixed Applications/Problem Solving

Listen. Solve.

1. 6 clowns bounced on a trampoline.
3 more clowns joined them.
How many clowns are there in all? *[9]*

2. 5 tigers stood on their hind legs.
3 tigers lay down and rolled over.
How many tigers were still standing? *[2]*

3. 10 circus performers marched in a parade.
The lion tamer and the ringmaster stopped to tie their shoes.
How many performers were still marching? *[8]*

4. Tanya has 3¢ in her right hand and 4¢ in her left hand.
Jesse has 5¢ in his right pocket and 5¢ in his left pocket.
Who has more money? *[Jesse]*

5. Kay counted 6 elephants in the circus parade.
Carlos counted 3 more elephants.
How many elephants did they count altogether? *[9]*

6. Sasha has 3 blue fish.
She also has 5 yellow fish.
She takes 1 blue fish and 2 yellow fish out of the tank.
How many fish are left? *[5]*

Subtract Money

OBJECTIVE Subtract money amounts, facts to 10.

Day 1 Subtract Money

RESOURCE REMINDER
Math Center Cards 33
Practice 44, Reteach 44, Extend 44

SKILLS TRACE	
GRADE K	• Explore subtracting facts to 6. *(Chapter 11)*
GRADE 1	• Subtract money amounts, facts to 10.
GRADE 2	• Subtract money amounts. *(Chapter 8)*

LESSON RESOURCES

MANIPULATIVE WARM-UP

Cooperative Pairs — **Logical/Analytical**

OBJECTIVE Explore estimating purchases up to 10¢.

Materials per pair: 10 pennies; 5–6 small classroom objects with price tags (TA 12) from 1¢ to 10¢; paper with 2 columns titled *Money Spent* and *Money Left?*

▶ Explain that each child has 10¢ to spend. Children take turns choosing two items they could buy with their money.

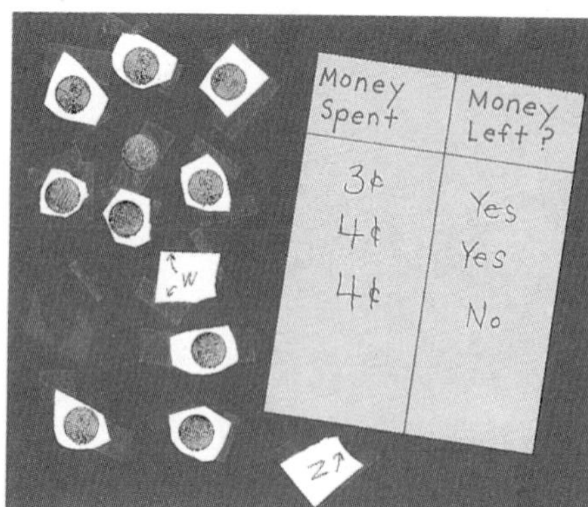

▶ When one child has chosen, the partner writes the total in the *Money Spent* column. He or she then decides whether the first child has any money left and writes *yes* or *no* in the *Money Left?* column.

CONNECTION ACTIVITY

Whole Class — **Auditory/Linguistic**

OBJECTIVE Connect addition and subtraction with music.

Resource Read-Aloud Anthology, page 47, "Five Little Ducks"

▶ Sing the first verse of the song "Five Little Ducks," found in the Read-Aloud Anthology, for the class. Have children sing it along with you. Then continue the song.

▶ After singing, ask volunteers to tell about the math in the song.
- **What is the subtraction fact in verse 1?** *[5 − 1 = 4]*

▶ Continue through all the subtraction verses. For the last verse, ask:
- **What is the addition fact for this verse?** *[0 + 5 = 5]*

DAILY MATH

PREVIOUS DAY QUICK REVIEW

Subtract.

1. $\begin{array}{r} 9 \\ -0 \\ \hline \end{array}$ *[9]* $\begin{array}{r} 9 \\ -9 \\ \hline \end{array}$ *[0]*

2. $\begin{array}{r} 8 \\ -5 \\ \hline \end{array}$ *[3]* $\begin{array}{r} 8 \\ -3 \\ \hline \end{array}$ *[5]*

FAST FACTS

1. 3 – 2 = *[1]*
2. 6 – 4 = *[2]*
3. 9 – 3 = *[6]*
4. 10 –7 = *[3]*

Problem of the Day • 33

Read aloud to children:

Suni's father gave him 10¢ to spend at the circus.
He spent 6¢ on a postcard of an elephant.
He spent 4¢ on a balloon.
How much money did Suni have left? *[0¢]*

TECH LINK

MATH FORUM

Idea I have children decorate a jar with construction-paper ears, eyes and snout, and a pipe-cleaner tail to make a piggy bank for the class supply of pennies.

Visit our Resource Village at http://www.mhschool.com to see more of the Math Forum.

MATH CENTER

Practice

OBJECTIVE Subtract money amounts to 10.

Materials per child: 10 pennies, Math Center Recording Sheet (TA 38 optional)

Children use 10 pennies to buy any ball and write the amount of money left over. In the second round, they must first choose a ball that they can buy with only 6¢. They then make up a problem, exchange, and solve their partner's problem. *[Possible answers include: 10 – 2 = 8¢, 10 – 7 = 3¢, 10 – 8 = 2¢, 10 – 4 = 6¢; 6 – 2 = 4¢, 6 – 4 = 2¢]*

PRACTICE ACTIVITY 33 — MATH CENTER, Partners

Manipulatives • Money Left

YOU NEED: 10 pennies each

Take turns.
Use pennies.

- You have 10¢.
  Buy a ball.
  How much is left?
  Write the subtraction fact.
- Do this again with 6¢.
- Make up a problem.
- Solve your partner's problem.

Beach Ball 2¢ · Football 8¢ · Soccer Ball 7¢ · Baseball 4¢

McGraw-Hill School Division · Grade Level 1

Chapter 5, Lesson 6 · Subtraction

NCTM Standards
✓ Problem Solving
✓ Communication
✓ Reasoning
✓ Connections

Problem Solving

OBJECTIVE Subtract cents from each price to find the sale price.

Materials per child: 20 pennies, 1–5 spinner (TA 7), Math Center Recording Sheet (TA 38 optional)

Children will find sale prices by spinning for a number and subtracting it from the prices shown on tags. They can use the pennies to solve the problems. *[Check children's answers.]*

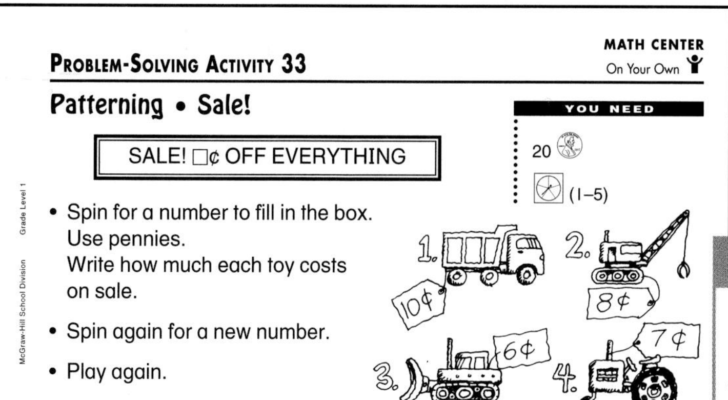

PROBLEM-SOLVING ACTIVITY 33 — MATH CENTER, On Your Own

Patterning • Sale!

YOU NEED: 20 pennies; spinner (1–5)

SALE! □¢ OFF EVERYTHING

- Spin for a number to fill in the box.
  Use pennies.
  Write how much each toy costs on sale.
- Spin again for a new number.
- Play again.

McGraw-Hill School Division · Grade Level 1

Chapter 5, Lesson 6 · Subtraction

NCTM Standards
✓ Problem Solving
Communication
✓ Reasoning
✓ Connections

Lesson 5.6

DAY 1

Subtract Money

OBJECTIVE Children subtract money amounts, facts to 10.

Materials per child: 10 penny models

1 Motivate — Whole Class

Materials 8 two-color counters, 8 pennies

Display 8 counters. Move 5 counters to the right and ask how many are left. *[3]* Have a volunteer write the subtraction fact on the chalkboard and read it aloud. *[8 – 5 = 3]*

Display 8 pennies, then move 5 of them to the right.

- **How many pennies are left?** *[3]*

Have another child write this subtraction on the chalkboard. Be sure the cents signs are included. *[8¢ – 5¢ =3¢]*

- **How is this subtraction sentence like the first one?** *[The numbers are the same.]* **How is it different?** *[Possible answers: This one has cents signs; it is about money.]*

2 Develop

Page 167

Explain that Josh has 10¢ to buy animal food to feed the circus animals. Discuss the worked-out example to find how much money Josh has left.

- **How much money did Josh start with?** *[10¢]* **Did he spend all of his money? How do you know?** *[No, because he has 5¢ left.]*

Have children use their pennies to subtract in exercises 1–6.

Critical Thinking
After children answer the question on the page, ask:

- **What could you buy that would cost all of your money?** *[Possible answers: fish food and corn; 2 apples]*

Page 168

Try These Assign practice exercises 1–7.

Children can use pennies to show the subtraction.

More to Explore Children use number patterns to help them subtract.

3 Close

Check for Understanding by having children subtract 7¢ from their 10 pennies and write the subtraction sentence. *[10¢ – 7¢ = 3¢]*

Name ______________________

Subtract Money

Find how much money Josh has left.

10¢
– 5¢
5¢

You need 10 (penny).
Subtract to find how much money is left.

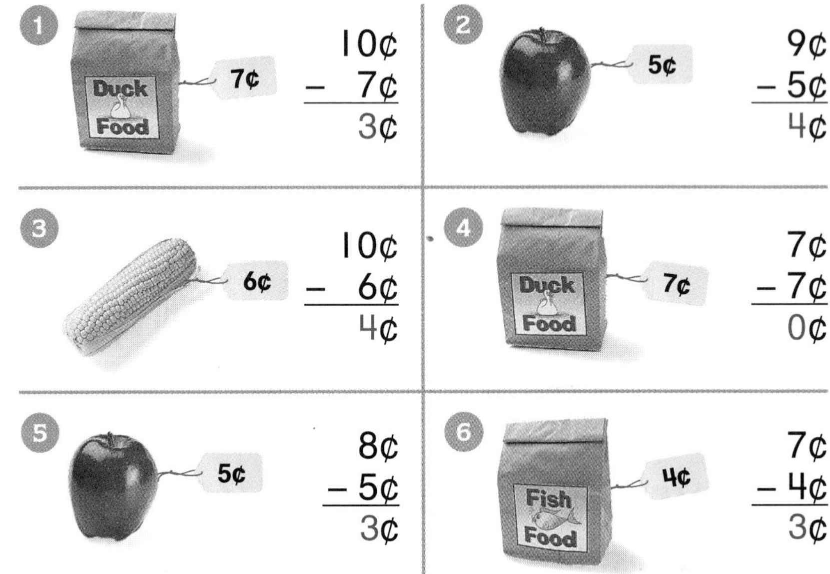

You have 5¢. How much more money do you need to buy duck food? 2¢

MEETING INDIVIDUAL NEEDS

EARLY FINISHERS

Have children draw something that costs 10¢ or less. Then have them exchange pictures with a partner and write the subtraction sentence for their pictures. Remind them to include the cents signs.

EXTRA SUPPORT

Have pairs of children use pennies to buy the items pictured on page 168 from each other. One child pays the total amount shown, and the other subtracts and gives back the change.

ONGOING ASSESSMENT

Interview Determine if children understand how to subtract money amounts by presenting 9 – 4 and 9¢ – 4¢.

- **How is subtracting money the same as subtracting numbers? How is it different?** *[Possible answer: You subtract the numbers the same way; you have to write the cents signs.]*

Follow Up For children having difficulty, assign **Reteach 44.**

For children who understand, assign **Extend 44.**

Try These!

Use pennies if you want to.

Subtract.

1.  6¢ 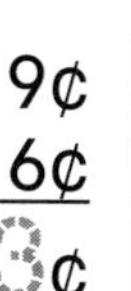
   9¢ − 6¢ = 3¢
2.  1¢
   7¢ − 1¢ = 6¢
3. 

   4¢
   10¢ − 4¢ = 6¢
4. 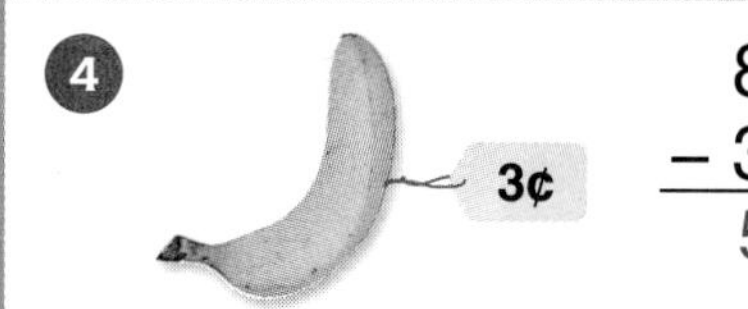 3¢
   8¢ − 3¢ = 5¢

5. 10¢ − 7¢ = 3¢ | 9¢ − 5¢ = 4¢ | 7¢ − 3¢ = 4¢ | 8¢ − 6¢ = 2¢ | 9¢ − 2¢ = 7¢ | 6¢ − 5¢ = 1¢
6. 8¢ − 2¢ = 6¢ | 10¢ − 5¢ = 5¢ | 4¢ − 1¢ = 3¢ | 9¢ − 9¢ = 0¢ | 5¢ − 2¢ = 3¢ | 7¢ − 6¢ = 1¢
7. 4¢ − 4¢ = 0¢ | 10¢ − 8¢ = 2¢ | 5¢ − 1¢ = 4¢ | 9¢ − 8¢ = 1¢ | 6¢ − 3¢ = 3¢ | 8¢ − 5¢ = 3¢

More to Explore — Patterns

Complete.

9	8	7	6	5	4	3
− 3	− 3	− 3	− 3	− 3	− 3	− 3
6	5	4	3	2	1	0

Show your child 10 pennies. Ask how many you would have left if you spent 6¢.

Alternate Teaching Strategy

Materials per child: 10 penny models; 5–6 small classroom objects, price tags (TA 12)

Prepare Label objects from 1¢ to 10¢.

Display the tagged items and explain that each child has 10¢ to spend. Have children take turns choosing an item they would like to buy.

Ask children to count enough pennies to purchase their item. Then have them count to see how many pennies they have left. Children then write the subtraction sentence that shows how much they spent and how much they have left. If necessary, remind them to write the cents signs next to the numbers.

PRACTICE • 44

HOMEWORK

Name: Practice 44

Subtract Money

Subtract.

1. Peanuts 3¢ — 10¢ − 3¢ = 7¢
2. 5¢ — 7¢ − 5¢ = 2¢
3. Orange Juice 8¢ — 8¢ − 8¢ = 0¢
4. 9¢ — 10¢ − 9¢ = 1¢
5. 8¢ − 4¢ = 4¢ | 9¢ − 4¢ = 5¢ | 4¢ − 3¢ = 1¢ | 3¢ − 3¢ = 0¢ | 9¢ − 3¢ = 6¢ | 10¢ − 1¢ = 9¢
6. 6¢ − 6¢ = 0¢ | 6¢ − 4¢ = 2¢ | 10¢ − 2¢ = 8¢ | 9¢ − 7¢ = 2¢ | 8¢ − 1¢ = 7¢ | 7¢ − 5¢ = 2¢
7. 9¢ − 1¢ = 8¢ | 10¢ − 5¢ = 5¢ | 8¢ − 7¢ = 1¢ | 4¢ − 2¢ = 2¢ | 5¢ − 5¢ = 0¢ | 6¢ − 2¢ = 4¢

RETEACH • 44

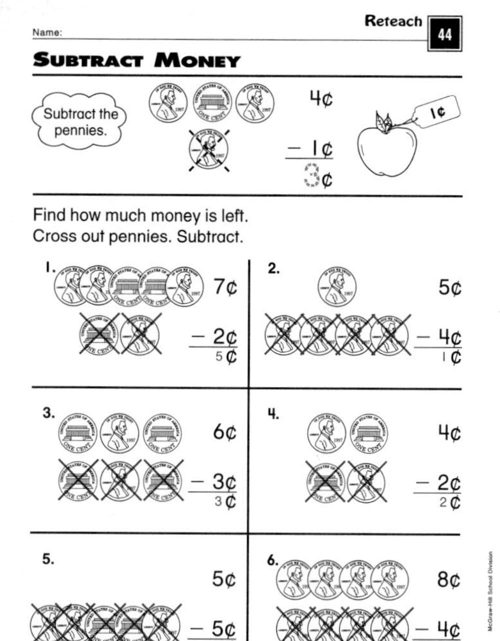

Name: Reteach 44

Subtract Money

Subtract the pennies. 4¢ − 1¢ = 3¢

Find how much money is left. Cross out pennies. Subtract.

1. 7¢ − 2¢ = 5¢
2. 5¢ − 4¢ = 1¢
3. 6¢ − 3¢ = 3¢
4. 4¢ − 2¢ = 2¢
5. 5¢ − 5¢ = 0¢
6. 8¢ − 4¢ = 4¢

EXTEND • 44

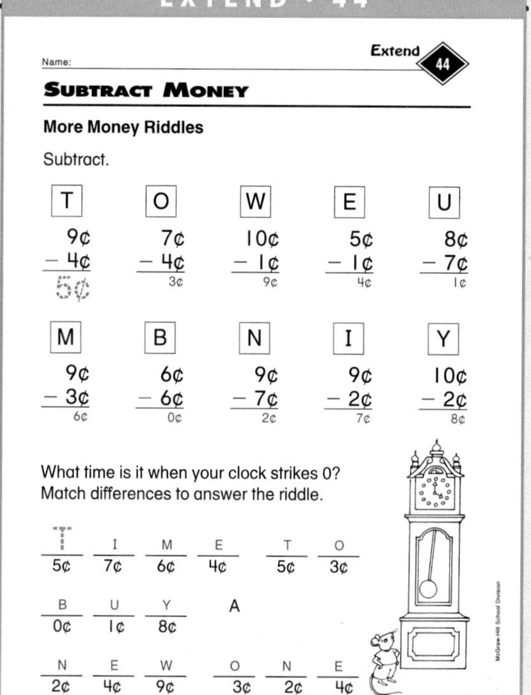

Name: Extend 44

Subtract Money

More Money Riddles

Subtract.

T	O	W	E	U
9¢ − 4¢ = 5¢	7¢ − 4¢ = 3¢	10¢ − 1¢ = 9¢	5¢ − 1¢ = 4¢	8¢ − 7¢ = 1¢

M	B	N	I	Y
9¢ − 3¢ = 6¢	6¢ − 6¢ = 0¢	9¢ − 7¢ = 2¢	9¢ − 2¢ = 7¢	10¢ − 2¢ = 8¢

What time is it when your clock strikes 0? Match differences to answer the riddle.

T I M E — 5¢ 7¢ 6¢ 4¢   T O — 5¢ 3¢

B U Y — 0¢ 1¢ 8¢   A

N E W — 2¢ 4¢ 9¢   O N E — 3¢ 2¢ 4¢

Addition and Subtraction

OBJECTIVE Relate addition and subtraction.

Day 1 Addition and Subtraction

Teaching With Technology
See alternate computer lesson, pp. 170A–170B.

RESOURCE REMINDER
Math Center Cards 34
Practice 45, Reteach 45, Extend 45

SKILLS TRACE

GRADE K	• Explore adding and subtracting, facts to 6. *(Chapter 11)*
GRADE 1	• Relate addition and subtraction.
GRADE 2	• Use related facts to complete fact families, facts to 18. *(Chapter 2)*

LESSON RESOURCES

MANIPULATIVE WARM-UP

Cooperative Pairs **Logical/Analytical**

OBJECTIVE Match related addition and related subtraction facts.

Materials index cards; per pair: 10 two-color counters

Prepare On index cards, write related addition facts to 10 and related subtraction facts to 10. Give each pair 12–16 fact cards.

▶ Have one child in each pair mix up the cards and place them face down. Children take turns turning over two cards. If the cards show related addition or subtraction facts, the child keeps the cards. If not, the child turns them face down again and the partner takes a turn.

▶ When all cards have been taken, the player with the most pairs is the winner. Children can use counters to help them if they wish.

CONNECTION ACTIVITY

Whole Class **Visual/Spatial**

OBJECTIVE Connect addition and map reading.

▶ Draw this map on the chalkboard.

▶ Have the class use the map to answer the questions.

- **How can you tell how far it is from the park to the school?** *[Possible answer: Read the number of miles between them.]*
- **How far is it from the park to the library? How can you tell?** *[5 miles; add the miles from the park to the school to the miles from the school to the library.]*
- **How much further is it from the school to the library than from the school to the park?** *[1 mile]*

DAILY MATH

PREVIOUS DAY QUICK REVIEW

Subtract.

1. 7¢ – 4¢ = ____ *[3¢]*
2. 6¢ – 5¢ = ____ *[1¢]*
3. 8¢ – 3¢ = ____ *[5¢]*
4. 9¢ – 5¢ = ____ *[4¢]*

FAST FACTS

1. 7 + 1 *[8]*
2. 8 + 1 *[9]*
3. 4 + 5 *[9]*
4. 3 + 4 *[7]*

Problem of the Day • 34

Read aloud to children:

3 acrobats are doing handstands in the ring.
2 more acrobats join the group.
How many acrobats are there in all? *[5]*
3 leave the group.
How many are there now? *[2]*

TECH LINK

MATH VAN

Activity You may wish to use *Dancing Cows* to teach this lesson.

MATH FORUM

Management Tip I keep a hundred chart on permanent display for children to use as a reference or to explore addition or subtraction patterns.

Visit our Resource Village at http://www.mhschool.com to see more of the Math Forum.

MATH CENTER

Practice

OBJECTIVE Write and identify related addition and subtraction facts.

Materials per pair: spinner (0–9); per child: Math Center Recording Sheet (TA 38 optional), 0–9 spinner (TA 7)

Children spin for a number, then write one addition fact. Their partner writes one related subtraction fact. They will do this for five numbers, writing the facts on cards. For fun, they can mix up the cards and then pair them back together. *[Check children's work for accuracy.]*

PRACTICE ACTIVITY 34 — MATH CENTER — Partners

Algebra Sense • Related Facts

YOU NEED: (0–9); 10 cards

- Spin the spinner to get a sum.
  Write an addition fact for that sum on a card.
  Your partner writes a related subtraction fact on a card.
- Do this four more times.
- Mix up all the cards.
  Now put together the cards in pairs.
  Each pair has related facts.

Grade Level 1 · McGraw-Hill School Division

Chapter 5, Lesson 7 — Addition/Subtraction

NCTM Standards

✓ Problem Solving
Communication
✓ Reasoning
Connections

Problem Solving

OBJECTIVE Practice addition and subtraction facts to 10.

Materials per pair: calculator, 9 connecting cubes; per child: Math Center Recording Sheet (TA 38 Optional)

Children will use related facts to find the missing addend that is subtracted on a calculator. They build a cube train as a visual reference of the starting number. *[Ask children to explain their thinking.]*

PROBLEM-SOLVING ACTIVITY 34 — MATH CENTER — Partners

Logical Reasoning • Calculator Differences

YOU NEED: calculator; 9 cubes

Player 1: Press ON/C.
Enter 6, 7, 8, or 9.
Press [–].

Player 2: Secretly enter 1, 2, 3, 4 or 5.
Press [=].

Player 1: Look at the number that is left.
What number did Player 2 subtract?
Write the subtraction fact.

Play 5 times.

Grade Level 1 · McGraw-Hill School Division

Chapter 5, Lesson 7 — Addition/Subtraction

NCTM Standards

✓ Problem Solving
✓ Communication
Reasoning
Connections

Lesson 5.7

DAY 1

Addition and Subtraction

OBJECTIVE Children relate addition and subtraction.

Materials per child: 9 red and 9 blue connecting cubes

1 Motivate — Cooperative Pairs

Materials per child: 9 red and 9 blue connecting cubes

Have children play "Make It and Break It." One child makes a cube train of up to 10 cubes with two colors and says an addition fact—for example, 5 + 4 = 9. The partner breaks the train into the two original parts and says the subtraction fact—9 − 4 = 5 or 9 − 5 = 4.

Have volunteers display their cube trains and say their facts.

- **Why do you think we call these addition and subtraction facts related facts?** *[They have the same parts and the same total.]*
- **If you know an addition fact, how could you say a related subtraction fact?** *[You could subtract one of the parts from the total.]*

2 Develop

Page 169

Have volunteers make up a story problem about the circus "strong cat" and the cubes. Discuss the worked-out example, and have children complete the page.

CRITICAL THINKING

- **Why can you show an addition fact and a subtraction fact with the same cubes?** *[Possible answer: because addition and subtraction both have parts and totals]*

Page 170

Try These Assign practice exercises 1–6.

Discuss the second exercise with children to be sure they understand that there are 0 cubes being added.

JOURNAL Look at children's drawings and facts to see if they show related addition and subtraction facts. You may wish to encourage them to write one or two sentences to tell about what they have drawn.

3 Close

Check for Understanding by having children make a two-color cube train and write the addition sentence. Then have them break the train apart into its original parts and write the related subtraction sentence.

Name ____________

Addition and Subtraction

5 + 3 = 8   8 − 3 = 5

Possible answer: The cat has 5 red cubes and 3 blue cubes. The cat has 8 cubes in all.

Talk Tell a story about the picture.

You need 9 red cubes and 9 blue cubes.

Show some red cubes and show some blue cubes.
Draw them.
Write the addition and subtraction.

Drawings and exercises may vary. Sample answers are given.

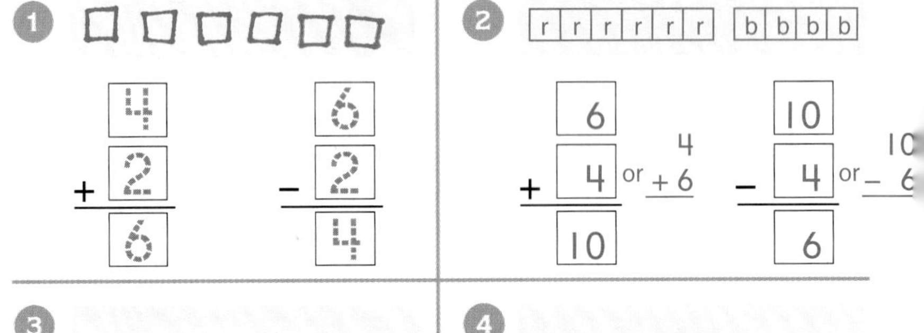

1. 4 + 2 = 6   6 − 2 = 4

2. 6 + 4 = 10 or 4 + 6   10 − 4 = 6 or 10 − 6

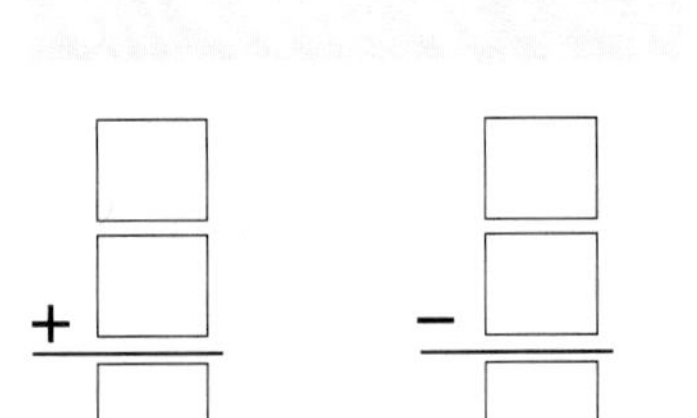

3. ☐ + ☐ = ☐   ☐ − ☐ = ☐

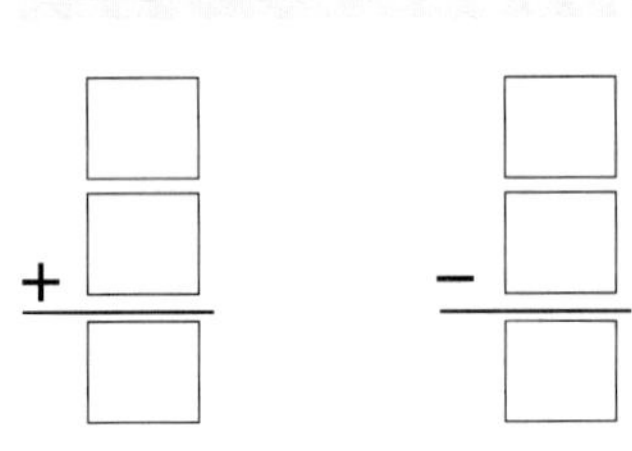

4. ☐ + ☐ = ☐   ☐ − ☐ = ☐

MEETING INDIVIDUAL NEEDS

EARLY FINISHERS

Have children write three subtraction facts and exchange them with a partner. Each writes related addition facts for the other's subtraction facts.

EXTRA SUPPORT

Help children recognize related facts by giving them a train of 8 connecting cubes. Have them take away 3 and tell how many are left. Then ask how many cubes have to be added back to make 8. *[3]*

ONGOING ASSESSMENT

Anecdotal Report Make notes on the drawings and exercises children do in their Journals. Look for an understanding of related facts—use of the same parts and totals. Some children may write a story to explain their drawings; others may simply illustrate with counters or cubes.

Follow Up For children having difficulty, assign **Reteach 45.**

For children who demonstrate understanding, assign **Extend 45.**

Use cubes if you want to.

Add or subtract.

1

2	7
+ 5	− 5
7	2

2

6	6
+ 0	− 6
6	0

3

8	10	3	7	1	4
+ 2	− 2	+ 4	− 4	+ 3	− 3
10	8	7	3	4	1

4

5	6	7	9	6	8
+ 1	− 1	+ 2	− 2	+ 2	− 2
6	5	9	7	8	6

5

0	5	4	7	3	6
+ 5	− 5	+ 3	− 3	+ 3	− 3
5	0	7	4	6	3

6

3	10	8	9	5	10
+ 7	− 7	+ 1	− 1	+ 5	− 5
10	3	9	8	10	5

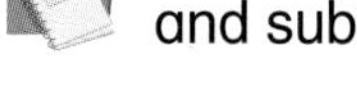

Draw a picture that shows addition and subtraction. Write the facts. mChildren should show the same parts and total for both exercises.

We learned how addition and subtraction can be related. Ask your child about the exercises on page 169.

Alternate Teaching Strategy

Materials per child: 10 two-color counters

Have children display 3 red and 4 yellow counters in a row.

Ask them to tell you the addition fact they have shown. *[3 + 4 = 7]* Write the fact on the chalkboard.

- **What are the parts in this fact?** *[3 and 4]*
- **What is the total?** *[7]*

Have children move the 4 yellow counters to the right.

Ask them to tell you the subtraction fact they have shown. *[7 − 4 = 3]* Write the fact on the chalkboard.

- **What is the total in this fact?** *[7]*
- **What are the parts?** *[3 and 4]*

Draw arrows between the totals in both facts. Then draw arrows between the parts. Explain that the two facts are related because they both have the same parts and the same total. Repeat with other facts.

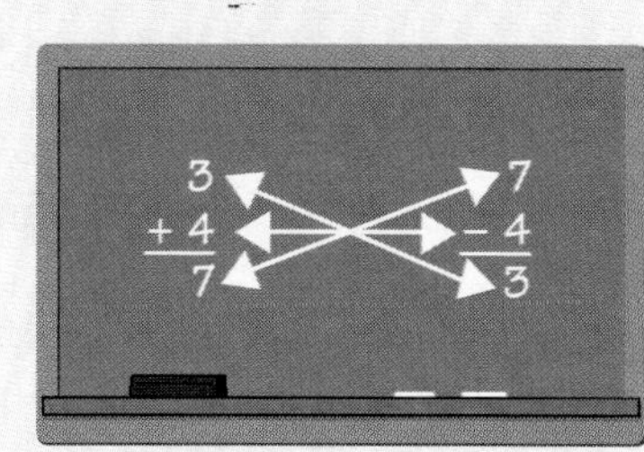

PRACTICE • 45

HOMEWORK

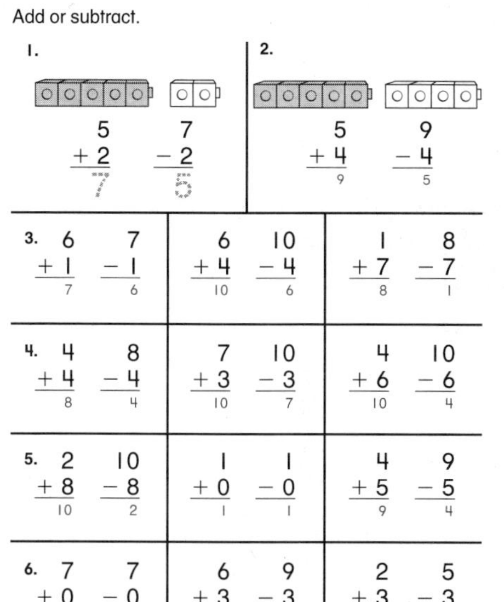

Name: Practice 45

ADDITION AND SUBTRACTION

Add or subtract.

1.

5	7
+ 2	− 2
7	5

2.

5	9
+ 4	− 4
9	5

3.	6 + 1 = 7	7 − 1 = 6	6 + 4 = 10	10 − 4 = 6	1 + 7 = 8	8 − 7 = 1
4.	4 + 4 = 8	8 − 4 = 4	7 + 3 = 10	10 − 3 = 7	4 + 6 = 10	10 − 6 = 4
5.	2 + 8 = 10	10 − 8 = 2	1 + 0 = 1	1 − 0 = 1	4 + 5 = 9	9 − 5 = 4
6.	7 + 0 = 7	7 − 0 = 7	6 + 3 = 9	9 − 3 = 6	2 + 3 = 5	5 − 3 = 2

RETEACH • 45

Name: Reteach 45

ADDITION AND SUBTRACTION

Both facts use the same numbers.

2	6
+ 4	− 4
6	2

2, 4, 6

Add or subtract.

1.	6 + 2 = 8	8 − 2 = 6
2.	4 + 4 = 8	8 − 4 = 4
3.	3 + 2 = 5	5 − 2 = 3
4.	1 + 6 = 7	7 − 6 = 1
5.	4 + 6 = 10	10 − 6 = 4
6.	6 + 3 = 9	9 − 3 = 6

EXTEND • 45

Name: Extend 45

ADDITION AND SUBTRACTION

Fact Trains

Write the missing numbers.
Color the trains that show related addition and subtraction facts. Children should color exercises 1, 4, and 5.

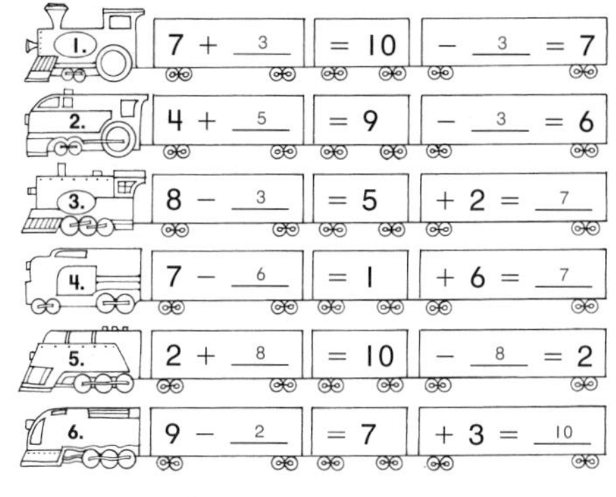

1.	7 + 3	= 10	− 3 = 7
2.	4 + 5	= 9	− 3 = 6
3.	8 − 3	= 5	+ 2 = 7
4.	7 − 6	= 1	+ 6 = 7
5.	2 + 8	= 10	− 8 = 2
6.	9 − 2	= 7	+ 3 = 10

Make up your own fact train. Answers may vary. Sample given.
Use related addition and subtraction facts.

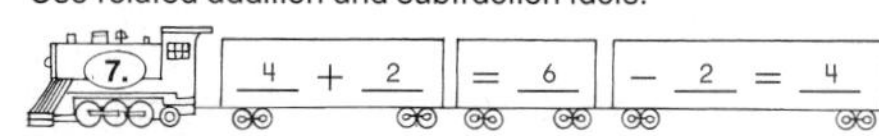

7.	4 + 2	= 6	− 2 = 4

Teaching With Technology

Addition and Subtraction

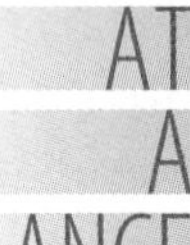

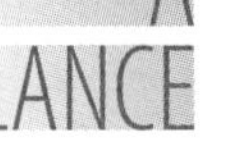

AT A GLANCE

OBJECTIVE Children solve pairs of problems relating addition and subtraction.

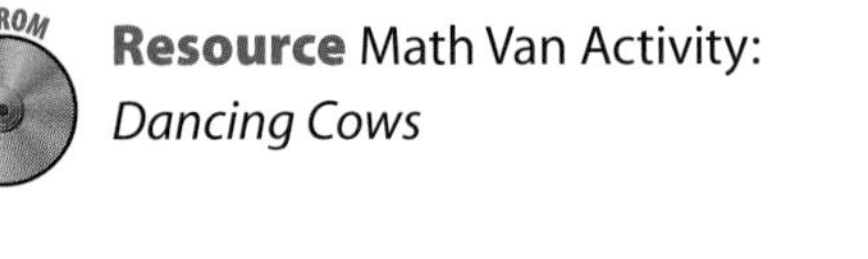

Resource Math Van Activity: *Dancing Cows*

SET UP

Launch the ***Math Van*** program. Click the right arrow to locate Activity 5, *Dancing Cows.* After listening to the activity's description, click *Start.*

USING THE MATH VAN ACTIVITY

1 **Getting Started** Have children review the use of the Open Mat within the Counters tool. Ask them to practice stamping, erasing, and moving counters.

2 **Practice and Apply** Children use counters to explore the relationship between addition and subtraction. They solve a pair of related problems that have the same parts and total. Children work with two groups of cows and find the total. They take away a group of cows and find out how many cows remain.

3 **Close** Have children show the pictures from their Math Journal and discuss their work with you, each other, or the class.

Extend Children can create pictures to show how addition and subtraction are related. Have them work with partners and take turns.

TIPS FOR TOOLS

Since children will be typing number sentences in their Math Journals, you may want to show them how to type the *plus, minus,* and *equal* signs on the computer.

SCREEN 1

Children listen to the first *Dancing Cows* problem, which asks them to find the total number of cows dancing on the stage.

SCREEN 2

In the first part of the activity children solve an addition problem. They stamp two groups of cows and find the total.

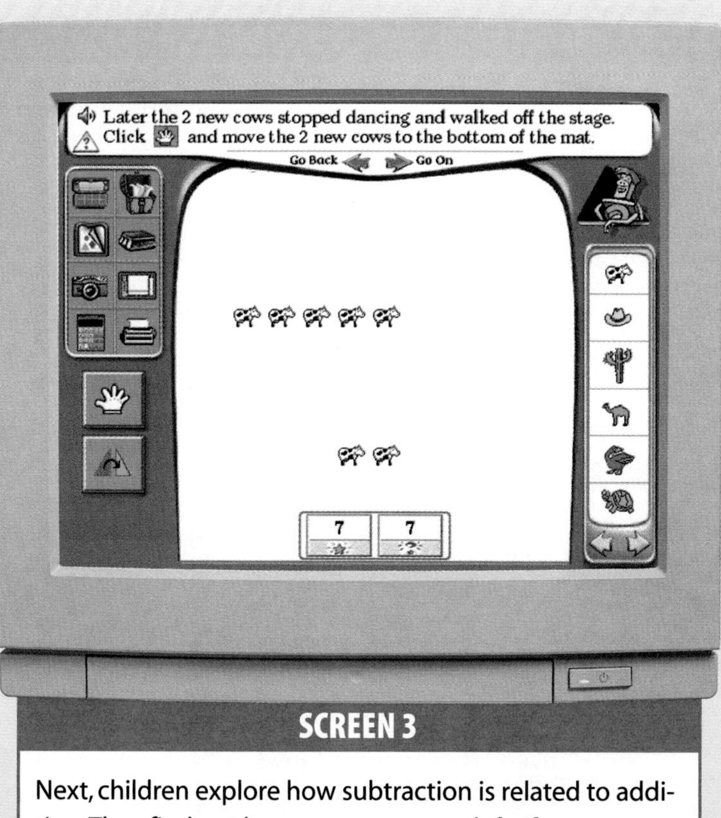

SCREEN 3

Next, children explore how subtraction is related to addition. They find out how many cows are left after one group is removed.

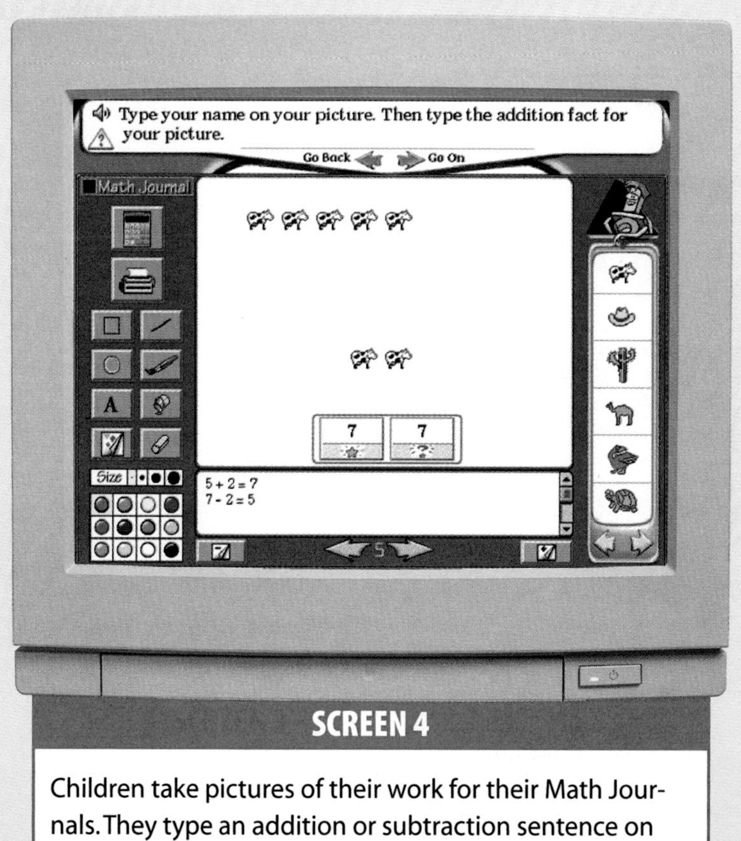

SCREEN 4

Children take pictures of their work for their Math Journals. They type an addition or subtraction sentence on each picture.

LESSON 5.8

Problem-Solving Strategy: Choose the Operation

OBJECTIVE Solve problems by choosing the operation.

Day 1 Problem-Solving Strategy: Choose the Operation

RESOURCE REMINDER
Math Center Cards 35
Practice 46, Reteach 46, Extend 46

SKILLS TRACE

GRADE K	• Solve problems by choosing the correct addition or subtraction sentence. *(Chapter 11)*
GRADE 1	• Solve problems by choosing the operation.
GRADE 2	• Solve problems by choosing the operation. *(Chapter 2)*

LESSON RESOURCES

MANIPULATIVE WARM-UP

Whole Class **Auditory/Linguistic**

OBJECTIVE Use addition and subtraction sentences to solve problems.

Resources Jumbo Activity Book, page 8; Stickers, sheet 3 (square counters)

▶ Illustrate the story by asking a volunteer to place red and blue squares on Jumbo Activity Book page 8. Make checkmarks in the "Read," "Plan," "Solve," and "Look Back" boxes as children work through the problem.

5 elephants march into the tent.
4 monkeys stand on the elephants' trunks.

▶ Have another child say the addition sentence that tells how many animals there are in all. *[5 + 4 = 9]* Repeat with a story about subtraction. You may wish to have volunteers show the story with stickers as you tell it.

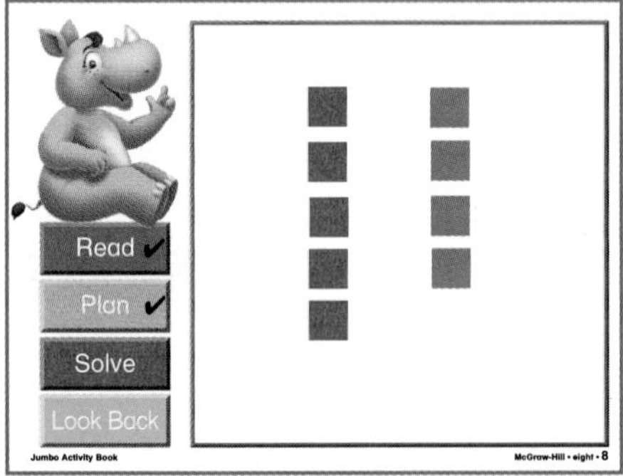

CONNECTION ACTIVITY

Cooperative Pairs **Auditory/Linguistic**

OBJECTIVE Connect addition to storytelling.

▶ Have children think of an addition fact and keep it secret. Then have them write or dictate a word problem that tells about the fact. Children switch papers with their partners, find and write the addition fact, and solve each other's word problem.

▶ After children have finished, ask volunteers to read their word problems for the class to solve.

DAILY MATH

PREVIOUS DAY QUICK REVIEW

Add or subtract.

1. 4 + 3 = [7] 7 − 3 = [4]
2. 2 + 7 = [9] 9 − 7 = [2]

FAST FACTS

1. 9 − 5 = __ [4]
2. 8 − 4 = __ [4]
3. 10 − 3 = __ [7]
4. 10 − 2 = __ [8]

Problem of the Day • 35

Read aloud to children:

5 lions are jumping through hoops.
3 lions are dancing.
How many lions are there in all? *[8]*

TECH LINK

MATH VAN

Tools You may wish to use the Counters tool with this lesson.

MATH FORUM

Multi-Age Classes I have older children who are more skilled readers help younger children read the word problems in this lesson.

Visit our Resource Village at http://www.mhschool.com to see more of the Math Forum.

MATH CENTER

Practice

OBJECTIVE Choose addition or subtraction and use it to solve a problem based on data in the picture.

Materials per child: 7 pennies, Math Center Recording Sheet (TA 38 optional)

Children use pennies to solve the problem. They choose addition or subtraction to solve the problems. Then they write the problems. *[**1.** 4¢, **2.** 1¢, **3.** 2¢]*

MATH CENTER
On Your Own

PRACTICE ACTIVITY 35

Using Data • Erasers for Sale

YOU NEED

Use pennies to solve each problem.
Do you add or subtract?
Write the addition or subtraction.

1. How much for a dog and a cat?
2. How much more is a rabbit than a dog?
3. You have 5¢. Buy a rabbit. How much do you have left?

Rabbit 3¢
Cat 2¢
Dog 2¢

Grade Level 1 · McGraw-Hill School Division

Chapter 5, Lesson 8 · Addition/Subtraction

NCTM Standards
- ✓ Problem Solving
- Communication
- ✓ Reasoning
- ✓ Connections

Problem Solving

OBJECTIVE Formulate problems choosing operations.

Materials per pair: 10 connecting cubes; per child: Math Center Recording Sheet (TA 38 optional)

Given one sample story to solve together, children take turns making up stories and writing addition or subtraction sentences to describe their partner's story.

You may want to ask students to name some key words that helped them decide whether to add or subtract for each story. *[Stories and number sentences may vary.]*

MATH CENTER
Partners

PROBLEM-SOLVING ACTIVITY 35

Formulating Problems • Picture Stories

YOU NEED

There were 4 birds and 2 flew away. How many are left?

- Solve together. Use cubes and write the number sentence.
- Now take turns. Tell an addition or subtraction story. Your partner shows the story. Write the number sentence.

Grade Level 1 · McGraw-Hill School Division

Chapter 5, Lesson 8 · Addition/Subtraction

NCTM Standards
- ✓ Problem Solving
- ✓ Communication
- ✓ Reasoning
- ✓ Connections

DAY 1

Problem-Solving Strategy: Choose the Operation

OBJECTIVE Children solve problems by choosing the operation.

Materials have available per child: 10 two-color counters

1 Motivate — Whole Class

Materials per child: 10 two-color counters

Write the following problem on the chalkboard, and then read it aloud. Ask children to use counters to show the problem.

8 cats are dancing in a circle.
3 cats run away.
How many cats are left?

Ask:

- **What does the problem tell you?** *[8 cats are dancing; 3 run away.]*
- **What do you need to find out?** *[how many cats are left]*
- **How could you find out how many cats are left?** *[subtract 8 – 3 or show 8 counters and take away 3.]*
- **Why do you use subtraction to solve this problem?** *[because you are taking some away from a group]*

2 Develop

Page 171

Ask a volunteer to read aloud the problem at the top of the page. Then review the four problem-solving steps together, asking children to explain what they do in each step.

- **What do you do in the Plan step?** *[Think about how you can solve the problem.]*

As children begin work on the page, point out the workspace at the right where they can write the addition or subtraction.

Critical Thinking
After children complete the page, ask:

- **How do you know if you can add or subtract to solve a problem?** *[Add to find a total; subtract when you have to find a part or how many are left.]*

Page 172

Try These Assign practice problems 1–4.

Talk about how the problems are alike and different. *[Problems 1 and 4 use addition; problems 2 and 3 use subtraction. All of the problems are about animals.]*

3 Close

Check for Understanding by having children choose a problem and explain how they solved it.

Name ______________________

Problem-Solving Strategy

Choose the Operation

Read · Plan · Solve · Look Back

Read There were 2 clowns in the ring.
3 more clowns came in.
How many clowns are in the ring now?

What do you know? Children should know that there were 2 clowns until 3 more clowns came in.

What do you need to find out? Children need to find a total, or "how many clowns in all."

Plan Do you add or subtract? (+) –

Solve Try your plan.

$$\begin{array}{r} 2 \\ +\ 3 \\ \hline 5 \end{array}$$

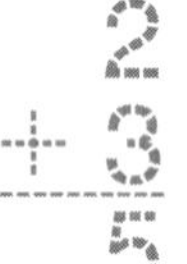

What is the answer? 5 clowns

Look Back Does your answer make sense? Yes.
Explain. Children should explain in their own words the joining of two parts to make a total.

Choose + or – . Solve.

Workspace

1. There were 7 clowns playing.
2 clowns went home.
How many clowns are playing now?

+ (–) 5 clowns

$$\begin{array}{r} 7 \\ -\ 2 \\ \hline 5 \end{array}$$

MEETING INDIVIDUAL NEEDS

EARLY FINISHERS

Have children make up their own word problem about some of the animals pictured at the top of page 172. They should share the problem with a partner and ask the partner to solve it.

EXTRA SUPPORT

Have children write each problem-solving step on a separate index card. Read a problem and help children locate the correct card for each part of the problem.

ONGOING ASSESSMENT

Anecdotal Report Make notes on each child's ability to apply the problem-solving steps to addition and subtraction problems. Note if they are able to follow the process and solve the problems independently.

Follow Up For children having difficulty, assign **Reteach 46.**

For children who demonstrate understanding, assign **Extend 46.**

Choose + or –. Solve.

Workspace

1. There are 3 dogs in one car. There are 5 dogs in another car. How many dogs are in the two cars?
   (+) – __8__ dogs
   $3 + 5 = 8$

2. 9 cats wear hats. 6 of the cats take off their hats. How many cats still wear hats?
   + (–) __3__ cats
   $9 - 6 = 3$

3. There were 9 pigs in a pen. 2 pigs get away. How many pigs are left?
   + (–) __7__ pigs
   $9 - 2 = 7$

4. 8 goats dance in a circle. I more goat joins them. How many goats are there now?
   (+) – __9__ goats
   $8 + 1 = 9$

We are learning how to read and solve problems. You may want to review those problems with your child.

Alternate Teaching Strategy

Materials per child: 9 red and 9 blue connecting cubes

Write the following problem on the chalkboard and have children show it with cubes.

9 clowns are standing on their heads.
3 clowns fall over.
How many clowns are still standing on their heads? *[6]*

Work through the problem-solving steps.

- **What does reading the problem tell you?** *[9 clowns stand on their heads; 3 clowns fall over.]*
- **What does the problem ask you?** *[How many clowns are still standing on their heads?]*
- **How could you solve the problem?** *[Subtract 9 – 3; show 9 cubes and take away 3 cubes.]*

Ask volunteers to show how they solved the problem. Ask the others to look back to see if the answer makes sense. Repeat, using an addition problem.

PRACTICE • 46

HOMEWORK

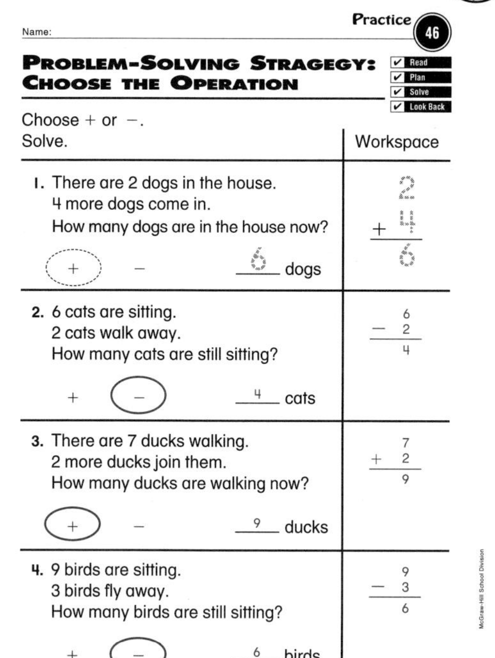
Name:

Practice 46

PROBLEM-SOLVING STRAGEGY: CHOOSE THE OPERATION

Read / Plan / Solve / Look Back

Choose + or –. Solve.

Workspace

1. There are 2 dogs in the house. 4 more dogs come in. How many dogs are in the house now?
   (+) – __6__ dogs
   $2 + 4 = 6$
2. 6 cats are sitting. 2 cats walk away. How many cats are still sitting?
   + (–) __4__ cats
   $6 - 2 = 4$
3. There are 7 ducks walking. 2 more ducks join them. How many ducks are walking now?
   (+) – __9__ ducks
   $7 + 2 = 9$
4. 9 birds are sitting. 3 birds fly away. How many birds are still sitting?
   + (–) __6__ birds
   $9 - 3 = 6$

McGraw-Hill School Division

RETEACH • 46

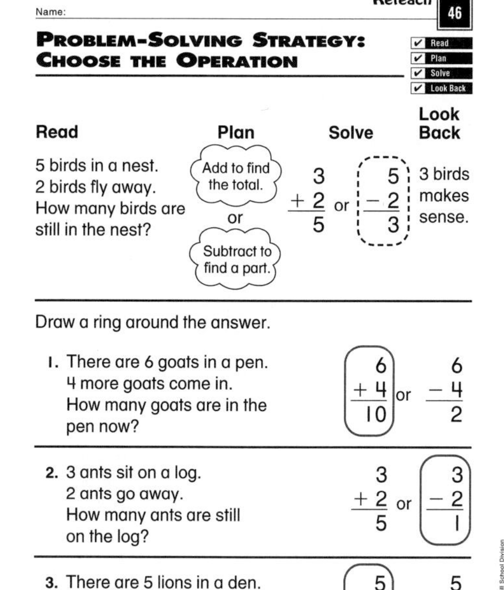
Name:

Reteach 46

PROBLEM-SOLVING STRATEGY: CHOOSE THE OPERATION

Read / Plan / Solve / Look Back

Read	Plan	Solve	Look Back
5 birds in a nest. 2 birds fly away. How many birds are still in the nest?	Add to find the total. or Subtract to find a part.	$3 + 2 = 5$ or $5 - 2 = 3$	3 birds makes sense.

Draw a ring around the answer.

1. There are 6 goats in a pen. 4 more goats come in. How many goats are in the pen now?
   ($6 + 4 = 10$) or $6 - 4 = 2$
2. 3 ants sit on a log. 2 ants go away. How many ants are still on the log?
   $3 + 2 = 5$ or ($3 - 2 = 1$)
3. There are 5 lions in a den. 4 more lions walk in. How many lions are in the den now?
   ($5 + 4 = 9$) or $5 - 4 = 1$

McGraw-Hill School Division

EXTEND • 46

Name:

Extend 46

PROBLEM SOLVING

Read / Plan / Solve / Look Back

Counter Give-Away

Beth has 10 red ○ and 7 yellow ○.
She gives 3 red ○ to Sam.
She gives 5 yellow ○ to Paco.
She gives 4 red ○ and 2 yellow ○ to Amber.

Write an addition or subtraction fact to solve. Use red and yellow ○.

Workspace

1. How many red counters does Beth give away?
   __7__ counters
   $3 + 4 = 7$
2. How many more yellow counters does Paco have than Amber?
   __3__ counters
   $5 - 2 = 3$
3. How many counters does Amber have in all?
   __6__ counters
   $4 + 2 = 6$

McGraw-Hill School Division

LESSON 5.9

Problem Solvers at Work: Use a Picture

OBJECTIVE Write and solve problems by using data from a picture.

Day 1 Problem Solvers at Work: Use a Picture

RESOURCE REMINDER
Math Center Cards 36
Practice 47, Reteach 47, Extend 47

SKILLS TRACE	
GRADE K	• Solve problems by using data from a picture. *(Chapter 12)*
GRADE 1	• Formulate and solve problems by using data from a picture.
GRADE 2	• Formulate and solve problems by using data from a picture. *(Chapter 4)*

LESSON RESOURCES

WARM-UP

Whole Class — **Visual/Spatial**

OBJECTIVE Explore solving addition and subtraction problems using data from a picture.

Resource Literature Big Book: *Number One Number Fun*

▶ Tell children that they will be making up addition and subtraction problems of their own, using pictures from the book, *Number One Number Fun*. To begin, display pages 5 and 6.

- **How could you find out how many pigs are in the pile?** *[Count them.]*

▶ Ask a volunteer to tell an addition story about the pigs. Write the problem on the chalkboard and have children solve it. Turn to page 7 and ask another child to tell a subtraction story about the pigs shown on this page and write the numbers on the chalkboard. *[10 – 1 = 9]*

▶ Continue having children tell stories about the animals and have the class solve them.

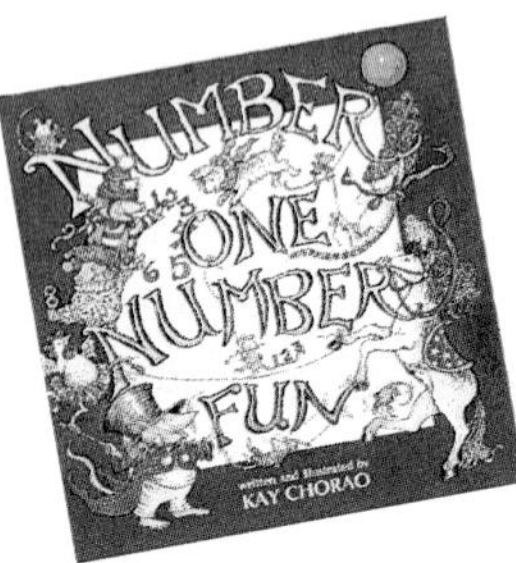

CONNECTION ACTIVITY

Cooperative Pairs — **Logical/Analytical**

OBJECTIVE Connect addition to using money.

Materials per child: 10 play pennies

▶ Ask volunteers to name four kinds of fruits. *[Possible answers: apple, banana, orange, pear]*

▶ Ask volunteers to suggest prices from 1¢ to 5¢ for each kind of fruit. Draw each fruit on the chalkboard and label it with the price.

▶ Partners talk about how many fruits they can buy with their 10 pennies. Encourage them to discuss their thinking and write or draw their choices.

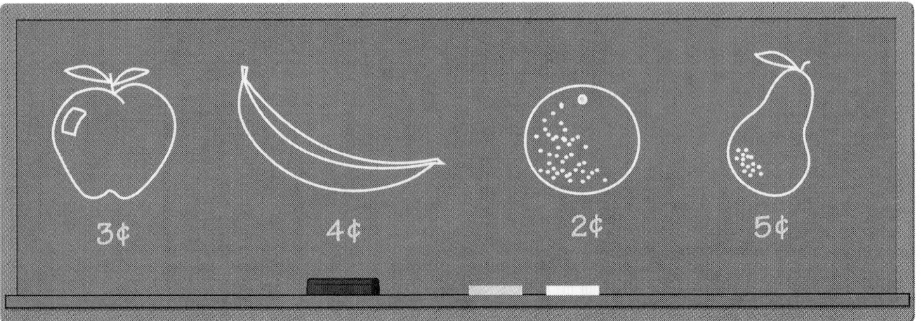

DAILY MATH

PREVIOUS DAY QUICK REVIEW

Add or subtract.

1. 6 + 2 = [8] 8 − 2 = [6]
2. 5 + 5 = [10] 10 − 5 = [5]

FAST FACTS

1. 5 + 4 = [9]
2. 6 + 3 = [9]
3. 3 + 7 = [10]
4. 8 + 2 = [10]

Problem of the Day • 36

Read aloud to children:

Sarah had 6¢ in one pocket.
She had 4¢ in the other pocket.
She spent 7¢ on a sticker.
How much money did she have left?
[3¢; 6¢ + 4¢ = 10¢ − 7¢ = 3¢]

TECH LINK

MATH VAN

Tools You may wish to use the Money Model tool with this lesson.

MATH FORUM

Idea When there is extra time, I ask children to look at pictures or maps around them and create story problems about what they see.

Visit our Resource Village at http://www.mhschool.com to see more of the Math Forum.

MATH CENTER

Practice

OBJECTIVE Use information from a picture to solve and write problems.

Materials per child: 10 pennies; Math Center Recording Sheet (TA 38 optional)

Children select two stickers and add their prices to find the total cost. They subtract the total cost from 10 to find how much is left. Children use art to create similar problems.

PRACTICE ACTIVITY 36 — MATH CENTER On Your Own

Formulating Problems • Stickers for Sale

YOU NEED

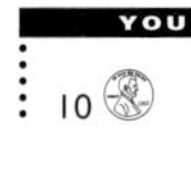

Use pennies. Write your answers.

- Choose two stickers.
  How much for both?
  How much is left from 10¢?
- Choose two different stickers.
  How much for both?
  How much is left from 10¢?
- Use the pictures to write two problems like these.

Chapter 5, Lesson 9 — Addition/Subtraction

NCTM Standards
- ✓ Problem Solving
- Communication
- ✓ Reasoning
- ✓ Connections

Problem Solving

OBJECTIVE Solve and write problems using a picture.

Materials per child: Math Center Recording Sheet (TA 38 optional)

Children write addition and subtraction sentences to solve problems using information they find in the pictures provided. *[**1.** 6; **2.** 6; **3.** 1]*

PROBLEM-SOLVING ACTIVITY 36 — MATH CENTER On Your Own

Using Data • How Many?

Use the pictures to solve.
Write the addition or subtraction problem.

1. John had some balloons.
   2 popped.
2. Luis has some cars.
   He buys 3 more cars.
3. Sheila has some cookies.
   She and her friends eat 4 cookies.

Chapter 5, Lesson 9 — Addition/Subtraction

NCTM Standards
- ✓ Problem Solving
- Communication
- ✓ Reasoning
- ✓ Connections

Problem Solvers at Work: Use a Picture

OBJECTIVE Children solve problems using data from a picture.

1 Motivate — Whole Class

Materials 6–8 small classroom items, with price tags from 2¢ to 9¢; per child: 10 play pennies

Display the tagged items and tell children they have 10¢ to spend. Ask them to choose two items and write a sentence that shows how much money they spent.

- **How did you find out what each item cost?** *[read the price on the price tag]*
- **Did you add or subtract? Why?** *[Add; because I was putting 2 parts together.]*

Have several volunteers tell what they bought and write their addition sentences on the chalkboard.

Continue by having children choose an item to buy and then find out how much money they have left.

- **Did you add or subtract? Why?** *[Subtract; because I was finding how much money was left.]*

Have volunteers tell what they bought and write their subtraction sentences on the chalkboard.

2 Develop

Page 173

Discuss the worked-out example with children. Remind them of the four problem-solving steps. After they answer the Talk questions, ask:

- **How can you decide what to do next?** *[Possible answer: Read the problem again to see what it asks.]*

Have children do problems 2 and 3. Point out that they need to write the cents signs in their problems because they are adding and subtracting money.

Critical Thinking
After children complete the page, ask:

- **Suppose you got an answer of 1¢ for problem 3. Does that answer make sense? Why or why not?** *[No. Katie had 7¢ and the hat cost 7¢, so she would have no money left.]*

Page 174

Try These Assign practice problems 1–4.

Discuss children's methods of solving.

3 Close

Check for Understanding by having pairs of children read the problems they wrote for problem 4 and explain how they solved them.

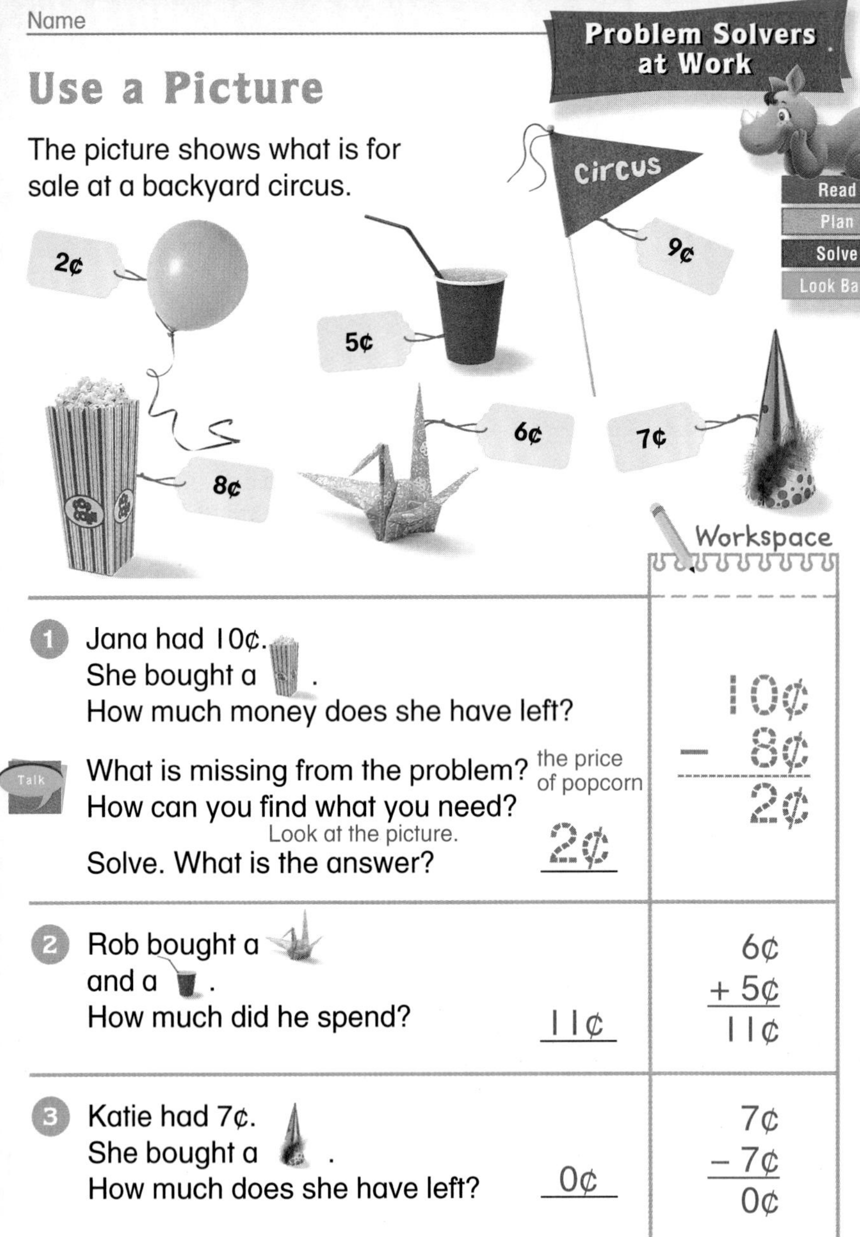

MEETING INDIVIDUAL NEEDS

EARLY FINISHERS

Have children use **Try These** problems 1 and 2 as an example, and write and solve two similar problems of their own. Have them draw pictures to illustrate their problems.

EXTRA SUPPORT

Have children use play pennies to show each of the problems on pages 173 and 174. Then have them write another problem about the stickers and use pennies to solve it.

ONGOING ASSESSMENT

Interview Determine if children understand how to get data from a picture by asking:

- **How do you know when some information you need is missing from a problem?** *[Possible answer: Read the problem to find out what you need to know. If a part is missing, you won't have enough information to solve the problem.]*

Follow Up For children having difficulty, assign **Reteach 47.**

For children who demonstrate understanding, assign **Extend 47.**

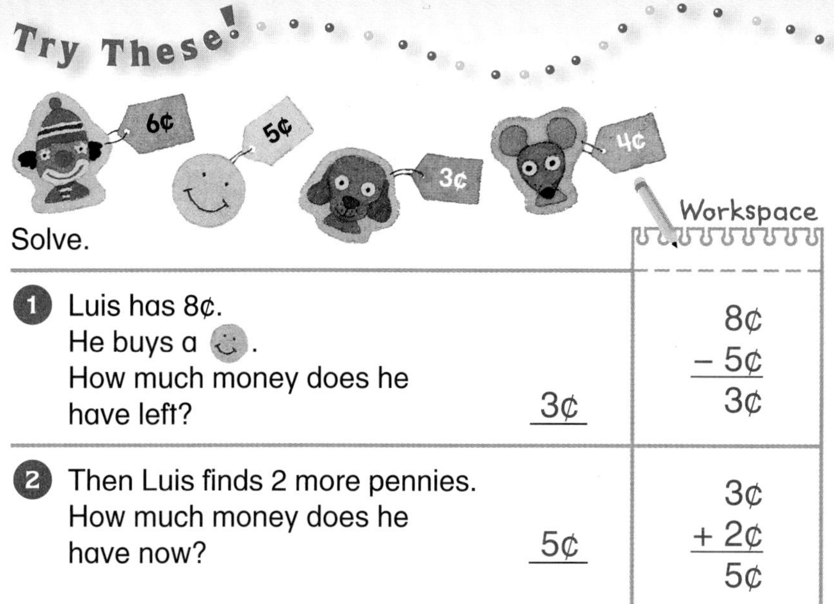

Solve.

		Workspace
1 Luis has 8¢. He buys a ☺. How much money does he have left?	3¢	8¢ − 5¢ = 3¢
2 Then Luis finds 2 more pennies. How much money does he have now?	5¢	3¢ + 2¢ = 5¢

Talk How did you solve problem 2? Children should realize that they have to use the answer for problem 1 to complete problem 2.

Neil wrote this problem.

Jennifer had 10¢. She bought a 🎈 for 2¢. How much does she have left?

Neil Perrette
O'Rourke School
Mobile, Alabama

3 Solve Neil's problem. 8¢

Talk How did you solve problem 3?
Possible answer: Subtracted 2¢ from 10¢ to get 8¢.

4 Write a problem.
Have a partner solve it.
Problems and solutions may vary.

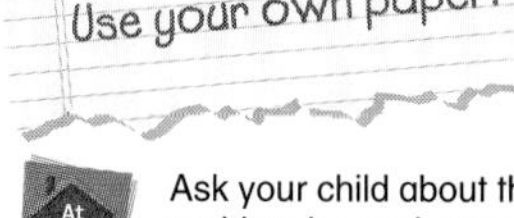

At Home Ask your child about the problem he or she wrote.

Alternate Teaching Strategy

Materials pictured food items from newspaper advertisements; per child: 10 play pennies

Display the pictures of food. Assign prices to each food item. Write the following problem on the chalkboard and read it aloud.

Hallie had 8¢.
She bought an apple.
How much money does she have left?

Have children tell you what the problem is asking. *[How much money does Hallie have left after buying an apple?]*

- **Does the problem tell you how much the apple costs?** *[No.]* **How can you find this information?** *[Look at the picture of the apple.]*

Let children use their pennies to show the subtraction and solve the problem.

Continue with an addition problem that is missing one or both of the amounts to be added. Have children tell you what is missing and how they can find the information. Then let them use pennies to solve the problem.

PRACTICE • 47

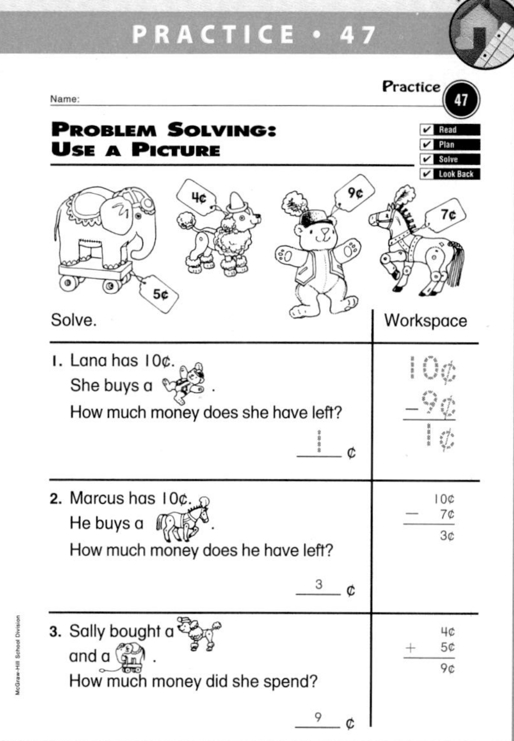

Name:
Practice 47

PROBLEM SOLVING: USE A PICTURE

Read / Plan / Solve / Look Back

4¢ 9¢ 7¢ 5¢

Solve. Workspace

1. Lana has 10¢. She buys a 🐩. How much money does she have left? 1 ¢ — 10¢ − 9¢ = 1¢
2. Marcus has 10¢. He buys a 🐴. How much money does he have left? 3 ¢ — 10¢ − 7¢ = 3¢
3. Sally bought a 🐩 and a 🐘. How much money did she spend? 9 ¢ — 4¢ + 5¢ = 9¢

McGraw-Hill School Division

RETEACH • 47

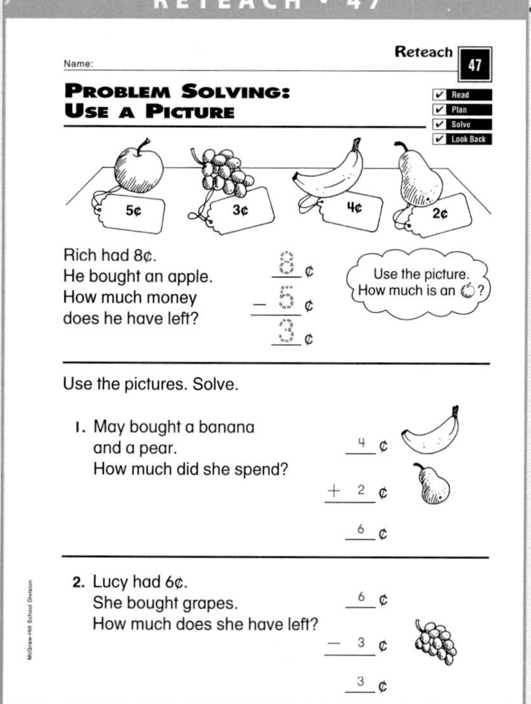

Name:
Reteach 47

PROBLEM SOLVING: USE A PICTURE

Read / Plan / Solve / Look Back

5¢ 3¢ 4¢ 2¢

Rich had 8¢. He bought an apple. How much money does he have left? 8 ¢ − 5 ¢ = 3 ¢

Use the picture. How much is an 🍎?

Use the pictures. Solve.

1. May bought a banana and a pear. How much did she spend? 4 ¢ + 2 ¢ = 6 ¢
2. Lucy had 6¢. She bought grapes. How much does she have left? 6 ¢ − 3 ¢ = 3 ¢

McGraw-Hill School Division

EXTEND • 47

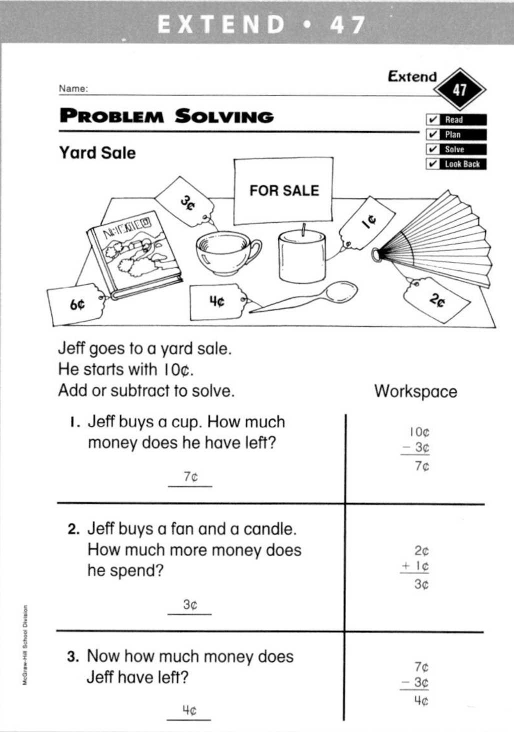

Name:
Extend 47

PROBLEM SOLVING

Read / Plan / Solve / Look Back

Yard Sale

FOR SALE 3¢ 1¢ 6¢ 4¢ 2¢

Jeff goes to a yard sale.
He starts with 10¢.
Add or subtract to solve. Workspace

1. Jeff buys a cup. How much money does he have left? 7¢ — 10¢ − 3¢ = 7¢
2. Jeff buys a fan and a candle. How much more money does he spend? 3¢ — 2¢ + 1¢ = 3¢
3. Now how much money does Jeff have left? 4¢ — 7¢ − 3¢ = 4¢

McGraw-Hill School Division

AT A GLANCE

PURPOSE Review and assess the concepts, skills, and strategies that children have learned in this chapter.

Chapter Objectives
- **5A** Add, facts to 10
- **5B** Subtract, facts to 10
- **5C** Solve problems including those that involve addition, subtraction, and choosing the operation

Using the Chapter Review

The **Chapter Review** can be used as a review, practice test, or chapter test.

You may need to read items 17–20 for some children.

What Do You Think? This feature gives children an opportunity for self-assessment. Assure children that there are no right or wrong answers. The emphasis is on what they think and how they justify their answers.

Children write about how to add and subtract money. They should mention that you use a cent sign to show money, and that adding money is the same as adding whole numbers.

Name

Chapter Review

Add.

1. 1 + 6 = 7
2. 5 + 4 = 9
3. 3 + 7 = 10
4. 9 + 0 = 9
5. 6 + 3 = 9
6. 2¢ + 3¢ = 5¢
7. 4¢ + 4¢ = 8¢
8. 2¢ + 8¢ = 10¢

Subtract.

9. 8 − 4 = 4
10. 6 − 0 = 6
11. 10 − 3 = 7
12. 7 − 5 = 2
13. 9 − 6 = 3
14. 5¢ − 1¢ = 4¢
15. 10¢ − 6¢ = 4¢
16. 8¢ − 3¢ = 5¢

Reinforcement and Remediation

CHAPTER OBJECTIVES	REVIEW ITEMS	STUDENT BOOK PAGES		TEACHER'S EDITION PAGES		TEACHER RESOURCES
		Lessons	Midchapter Review	Activities	Alternate Teaching Strategy	Reteach
5A	1–8	145–150, 153–159, 169–170	155	144A, 148A, 152A	148, 150, 154	37–40, 45
5B	9–16	159–164, 167–170		158A, 162A, 166A	162, 164, 168	41–45
5C	17–20	171–174		170A, 172A	172, 174	46–47

Choose + or –. Solve.

17 There are 6 cats playing.
3 more cats come to play.
How many cats are playing now?
(+) – 9 cats

18 There are 8 dogs playing.
5 dogs run home.
How many dogs are playing now?
+ (–) 3 dogs

Solve.

19 Jill had 9¢.
She bought a [elephant].
How much money does she have left? 3¢

20 Carl bought a [cat] and a [clown].
How much money did he spend? 8¢

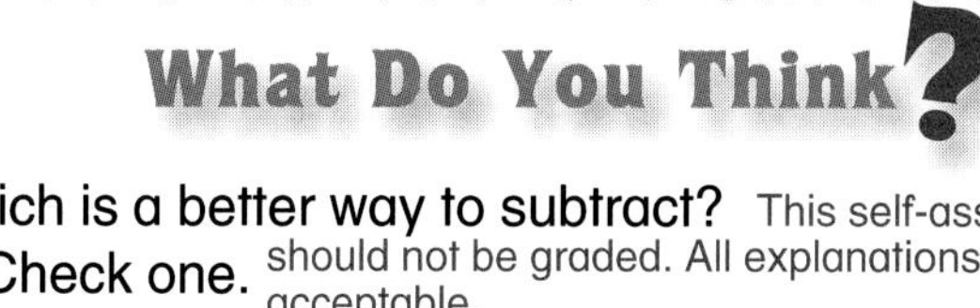

What Do You Think?

Which is a better way to subtract? This self-assessment should not be graded. All explanations are acceptable.
☑ Check one.

☐ $\begin{array}{r} 7 \\ -2 \\ \hline \end{array}$ ☐ 7 – 2 = ____ ☐ Either way

Why? ______________________

Show how you add and subtract money.
Children may draw pictures, relate money to counters, or relate addition and subtraction.

AT A GLANCE

PURPOSE Assess the concepts, skills, and strategies that children have learned in this chapter.

Chapter Objectives

5A Add, facts to 10
5B Subtract, facts to 10
5C Solve problems including those that involve addition, subtraction, and choosing the operation

Using the Chapter Test

The **Chapter Test** can be used as a practice test, a chapter test, or as an additional review. The **Performance Assessment** on Student Book page 178 provides an alternate means of assessing children's ability to identify the number of objects in a set, to 10.

The table below correlates the test items to the chapter objectives and to the Student Book pages on which the skills are taught.

Assessment Resources

TEST MASTERS

The Testing Program Blackline Masters provide three forms of the Chapter Test. Form C uses a free-response format. Forms A and B use a multiple-choice format.

TEACHER'S ASSESSMENT RESOURCES

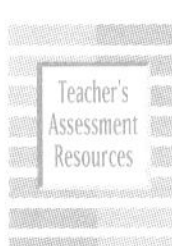

Teacher's Assessment Resources provides resources for alternate assessment. It includes guidelines for Building a Portfolio, page 6, and the Holistic Scoring Guide, page 27.

Name

Chapter Test

Add.

1.  2 + 3 = 5

2.  3 + 5 = 8

3. 9 + 1 = 10 | 8 + 0 = 8

4. 1¢ + 5¢ = 6¢ | 4¢ + 3¢ = 7¢

Subtract.

5. 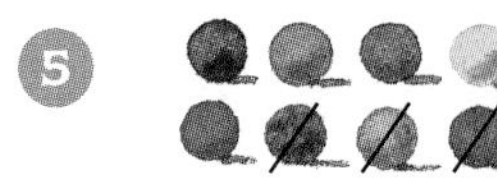 8 − 3 = 5

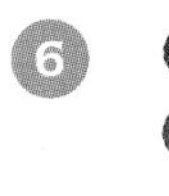
6. 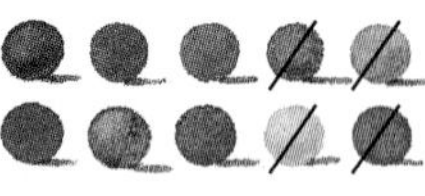 10 − 4 = 6

7. 7 − 2 = 5 | 8 − 0 = 8

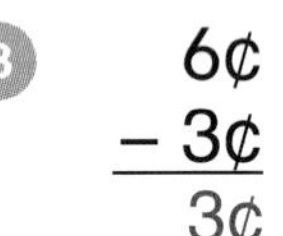
8. 6¢ − 3¢ = 3¢ | 9¢ − 5¢ = 4¢

Choose + or −. Solve.

9. There are 6 clowns on a slide.
There are 4 clowns on a swing.
How many clowns is that in all?

(+) − 10 clowns

Solve.

10. Rhonda has 8¢.
She spends 6¢.
How much money does she have left? 2¢

Test Correlation		
CHAPTER OBJECTIVES	TEST ITEMS	STUDENT BOOK PAGES
5A	1–4	145–150, 153–154, 169–170
5B	5–8	159–164, 167–170
5C	9, 10	171–174

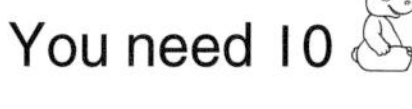

Performance Assessment

What Did You Learn?

You need 10 counters.

Tell a circus story.
Use addition or subtraction.

Use counters to act it out.
Draw a picture of your problem.

Children's drawings may vary.

Show how you solve your problem.

Solutions may vary.

You may want to put this page in your portfolio.

REVIEWING A PORTFOLIO

Have children review their portfolios. Consider including the following items:

- Finished work on a project, page 142F.
- Selected math journal entries, pages 154, 155, 170, and 176.
- Products from investigations, pages 157–158.
- Children's self-selected "best piece" drawn from the work completed during the chapter. Have them attach a note explaining why they chose that piece.
- Any work that you or individual children wish to keep for future reference.

You may wish to take this opportunity to conduct conferences with children.

The Portfolio Analysis Form can help you in the reporting of children's progress. See Teacher's Assessment Resources, page 33.

AT A GLANCE

PURPOSE Review and assess the concepts, skills, and strategies that children have learned in this chapter.

Materials per pair: 10 counters

Using the Performance Assessment

Divide children into pairs. Discuss the directions next to the word *Talk*. Each child is to tell an addition or subtraction story to his or her partner. Then each child is to use counters to model his or her problem and draw a picture of the problem in the circus ring. Each child is to show how she or he solved her or his problem below the circus ring. Make sure children understand what they are to do. Give each pair 10 counters. Observe children as they work.

Evaluating Student Work

As you read children's papers, look for the following:

- *Can the problem be solved by adding or subtracting?*
- *Does the picture show the problem?*
- *Did the child solve the problem correctly?*

You may wish to use the Holistic Scoring Guide and annotated samples of children's work to assess this task. See pages 29–32 and 37–61 in Teacher's Assessment Resources.

Follow-Up Interviews

Meet with children individually or in small groups to reflect on the Performance Assessment task. You can use the following questions to gain insight into children's thinking and evaluate their level of understanding:

- **What is your problem?**
- **Show me how you used counters to act out your problem.**
- **What does this mean in your picture? (Point to part of the picture.)**
- **How did you solve your problem?**
- **Could you solve your problem another way?**

OBJECTIVE Use addition and subtraction patterns to complete tables.

Using the Math Connection

Working Together Discuss patterns.

- **What is a pattern?** *[Possible answer: something that repeats over and over again]*
- **Where can you find any patterns around you?** *[Possible answers: on clothes; on the walls; on the floor]*

Discuss the pattern in the table at the top of the page. Have children complete the tables in the center of the page.

Have pairs work together to create their own tables. One child fills in the first column of the table, and the other fills in the second column to complete the table. Children switch roles to create a second table.

Discuss all the different tables that children made.

Developing Algebra Sense The input/output tables found in this activity extend children's understanding of the concept of function.

Extending the Activity Children can play "What's the Pattern?" by making addition and subtraction input/output tables, trading papers, and guessing the patterns.

Math Connection
Patterns and Functions

Name

Addition and Subtraction

Talk What patterns do you see?

Add 2.	
4	6
5	7
6	8

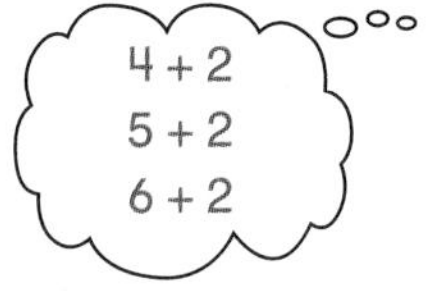

Each number in the second column is 2 more than the number in the first column.

Complete the table.

Add 5.	
2	7
3	8
4	9

Subtract 3.	
5	2
6	3
7	4

Add 0.	
7	7
8	8
9	9

Make your own tables. Tables may vary. Sample answers are given.

Add 3.	
2	5
3	6
4	7

Subtract 2.	
7	5
6	4
5	3

Subtraction Song

Sing the song.

1. How many monkeys are left on the bed?

   10 – 1 = 9   9 are left.

2. What if 2 monkeys fell off the bed. How many monkeys are left on the bed?

   10 – 2 = 8   8 are left.

3.  Write a problem about monkeys jumping off the bed.

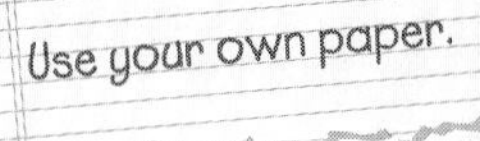

OBJECTIVE Connect subtraction patterns with music.

Using the Curriculum Connection

Read the words or sing the song "Ten Little Monkeys," and have children join in as soon as they are able to follow the pattern. Ask volunteers to describe the pattern. You may wish to write the number sentences children describe on the chalkboard.

Be sure children are writing accurate numbers based on the song. Partners can check each other's work.

Extending the Activity Children can brainstorm and pantomime other situations that fit the 10 little monkeys pattern, such as jumping up and down, climbing a tree, banging on a drum, and so on.

Family Activities

PURPOSE Give family members an opportunity to help children maintain concepts and skills learned in the chapter.

Using the Wrap-Up

Page 181

Tell children that this side of the page will help them show their parents what they have been learning in this chapter.

Explain the rules and allow children time to practice the game before they play it at home.

Name

Circus Sums!

PLAYERS 2

MATERIALS 2 coins

DIRECTIONS Drop 2 coins on the balloons. Add the 2 numbers. Find the sum below. Write the addition.

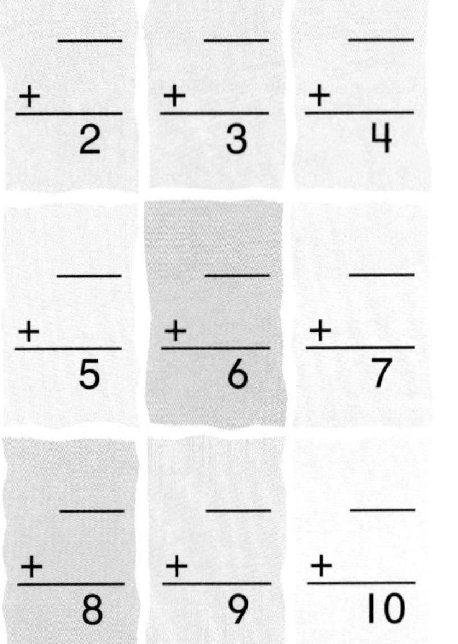

Play the game with your child to practice addition facts.

Dear Family,

Our new chapter in mathematics will be about numbers. We will explore different ways to count and to show numbers.

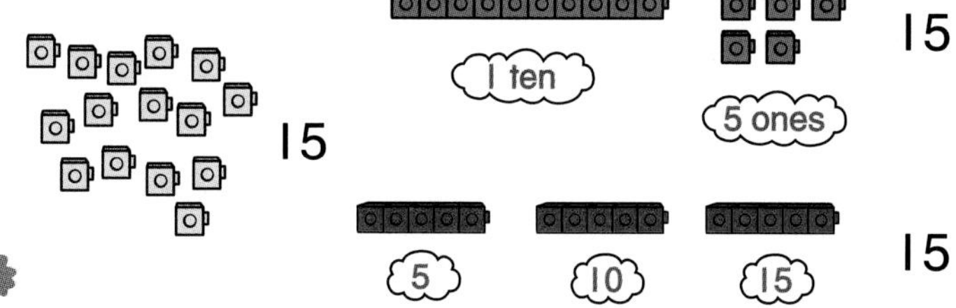

We will also be making graphs and counting people and things. Please help me complete this interview.

Your child,

____
Signature

Interview

How many people are in my family? ________
Whom do we count? (You may check more than one.)

- ❑ Parents
- ❑ Aunts/Uncles
- ❑ Grandparents
- ❑ Cousins
- ❑ Brothers/Sisters
- ❑ Friends
- ❑ Other ______________________

Our family is ❑ small. ❑ big. ❑ huge.

Family Activities

PURPOSE Give family members an opportunity to share in their child's mathematics learning.

Using the Preview

Page 182

Discuss the contents of the page with children and have them sign the letter at the top. Be sure they understand how to conduct an interview with a family member, friend, or neighbor.

Explain to children that they may share what they learn during their next math lesson. You may wish to have children bring back the page.

NUMBERS TO 100 AND GRAPHING

Planning for Learning

CHAPTER 6 ORGANIZER

Suggested Pacing: 18–20 days **Theme: One Big Family**

Lesson Title/Description	Pages	Pacing	Real-life Connection	Chapter Objectives	Materials	Reteach/ Practice/Extend	Math Center Cards
Preview	182						
Introduction	183		family reunion				
What Do You Know? (J) (P)	184						
▶ 1. Count to 20 (J)	185–188	2-day lesson		6A, 6D	counters, index cards, markers, Workmat 2	48–49	37
▶ 2. Count to 50	189–192	2-day lesson		6A, 6D	counters, connecting cubes, beans	50–51	38
▶ 3. Problem-Solving Strategy: Use Estimation	193–194	1-day lesson	guessing how many beans	6F	pennies	52	39
▶ 4. Count to 100	195–198	2-day lesson		6A, 6D	beans, hundred chart (TA 22), connecting cubes	53–54	40
Midchapter Review (J)	199		singing a counting song		counters, connecting cubes, Workmat 2 (10-frame)		
Extra Practice Game: Around the Neighborhood	200				blank spinners (TA 7)		
Real-life Investigation: Applying Counting (P)	201–202						
▶ 5. Order to 100	203–206	2-day lesson		6B	have available: hundred chart (TA 22)	55–56	41
▶ 6. Skip-Count	207–210	2-day lesson	stacking pennies	6D	connecting cubes; play pennies, 2-color counters	57–58	42
▶ 7. Greater and Less	211–212	1-day lesson		6B	red and blue connecting cubes	59	43
▶ 8. Ordinal Numbers	213–214	1-day lesson		6E		60	44
Math Van ▶ 9. Picture Graphs Teaching with Technology	215–218	2-day lesson	making a picture graph	6C	pattern blocks, counters, red and blue cubes, crayons	61–62	45
▶ 10. Problem Solvers at Work	219–220	1-day lesson	graphing family-member sizes	6C, 6F	colored chalk	63	46
ASSESSMENT OPTIONS (J) (P) Chapter Review Chapter Test Performance Assessment	 221–222 223 224						
CONNECTIONS MATH: Calculator TECHNOLOGY Home Connection	 225 226 229						
Cumulative Review	227–228						

(J) = JOURNAL OPPORTUNITY (P) = PORTFOLIO OPPORTUNITY TA = TEACHER AID

	Technology Links	NCTM Standards
	Online Exploration, p. 184B Math Forum, p. 184B	4, 6
	Math Van: Counters tool Math Forum, p. 188B	4, 6
	Math Forum, p. 192B	1, 2, 3, 4, 5, 6
	Math Van: Counters tool Math Forum, p. 194B	4, 6
		1, 2, 3, 4, 5, 6
	Math Van: Calculator tool Math Forum, p. 202B	6
	Math Van: Calculator tool Math Forum, p. 206B	6, 13
	Math Van: Counters tool Math Forum, p. 210B	4, 6
	Math Forum, p. 212B	6
	Math Van: *Pet Show* Math Forum, p. 214B	4, 11
	Math Van: Table and Graph Math Forum, p. 218D	1, 2, 3, 4, 8
	Math Van: Calculator tool Math Van Aid, p. 226	1, 4, 6, 8

ASSESSMENT OPTIONS

INFORMAL

Ongoing Assessment

- Observation Checklist, pp. 187, 191, 193, 203, 207, 211, 213
- Interview, pp. 185, 189, 195, 205, 209, 213, 215, 219
- Anecdotal Report, pp. 197, 217

Portfolio Opportunities

- Chapter Project, p. 182F
- What Do You Know? p. 184
- Investigation, pp. 201–202
- Journal Writing, pp. 184, 188, 199, 222
- Performance Assessment, p. 224

FORMAL

Chapter Tests

Student Book

- Midchapter Review, p. 199
- Chapter Review, pp. 221–222
- Chapter Test, p. 223
- Cumulative Review, pp. 227–228

Test Masters

- Free-Response Test: Form C
- Multiple-Choice Test: Forms A and B

Performance Assessment

- What Do You Know? p. 184
- Performance Assessment, p. 224
- Self-Assessment: What Do You Think? p. 221
- Holistic Scoring Guide, Teacher's Assessment Resources, pp. 29–32
- Follow-Up Interviews, p. 224

Teacher's Assessment Resources

- Portfolio Guidelines and Forms, pp. 6–9, 27–36
- Holistic Scoring Guide, pp. 29–32
- Samples of Student Work, pp. 37–61

Chapter Objectives		Standardized Test Correlations
6A	Read, write, and represent numbers, to 100	MAT, CAT, SAT, ITBS, CTBS
6B	Compare and order numbers, to 100	MAT, CAT, SAT, ITBS, CTBS
6C	Read and interpret graphs	MAT, CAT, SAT, ITBS, CTBS
6D	Count by ones, twos, fives, or tens	MAT, CAT, CTBS
6E	Identify ordinal position	SAT, ITBS, CTBS
6F	Solve problems, including those that involve numbers to 100, graphs, and estimation	MAT, CAT, SAT, ITBS, CTBS

NCTM Standards Grades K–4

1 Problem Solving
2 Communication
3 Reasoning
4 Connections
5 Estimation
6 Number Sense and Numeration
7 Concepts of Whole Number Operations
8 Whole Number Computation
9 Geometry and Spatial Sense
10 Measurement
11 Statistics and Probability
12 Fractions and Decimals
13 Patterns and Relationships

Meeting Individual Needs

LEARNING STYLES

- AUDITORY/LINGUISTIC
- LOGICAL/ANALYTICAL
- VISUAL/SPATIAL
- MUSICAL
- KINESTHETIC
- SOCIAL
- INDIVIDUAL

Children who are talented in art, language, and physical activity may better understand mathematical concepts when these concepts are connected to their areas of interest. Use the following activity to stimulate the different learning styles of some of your children.

Logical/Analytical Learners

Children may enjoy solving riddles. Some riddles can have one clue:
My number is two more than 7.
What is my number?

Other riddles can have two or more clues:
My number is more than 10.
My number is less than 14.
It has one ten and 2 ones.
What is my number?

See Lesson Resources, pp. 184A, 188A, 192A, 194A, 202A, 206A, 210A, 212A, 214A, 218C.

GIFTED AND TALENTED

Children who are ready for a challenge may enjoy working with abstract models. Different kinds of beans could be used as models for tens and ones. Black beans could be ones, red beans tens, and lima beans hundreds. Encourage children to model numbers. Then have children compare their numbers with those others have made. You may wish to have children place the numbers in order from least to greatest.

See also Meeting Individual Needs, pp. 191, 197.

EXTRA SUPPORT

Specific suggestions for ways to provide extra support to children appear in every lesson in this chapter.

See Meeting Individual Needs, pp. 185, 189, 193, 195, 203, 209, 211, 213, 215, 219.

EARLY FINISHERS

Children who finish their class work early may list names of products that are available in at least 100 items to a package—for example, toothpicks, drinking straws, certain brands of cereal. Have the children draw pictures of the packaged items and paste them on a poster to be displayed on the bulletin board. (See *Chapter Project,* p. 182F.)

See also Meeting Individual Needs, pp. 185, 189, 193, 195, 203, 209, 211, 213, 215, 219.

STUDENTS ACQUIRING ENGLISH

Because of language differences, children may need practice reading and saying numbers. Check to see if children have a stable counting sequence. If not, have them practice counting while pointing to the numbers. Spanish speakers may confuse the numbers 15 and 50 because of the similar pronunciations. Be sure they are saying 15 and not 50 when referring to that number.

See also Meeting Individual Needs, pp. 187, 205, 217.

INCLUSION

- **For inclusion ideas, information, and suggestions, see pp. 187, 205, 207, 217, T15.**
- **For gender fairness tips, see p. T15.**

USING MANIPULATIVES

Building Understanding Most children do not fully grasp the concept of place value until third or fourth grade. Six-year-olds generally are *unit counters*; thus tens and ones models should be decomposable—made of materials that can be attached and taken apart. This program recommends connecting cubes or similar models grouped as tens and ones. Children should construct tens before using models to show numbers to 100.

Children can play "What's My Number?" Place tens and ones for a specific number in a box. Without looking, have a child feel the models in the box and say how many tens and ones and the number. Have other children repeat the tens and ones and write the number.

Easy-to-Make Manipulatives Make tens and ones models from pop-beads or easy-to-string beads; paper clips or plastic links; or buttons or beans in small plastic bags.

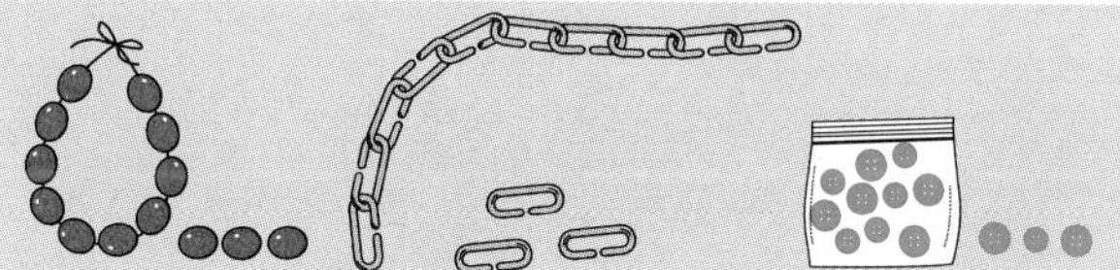

USING COOPERATIVE LEARNING

Partners Think and Share This strategy develops simple teamwork by bringing children together for discussion.

- **Teacher poses a question.**
- **Children think about their answer individually.**
- **Children meet with a partner and discuss their answers.**
- **Partners share their ideas with the whole class.**

USING LITERATURE

Use the Literature Big Book *I Go With My Family to Grandma's* to introduce the chapter theme, One Big Family.

Also available in the Read-Aloud Anthology are the poems "The Chickens," page 30; "Bleezer's Ice Cream," page 31; and "Band-Aids," page 33.

Linking Technology

This integrated package of programs and services allows students to explore, develop, and practice concepts; solve problems; build portfolios; and assess their own progress. Teachers can enhance instruction, provide remediation, and share ideas with other educational professionals.

MATH VAN ACTIVITY

In *Pet Show,* students use the graph tool to create a picture graph of a pet show. Students can use the online notebook to write about how they made their graph. To extend the activity, students use the Math Van tools to create a bar graph using data provided. *Available on CD-ROM.*

MATH VAN TOOLS

Students can use Math Van's counters to explore numbers to 100. The Tech Links on the Lesson Resources pages highlight opportunities for students to use this and other tools such as graphs, online notes, and calculator to provide additional practice, reteaching, or extension. *Available on CD-ROM.*

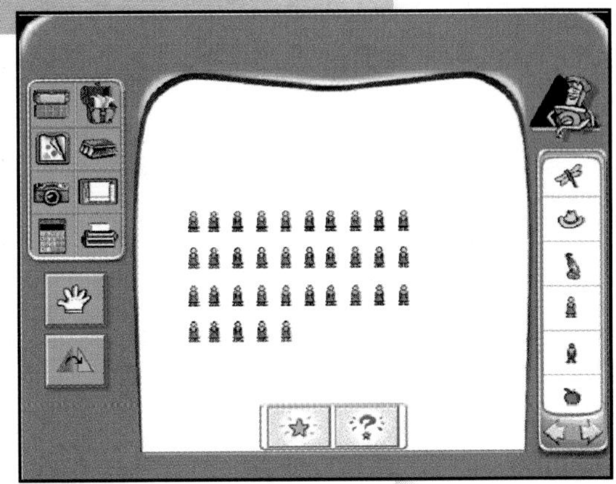

WEB SITE http://www.mhschool.com

Teachers can access the McGraw-Hill School Division World Wide Web site for additional curriculum support at http://www.mhschool.com. Click on our Resource Village for specially designed activities linking Web sites to numbers to 100 and graphing. Motivate children by inviting them to explore Web sites that develop the chapter theme of "One Big Family." Exchange ideas on classroom management, cultural diversity, and other areas in the Math Forum.

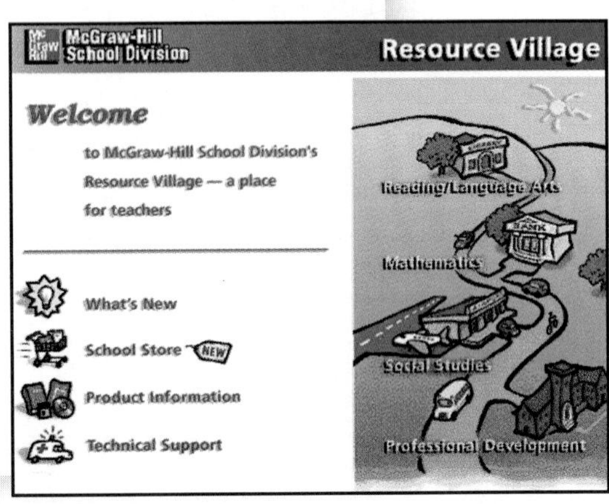

Chapter Project COLLECTIONS OF 100

Highlighting the Math

- count and record 100 objects
- make groups of 10
- sort objects in a collection

1 Starting the Project

Discuss the quantity 100. Is 100 a lot more than 10? Have children bought something for 100 pennies? Tell children they will work with a partner to collect 100 objects. Brainstorm found items to collect—for example, paper stars, buttons, shells.

Using index cards, have each set of partners write and illustrate the name of the item they will collect. Display these cards on a bulletin board. Consider ways in which family and community members can participate.

2 Continuing the Project

As the collections grow, have children arrange the objects to make the counting to 100 easier. For example, they may show 10 rows of 10. Or they might paste small objects on tag board or shallow box tops.

3 Finishing the Project

Children count the objects in their collections and at least one other collection.

Establish that within the category collected there can be a variety of shapes, sizes, and colors; yet the total number remains 100. The class might make a graph showing the numbers of collections for each category.

Community Involvement

Challenge children to think of a use for their collections. For example, a collection of shells could be displayed in the school library. You may wish to invite local collectors to share their collections with the class.

BUILDING A PORTFOLIO

Have children write a sentence or two about their collections.

Each child's portfolio should include the writing and any notes you made about the child's work.

To assess the work, refer to the Holistic Scoring Guide on page 27 in the Teacher's Assessment Resources.

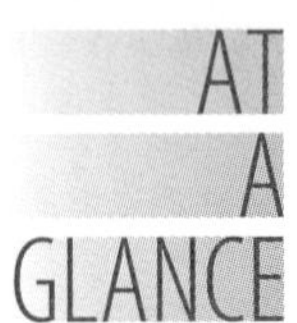

PURPOSE Introduce the theme of the chapter.

Resource Literature Big Book: *One Hundred Is a Family*

Using Literature

Page 183

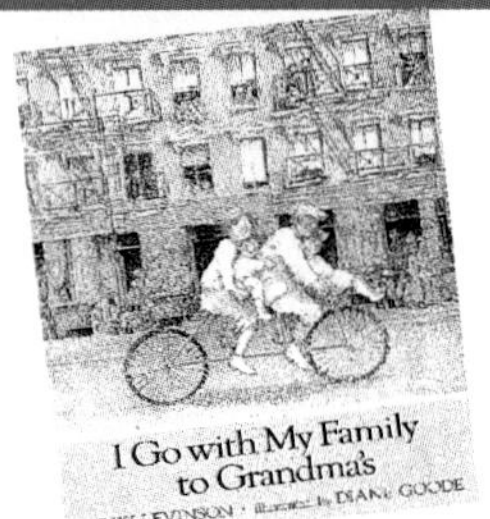

Synopsis of the Book

I Go with My Family to Grandma's, set in the early 20th century, tells how grandchildren and their parents travel from many areas of New York City to visit their grandmother in Manhattan.

Read the story aloud once or twice to enjoy the repetition and to allow children to comment on the number and variety of the characters. Then read it again and invite children to join in with you on the predictable phrases *I go with my family* and *to Grandma's.*

Developing the Theme

The chapter theme is "One Big Family." Begin by asking each child to tell something about his or her own family. Point out that families are different sizes and may include various kinds of relatives and caretakers. List some of the different members of children's families. Children may wish to draw pictures to show the members of their families.

The theme will be revisited throughout the chapter on pages 184, 193, 194, 200, 203, 209, 213, 219, and 229.

Making Cultural Connections

Discuss with children families' different customs, traditions, and holidays. Invite children to tell about a favorite custom or holiday that their family celebrates.

Some families have two New Year's celebrations—one on January 1 and the other relating to their cultural heritage. For instance, the Jewish New Year begins at the end of summer, while people from Nigeria celebrate the New Year in March.

One Big Family

Numbers to 100 and Graphing

Listen to the story *One Hundred Is a Family.*

Tell about one of the families in the story.

CHAPTER BIBLIOGRAPHY

Count! by Denise Fleming. New York: Henry Holt and Company, Inc., 1992. ISBN 0–8050–1595–7.

Ocean Parade by Patricia MacCarthy. New York: Dial Books for Young Readers, 1990. ISBN 0–8037–0780–0.

One Tortoise, Ten Wallabies: A Wildlife Counting Book by Jakki Wood. New York: Bradbury Press, 1994. ISBN 0–02–793393–8.

COMMUNITY INVOLVEMENT

Display a map of the world. Place shiny stickers on places where children's out of town family members live. Brainstorm ways that children can stay in touch with family that is far away. Create a chart or a class book, and make it available to a local newspaper before a major holiday so they can reprint its ideas.

DAILY MATH

PREVIOUS DAY QUICK REVIEW

Add or subtract.

1.	2.	3.	4.
2	6	5	9
+ 4	− 2	+ 4	− 5
[6]	*[4]*	*[9]*	*[4]*

FAST FACTS

1. 8 + 2 *[10]*
2. 7 + 3 *[10]*
3. 6 + 4 *[10]*
4. 5 + 5 *[10]*

Problem of the Day • 37

Read aloud to children:

There are 11 children on a bus.
At the first stop, 1 child gets on the bus.
At the next stop, 1 more child gets on.
How many children are now on the bus?
[13; 11 + 1 + 1 = 13]

TECH LINK

ONLINE EXPLORATION

Use our Web-linked activities and lesson plans to connect your children to the real world of families.

MATH FORUM

Management Tip I have children prepare plastic zip-closing bags of 20 two-color counters to facilitate distributing and gathering the counters for this lesson.

Visit out Resource Village at http://www.mhschool.com to access the OnLine Exploration and the Math Forum.

MATH CENTER

Practice

OBJECTIVE Explore numbers 11-20.

Materials per child: number cards, connecting cubes, crayons, Math Center Recording Sheet (TA 38 optional)

Prepare Number index cards from 10 to 20.

Children find the card for 10 and make a matching cube train. Then they write the number and draw a picture of the cubes. Children play again, finding the next chronological number card. *[Check children's work.]*

PRACTICE ACTIVITY 37 — MATH CENTER, On Your Own

Number Sense • Show Off

YOU NEED: number cards

- Find the card for 10.
  Make a cube train for 10.
  Write the number and draw a picture of the cubes.
- Add 1 cube.
  Find the card.
  Write the number and draw a picture.
- Keep playing.
  Add one cube at a time.
  Put all the cards in order.

13

Chapter 6, Lesson 1 — Number

Grade Level 1 — McGraw-Hill School Division

NCTM Standards

✓ Problem Solving
✓ Communication
✓ Reasoning
Connections

Problem Solving

OBJECTIVE Count numbers to 20.

Materials per child: calculator, number cards, Math Center Recording Sheet (TA 38 optional)

Prepare Make number cards 11, 13, 15, 17, 19, 20

Children use a calculator to count to 20. Then they put the number cards in order and write the missing numbers. They write about a "pattern" that is shown. *[By pressing =, children count to 20. Missing numbers are 12, 14, 16, 18; the numbers go up.]*

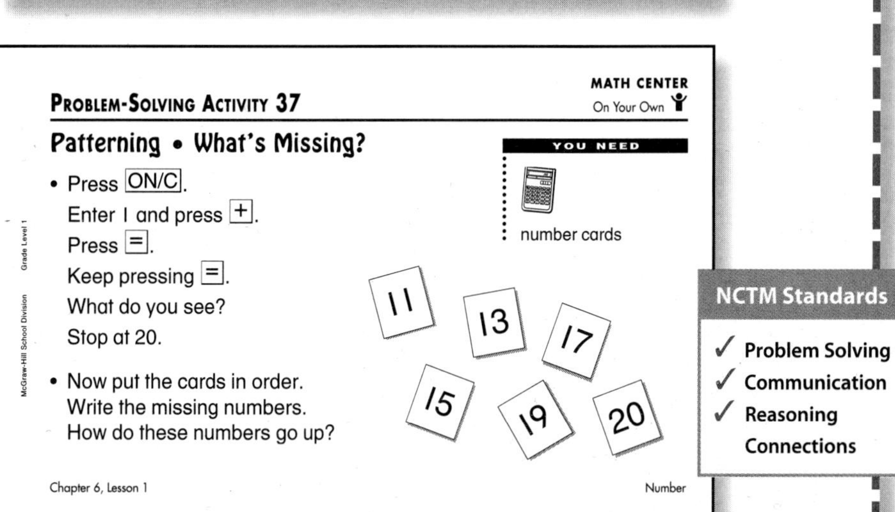
PROBLEM-SOLVING ACTIVITY 37 — MATH CENTER, On Your Own

Patterning • What's Missing?

YOU NEED: number cards

- Press ON/C.
  Enter 1 and press +.
  Press =.
  Keep pressing =.
  What do you see?
  Stop at 20.
- Now put the cards in order.
  Write the missing numbers.
  How do these numbers go up?

Chapter 6, Lesson 1 — Number

Grade Level 1 — McGraw-Hill School Division

NCTM Standards

✓ Problem Solving
✓ Communication
✓ Reasoning
Connections

Lesson 6.1

EXPLORE ACTIVITY
Count to 20

OBJECTIVE Children count sets of objects and write the numeral.

Materials per pair: 20 two-color counters

1 Motivate — Whole Class

Materials 11 5" × 7" index cards, marker

Prepare Prepare a set of object/numeral cards similar to those on Student Book page 185, and place them in order on the chalk tray.

Introduce and practice the numbers ten (10) through twenty (20) by having children recite the numbers in unison as a volunteer points to each card in order.

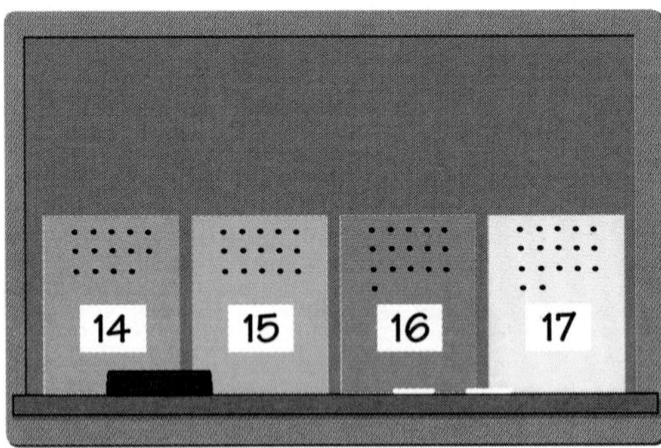

Talk about each number as being one more than the previous number and one less than the next number. Reinforce the concept of these numbers being "ten and some ones." Note that the numbers with a ten and 3 to 9 ones are "teen" numbers.

2 Develop

Page 185

Working Together Discuss with children the pattern they see in the numbers at the top of the page. Demonstrate the activity using two-color counters. Then have pairs of children work together to show how to count the numbers. Each child must choose three different numbers to complete exercises 1, 2, and 3.

Critical Thiinking
After children finish the exercises on this page, ask:

- **What number is 3 more than 10?** *[13]* **6 more than 10?** *[16]* **9 more than 10?** *[19]*

Name ______________________

Explore Activity
Count to 20

10 11 12 13 14 15 16 17 18 19 20

Talk about the numbers. Tell what pattern you see.

Children may see that each number is one more than the previous number.

Working Together

You need 20 counters.

Take turns.

- You show some counters.
- Your partner counts.
- Draw and write to show the number.

Numbers and drawings may vary. Sample answers are given.

1 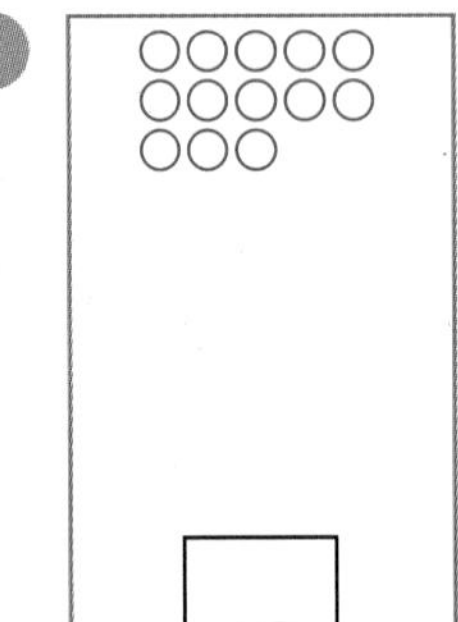

2 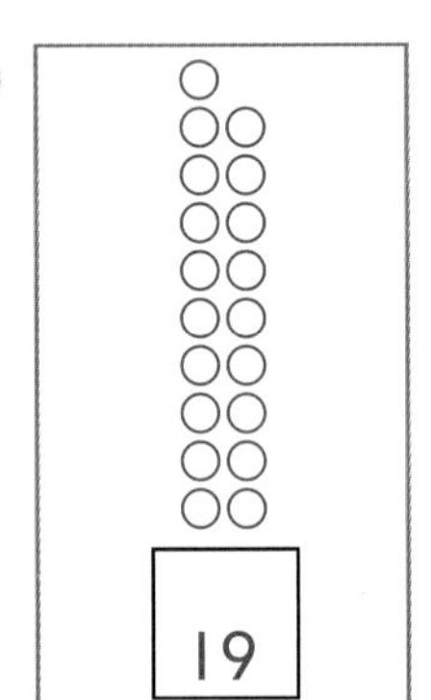

3 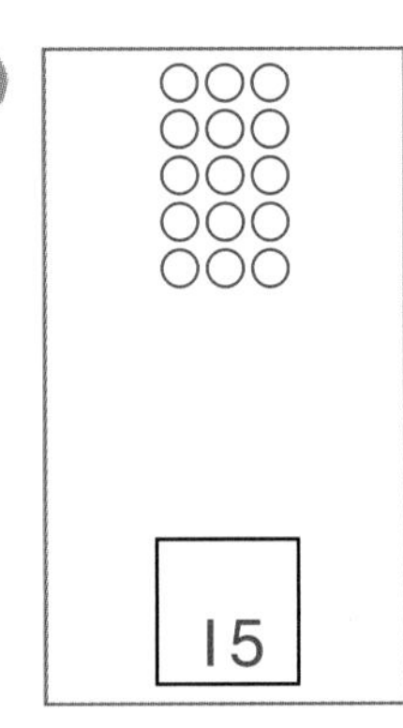

MEETING INDIVIDUAL NEEDS

EARLY FINISHERS

Have various dot-to-dot puzzles for numbers 1–20 available for children to do.

EXTRA SUPPORT

For children having difficulty counting the counters, use either the red or the yellow side of the two-color counters to reduce confusion. Have children line up the counters in a row.

ONGOING ASSESSMENT

Interview Determine if children can count a set of objects and write a numeral for it . For children having difficulty counting, use 16 counters and say:

- **Count these counters.** *[1, 2, 3, ..., 16.]*
- **Write the number.** *[16]*

Follow Up Use counters to work individually with children before assigning **Reteach 48.**

For children who are counting and recording correctly, assign **Extend 48.**

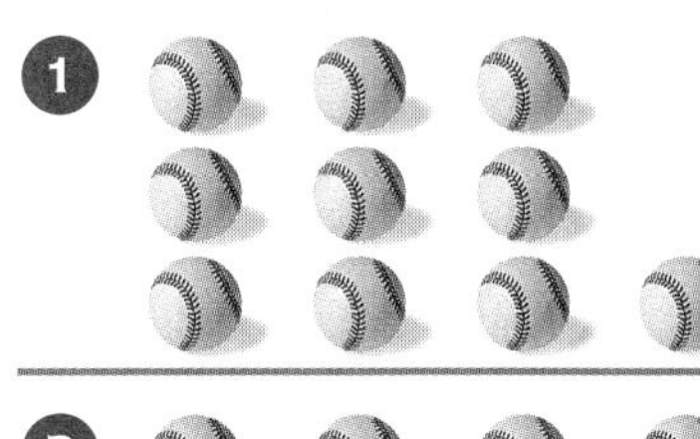

Count. Draw 1 more. Write the number.

1. 11

2. 13

3. 19

4. 16

10 11 12 13 14 15 16 17 18 19 20

Write the missing numbers.

5. 10, 11, 12, 13, 14, 15, 16, 17, 18, 19, 20

6. 10, 11, 12, 13, 14, 15, 16, 17, 18, 19, 20

Practice counting to 20 with your child.

Page 186

Try These Work through exercise 1 with children.

Assign practice exercises 2–6.

Point out the number line above exercises 5 and 6 to help children find the missing numbers in each sequence.

3 Close

Check for Understanding by having children explain how they count a set of 14 counters. Ask:

- **How do you know how many counters are in this group?** *[Possible answer: I started from 1 and went on until I got to the last counter.]*

Tomorrow children will represent numbers 11 through 20 as tens and ones.

PRACTICE • 48

HOMEWORK

Name: Practice 48

MIXED REVIEW

Add.

1. 4¢ + 5¢ = 9¢
2. 6¢ + 3¢ = 9¢
3. 8¢ + 2¢ = 10¢
4. 5¢ + 3¢ = 8¢

5.	4¢ + 2¢ = 6¢	6¢ + 3¢ = 9¢	1¢ + 7¢ = 8¢	3¢ + 4¢ = 7¢	5¢ + 4¢ = 9¢	3¢ + 3¢ = 6¢
6.	1¢ + 5¢ = 6¢	1¢ + 6¢ = 7¢	4¢ + 4¢ = 8¢	3¢ + 7¢ = 10¢	6¢ + 4¢ = 10¢	1¢ + 8¢ = 9¢
7.	2¢ + 2¢ = 4¢	3¢ + 6¢ = 9¢	5¢ + 5¢ = 10¢	7¢ + 1¢ = 8¢	3¢ + 2¢ = 5¢	7¢ + 1¢ = 8¢

RETEACH • 48

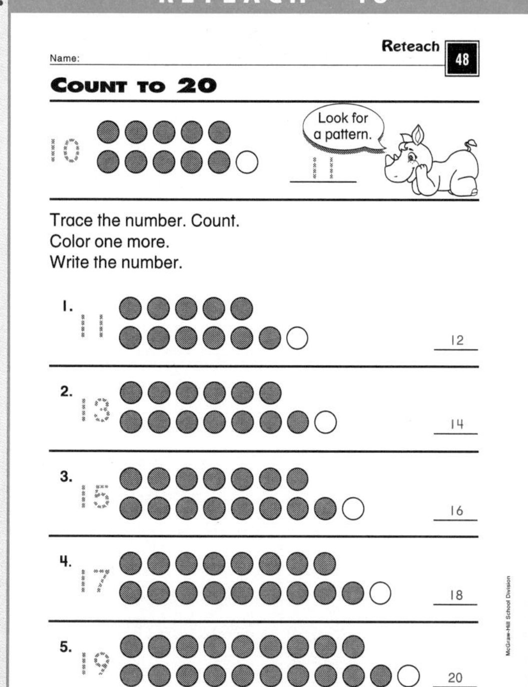
Name: Reteach 48

COUNT TO 20

10 — 11

Trace the number. Count. Color one more. Write the number.

1. 11 — 12
2. 13 — 14
3. 15 — 16
4. 17 — 18
5. 19 — 20

EXTEND • 48

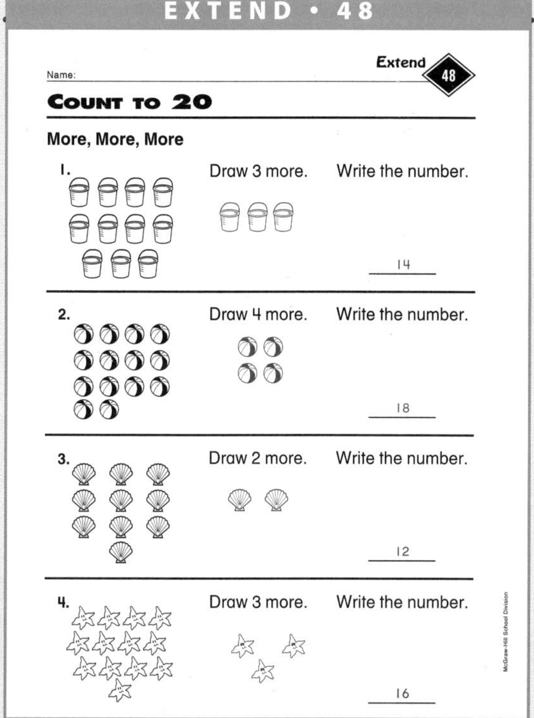
Name: Extend 48

COUNT TO 20

More, More, More

1. Draw 3 more. Write the number. 14
2. Draw 4 more. Write the number. 18
3. Draw 2 more. Write the number. 12
4. Draw 3 more. Write the number. 16

Lesson 6.1

DAY 2

EXPLORE ACTIVITY
Numbers to 20

OBJECTIVE Children represent numbers as tens and ones.

Materials per pair: 20 two-color counters; Workmat 2 (10-frame)

1 Motivate Whole Class

Materials per child: 20 two-color counters; Workmat 2 (10-frame)

Demonstrate how to organize counting to show numbers. Draw a 10-frame on the chalkboard, and show children how the 10-frame makes it easy to count "10 and ___ more." Have children organize the counters on their workmats and then count the numbers out loud.

2 Develop

Page 187

Working Together Help pairs of children organize their counters in 10-frames and "more" in exercise 1. Tell children to use three different numbers in exercises 2, 3, and 4. After they complete the exercises, ask children to say the number name for each "10 and ___ more" answer.

CRITICAL THINKING
After children complete the exercises on the page, ask:

- **What is the number for 10 and 6 more?** *[16]* **10 and 9 more?** *[19]*

Page 188

Try These Assign practice exercises 1–6.

Children may write the numeral, the word name, or how they remember the number.

3 Close

Check for Understanding by having children say the number for a group of "10 and ___ more." Ask:

- **What is the number for 10 and 7 more?** *[17]*
- **How can you show that the number 16 is 10 and some more?** *[Possible answer: Show 10 counters on a 10-frame and 6 counters left outside the 10-frame.]*

Name ____________________

Working Together

You need 20 counters and a 10-frame.

Take turns.

- Show 10 counters.
- Your partner adds more counters.
- Draw and write to show the numbers.

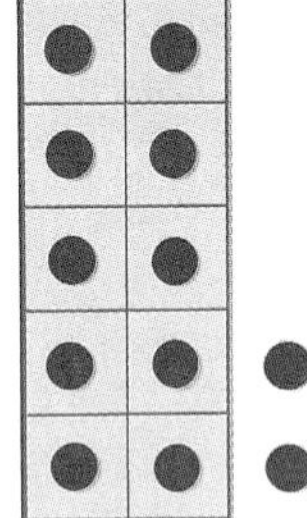

Numbers and drawings may vary. Sample answer is given.

1. 10 and 2 more — 12
2. 10 and 6 more — 16
3. 10 and ___ more — ___
4. 10 and ___ more — ___

MEETING INDIVIDUAL NEEDS

INCLUSION

To give children realistic number experiences, have them find groups of 10 to 20 objects in the classroom, identify them as "10 and ___ more," and then say the number.

STUDENTS ACQUIRING ENGLISH

Have children make a book of the numbers 11 to 20 with separate pages to show a set of objects for each number. Ask them about the objects and about each numeral.

ONGOING ASSESSMENT

Observation Checklist Determine if children understand using a 10-frame to show numbers 11 to 20 by observing the following:

- **Group 10 counters in the 10-frame to show "10 and ___ more."**
- **Write the correct numeral for the 10-frame grouping.**

Follow Up For children needing more developmental work, assign **Reteach 49.**

For children displaying an understanding of the lesson, assign **Extend 49.**

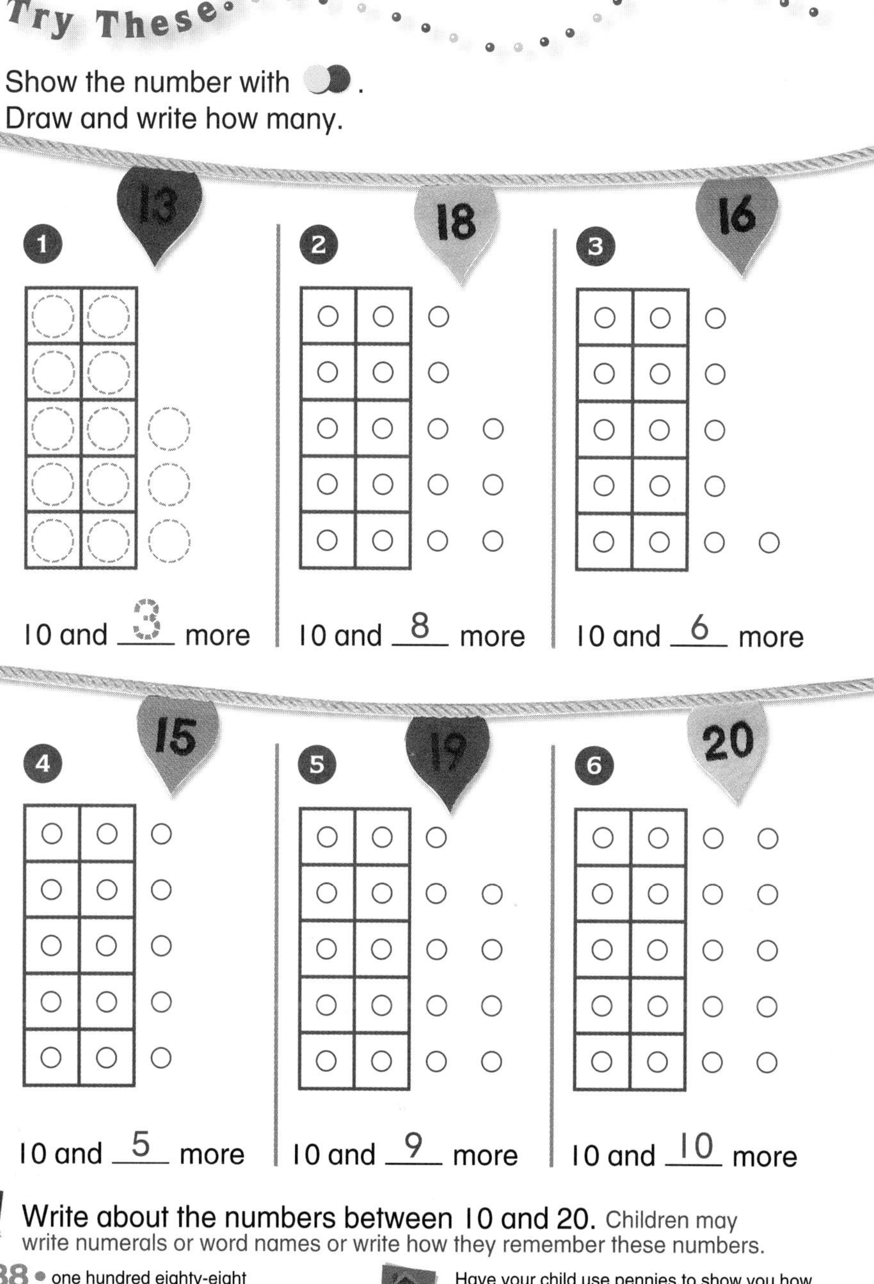

Try These!

Show the number with [counter].
Draw and write how many.

1. 13 — 10 and 3 more
2. 18 — 10 and 8 more
3. 16 — 10 and 6 more
4. 15 — 10 and 5 more
5. 19 — 10 and 9 more
6. 20 — 10 and 10 more

Journal: Write about the numbers between 10 and 20. Children may write numerals or word names or write how they remember these numbers.

At Home: Have your child use pennies to show you how to make a *group of 10* and some *more*.

Alternate Teaching Strategy

Materials 155 blue connecting cubes

Prepare Make 11 cube trains with 10 cubes. Then make cube trains for each of the numbers 1–9.

Display the cube trains to show 10, 10 and 1 more, 10 and 2 more, until there is 10 and 10 more. Point to the cube train 10 and 4 and ask:

- **What kind of cube trains do you see?** *[I see a train for 10 and a train for 4.]*
- **So, it's a train of 10 and how many more?** *[4 more]*
- **How many cubes are there altogether?** *[14]*

Have children write the number 14. Then continue this activity until all children have had an opportunity to talk about each set of cube trains.

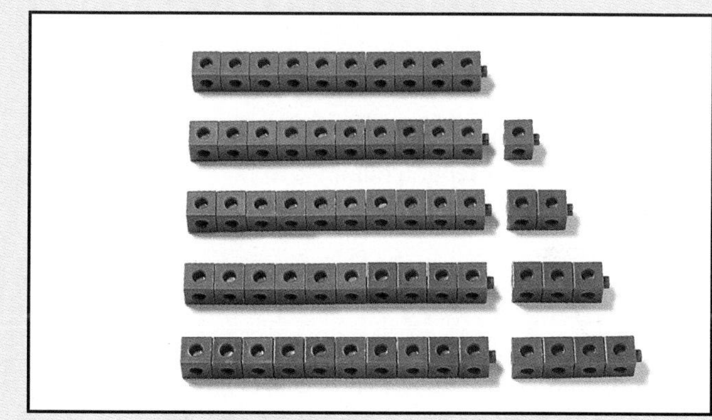

PRACTICE • 49

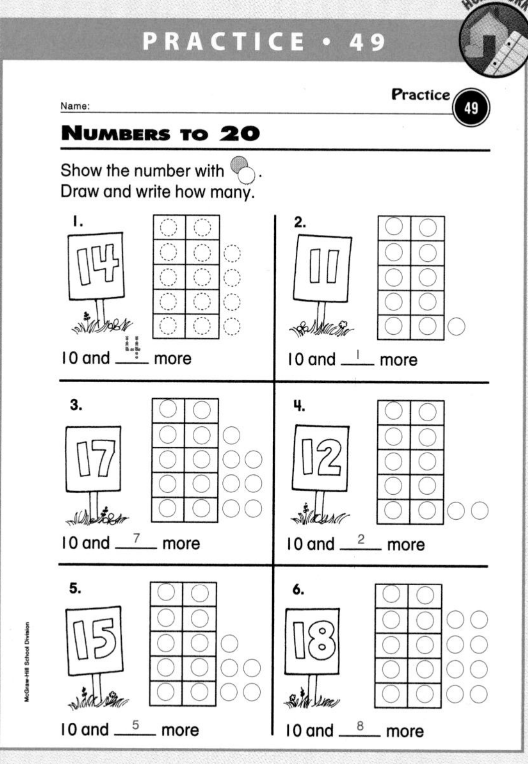

Practice 49

Name:

NUMBERS TO 20

Show the number with [counter].
Draw and write how many.

1. 14 — 10 and 4 more
2. 11 — 10 and 1 more
3. 17 — 10 and 7 more
4. 12 — 10 and 2 more
5. 15 — 10 and 5 more
6. 18 — 10 and 8 more

McGraw-Hill School Division

RETEACH • 49

Reteach 49

Name:

NUMBERS TO 20

12 — 10 and 2 more

Ring 10. Write how many more.

1. 16 — 10 and 6 more
2. 20 — 10 and 10 more
3. 17 — 10 and 7 more

McGraw-Hill School Division

EXTEND • 49

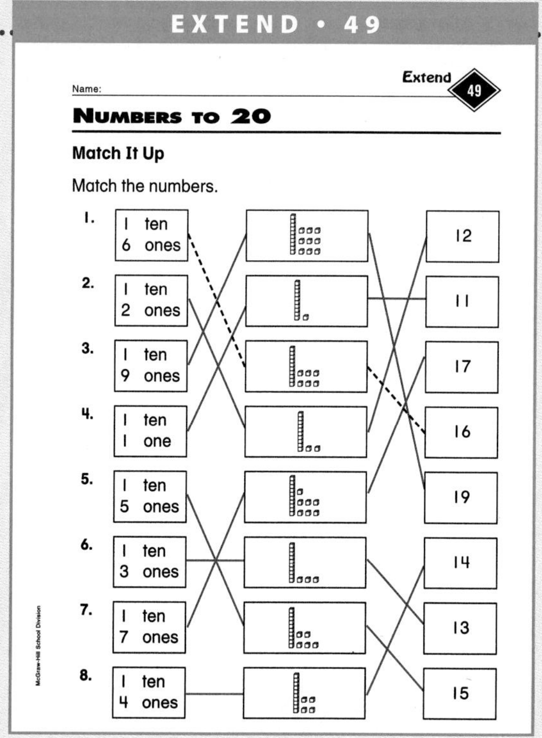

Extend 49

Name:

NUMBERS TO 20

Match It Up

Match the numbers.

1. 1 ten 6 ones
2. 1 ten 2 ones
3. 1 ten 9 ones
4. 1 ten 1 one
5. 1 ten 5 ones
6. 1 ten 3 ones
7. 1 ten 7 ones
8. 1 ten 4 ones

12, 11, 17, 16, 19, 14, 13, 15

McGraw-Hill School Division

Numbers to 50

OBJECTIVE Read, write, and represent numbers to 50.

Day 1 Explore Activity: Counting to 50

Day 2 Explore Activity: Numbers to 50

RESOURCE REMINDER
Math Center Cards 38
Practice 50–51, Reteach 50–51, Extend 50–51

SKILLS TRACE	
GRADE K	• Explore reading, writing and representing numbers to 12. *(Chapter 8)*
GRADE 1	• Explore reading, writing, and representing numbers to 50.
GRADE 2	• Explore reading, writing, and representing numbers to 100. *(Chapter 3)*

LESSON RESOURCES

MANIPULATIVE WARM-UP

Cooperative Pairs — **Visual/Spatial**

OBJECTIVE Explore counting numbers to 50

Materials per pair: 50 two-color counters

▶ Tell partners to count out 10 counters in a row. Draw 10 small circles to represent counters on the chalkboard. Write the numeral 10 beside them and say "ten." Then tell children to count out another row of 10 counters. Draw another row of 10 circles on the chalkboard under the first row. Write the numeral 20 beside it and say "twenty."

▶ Repeat for the numbers 30, 40, and 50. Have partners take turns counting each row from 1 to 10, then 11 to 20, and so on, to 50. Ask:

- **What pattern do you see for the numbers 10, 20, 30, 40, and 50?** *[Possible answer: There is a zero at the end of each number, just like 10.]*

CONNECTION ACTIVITY

Cooperative Pairs — **Auditory/Linguistic**

OBJECTIVE Connect counting with literature.

Resource Read-Aloud Anthology, pages 31–32

Materials per pair: 30 two-color counters

▶ Read the poem "Bleezer's Ice Cream," found in the Read-Aloud Anthology. Talk about children's favorite flavors and those that are unusual.

▶ Give each pair of children 30 counters and then reread the poem. Each partner helps the other keep track of the flavors with the counters. At the end of the poem, ask:

- **How many flavors are there?** *[28]*

▶ After children agree on the number of flavors, have them group their counters by "__ tens and __ more." *[2 tens and 8 more]* Children may enjoy brainstorming 50 of their own unusual flavors.

DAILY MATH

PREVIOUS DAY QUICK REVIEW

Show with counters.

1. 10 and 1 more *[11]*
2. 10 and 4 more *[14]*
3. 10 and 9 more *[19]*
4. 10 and 5 more *[15]*

FAST FACTS

1. 5 + 2 *[7]*
2. 6 + 2 *[8]*
3. 8 + 0 *[8]*
4. 1 + 6 *[7]*

Problem of the Day • 38

Read aloud to children:

Mr. Hirota picked 30 apples from his apple tree.
He wants to put them in bags of 10.
How many bags of 10 apples will he have? *[3]*

TECH LINK

MATH VAN

Tools You may wish to use the Counter tool with this lesson.

MATH FORUM

Idea I have children use egg cartons trimmed to 10 cups to help them make groups of ten in order to help them count large groups of objects.

Visit our Resource Village at http://www.mhschool.com to see more of the Math Forum.

MATH CENTER

Practice

OBJECTIVE Use models to build numbers to 50.

Materials per pair: 50 connecting cubes, crayons

Prepare Assemble 4 ten-cube trains and leave the remaining cubes as singles.

Children use cubes to build greater and greater numbers to 50. They draw and write the numbers. *[Check children's work.]*

PRACTICE ACTIVITY 38 — MATH CENTER — Partners

Manipulatives • Build Them Up

YOU NEED

- Think of a number with 1 ten.
  Show the number with cubes.
  Draw a picture of the cubes.
  Write the number.
- Your partner puts more cubes next to yours.
  Draw and write the new number.
- Now take turns.
  Use more cubes to make a new number.

12

Grade Level 1 — McGraw-Hill School Division

Chapter 6, Lesson 2 — Number

NCTM Standards
- ✓ Problem Solving
- ✓ Communication
- ✓ Reasoning
- Connections

Problem Solving

OBJECTIVE Read, write, and model numbers to 50.

Materials per child: 1–50 chart, connecting cubes, 2 crayons (different colors), Math Center Recording Sheet (TA 38 optional)

Prepare Make a 1–50 chart by cutting off the bottom half of a copy of a hundred chart.

Suggest that children color the numbers with 2 lightly. They will use cubes to show any 5 numbers from the pattern. They can play again with 4. *[Pattern is one column down and one row across.]*

PROBLEM-SOLVING ACTIVITY 38 — MATH CENTER — On Your Own

Patterning • Pattern, Please!

YOU NEED
2 crayons
number chart (1–50)

- Color the numbers with a 2 in them.
  What do you see?
  Use cubes to show five of these numbers.
  Write the numbers.
- Play again.
  Use another color.
  This time, color the numbers with a 4 in them.

22

1	2	3	4	5	6	7	8	9	10
11	12	13	14	15	16	17	18	19	20
21	22	23	24	25	26	27	28	29	30
31	32	33	34	35	36	37	38	39	40
41	42	43	44	45	46	47	48	49	50

Grade Level 1 — McGraw-Hill School Division

Chapter 6, Lesson 2 — Number

NCTM Standards
- ✓ Problem Solving
- ✓ Communication
- ✓ Reasoning
- Connections

Lesson 6.2

DAY 1

EXPLORE ACTIVITY
Count to 50

OBJECTIVE Children count sets of objects and organize as tens and ones.

Materials per pair: 50 two-color counters, connecting cubes, beans, or other small counters

1 Motivate — Cooperative Pairs

Materials per pair: 50 two-color counters

Write the numeral 20 on the chalkboard. Tell pairs of children to count out 20 counters into two groups of ten. Say "twenty." Write the numeral 23 on the chalkboard and ask children how they could show it using two groups of ten and some more. *[2 tens and 3 more]* Say "twenty-three."

Try numbers 30 and 37, 40 and 48, and then 50. Include the words *thirty, forty,* and *fifty.*

Look at the chart to 50 at the top of the page. Point out the "one more" pattern across each row and the "ten more" pattern going down. Have children repeat or chant the numbers 1 through 50 as you point to each number on the chart.

2 Develop

Page 189

Working Together Have children take a handful or two of counters, connecting cubes, beans, or whatever is available for their partners to count. Discuss ways they might organize the objects to make counting easier. Encourage children to group objects by tens.

Critical Thinking
After children answer the question on the page, have them look at the number 35. Ask:

- **How many groups of 10 are in 35?** *[3 groups of ten]*
- **How do you know?** *[Possible answer: The digit 3 in 35 tells how many tens.]*

Name ______________________

Explore Activity
Count to 50

1	2	3	4	5	6	7	8	9	10
11	12	13	14	15	16	17	18	19	20
21	22	23	24	25	26	27	28	29	30
31	32	33	34	35	36	37	38	39	40
41	42	43	44	45	46	47	48	49	50

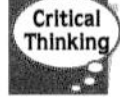

Tell what patterns you see. Children may see the one-more pattern going across and the ten-more pattern going down.

50 apples

Working Together

You need 50 counters.

Take turns.

- ▶ Show some counters.
- ▶ Your partner counts.
- ▶ Draw and write the number.

Numbers may vary. Sample answer is given.

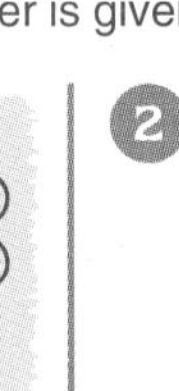

1. ○○○○○○○○○○ ○○○○○○○○○○ ○○○○○○○ 27
2. ____

How many groups of 10 in 25? Some children may have to use counters to find the answer of 2 groups of 10.

MEETING INDIVIDUAL NEEDS

EARLY FINISHERS

On the chalkboard, write one missing number sequence each for the 20s, 30s, and 40s, such as 21, 22, 23, ___, 25, 26, ___, 28, ___, 30. Have children fill in the sequences in their journals.

EXTRA SUPPORT

Organize objects into groups of 10 to help children count. Also make this the basis of number sense so they can grasp how large a number is.

ONGOING ASSESSMENT

Interview Determine if children can count to 50. Show 43 counters and ask:

- **Count the counters out loud.** *[1, 2, 3, . . ., 43]*

If a child groups by tens, ask:

- **Why did you group the counters by tens?** *[It is easier to keep track.]*

Follow Up Assign **Reteach 50** to those children needing more developmental practice.

Assign **Extend 50** to children who can count objects to 50.

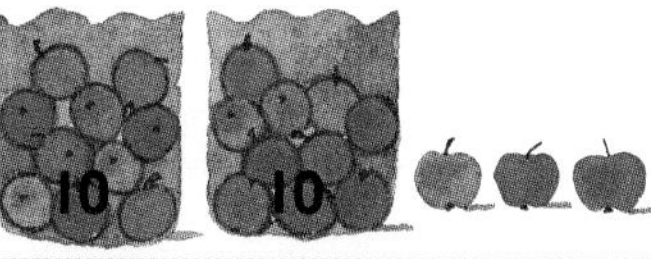

Try These!

Count. Write the number.

1. 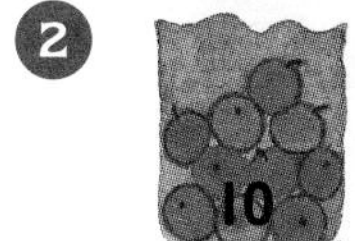 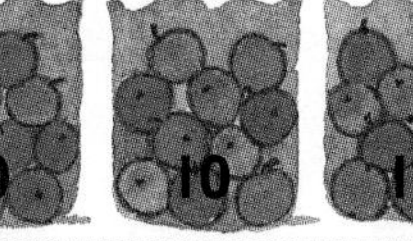 23

2.  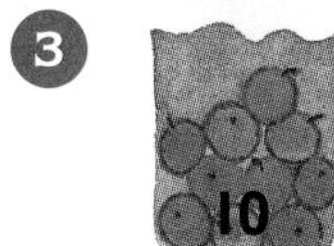 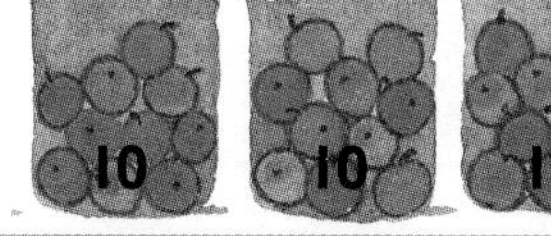 37

3. 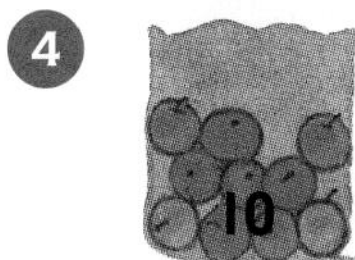 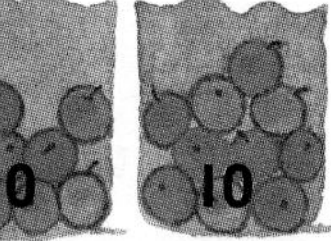 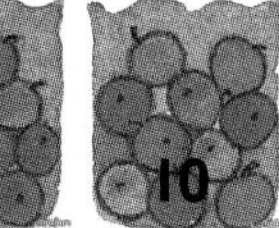 35

4. 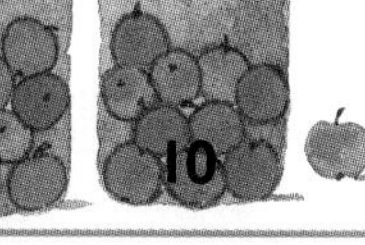  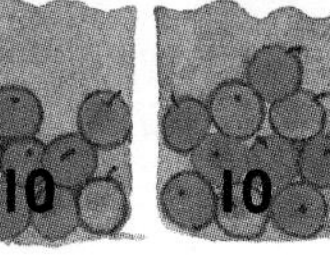 41

5. 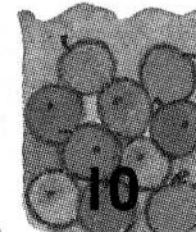 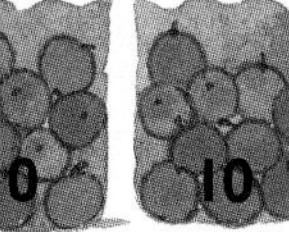  49

Mixed Review

Add.

6. 4 + 1 = 5 5 + 3 = 8 3 + 2 = 5

7. 6 + 3 = 9 7 + 2 = 9 9 + 1 = 10

At Home Practice counting to 50 with your child.

Pages 189–190

Page 190

Try These Work through exercise 1. Assign practice exercises 2–5.

Discuss how children counted to see who is counting by ones and who is counting by tens and ones.

Mixed Review Children review addition facts to 10 from Chapter 3.

3 Close

Check for Understanding by having children explain the number they wrote, and why, for a picture of objects on page 190.

Tomorrow children will identify the number of tens and ones in numbers to 50.

PRACTICE • 50

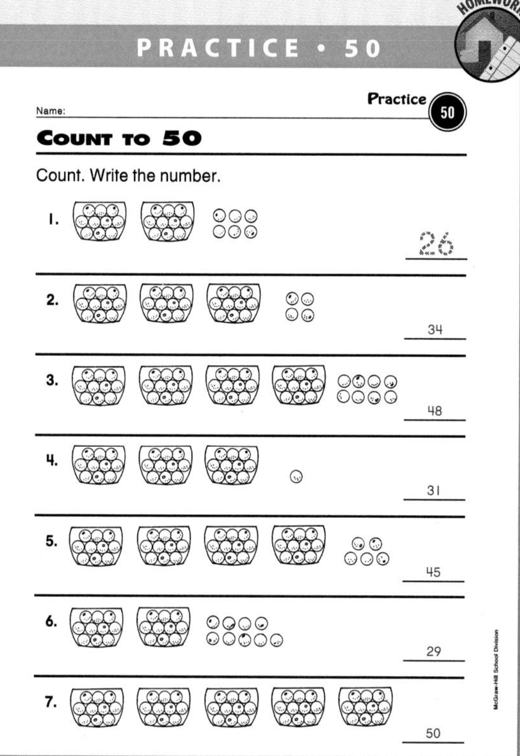
HOMEWORK

Name: Practice 50

COUNT TO 50

Count. Write the number.

1. 26
2. 34
3. 48
4. 31
5. 45
6. 29
7. 50

RETEACH • 50

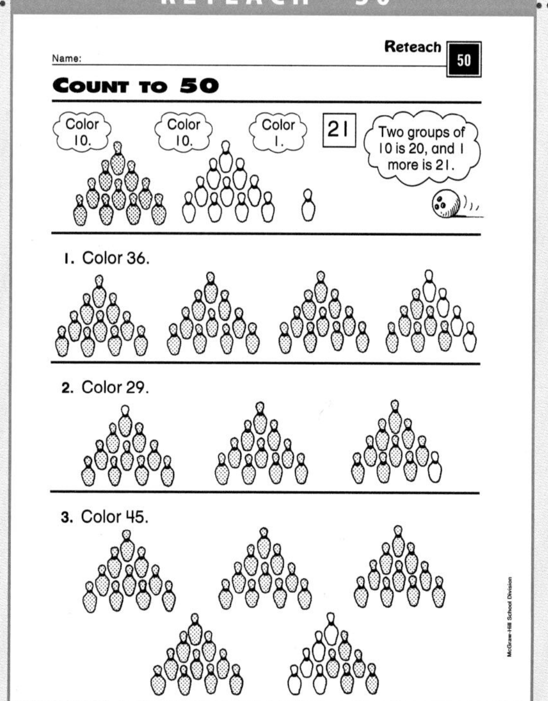
Name: Reteach 50

COUNT TO 50

1. Color 36.
2. Color 29.
3. Color 45.

EXTEND • 50

Name: Extend 50

COUNT TO 50

Vegetable Stew

Mr. Mott is making soup. Help him count. Ring groups of 10.

1.
2.
3.

Write how many.

4. 42 5. 37 6. 25

Lesson 6.2

EXPLORE ACTIVITY

Numbers to 50

OBJECTIVE Children read, write, and represent numbers to 50.

Materials per pair: 50 connecting cubes in one color

1 Motivate — Whole Class

Materials per pair: 50 connecting cubes in one color

Write the numeral 27 on the chalkboard. Tell pairs of children to count out 27 cubes. Then have them make as many cube trains for 10 and some more. Call the cube trains for ten "tens" and the cubes left over "ones." Ask:

- **How many tens?** *[2 tens]* **How many ones?** *[7 ones]*
- **How can counting by tens help you?** *[It helps me count more easily.]*

Repeat the activity for numbers 35 and 49.

2 Develop

Page 191

Working Together Some children may have to count every cube. Encourage them to group by 10 to "make it easier" for you to count. Be sure they make cube trains for 10 to find how many tens. Tell them to call the loose ones *ones*.

CRITICAL THINKING
After children answer the question on the page, ask:

- **If you have 3 ones and 4 tens, how many cubes do you have?** *[43]*

By switching the tens and ones in the question, you can see if children are concentrating on the concept and not just the format of the problem.

Page 192

Try These Assign practice exercises 1–6.

Children may use connecting cubes to help them find the answers. Observe children as they discuss the Talk question with each other to learn how each child counts.

3 Close

Check for Understanding by having children explain how to count a group of objects by grouping them into tens and ones. Ask them if they like to use the two-color counters or the connecting cubes and why.

Name ______________________

Working Together

Your group needs 50 cubes.

- You each take a handful of cubes.
- Count how many in all.
- Make groups of ten.
- Count again.
- Write how many **tens and ones.**

Numbers may vary. Sample answer is given.

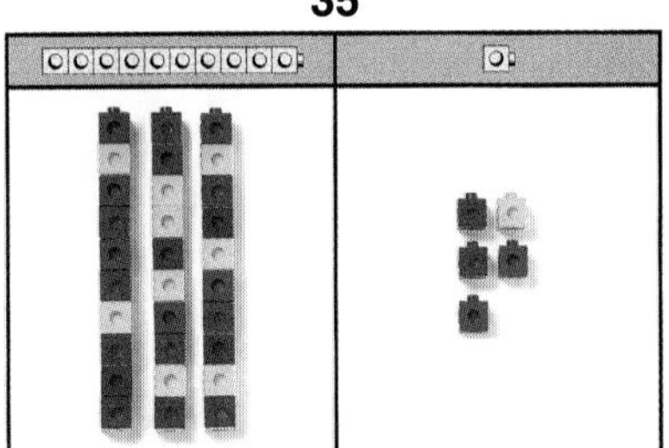

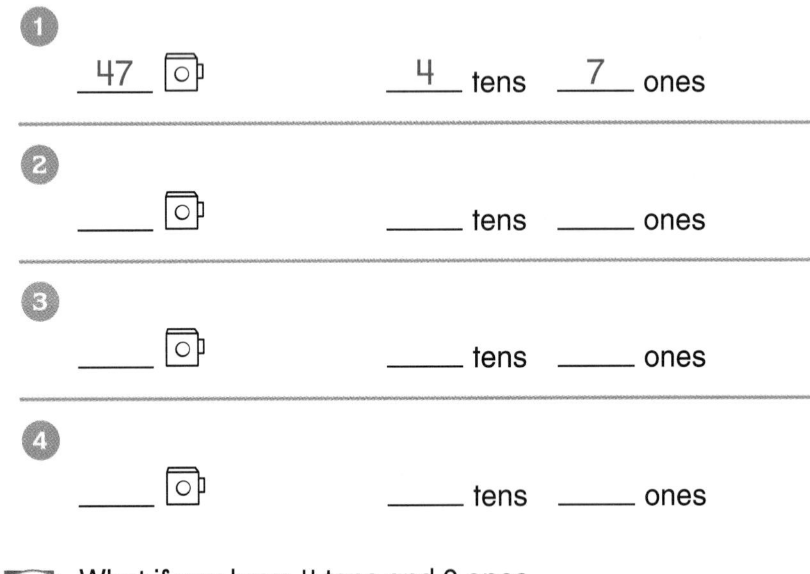

1. 47 cubes — 4 tens 7 ones
2. ____ cubes — ____ tens ____ ones
3. ____ cubes — ____ tens ____ ones
4. ____ cubes — ____ tens ____ ones

Critical Thinking: What if you have 4 tens and 0 ones. How many cubes do you have? 40

MEETING INDIVIDUAL NEEDS

COMMON ERROR

When counting a large group of counters, children may count some of them twice or skip some. Have them use a 10-frame or make rows of ten to keep track of the counters.

GIFTED AND TALENTED

Challenge children to count backward from 50 to 1. They may use counters.

ONGOING ASSESSMENT

Observation Checklist
Observe children as they use cubes to count to 50. Do they:

- **Make trains of 10 first to show tens and ones?**
- **Count by tens, then count on by ones?**

Follow Up Have more able children help children having difficulty understanding tens and ones before assigning **Reteach 51.**

For those children who demonstrate understanding of the lesson, assign **Extend 51.**

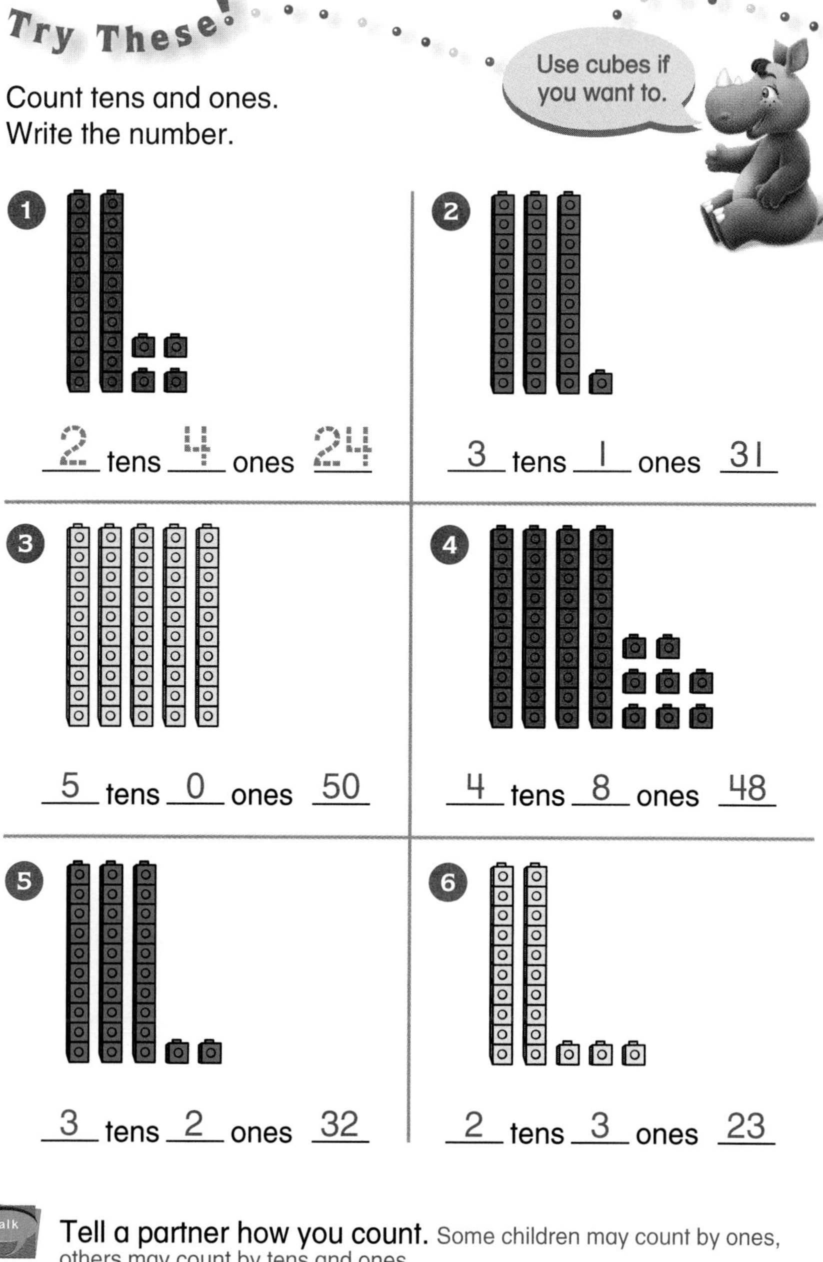

Tell a partner how you count. Some children may count by ones, others may count by tens and ones.

At Home: Have your child count sets of fewer than 50 objects.

Alternate Teaching Strategy

Materials per pair: 50 paper clips (large or small), paper cup

Prepare Put 20 paper clips into each cup for each pair of children.

Tell children to count the paper clips and organize them into groups of ten. Children should make paper-clip chains of ten.

- **How many tens do you have?** *[2 tens]*
- **How many paper clips do you have?** *[20]*

Continue the activity with 30, 40, and 50 paper clips. Then go around to each pair of children and put a handful of paper clips (21–50) in each cup. Tell them to count the paper clips.

- **How did you count the paper clips?** *[Possible answers: counted by ones, grouped them into tens and ones.]*

Have each pair make paper-clip chains using the paper clips in their cup. Encourage children to talk about their paper-clip chains of tens and ones.

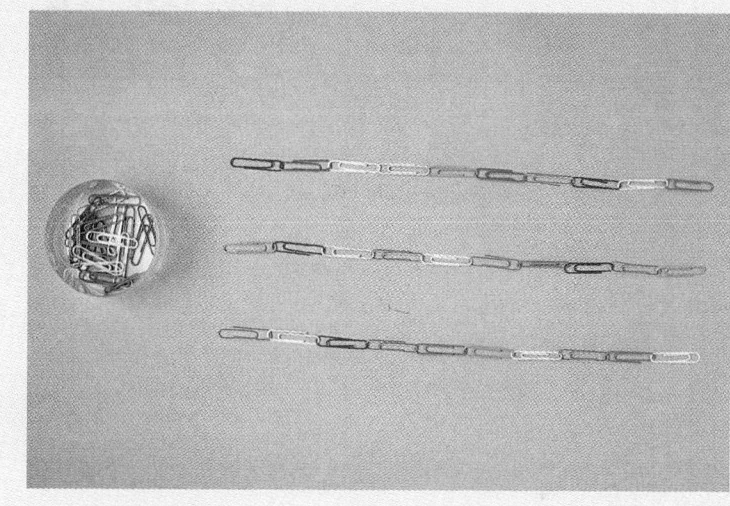

PRACTICE • 51

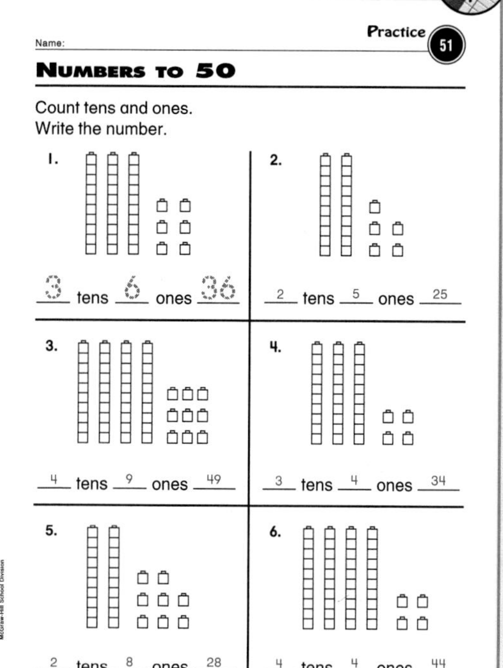

RETEACH • 51

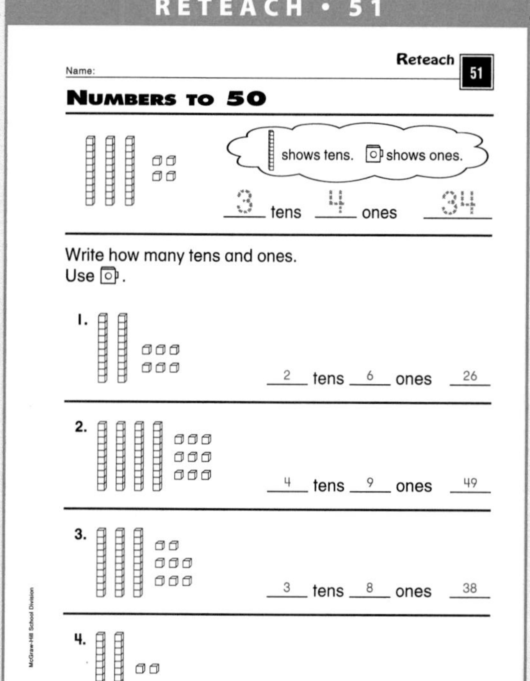

EXTEND • 51

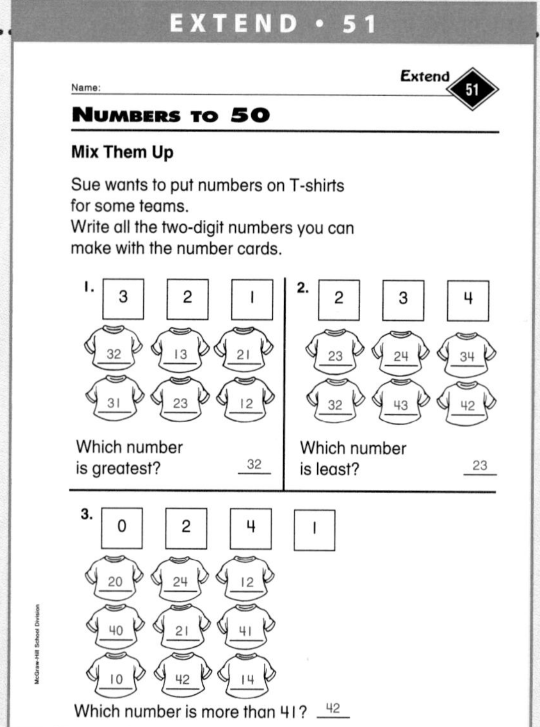

LESSON 6.3

Problem-Solving Strategy: Use Estimation

OBJECTIVE Solve problems by estimating quantity.

Day 1 Problem-Solving Strategy: Use Estimation

RESOURCE REMINDER
Math Center Cards 39
Practice 52, Reteach 52, Extend 52

SKILLS TRACE	
GRADE K	• Solve problems by estimating quantity. *(Chapter 12)*
GRADE 1	• Solve problems by estimating quantity.
GRADE 2	• Solve problems involving addition and estimation. *(Chapter 7)*

LESSON RESOURCES

MANIPULATIVES

MANIPULATIVE WARM-UP

Whole Class — Visual/Spatial

OBJECTIVE Explore estimating quantity.

▶ Display a large square and draw a cluster of counters in it. Ask children to try to guess how many counters are shown.

▶ Make a tally of the estimates for 10, 20, 30, and 40. Discuss how children made their guesses.

▶ Point to the counters. Ask:

- **How can the 10 counters help you make a good guess?** *[It helps me see about how many groups of 10 are in a larger group.]*

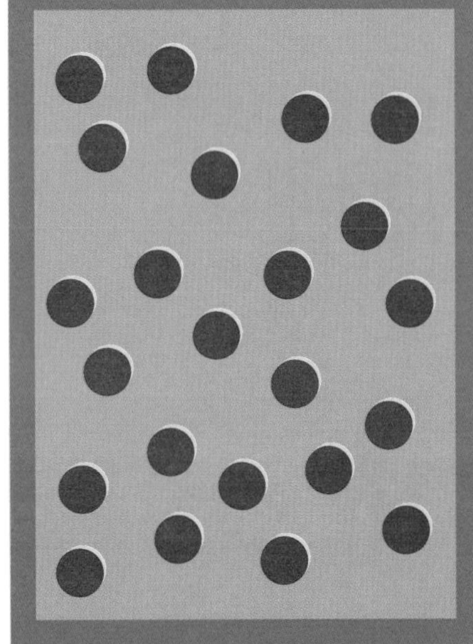

MONEY

CONNECTION ACTIVITY

Cooperative Pairs — Social

OBJECTIVE Connect estimation and money.

Materials per pair: 50 play pennies; paper plate

▶ One partner spreads a large handful of pennies out on a paper plate.

▶ Each child says and records an estimate for the group of pennies. One partner then counts out 10 pennies (as a referent set). Comparing the group of 10 to the pennies on the plate, children can keep or revise their original estimate.

▶ Partners count the pennies on the plate. The child with the closest estimate gets a point. Play continues until one partner scores 5 points.

DAILY MATH

PREVIOUS DAY QUICK REVIEW

Show as tens and ones with cubes.

1. 32 *[3 tens, 2 ones]*
2. 43 *[4 tens, 3 ones]*
3. 19 *[1 ten, 9 ones]*
4. 27 *[2 tens, 7 ones]*

FAST FACTS

1. 2 + 2 *[4]*
2. 3 + 3 *[6]*
3. 4 + 4 *[8]*
4. 5 + 5 *[10]*

Problem of the Day • 39

Read aloud to children:

Suki has 27 stickers.
Her sticker book can hold 10 stickers on each page.
Can she fill 3 full pages?
Explain. *[No; only 2 pages and part of another page.]*

TECH LINK

MATH FORUM

Idea I take my class to visit a neighboring classroom and have children make estimates of the number of students, or during recess, I have them estimate the number of bicycles in the bike racks or the number of cars in the teachers' parking lot.

Visit our Resource Village at http://www.mhschool.com to see more of the Math Forum.

MATH CENTER

Practice

OBJECTIVE Use known amounts to estimate unknown amounts.

Materials per child: 70 connecting cubes, paper bag, Math Center Recording Sheet (TA 38 optional)

Prepare Put 50 cubes in a bag. Give the child 20 cubes to build 2 ten-cube trains.

Children make 2 trains of ten cubes. They take cubes from a bag, estimate the amount, compare the loose cubes to the 2 ten-cube trains, and count the cubes to show how close they got.

PRACTICE ACTIVITY 39 — MATH CENTER On Your Own

Logical Reasoning • About How Many?

YOU NEED: bag with [cubes]

- Use the cubes to make trains of ten.
- Take some more cubes from the bag. About how many do you have? Don't count, estimate. Look at the cube trains for help.
- Now count. How close did you get?
- Put the cubes back and try again.

Grade Level 1 · McGraw-Hill School Division

Chapter 6, Lesson 3 — Number

NCTM Standards
- ✓ Problem Solving
- ✓ Communication
- ✓ Reasoning
- Connections

Problem Solving

OBJECTIVE Draw an estimated number of items.

Materials per child: spinner (TA 7), crayons, Math Center Recording Sheet (TA 38 optional)

Prepare Label the sections of the spinner 10, 20, 30, 40, 50.

Children spin for a target number and draw items without counting to reach the target number. *[Estimates may vary.]*

PROBLEM-SOLVING ACTIVITY 39 — MATH CENTER On Your Own

Spatial Reasoning • Bird Watch!

YOU NEED

The picture shows how to draw 10 birds.

- Spin for a number. That is the number of birds to draw. Draw very fast. Don't count. Stop when you think you have enough.
- Now count. Were you close? Play again and again.

Grade Level 1 · McGraw-Hill School Division

Chapter 6, Lesson 3 — Number

NCTM Standards
- ✓ Problem Solving
- Communication
- ✓ Reasoning
- Connections

Lesson 6.3

DAY 1

Problem-Solving Strategy: Use Estimation

OBJECTIVE Children solve problems by estimating quantity.

1 Motivate — Whole Class

Materials 30 pennies

Display 22 pennies and write the following.

About how many pennies are there?

About 10 About 20 About 30

Ask children to make a guess, or *estimate*, of the number of pennies shown. Tell them to follow the 4-step process:

- **Read—How many are there?**
- **Plan—Estimate.**
- **Solve—Say your estimate.**
- **Look Back—Does it make sense? Count.**

Tally their estimates as children raise their hands to indicate 10, 20, 30, or more.

Ask for a volunteer to count the pennies. Compare the exact amount to the estimates. Tell them to use the word *about* when they make an estimate.

2 Develop

Page 193

Guide children through the problem-solving steps. Discuss the Look Back questions. Then go through the four steps again for problem 1.

CRITICAL THINKING

After children answer the **Critical Thinking** question on the page, ask:

- **How can there be more people in the little picture?** *[Possible answer: The people are smaller and closer together.]*

Page 194

Try These Assign practice problems 1–4.

3 Close

Check for Understanding by having children make an estimate for a set of objects. Show 32 counters and ask:

- **How can you make an estimate for this group?** *[Possible answer: Use 10 counters as a guide.]*
- **About how many counters are there?** *[about 30]*

Name

Problem-Solving Strategy

Use Estimation

Read | Plan | Solve | Look Back

Read About how many children are in the picture?

Plan You can **estimate** about how many.

Solve Ring your estimate. (about 20) about 40

Look Back Does your answer make sense? Yes.
How can you check? Most children will say to count.

Estimate to solve.

1 About how many people are in the picture?

about 20 (about 40)

Critical Thinking: Are there more people in the big picture or the little picture? There are more in the little picture.

MEETING INDIVIDUAL NEEDS

EARLY FINISHERS

Ask children to think about times when they have to make an estimate quickly rather than having time to count objects in a group. Have them draw a picture of it.

EXTRA SUPPORT

Be sure that children understand that an exact answer is not required. Review the definitions of estimate and about.

ONGOING ASSESSMENT

Observation Checklist Determine if children understand how to estimate to solve problems by having them explain to a partner how they estimated to solve the problems on p. 194.

- **About how many children are in line to go to recess?** *[Answers may vary.]*

Follow Up Children should practice making estimates using counters before doing **Reteach 52.**

For those children grasping the estimation strategy, assign **Extend 52.**

Try These!

Estimate to solve.

1. About how many people?

about 10 (circled)

about 20

2. About how many people?

about 20 (circled)

about 40

3. About how many people?

about 10

about 30 (circled)

4. About how many children?

about 20

about 40 (circled)

Show your child a handful of small objects. Ask about how many objects you have. Then count.

Alternate Teaching Strategy

Materials per pair: 50 rhino counters in a bowl

Prepare Make sets of four number cards labeled 10, 20, 30, 40 for each pair of children.

One partner pours some counters out of the bowl. Then each child must make an estimate by showing one of the four cards. The other partner counts out a group of 10. Ask:

- **How can a group of 10 help you make a good estimate for the group of rhinos?** *[Possible answer: If I know what a group of 10 looks like, that can help me to see how many groups of 10 might be in a large group.]*

After counting the number of rhinos shown, the child with the closest number on the card explains how he or she made the estimate. Repeat the activity several times.

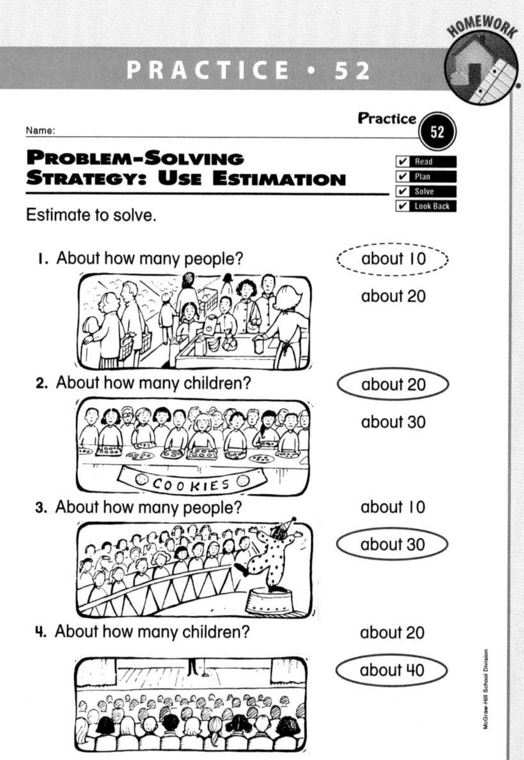

PRACTICE • 52

HOMEWORK

Name: Practice 52

PROBLEM-SOLVING STRATEGY: USE ESTIMATION

✔ Read ✔ Plan ✔ Solve ✔ Look Back

Estimate to solve.

1. About how many people? about 10 (circled) / about 20
2. About how many children? about 20 (circled) / about 30
3. About how many people? about 10 / about 30 (circled)
4. About how many children? about 20 / about 40 (circled)

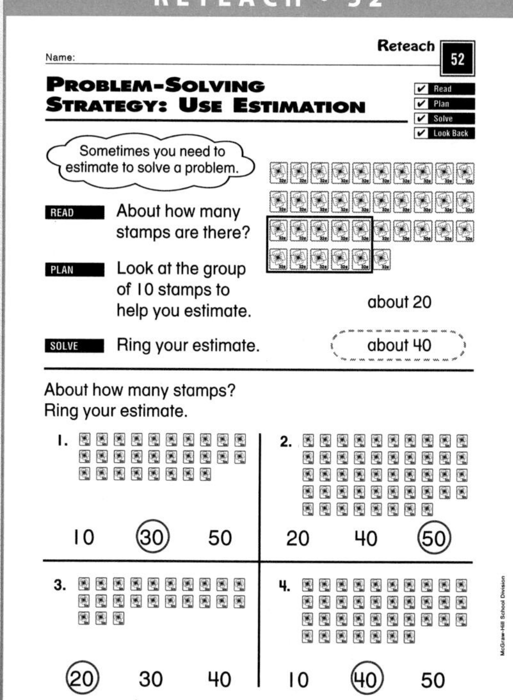

RETEACH • 52

Name: Reteach 52

PROBLEM-SOLVING STRATEGY: USE ESTIMATION

✔ Read ✔ Plan ✔ Solve ✔ Look Back

Sometimes you need to estimate to solve a problem.

READ About how many stamps are there?

PLAN Look at the group of 10 stamps to help you estimate.

SOLVE Ring your estimate.

about 20

about 40 (circled)

About how many stamps? Ring your estimate.

1. 10 / 30 (circled) / 50
2. 20 / 40 / 50 (circled)
3. 20 (circled) / 30 / 40
4. 10 / 40 (circled) / 50

EXTEND • 52

Name: Extend 52

PROBLEM SOLVING

✔ Read ✔ Plan ✔ Solve ✔ Look Back

Picture How Many

About how many [flower] in the picture?

About how many [duck] in the picture?

About how many [apple] in the picture?

1. 10 [flower] 2. 20 [duck] 3. 30 [apple]

LESSON 6.4

Numbers to 100

OBJECTIVE Explore reading, writing, and representing numbers to 100.

Day 1 Explore Activity: Count to 100
Day 2 Explore Activity: Numbers to 100

RESOURCE REMINDER
Math Center Cards 40
Practice 53–54, Reteach 53–54, Extend 53–54

SKILLS TRACE	
GRADE K	• Explore reading, writing and representing numbers to 12. *(Chapter 8)*
GRADE 1	• Explore reading, writing, and representing numbers to 100.
GRADE 2	• Explore reading, writing, and representing numbers to 100. *(Chapter 3)*

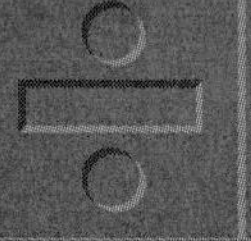

LESSON RESOURCES

MANIPULATIVE WARM-UP

Cooperative Pairs — **Visual/Spatial**

OBJECTIVE Review counting numbers to 50 on a hundred chart.

Materials per child: hundred chart (TA 22); 1 rhino counter

▶ Have children count each row to 50 on the hundred chart in unison.

▶ Write the numeral 32 on the chalkboard. Tell children to put their rhino counter on 32 on their hundred chart. Have partners take turns counting to 32 without looking at the chart as the other keeps track of the counting.

▶ Repeat the activity several times.

CONNECTION ACTIVITY

Whole Class — **Auditory/Linguistic**

OBJECTIVE Connect counting to 100 with literature.

Resources Read-Aloud Anthology, page 33

Materials per child: 40 two-color counters; chart paper

▶ Talk about the largest number of plastic strips children have ever worn at one time. Then read the poem "Band-Aids," found in the Read-Aloud Anthology.

▶ Give each child 40 counters. Reread the poem slowly so that they can keep track of the numbers in it. Have children group counters by tens and ones for a total of 35.

▶ Reread the poem again, increasing the total number of plastic strips on the different body parts to between 50 and 100. Have children trace one child on the chart paper and draw several plastic strips.

DAILY MATH

PREVIOUS DAY QUICK REVIEW

How many cubes?

1. 3 tens 6 ones *[36]*
2. 2 tens 1 ones *[21]*
3. 4 tens 5 ones *[45]*
4. 1 ten 9 ones *[19]*

FAST FACTS

1. 9 – 8 *[1]*
2. 7 – 6 *[1]*
3. 6 – 5 *[1]*
4. 5 – 4 *[1]*

Problem of the Day • 40

Read aloud to children:

The Teddy Bear Store has 3 bears on the shelf.
Then 6 boxes of bears arrive.
There are 10 bears in each box.
How many bears does the Teddy Bear Store have now? *[63]*

TECH LINK

MATH VAN

Tools You may wish to use the Counter tool with this lesson.

MATH FORUM

Management Tip I display a large hundred chart in the classroom for children to refer to as they count or find numbers on the chart.

Visit our Resource Village at http://www.mhschool.com to see more of the Math Forum.

MATH CENTER

Practice

OBJECTIVE Read and represent numbers 51–100.

Materials per pair: 2 cards

Prepare Choose 10 numbers between 10 and 100. Make one card with the numeral and a second card showing tens and ones for each number. The numeral cards should have a red dot on the blank side. The "picture" cards should have a blue dot on the blank side. Children play a memory game, matching number cards with cards that show tens and ones.

PRACTICE ACTIVITY 40 — MATH CENTER — Partners

Game • Make a Match

YOU NEED: cards

See the red cards.
See the blue cards.
Take turns.

- Turn over a blue card and a red card.
- If they match, take them.
  If they don't, turn them facedown.
- The player with more cards at the end wins.

12

Chapter 6, Lesson 4 — Number

Grade Level 1 — McGraw-Hill School Division

NCTM Standards
- Problem Solving
- ✓ Communication
- ✓ Reasoning
- Connections

Problem Solving

OBJECTIVE Read and compare two 2-digit numbers to 100 that contain the same digits, but in different places.

Materials per child: 75 connecting cubes, Math Center Recording Sheet (TA 38 optional)

Children will show a number with cubes and write it. Then they reverse the digits and show the next number with cubes. Children tell how the numbers are alike and different. Children play again with two other numbers.

PROBLEM-SOLVING ACTIVITY 40 — MATH CENTER — On Your Own

Decision Making • What's the Difference?

YOU NEED

- Show 15 with cubes.
  Write the number.
  Now show 51 with cubes.
  Write that number.
  How are 15 and 51 the same?
  How are they different?
- Now show 57 and 75 with cubes.
- Write what you learned.
- Play again with two other numbers.

15

Chapter 6, Lesson 4 — Number

Grade Level 1 — McGraw-Hill School Division

NCTM Standards
- ✓ Problem Solving
- ✓ Communication
- ✓ Reasoning
- Connections

Lesson 6.4

EXPLORE ACTIVITY
Count to 100

OBJECTIVE Children count sets of objects and organize as tens and ones.

Materials per pair: 100 beans; hundred chart (TA 22)

1 Motivate — Cooperative Pairs

Materials per pair: 100 beans; hundred chart (TA 22)

Prepare Make a 10-by-10 grid and write the numbers 1–100 to make a hundred chart on a chalkboard.

Partners make rows of 10 beans on the hundred chart as they count aloud with you from 1 to 10, 11 to 20, until they get to 100.

Cover all but the last row of the hundred chart on the chalkboard, showing the tens.

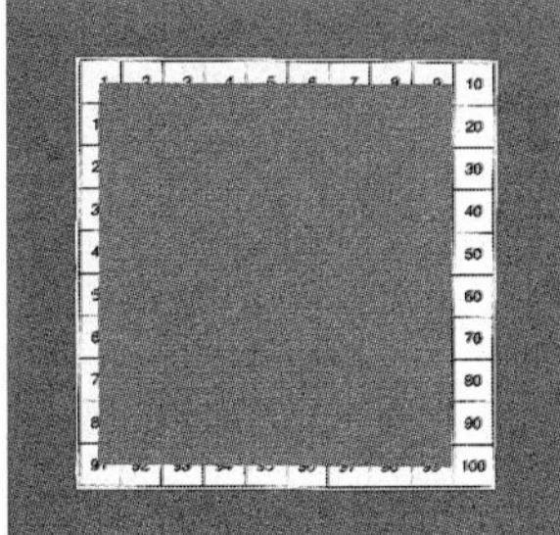

Focus on *60, 70, 80, 90,* and *100.* Have children say the number names *sixty, seventy, eighty, ninety,* and *one hundred* aloud with you.

2 Develop

Page 195

Working Together Have children take several handfuls of counters to show more than 50. Ask how they can organize them to make the counting easier. Observe as they draw and write the number for their set of counters.

Have children study the hundred chart on the page. Discuss how the packets of seeds relate to the numbers in the chart.

Critical Thinking
After children complete the exercises on the page, ask:
- **How many groups of 10 in 76?** *[7; some children may have to use counters to find the answer.]*

Name ______________________

Explore Activity
Count to 100

51	52	53	54	55	56	57	58	59	60
61	62	63	64	65	66	67	68	69	70
71	72	73	74	75	76	77	78	79	80
81	82	83	84	85	86	87	88	89	90
91	92	93	94	95	96	97	98	99	100

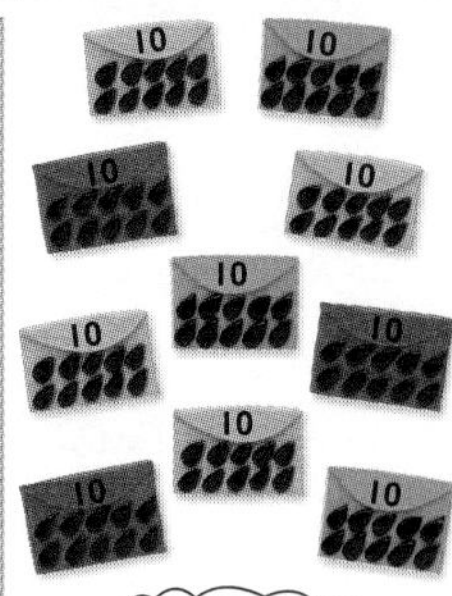

Tell what patterns you see. Children may see the one-more pattern going across and the ten-more pattern going down.

Working Together

Your group needs 100 counters.

- Each of you take a big handful of counters.
- Count how many in all.
- Draw and write the number.

Numbers may vary. Sample answer is given.

1. Some children may draw tens. 76

2. ____

MEETING INDIVIDUAL NEEDS

EARLY FINISHERS

Have pairs of children count out groups of 100 connecting cubes and put them into bags or bowls for the next day's lesson.

EXTRA SUPPORT

Provide two sets of cards for children to practice with, one set with decade numbers *10, 20, ..., 100,* and another set with words *ten, twenty, ..., one hundred.* Have children match the numerals and number names.

ONGOING ASSESSMENT

Interview Determine if children can count a set of objects to 100. Show 74 counters and ask:
- **Count the counters out loud.** *[1, 2, 3, ..., 74]*
- **How many counters?** *[74]*

See if the child groups the counters by tens and ones.

Follow Up Help children organize large numbers of objects by tens and ones before counting them. Then assign **Reteach 53.**

Assign **Extend 53** to children who can count objects to 100.

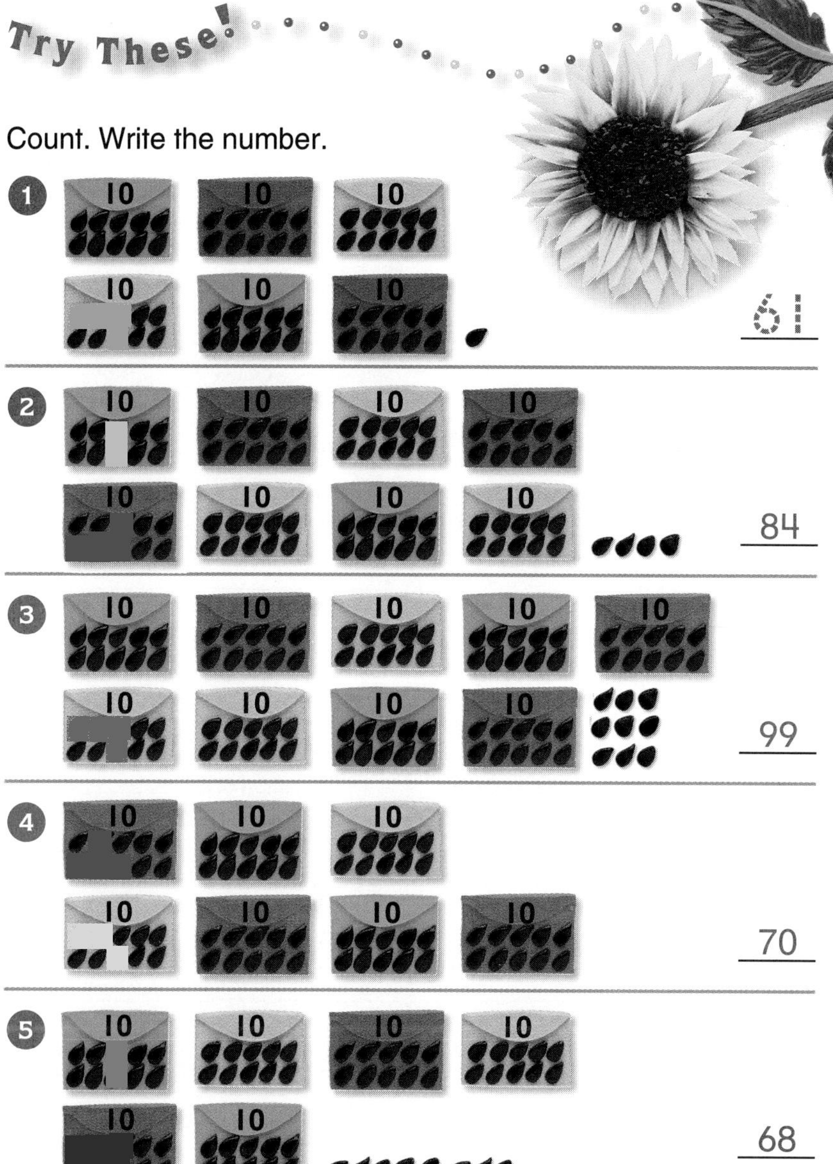

Try These!

Count. Write the number.

1. 61
2. 84
3. 99
4. 70
5. 68

Talk **Tell a partner how you counted.** Some children may count tens and ones, while many children may count each seed.

196 • one hundred ninety-six

At Home: Practice counting to 100 with your child.

Page 196

Try These Assign practice exercises 1–5.

As children discuss the Talk question, guide them to tell whether they counted the packs of seeds or every seed shown in the exercises, and whether they found it a good way to count.

3 Close

Check for Understanding by having children explain how they got the number for one of the exercises on page 196.

Tomorrow children will identify the number of tens and ones in numbers to 100.

PRACTICE • 53

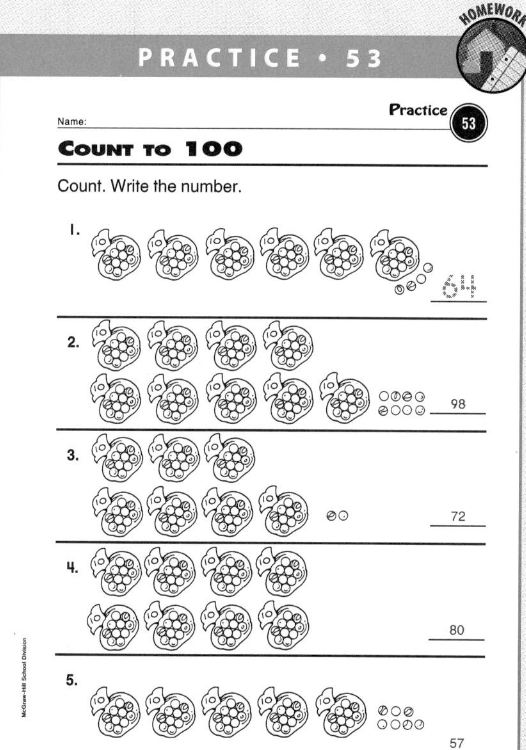

Practice 53

Name:

Count to 100

Count. Write the number.

1. 64
2. 98
3. 72
4. 80
5. 57

RETEACH • 53

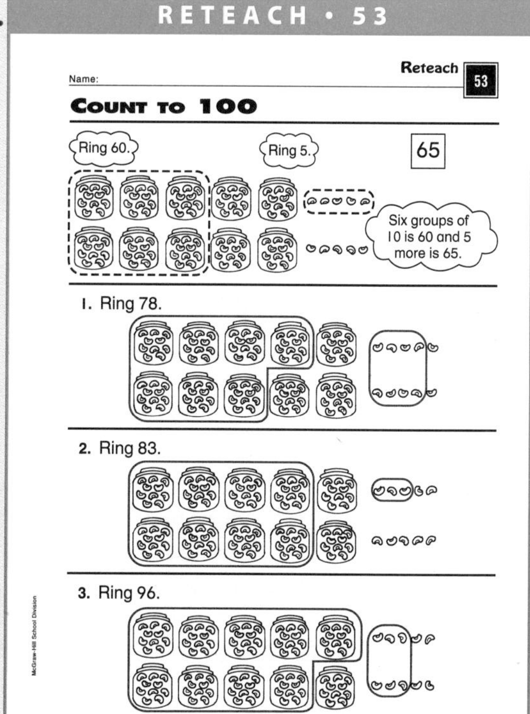

Reteach 53

Name:

Count to 100

Ring 60. Ring 5. 65

Six groups of 10 is 60 and 5 more is 65.

1. Ring 78.
2. Ring 83.
3. Ring 96.

EXTEND • 53

Extend 53

Name:

Count to 100

Lots of Peanuts

Help Maria count the peanuts. Ring groups of 10. Write the number.

Answers may vary. Samples given.

1. 68
2. 84

Lesson 6.4

DAY 2

EXPLORE ACTIVITY

Numbers to 100

OBJECTIVE Children read, write, and represent numbers to 100.

Materials per pair: 100 connecting cubes

1 Motivate — Whole Class

Resources Jumbo Activity Book, page 11 (place-value chart); Stickers, sheet 3 (square counters)

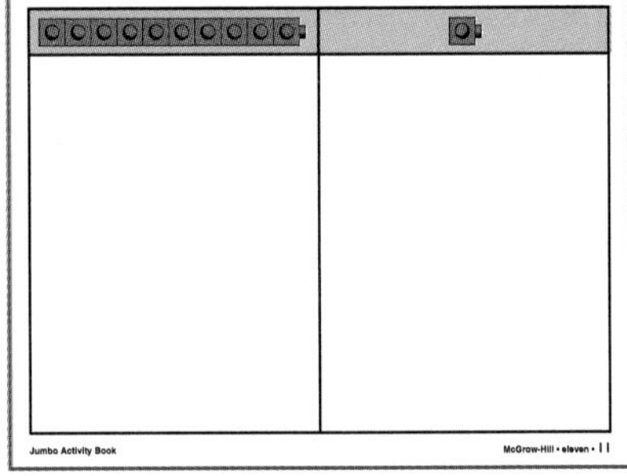

Point out the two sections of the chart—*Tens* and *Ones*. Place 63 square counters in the Ones section of the chart. Ask one or two children to count them.

Then have volunteers come to the chart to show rows of 10 squares in the Tens section of the chart to finally show 6 tens and 3 ones, or 63. Then have children show 71, 80, and 96 as tens and ones on the chart.

2 Develop

Page 197

Working Together Have pairs work together to share materials. Tell them to work with more than 50 cubes at a time as they do exercises 1–6. Observe as they make cube trains for 10 to help them count the cubes.

CRITICAL THINKING
After children complete the exercises on the page, ask:

- **How can you show tens and ones when you count pennies?** *[Possible answer: Make stacks of 10 pennies.]*

Page 198

Try These Assign practice exercises 1–6.

3 Close

Check for Understanding by having children explain how they counted the cubes on page 198, such as in exercise 5. *[Possible answer: There are six trains of ten and 1 cube left over to show 6 tens and 1 one. That's 61 cubes.]*

Name ____________________

Working Together

Your group needs 100 cubes.

- Each of you take a big handful of cubes.
- Count how many in all.
- Make groups of ten.
- Count again.
- Write how many.

Numbers may vary. Sample answer is given.

86

8 tens 6 ones

1. 92 cubes — 9 tens 2 ones
2. ____ cubes — ____ tens ____ ones
3. ____ cubes — ____ tens ____ ones
4. ____ cubes — ____ tens ____ ones
5. ____ cubes — ____ tens ____ ones
6. ____ cubes — ____ tens ____ ones

Critical Thinking: How can you show tens and ones with 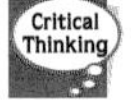? Possible answer: Stack counters in piles of ten to show tens, and use loose counters for ones.

MEETING INDIVIDUAL NEEDS

COMMON ERROR

Some children may switch the digits for the tens and ones blanks on pages 197–198. Have them use a place-value chart (TA 24) to help them keep track of tens and ones.

GIFTED AND TALENTED

Give children sheets of centimeter dot paper (TA 25). Tell them to find at least one group of 100 dots and draw a line around it.

ONGOING ASSESSMENT

Anecdotal Report Note the progress in each child's ability to count a large group of objects to 100 by ones and then by tens and ones. Store samples and your notes in their portfolios.

Follow Up Assign **Reteach 54** to children who need more guided practice. Also have them group and count objects such as crayons or paper clips.

For children who demonstrate the ability to read, write, and represent numbers to 100, assign **Extend 54.**

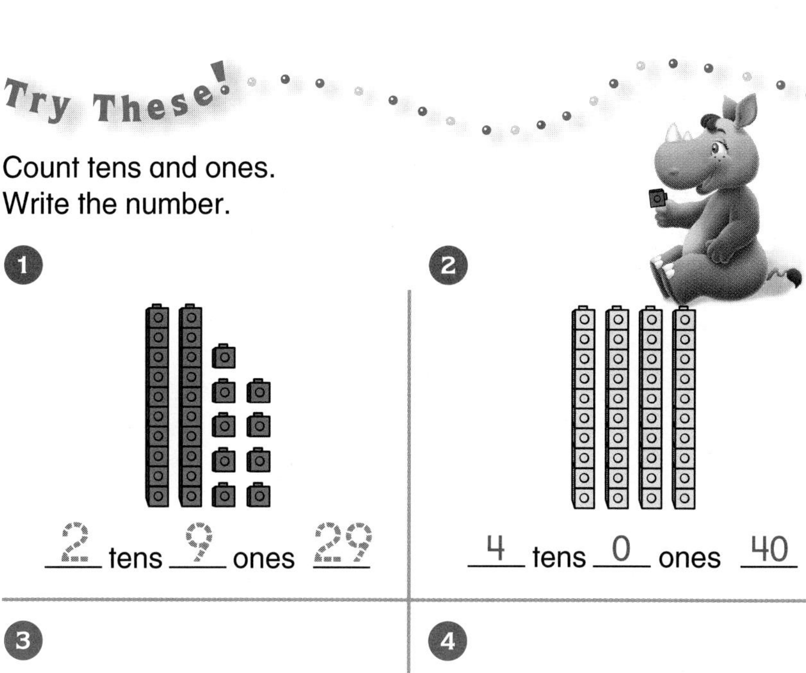

Try These!

Count tens and ones.
Write the number.

1. 2 tens 9 ones 29

2. 4 tens 0 ones 40

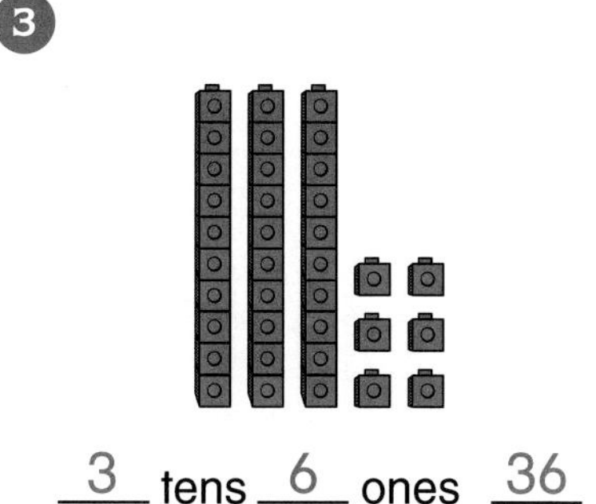

3. 3 tens 6 ones 36

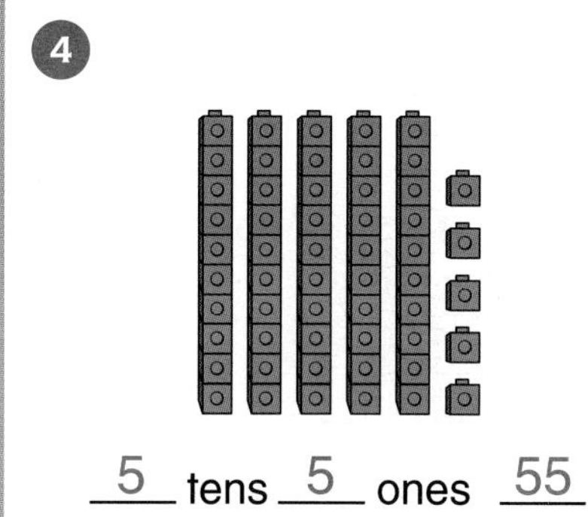

4. 5 tens 5 ones 55

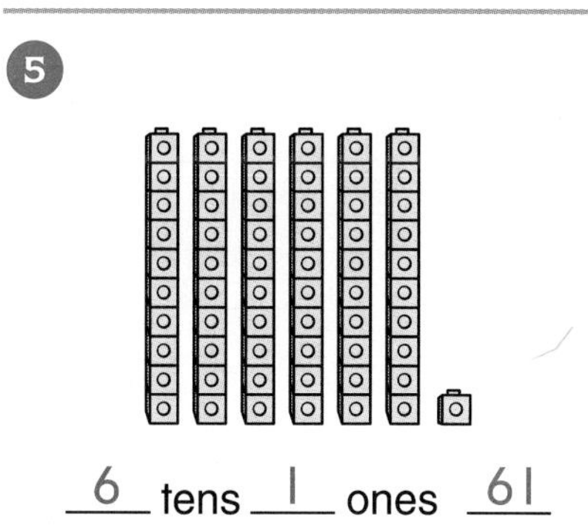

5. 6 tens 1 ones 61

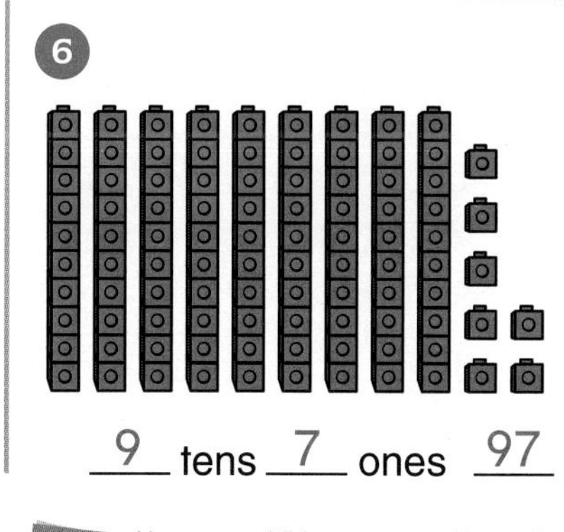

6. 9 tens 7 ones 97

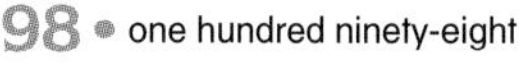

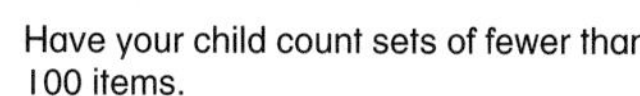

At Home: Have your child count sets of fewer than 100 items.

Alternate Teaching Strategy

Materials per pair: 100 small paper clips; 2 blank spinners (TA 8)

Prepare per pair: Label one spinner with numbers 40, 50, 60, 70, 80, 90, and the other with numbers 4–9.

Partners take turns spinning both spinners to get and record a number of tens and a number of ones. Then partners should make paper-clip chains of ten and single paper clips to show the number spun.

After partners count the paper-clip chains and leftover paper clips, have them record the number of tens, the number of ones, and the total number of paper clips for the spin on a sheet of paper. Repeat several times.

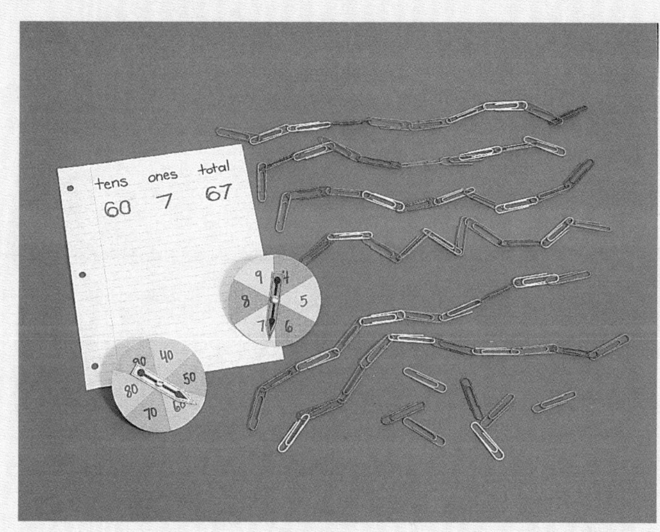

PRACTICE • 54

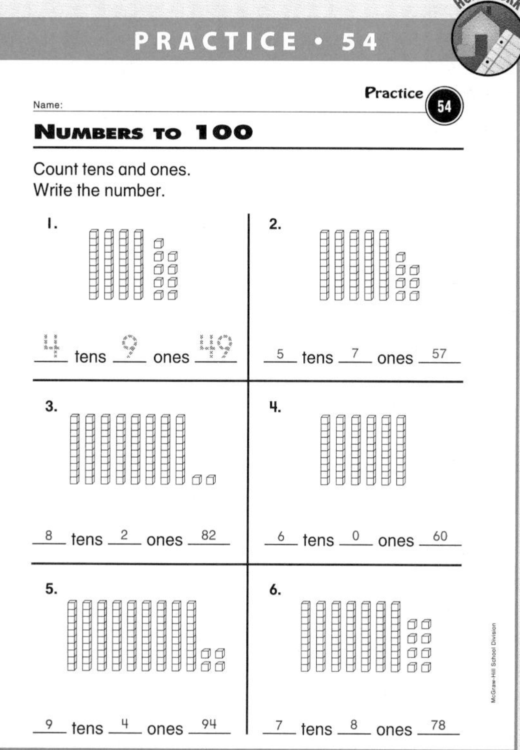

Practice 54

Name:

NUMBERS TO 100

Count tens and ones.
Write the number.

1. 4 tens 9 ones 49
2. 5 tens 7 ones 57
3. 8 tens 2 ones 82
4. 6 tens 0 ones 60
5. 9 tens 4 ones 94
6. 7 tens 8 ones 78

RETEACH • 54

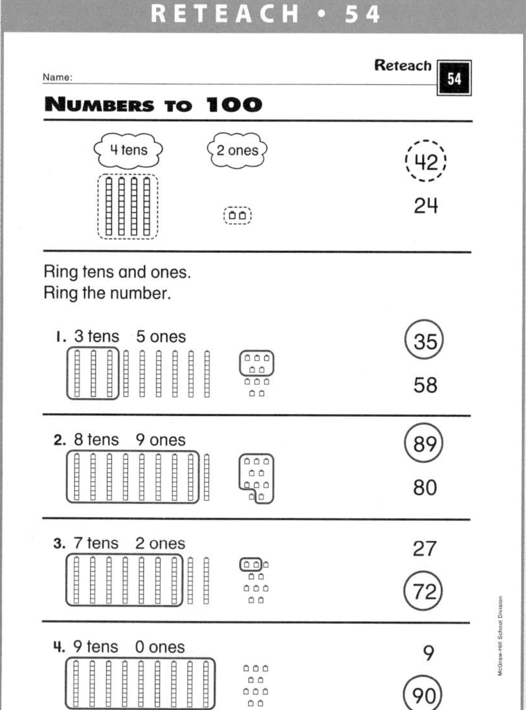

Reteach 54

Name:

NUMBERS TO 100

4 tens 2 ones (42) 24

Ring tens and ones.
Ring the number.

1. 3 tens 5 ones (35) 58
2. 8 tens 9 ones (89) 80
3. 7 tens 2 ones 27 (72)
4. 9 tens 0 ones 9 (90)

EXTEND • 54

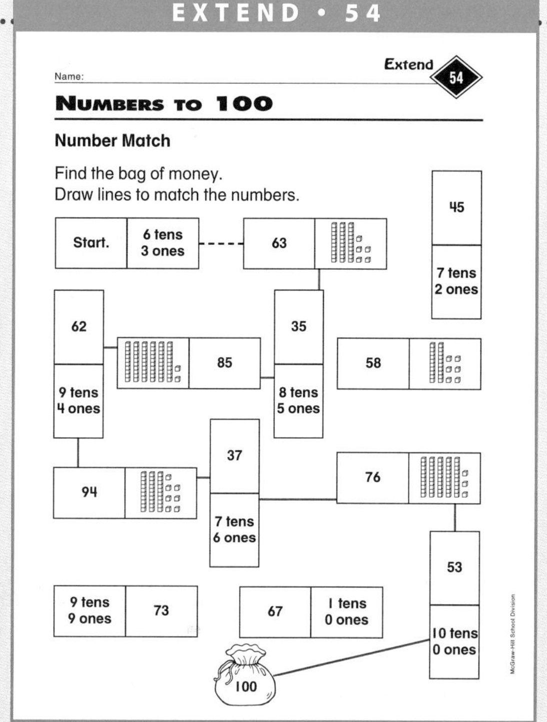

Extend 54

Name:

NUMBERS TO 100

Number Match

Find the bag of money.
Draw lines to match the numbers.

Start. | 6 tens 3 ones | 63 | 45 | 7 tens 2 ones | 62 | 9 tens 4 ones | 85 | 35 | 8 tens 5 ones | 58 | 37 | 7 tens 6 ones | 94 | 76 | 53 | 10 tens 0 ones | 9 tens 9 ones | 73 | 67 | 1 tens 0 ones | 100

AT A GLANCE

PURPOSE Maintain and review the concepts, skills, and strategies that children have learned thus far in the chapter.

Materials have available: sets of 100 two-color counters, 100 connecting cubes; Workmat 2 (10-frame)

Using the Midchapter Review

Page 199

The **Midchapter Review** may be completed independently or by the class as a whole. Children may use counters to complete exercises 1–8. Discuss exercises 9–10 to check childrens' understanding of making an estimate for a group of objects.

JOURNAL Have children write how they estimate to find about how many objects are in a group. Children who have difficulty writing or using the vocabulary may dictate the estimate and their explanations to you, a classroom aide, or an older child to write in the journal.

Vocabulary Review

Write the following on the chalkboard:

eighteen, 18	**fourteen, 14**	**sixteen, 16**
eighty, 80	**nineteen, 19**	**sixty, 60**
eleven ,11	**ninety, 90**	**thirteen, 13**
estimate	**one hundred, 100**	**thirty, 30**
fifteen, 15	**seventeen, 17**	**twelve, 12**
fifty, 50	**seventy, 70**	**twenty, 20**
forty, 40		

Ask for volunteers to explain, show, or act out the meanings of these words.

Name

Midchapter Review

Write the number.

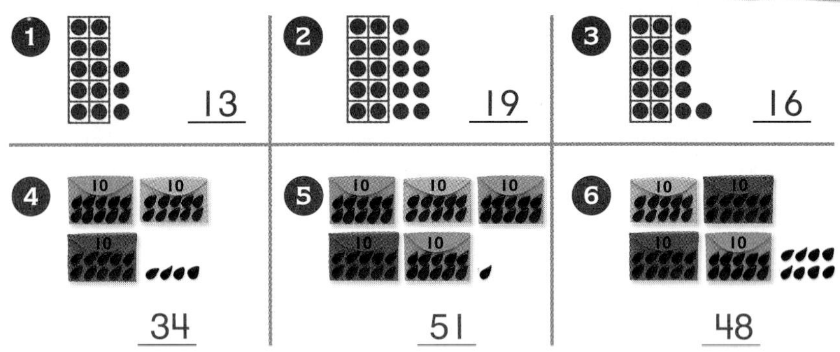

1. 13
2. 19
3. 16
4. 34
5. 51
6. 48

Count tens and ones. Write the number.

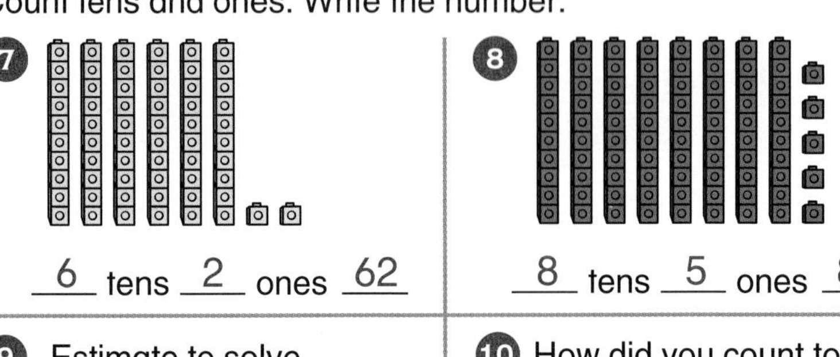

7. 6 tens 2 ones 62
8. 8 tens 5 ones 85

9. Estimate to solve. About how many?

about 10 (about 20)

10. How did you count to answer exercise 8? Children may count tens and ones and then write the number 85, and some children may recount to get 85.

Journal: Tell how you estimate about how many. Children may count part of the set, they may guess, or they may feel they can judge about how many by sight.

Reinforcement and Remediation

CHAPTER OBJECTIVES	MIDCHAPTER REVIEW ITEMS	STUDENT BOOK PAGES	TEACHER'S EDITION PAGES		TEACHER RESOURCES
			Activities	Alternate Teaching Strategy	Reteach
*6A	1–8	185–192, 195–198	184A, 188A, 194A	188, 192, 198	48–51, 53–54
*6F	9–10	193–194	192A	194	52

*6A Read, write, and represent numbers, to 100
*6F Solve problems, including those that involve numbers to 100, graphs, and estimation

Extra Practice
Game !

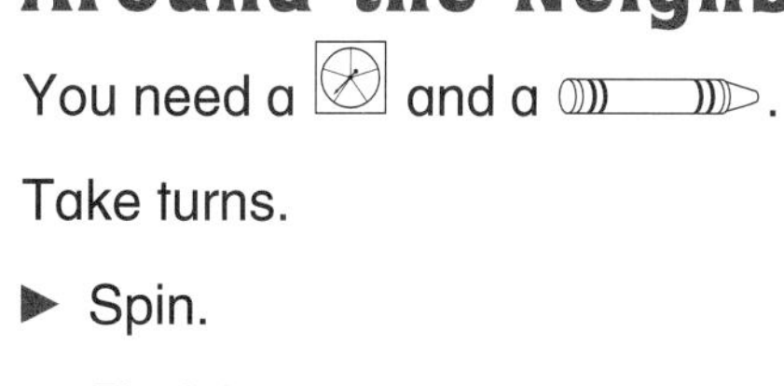

Around the Neighborhood

You need a spinner and a crayon.

Take turns.

- ▶ Spin.
- ▶ Find the number.
- ▶ Color the tens and ones.
- ▶ Play until you color all the spaces.

AT A GLANCE

PURPOSE Provide an opportunity for review and practice.

Materials per pair: blank spinner (TA 8) with numbers 49, 36, 25, 27, 40, 71, 18, 52

Using the Extra Practice

Page 200

Explain the rules of the game. Although pairs of children play, each child finds and colors the tens and ones on his or her own page. Play until both children color all the tens and ones. If a child spins a number more than once, it becomes the other player's turn.

Using the Additional Practice

The section below provides additional practice that you may want to write on the chalkboard or on a reproducible master.

ADDITIONAL PRACTICE

Count tens and ones. Write the number.

1. [2] tens [6] ones [26]

2. [1] tens [8] ones [18]

3. [4] tens [3] ones [43]

4. [3] tens [0] ones [30]

5. [6] tens [1] ones [61]

6.

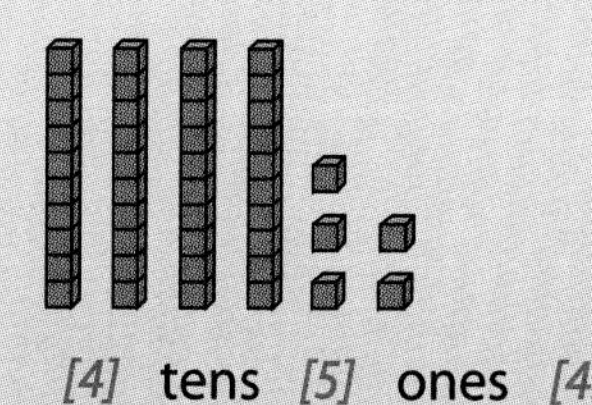

[4] tens [5] ones [45]

7. [7] tens [0] ones [70]

8. [5] tens [2] ones [52]

Applying Counting

OBJECTIVE Children count 100 objects in a social studies context.

Resource Literature Big Book: *I Go With My Family to Grandma's*

Materials clear plastic containers of various sizes; per group: a collection of 100 objects such as connecting cubes, beans, pennies, counters, crayons, half-pint milk cartons, and paper clips

1 Engage

Materials 250 connecting cubes

Display three piles of connecting cubes containing 50, 80, and 120 cubes, respectively. Point to the pile of 50 cubes. Ask:

- **Do you think this pile has more than 100 cubes or less than 100?**

Have a volunteer count the cubes. Then repeat the activity for the other two piles of cubes.

2 Investigate — Cooperative Pairs

Page 201

Working Together Using the Partners Think and Share Strategy, have the teacher ask children what they want to count. Children think about their answer individually. Children meet with a partner and discuss their answers. Partners share their ideas with the whole class.

3 Reflect and Share

Page 202

Write a Report After children choose a container and check to see if it can hold 100, they begin their portfolio reports. Children's descriptions of how their collections fit in the container should indicate whether or not the objects filled the container and whether there were more objects than the container could hold.

Name

Container Collections

Tell what you know about 100.
Is 100 a lot? Is 100 a little?

Answers may vary.

Working Together

Work in small groups.

- Talk about what you want to count.
- Choose an object.
- Find different ways to count 100 objects.

MORE TO INVESTIGATE

Predict Sample answer: Our collection did not fill our container, so the collection will fit in a smaller container.

Explore Have children in each group discuss which container to choose next.

Find Have two groups compare their results.

Bibliography Children may enjoy reading the following books:

Count Your Way Through Africa by Jim Haskins. Minneapolis, MN: Carolrhoda Books, 1989. ISBN 0–87614–347–8.

The 329th Friend 2nd edition by Marjorie Weinman Sharmat. New York: Four Winds Press, 1992. ISBN 0–02–782259–1.

Decision Making

Answers may vary. See Teacher's Edition for sample of children's work.

1. Choose a container that you think will hold 100. Then see if it does.
2. How many objects did the container hold?

____

Write a report.

3. Tell what you collected. Tell how you counted.
4. Describe how your collection fit in the container you chose.

More to Investigate

See Teacher's Edition.

PREDICT Can your collection fit in a smaller container?

EXPLORE Choose a smaller container. Then try it.

FIND How did your collection fit in the container you chose?

BUILDING A PORTFOLIO

This assignment will provide insight into children's ability to use different ways to count 100 objects and to relate the size of 100 objects to the space the objects fill.

Allow children to revise their work for the portfolio. Each child's portfolio piece should consist of his or her written report and any notes you made about the child's work.

You may wish to use the Holistic Scoring Guide to assess this task. See page 27 in Teacher's Assessment Resources.

Children's Work

Justin

I counted crayons and they were different colons. And we counted by fives, twos, twenties, and tens. And this is how they go into the bucket- you just drop them in!

Courtney

I counted cubes by twos and tens and fives. Then we counted peanuts counting by fives and ten's. 100 peanuts is not alot. It is a small type of food. It was a pound.

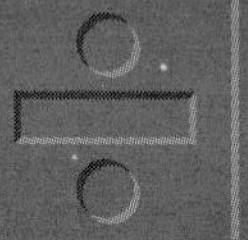

LESSON RESOURCES

Order to 100

OBJECTIVE Order numbers to 100.

Day 1 Order to 100
Day 2 Before, After, Between

RESOURCE REMINDER
Math Center Cards 41
Practice 55–56, Reteach 55–56, Extend 55–56

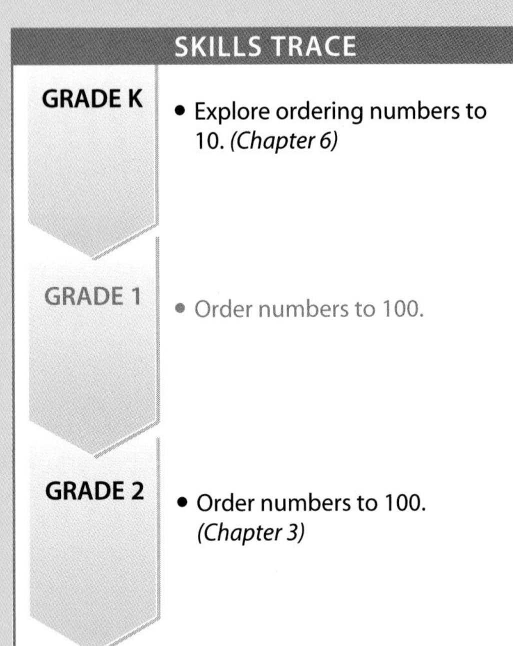

SKILLS TRACE	
GRADE K	• Explore ordering numbers to 10. *(Chapter 6)*
GRADE 1	• Order numbers to 100.
GRADE 2	• Order numbers to 100. *(Chapter 3)*

WARM-UP

Cooperative Pairs — **Visual/Spatial**

OBJECTIVE Explore ordering numbers to 100.

Materials per pair: 2 hundred charts (TA 22); scissors

▶ Each partner cuts out the hundred chart and then cuts the hundred chart horizontally into strips showing the rows 1–10, 11–20, and so on. Then the strips are mixed up in a pile.

▶ The partners exchange their piles of strips and then work independently to put the strips in order to recreate the hundred charts.

▶ The partners compare their work and correct any errors.

▶ Have partners exchange their mixed-up pile of strips again. This time have them see which one recreates the hundred chart faster.

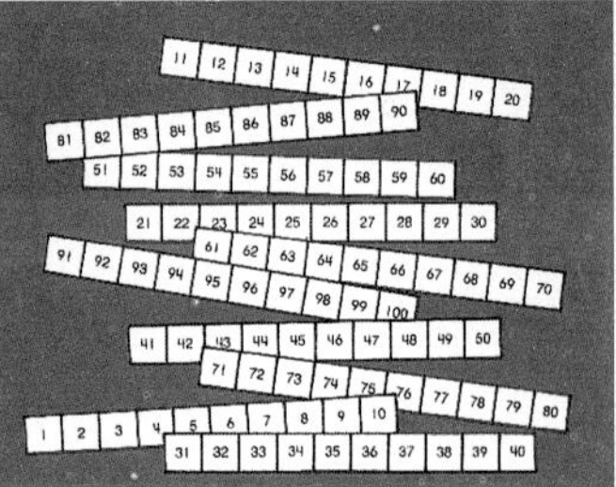

CONNECTION ACTIVITY

Whole Class — **Individual**

OBJECTIVE Connect ordering numbers to 100 with art.

Materials chart paper, 3" x 3" self-stick notes, marker

Prepare Outline a very large rhino on chart paper. Make number cards 1–100 using self-stick notes. Make the decade numbers in another color.

▶ Place number cards 1–5 in order on the rhino. Then place number cards in order, including the numbers 10, 20, 30, ..., 100.

▶ Ask questions such as these:
- **Which number comes just after 5?** *[6]*
- **Which number is between 45 and 47?** *[46]*

▶ Use this as an ongoing activity children can return to time after time by placing different number cards on the outline each day.

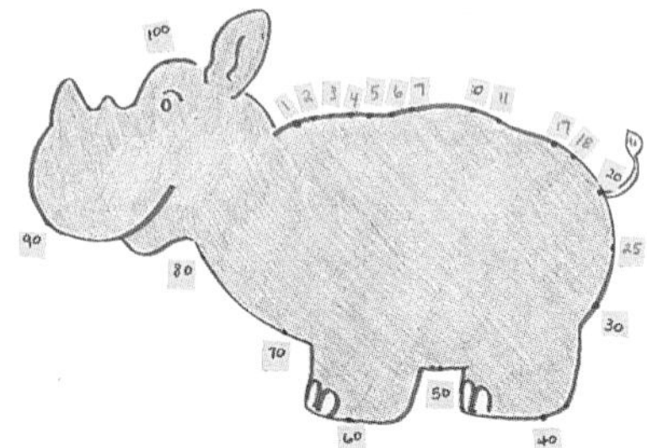

DAILY MATH

PREVIOUS DAY QUICK REVIEW

How many tens and ones?

1. 16 *[1 ten, 6 ones]*
2. 27 *[2 tens, 7 ones]*
3. 84 *[8 tens, 4 ones]*
4. 99 *[9 tens, 9 ones]*

FAST FACTS

1. 9 – 7 *[2]*
2. 6 – 4 *[2]*
3. 10 – 8 *[2]*
4. 5 – 3 *[2]*

Problem of the Day • 41

Read aloud to children:

Ann, Dan, and Sam were born exactly one year apart.
Sam is the oldest.
Ann is 8.
Dan is 9.
How old is Sam? *[10]*

TECH LINK

MATH VAN

Tools You may wish to use the Calculator with this lesson.

MATH FORUM

Cultural Diversity I encourage non-English-speaking children to share counting aloud to 100 in their language of origin. If a child's culture uses different number symbols, I have him or her write the symbols for 1–10 on the chalkboard for everyone to learn.

Visit our Resource Village at http://www.mhschool.com to see more of the Math Forum.

MATH CENTER

Practice

OBJECTIVE Order numbers to 100.

Materials per pair: number cards, bag, hundred chart (TA 22); per child: Math Center Recording Sheet (TA 38 optional)

Prepare Prepare a set of 20 number cards and place it in the bag. Write a number from 1 to 100 on each.

One child picks 4 cards from the bag. The partner puts the cards in order. Both children check the order with a hundred chart. Children may play until all cards are used.

PRACTICE ACTIVITY 41

MATH CENTER
Partners

Number Sense • What's the Order?

YOU NEED
- number cards
- bag

- Shake the bag.
- Pick four cards.
  Give them to your partner.
- Your partner puts them in order.
- Together you check the order.
- Write the numbers in order.

Do it again and again. Take turns.

1	2	3	4	5	6	7	8	9	10
11	12	13	14	15	16	17	18	19	20
21	22	23	24	25	26	27	28	29	30
31	32	33	34	35	36	37	38	39	40
41	42	43	44	45	46	47	48	49	50
51	52	53	54	55	56	57	58	59	60
61	62	63	64	65	66	67	68	69	70
71	72	73	74	75	76	77	78	79	80
81	82	83	84	85	86	87	88	89	90
91	92	93	94	95	96	97	98	99	100

Chapter 6, Lesson 5 Number

NCTM Standards
- ✓ Problem Solving
- ✓ Communication
- ✓ Reasoning
- Connections

Problem Solving

OBJECTIVE Count on a hundred chart.

Materials per pair: number cube (1-6), hundreds chart, per child: penny, Math Center Recording Sheet (TA 38 optional)

Children move forward on a hundred chart the number of spaces they roll. *[Check children's written numbers — the numbers should increase toward 100.]*

PROBLEM-SOLVING ACTIVITY 41

MATH CENTER
Partners

Spatial Reasoning • Count On

YOU NEED
2

- Put your penny on 1 on the chart.
  Use heads.
  Your partner does the same.
  Your partner uses tails.
- Roll a number.
  Move your penny that many spaces.
  Write the number that is in the space.
  Your partner does the same.
- Keep playing until one of you reaches 100.

1	2	3	4	5	6	7	8	9	10
11		13	14	15		17	18	19	20
21	22	23	24	25	26	27	28	29	30
31	32	33	34	35	36	37	38	39	40
41	42	43	44	45	46	47	48	49	50
51	52	53	54	55	56	57	58	59	60
61	62	63	64	65	66	67	68	69	70
71	72	73	74	75	76	77	78	79	80
81	82	83	84	85	86	87	88	89	90
91	92	93	94	95	96	97	98	99	100

Chapter 6, Lesson 5 Number

NCTM Standards
- ✓ Problem Solving
- ✓ Communication
- ✓ Reasoning
- ✓ Connections

Lesson 6.5

Order to 100

OBJECTIVE Children order numbers to 100.

Materials have available: hundred chart (TA 22)

1 Motivate — Whole class

Resources Jumbo Activity Book, page 10; Sticker sheet 3 (square counters)

Display Jumbo Activity Book page 10. Ask children to look at each row across and each column down. Cover numbers 27, 28, and 29. Ask:

- **What numbers come after 26 in this row? How do you know?** *[27, 28, 29; follow the same pattern used when counting 6, 7, 8, 9.]*
- **How does knowing how to count from 1 to 9 help you to find and read the numbers on this chart?** *[Possible answer: No matter what row I'm in, there are numbers 1–9 following a tens number.]*

Cover number 43. Ask:

- **If you look at the box just below 43, what number is that?** *[53]* **What number is just below 53?** *[63]*

2 Develop

Page 203

Draw a 10-by-10 grid on the chalkboard. Have volunteers write the numbers in order starting with 1 at the top left corner of the grid to make a hundred chart. As each row is completed on the chalkboard, have children write in the missing numbers on the hundred chart on their book page.

CRITICAL THINIKING

After children answer the question on the page, ask:

- **What numbers do you see in each row?** *[1, 2, 3, ..., 0]*

Name ______________________

Order to 100

Count.
Write the numbers in **order.**

1	2	3	4	5	6	7	8	9	10
11	12	13	14	15	16	17	18	19	20
21	22	23	24	25	26	27	28	29	30
31	32	33	34	35	36	37	38	39	40
41	42	43	44	45	46	47	48	49	50
51	52	53	54	55	56	57	58	59	60
61	62	63	64	65	66	67	68	69	70
71	72	73	74	75	76	77	78	79	80
81	82	83	84	85	86	87	88	89	90
91	92	93	94	95	96	97	98	99	100

What patterns do you see? Possible answer: Every number in the first column has 1 one.

MEETING INDIVIDUAL NEEDS

EARLY FINISHERS

Have several sets of 10 number cards for children to put in order. The sets of cards can represent each row of the hundred chart or have a sequence such as 17, 18, ..., 26.

EXTRA SUPPORT

Some children may skip numbers in a sequence. Have them count aloud to a partner.

ONGOING ASSESSMENT

Observation Checklist Determine if children understand how to order the numbers by giving them sequences to complete.

Follow Up Help children who are having trouble by working with them on a hundred chart. Assign **Reteach 55.**

Assign **Extend 55** to those children who have successfully completed page 204.

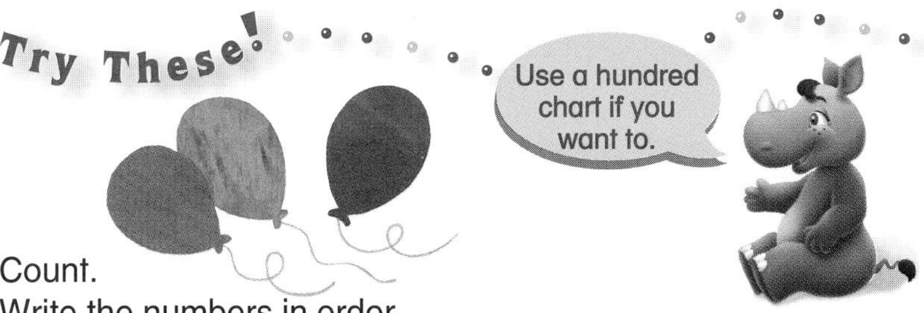

Count.
Write the numbers in order.

1. 11, 12, 13, 14, 15, 16, 17, 18, 19

2. 33, 34, 35, 36, 37, 38, 39, 40, 41

3. 51, 52, 53, 54, 55, 56, 57, 58, 59

4. 65, 66, 67, 68, 69, 70, 71, 72, 73

5. 79, 80, 81, 82, 83, 84, 85, 86, 87

6. 92, 93, 94, 95, 96, 97, 98, 99, 100

More to Explore Calculator

Press 2 3 + 1. Cover the number.
Press = three times.
What number do you think is hidden? 26
Check your answer by looking.
Do the same steps. Start with other numbers.

Ask your child to count on from numbers such as 11, 32, 69, and 90.

Page 204

Try These Assign practice exercises 1–6.

Allow children to use their completed chart on page 203, copies of TA 22, or a hundred chart displayed in the classroom to help them complete the exercises.

More to Explore Show children how to clear the display, enter the numbers, and press the equals (=) key. Children may check their work by counting on a hundred chart.

3 Close

Check for Understanding by having children complete a number sequence orally from 36 to 42. *[37, 38, 39, 40, 41, 42]* Then ask:

- **How did you know the order of the numbers?** *[Possible answer: Each number was one more.]*

Tomorrow children will identify numbers just before, just after, and between given numbers.

PRACTICE • 55

HOMEWORK

Name: Practice 55

ORDER TO 100

Write the numbers in order.

1. 9, 10, 11, 12, 13, 14, 15, 16
2. 21, 22, 23, 24, 25, 26, 27, 28
3. 39, 40, 41, 42, 43, 44, 45, 46
4. 57, 58, 59, 60, 61, 62, 63, 64
5. 70, 71, 72, 73, 74, 75, 76, 77
6. 83, 84, 85, 86, 87, 88, 89, 90
7. 92, 93, 94, 95, 96, 97, 98, 99

RETEACH • 55

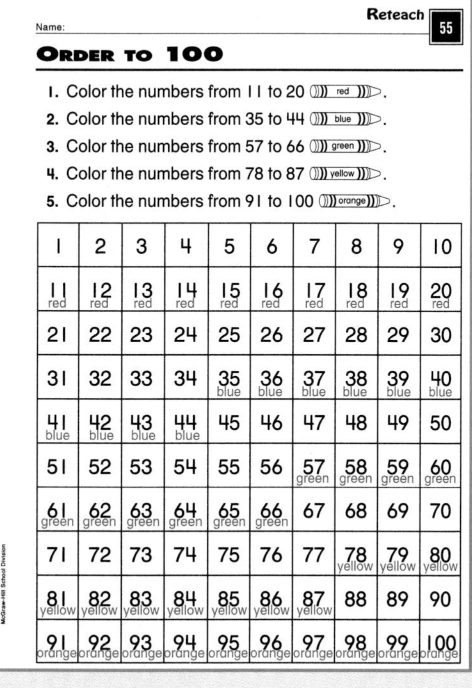
Name: Reteach 55

ORDER TO 100

1. Color the numbers from 11 to 20 red.
2. Color the numbers from 35 to 44 blue.
3. Color the numbers from 57 to 66 green.
4. Color the numbers from 78 to 87 yellow.
5. Color the numbers from 91 to 100 orange.

1	2	3	4	5	6	7	8	9	10
11 red	12 red	13 red	14 red	15 red	16 red	17 red	18 red	19 red	20 red
21	22	23	24	25	26	27	28	29	30
31	32	33	34	35 blue	36 blue	37 blue	38 blue	39 blue	40 blue
41 blue	42 blue	43 blue	44 blue	45	46	47	48	49	50
51	52	53	54	55	56	57 green	58 green	59 green	60 green
61 green	62 green	63 green	64 green	65 green	66 green	67	68	69	70
71	72	73	74	75	76	77	78 yellow	79 yellow	80 yellow
81 yellow	82 yellow	83 yellow	84 yellow	85 yellow	86 yellow	87 yellow	88	89	90
91 orange	92 orange	93 orange	94 orange	95 orange	96 orange	97 orange	98 orange	99 orange	100 orange

EXTEND • 55

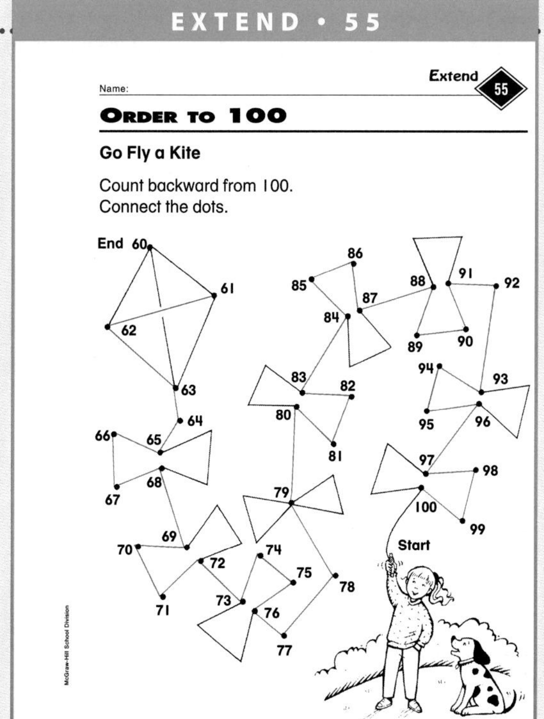
Name: Extend 55

ORDER TO 100

Go Fly a Kite

Count backward from 100.
Connect the dots.

Lesson 6.5

DAY 2

Before, After, Between

OBJECTIVE Children identify the number just before, just after, and between given numbers.

Materials per child: hundred chart (TA 22)

1 Motivate — Whole Class

Materials current calendar month displayed in the classroom

Look at the current calendar month. Have volunteers count the numbers for each week. Then ask:

- **Which number is just after 15?** *[16]*
- **Which number is just before 30?** *[29]*
- **Which number is between 23 and 25?** *[24]*

Continue the activity until all children have had an opportunity to respond. To add interest, ask questions such as these:

- **Whose birthday is this month? Which day is it? Which day is just before (or after) it?** *[Answers may vary.]*

2 Develop

Page 205

Discuss the example at the top of the page, emphasizing the words before, after, and between.

CRITICAL THINKING

After children discuss the example, ask:

- **How do you know what number comes just before 60?** *[Possible answer: I know that 9 is before 10, so 59 is before 60.]*

Page 206

Try These Assign the dot-to-dot puzzle.

Have children take turns counting aloud from 19 through 44.

Cultural Connection Talk about Roman numerals. Ask:

- **Why are the numbers 1, 2, and 3 easy to write and remember?** *[There is one mark for 1, two marks for 2, and three marks for 3.]*

3 Close

Check for Understanding by asking children questions such as these:

- **What number is just after 27?** *[28]*
- **What number is just before 46?** *[45]*
- **What number is between 69 and 71?** *[70]*

Name ______________________

Before, After, Between

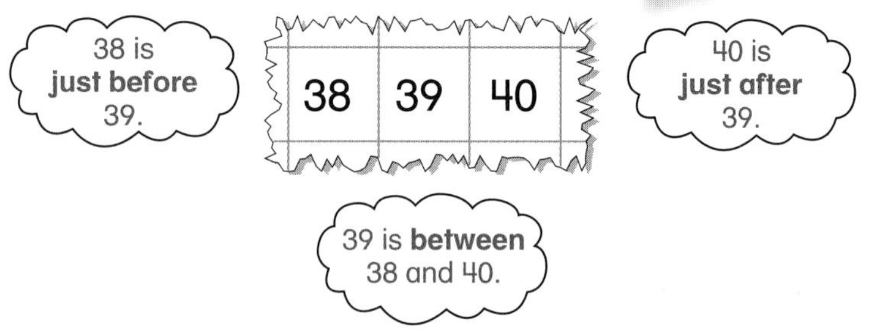

Write the number that comes just before.

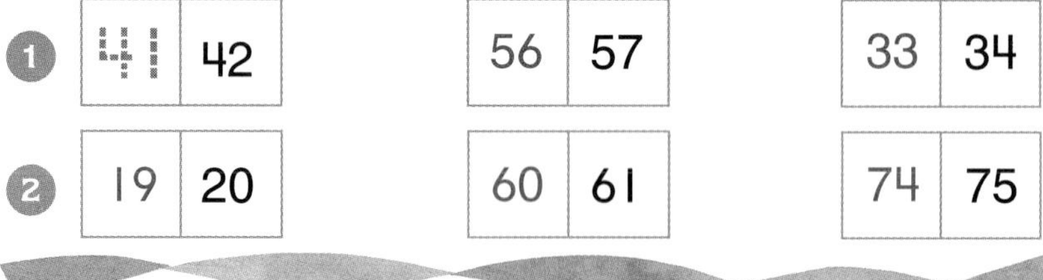

1	41 42	56 57	33 34
2	19 20	60 61	74 75

Write the number that comes just after.

3	89 90	14 15	97 98
4	50 51	29 30	22 23

Write the number that comes between.

5	71 72 73	48 49 50
6	98 99 100	69 70 71

MEETING INDIVIDUAL NEEDS

STUDENTS ACQUIRING ENGLISH

Use the words *before, after,* and *between* with three numbers. For example, write 35, 36, and 37 on the chalkboard. Point while you say, "35 is before 36, 37 is after 36, and 36 is between 35 and 37."

INCLUSION

Cut apart a hundred chart into 2- or 3-number strips, and use your finger to cover one of the numbers. Have the child say the number just before, after, or between.

ONGOING ASSESSMENT

Interview Determine if children understand the concepts of before, after, and between. Ask:

- **What number is just before 39?** *[38]* **just after 39?** *[40]*
- **What number is between 56 and 58?** *[57]*

Follow Up Do the Inclusion activity before assigning **Reteach 56.**

Assign **Extend 56** to those children who understand this lesson.

Try These!

Count.
Connect the dots.

What do you see? rhino

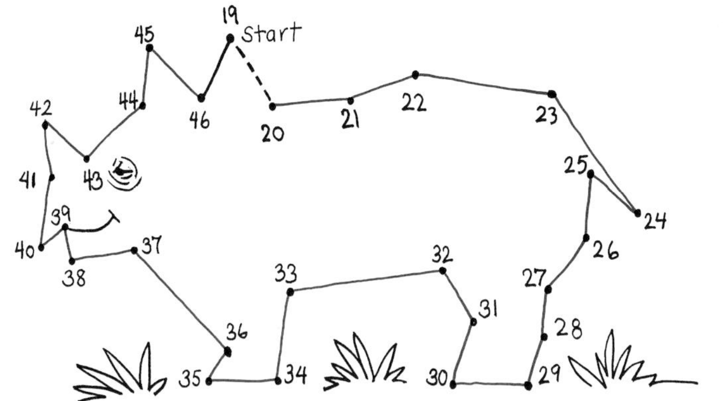

Cultural Connection

Roman Numerals

I	II	III	IV	V	VI	VII	VIII	IX	X
1	2	3	4	5	6	7	8	9	10

Write the Roman numeral that comes just after.

III IV   VI VII   II III

IX X   VIII IX   V VI

Pick a number from 10 to 99. Ask your child what number comes just before and just after the number you pick.

Alternate Teaching Strategy

Draw a number line from 24 to 35 on the chalkboard with some missing numbers. Call on volunteers to fill in the missing numbers. Then have the class read the numbers in order in unison.

Point to 27 on the number line and ask:

- **What number comes just after 27?** *[28]*
- **What number comes just before 27?** *[26]*

Point to 24 and 26 on the number line and ask:

- **What number is between 24 and 26?** *[25]*

Repeat the activity with other numbers and other number lines.

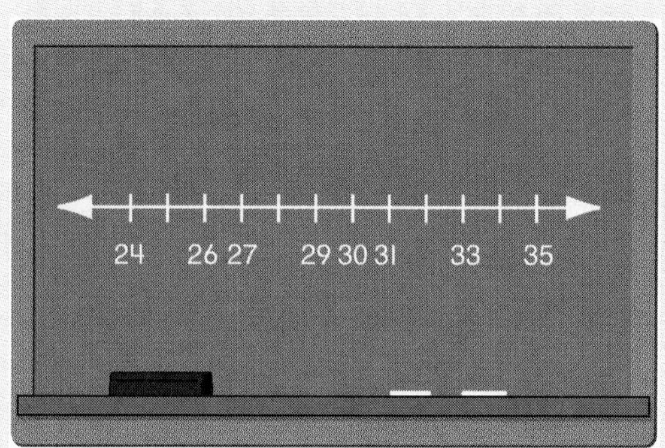

PRACTICE • 56

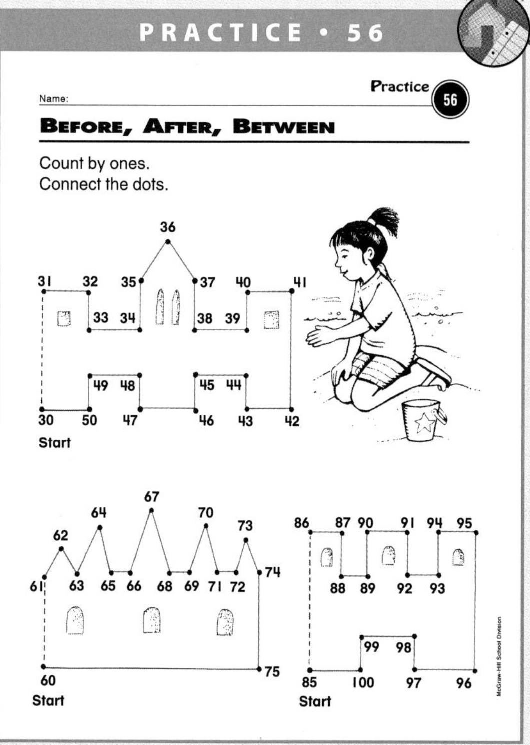

Name:

Practice 56

BEFORE, AFTER, BETWEEN

Count by ones.
Connect the dots.

Start

Start

Start

RETEACH • 56

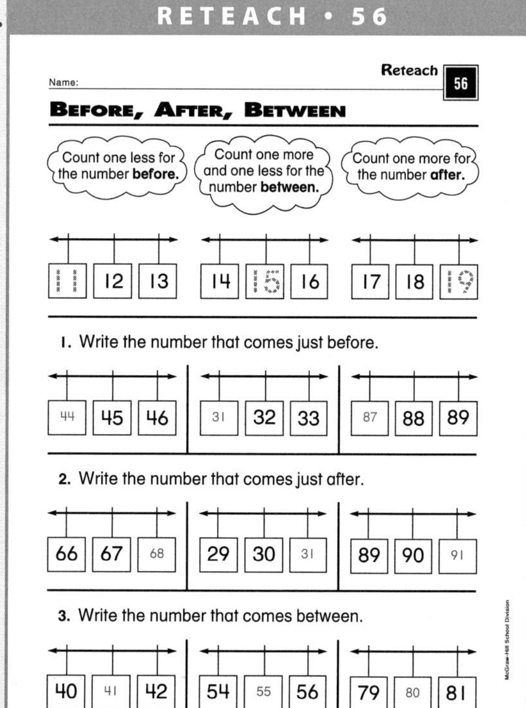

Name:

Reteach 56

BEFORE, AFTER, BETWEEN

Count one less for the number **before.**

Count one more and one less for the number **between.**

Count one more for the number **after.**

11 12 13 | 14 15 16 | 17 18 19

1. Write the number that comes just before.

44 45 46 | 31 32 33 | 87 88 89

2. Write the number that comes just after.

66 67 68 | 29 30 31 | 89 90 91

3. Write the number that comes between.

40 41 42 | 54 55 56 | 79 80 81

EXTEND • 56

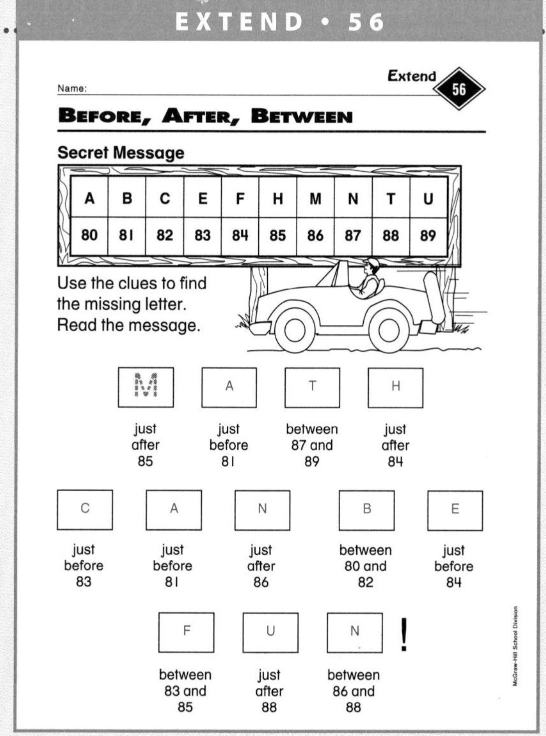

Name:

Extend 56

BEFORE, AFTER, BETWEEN

Secret Message

A	B	C	E	F	H	M	N	T	U
80	81	82	83	84	85	86	87	88	89

Use the clues to find the missing letter. Read the message.

M — just after 85; A — just before 81; T — between 87 and 89; H — just after 84

C — just before 83; A — just before 81; N — just after 86; B — between 80 and 82; E — just before 84

F — between 83 and 85; U — just after 88; N — between 86 and 88 !

Skip-Counting

OBJECTIVE Skip-count to 100 by twos, fives, and tens.

Day 1 Skip-Counting

Day 2 More Skip-Counting

RESOURCE REMINDER
Math Center Cards 42
Practice 57–58, Reteach 57–58, Extend 57–58

SKILLS TRACE	
GRADE K	• Introduced at Grade 1.
GRADE 1	• Skip count to 100 by twos, fives, and tens.
GRADE 2	• Skip count to 100 by twos, fives, and tens. *(Chapter 3)*

LESSON RESOURCES

MANIPULATIVE WARM-UP

Cooperative Pairs **Visual/Spatial**

OBJECTIVE Explore counting to 100 by fives and tens.

Materials per pair: hundred chart (TA 22), 100 counters, red and yellow crayon

▶ Have partners group counters by tens and count. Each time they find a ten, they should mark it on the hundred chart in yellow.

▶ Have children repeat the activity, grouping the counters by five. Each group of five is marked with a red crayon. Ask:

- **Why are the tens orange?** *[They have been colored yellow with the tens and red with the fives.]*

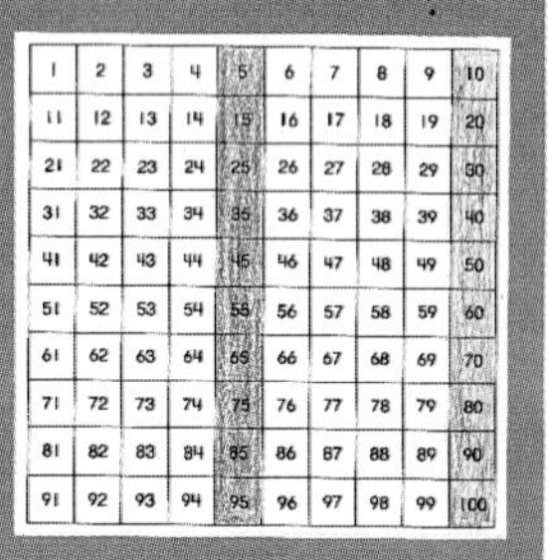

CONNECTION ACTIVITY

Cooperative Pairs **Logical/Analytical**

OBJECTIVE Connect counting to 100 by fives and tens with money.

Materials per pair: 100 play pennies; hundred chart (TA 22)

▶ Partners make stacks of 10 pennies each. Then each partner counts by tens and circles the numbers 10, 20, 30, …, 100 on his or her hundred chart.

▶ Next, partners make stacks of 5 pennies each, count each stack by fives, and cross through the numbers 5, 10, 15 up to 100 on the hundred chart. Ask:

- **If you had many pennies to count, which method would you use? Why?** *[Possible answer: I'd count by tens because it's easier and faster.]*

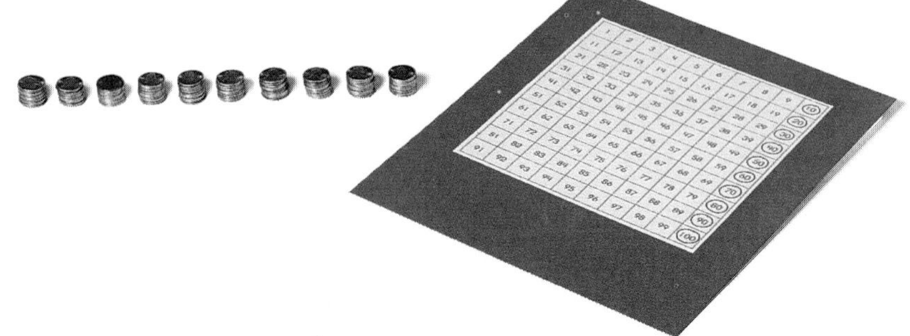

DAILY MATH

PREVIOUS DAY QUICK REVIEW

Write the missing number.

1. 49, __ *[50]*
2. ___, 62 *[61]*
3. 98, __, 100 *[99]*
4. 83, __, 85 *[84]*

FAST FACTS

1. 7 – 7 *[0]*
2. 6 – 0 *[6]*
3. 8 – 8 *[0]*
4. 1 – 0 *[1]*

Problem of the Day • 42

Read aloud to children:

Frank puts 10 stickers on each page of his sticker book.
He has filled 6 pages.
Count by tens to tell how many stickers he has. *[10, 20, 30, 40, 50, 60]*

TECH LINK

MATH VAN

Tools You may wish to use the Calculator with this lesson.

MATH FORUM

Idea I make a "3-dimensional hundred chart" out of 5 egg cartons that have been trimmed so there are only 10 cups. Children place small objects such as beans in each cup, and then count by tens.

Visit our Resource Village at http://www.mhschool.com to see more of the Math Forum.

MATH CENTER

Practice

OBJECTIVE Skip count to 100.

Materials per child: calculator, Math Center Recording Sheet (TA 38 optional)

Children will skip-count on the calculator and arrive at a target number. *[This is a self-checking activity.]*

PRACTICE ACTIVITY 42 — MATH CENTER, On Your Own

Calculator • What's the Last Number?

YOU NEED

- Press ON/C.
  Enter 2.
  Press +.
  Press = ten times.
  Write each number you see.
  What is the last number you see?
  What number are you skip-counting by?
- Press ON/C.
  Do it again with 5.

Grade Level 1 — McGraw-Hill School Division

Chapter 6, Lesson 6 — Number

NCTM Standards

- Problem Solving
- ✓ Communication
- Reasoning
- ✓ Connections

Problem Solving

OBJECTIVE Skip count to 100 by twos, fives, and tens.

Materials per child: crayons or markers, Math Center Recording Sheet (TA 38 optional)

Children choose a number to skip-count by to 100. They draw a picture to show it. Then they exchange pictures with their partner who writes the numbers.

PROBLEM-SOLVING ACTIVITY 42 — MATH CENTER, Partners

Decision Making • 100 Count

How do you like to skip-count to 100?

- Pick a number to skip-count by.
  Do you like to skip-count by twos?
  How about by fives? by tens?
- You and your partner each draw a picture.
- Trade pictures.
- Write the numbers.

Grade Level 1 — McGraw-Hill School Division

Chapter 6, Lesson 6 — Number

NCTM Standards

- ✓ Problem Solving
- ✓ Communication
- ✓ Reasoning
- ✓ Connections

Lesson 6.6

DAY 1

Skip-Count

OBJECTIVE Children skip-count by tens and fives.

Materials per pair: 100 connecting cubes in one color; have available: play pennies

1 Motivate — Cooperative Pairs

Materials per pair: 100 connecting cubes

Tell each pair to count their set of cubes. Ask:

- **How could you make the counting easier for this large amount of cubes?** *[Possible answers: Group by tens, group by fives.]*
- **Will you get the same number of cubes if you count by ones and then count by tens? Why?** *[Yes; the same number of cubes are counted.]*

After children count the cubes out loud by tens, have them unsnap each 10-cube train into two 5-cube trains. Then ask children to count the cubes out loud by fives.

Tell them they are *skip-counting* to find the number of cubes. Ask children about the word *skip* and discuss how this describes the way they are counting. *[Not counting every number, "skipping" over some numbers.]*

2 Develop

Page 207

Have children count by tens and fives using their cube trains or looking at the pictures at the top of the page. Discuss how 10-frames in exercise 1 and the 5-frames in exercise 3 help to count objects.

CRITICAL THINKING

After children complete the exercises on the page, ask:

- **How can you tell when someone is counting by tens instead of fives?** *[Possible answer: There is no "five" in the number name.]*

Name ______________ **Skip-Count**

10 20 30 40 50 60 70 80 90 100

5 10 15 20 25 30 35 40 45 50

How many? Skip-count by tens.

1. 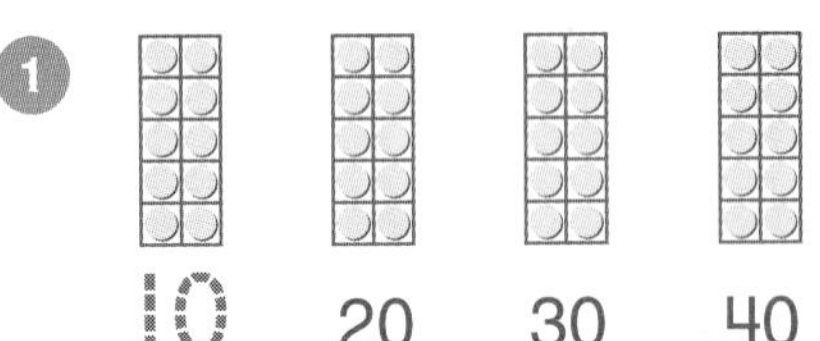

10 20 30 40 — 40 in all

2. 

60 in all

How many? Skip-count by fives.

3. 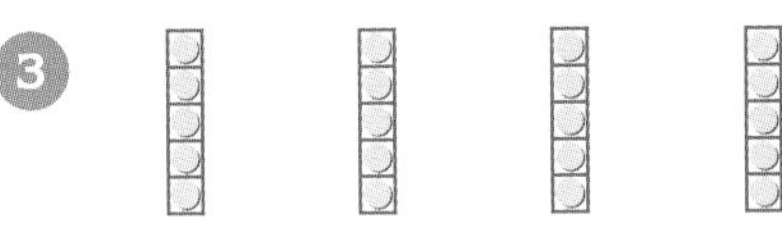

5 10 15 20 — 20 in all

4.   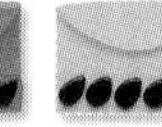   

30 in all

MEETING INDIVIDUAL NEEDS

COMMON ERROR

Some children may say "5, 15, 25, 35, ..." when they count by fives. Using 5-cube trains rather than the hundred chart can help them verify that counting a ten also includes counting a five.

INCLUSION

Determine whether children who seem to make careless color mistakes are able to see the full spectrum. Some individuals have difficulty seeing red and green and colors that derive from them.

ONGOING ASSESSMENT

Observation Checklist Determine if children understand counting by tens and fives. Observe their work in exercises 1 and 2 on page 208.

Follow Up Allow children to use cube trains when you assign **Reteach 57.**

Assign **Extend 57** to children who can count by fives and tens proficiently.

Try These!

How much money? Skip-count by tens.

1

10 20 30 40 50 60 — 60 ¢

How much money? Skip-count by fives.

2

5 10 15 20 25 — 25 ¢

Skip-count by tens. Color the boxes yellow.
Skip-count by fives. Color the boxes red.

3

1	2	3	4	5 r	6	7	8	9	y 10 r
11	12	13	14	15 r	16	17	18	19	y 20 r
21	22	23	24	25 r	26	27	28	29	y 30 r
31	32	33	34	35 r	36	37	38	39	y 40 r
41	42	43	44	45 r	46	47	48	49	y 50 r

Children should have colored the fives column once (red) and colored the tens column twice (red and yellow), and some children may have produced orange boxes in the tens column.

Talk: Tell a partner about what happened when you colored the chart.

At Home: Help your child practice skip-counting by fives.

Page 208

Try These Assign practice exercises 1–3.

Have play pennies available for those children having difficulty seeing the stacks of 10 pennies on the page. For exercise 3, suggest they color lightly with the red crayon so they can see both the colors in the tens column.

Talk about the pattern shown on the chart in exercise 3. Ask why the last column was colored red and yellow.

3 Close

Check for Understanding by having children use a soft/loud oral counting technique to count by fives from 1 to 100.

Tomorrow children will skip-count by twos.

PRACTICE • 57

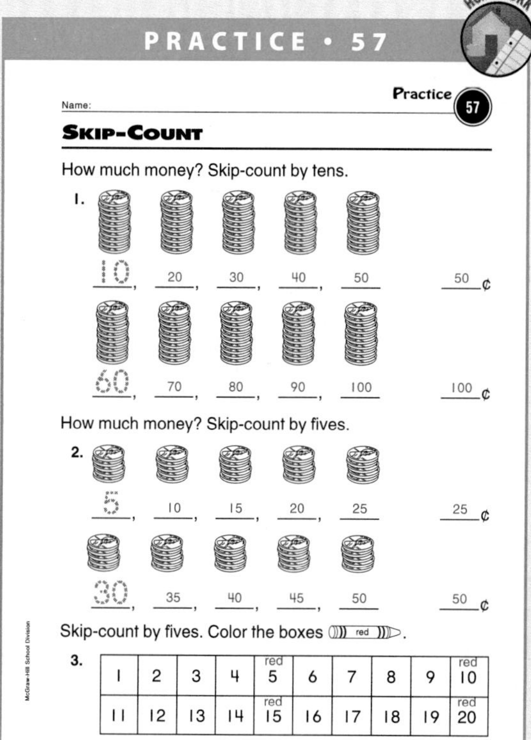

Practice 57

Name:

Skip-Count

How much money? Skip-count by tens.

1. 10, 20, 30, 40, 50 — 50 ¢
60, 70, 80, 90, 100 — 100 ¢

How much money? Skip-count by fives.

2. 5, 10, 15, 20, 25 — 25 ¢
30, 35, 40, 45, 50 — 50 ¢

Skip-count by fives. Color the boxes red.

3.

1	2	3	4	red 5	6	7	8	9	red 10
11	12	13	14	red 15	16	17	18	19	red 20

RETEACH • 57

Reteach 57

Name:

Skip-Count

1	2	3	4	5	6	7	8	9	10
11	12	13	14	15	16	17	18	19	20
21	22	23	24	25	26	27	28	29	30
31	32	33	34	35	36	37	38	39	40
41	42	43	44	45	46	47	48	49	50

Skip-count by tens.

1. 10, 20, 30
2. 40, 50, 60

Skip-count by fives.

3. 5, 10, 15
4. 20, 25, 30

EXTEND • 57

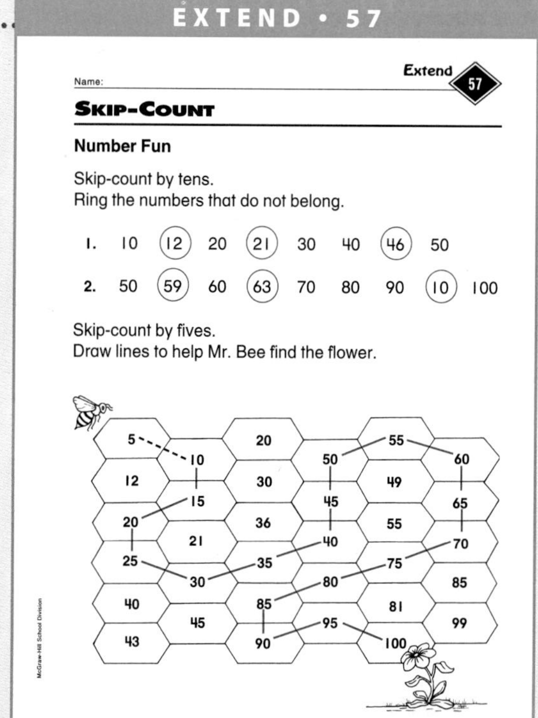

Extend 57

Name:

Skip-Count

Number Fun

Skip-count by tens.
Ring the numbers that do not belong.

1. 10 (12) 20 (21) 30 40 (46) 50
2. 50 (59) 60 (63) 70 80 90 (10) 100

Skip-count by fives.
Draw lines to help Mr. Bee find the flower.

Lesson 6.6

More Skip-Counting

OBJECTIVE Children skip-count by twos.

Materials have available: 20 two-color counters or 20 play pennies

1 Motivate — Whole Class

Have children pair up and march around the classroom in twos. Stop and then have them count off "1, 2" for the first pair, "3, 4" for the next pair, and so on. Then have the second child of each pair say the numbers for others to hear: "2, 4, 6,", and so on.

2 Develop

Page 209

Ask children to think of things that come in pairs, or twos—eyes, ears, hands, pant legs. Then have them complete and discuss the exercises on the page.

CRITICAL THINKING

Before children answer the question on the page, ask:

- **What comes in groups of 3?** *[Possible answers: wheels on a tricycle; triplets]*

Page 210

Try These Assign practice exercises 1–3.

Have play pennies available for exercises 1 and 2.

More to Explore Discuss with children what it means to press the equals key in this exercise. *[It's like adding 2 each time.]*

3 Close

Check for Understanding by counting 12 pennies by twos.

- **Count the pennies by twos. How many pennies are there?** *[2, 4, 6, 8, 10, 12; 12]*

Name ____________

More Skip-Counting

How many children?

2 4 6 8 10 10 in all

Skip-count by twos.

1. How many shoes?

   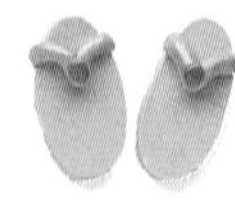

2 4 6 8 8 in all

2. How many mittens?

2 4 6 8 10 12 12 in all

3. How many boots?

2 4 6 8 10 10 in all

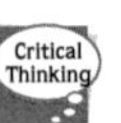

How could you count sets of triplets? Count sets of triplets by threes.

MEETING INDIVIDUAL NEEDS

EARLY FINISHERS

Have children draw pictures in their journals of things that come in twos, threes, or fours.

EXTRA SUPPORT

The poem "One, Two, Buckle My Shoe" may help some children count by twos to 10. Have children color by twos on a hundred chart (TA 22) as they recite the rhyme.

ONGOING ASSESSMENT

Interview Determine if children can count by twos. Show 14 counters and say:

- **Count by twos.** *[2, 4, 6, 8, 10, 12, 14]*

Follow Up Assign **Reteach 58** and give additional guidance as needed using cubes or a hundred chart.

For children who can skip-count by tens, fives, and twos, assign **Extend 58.**

Try These!

Skip-count by twos. How much money?

1   

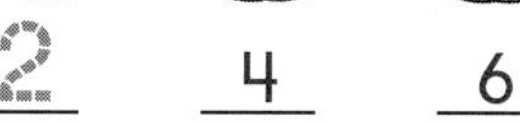

2 4 6 6 ¢

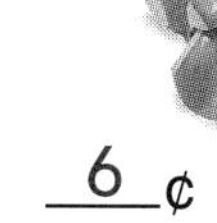

2     

2 4 6 8 10 10 ¢

Skip-count by twos. Color the boxes  blue.

3

1	2	3	4	5	6 b	7	8 b	9	10 b
11	12 b	13	14 b	15	16 b	17	18 b	19	20 b
21	22 b	23	24 b	25	26 b	27	28 b	29	30 b
31	32 b	33	34 b	35	36 b	37	38 b	39	40 b
41	42 b	43	44 b	45	46 b	47	48 b	49	50 b

More to Explore Calculator

Press ON/C 0 + 2.
Press = 8 times.
Write each number you see.

2 4 6 8 10 12 14 16

At Home Help your child practice skip-counting by twos.

Alternate Teaching Strategy

Materials per pair: 40 play pennies, hundred chart (TA 22)

Have children work together in pairs, one stacking and counting and one recording. One partner makes four rows of 10 pennies on a sheet of paper. The other partner writes the number of pennies (1–10, 11–20, 21–30, and 31–40) below the appropriate row, counting by ones.

Then children stack the pennies on top of the tenth penny in each row. Finally, they count the pennies by tens.

Repeat the activity for counting by fives and then by twos. Let children switch roles when they switch from tens to fives and from fives to twos.

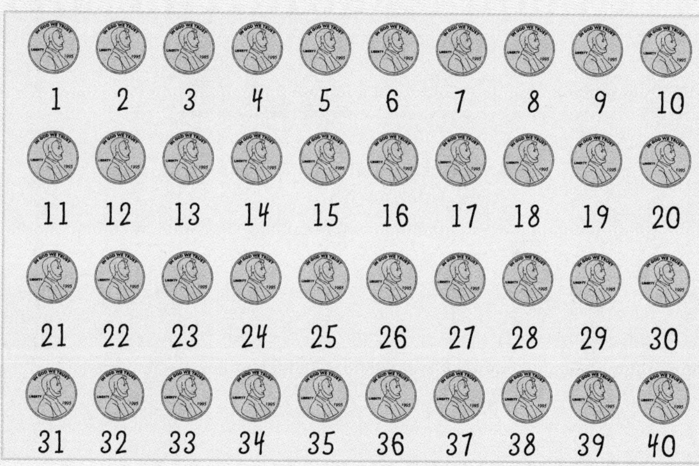

HOMEWORK

PRACTICE • 58

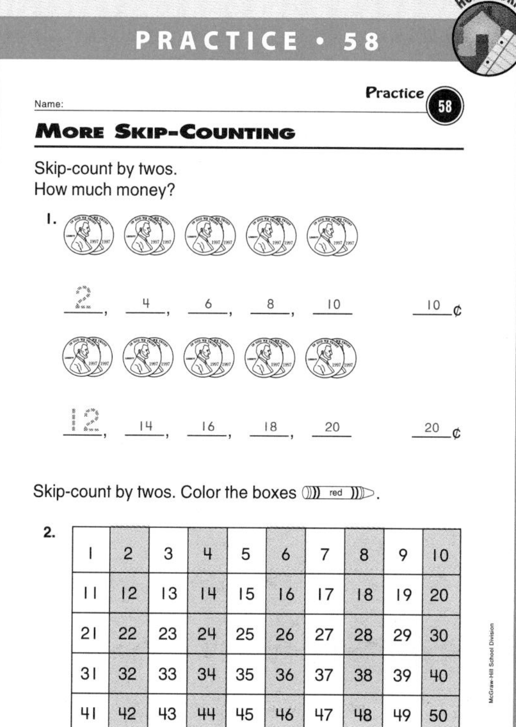

Name: Practice 58

More Skip-Counting

Skip-count by twos.
How much money?

1. 2, 4, 6, 8, 10 10 ¢

12, 14, 16, 18, 20 20 ¢

Skip-count by twos. Color the boxes red.

2.

1	2	3	4	5	6	7	8	9	10
11	12	13	14	15	16	17	18	19	20
21	22	23	24	25	26	27	28	29	30
31	32	33	34	35	36	37	38	39	40
41	42	43	44	45	46	47	48	49	50

RETEACH • 58

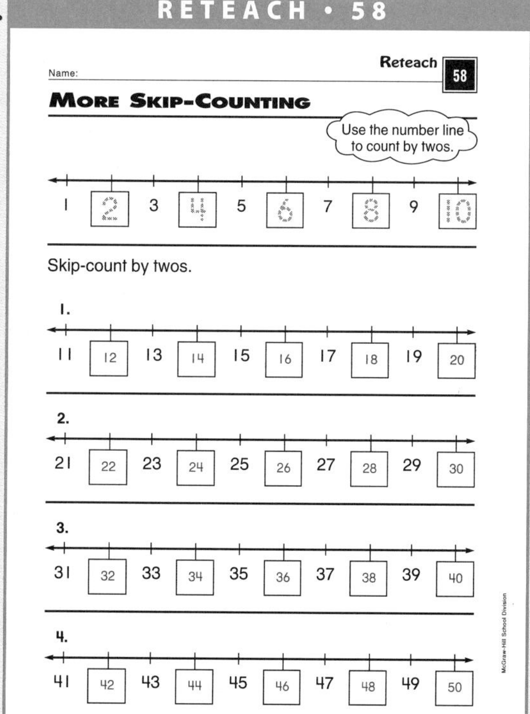

Name: Reteach 58

More Skip-Counting

Use the number line to count by twos.

1 2 3 4 5 6 7 8 9 10

Skip-count by twos.

1. 11 12 13 14 15 16 17 18 19 20

2. 21 22 23 24 25 26 27 28 29 30

3. 31 32 33 34 35 36 37 38 39 40

4. 41 42 43 44 45 46 47 48 49 50

EXTEND • 58

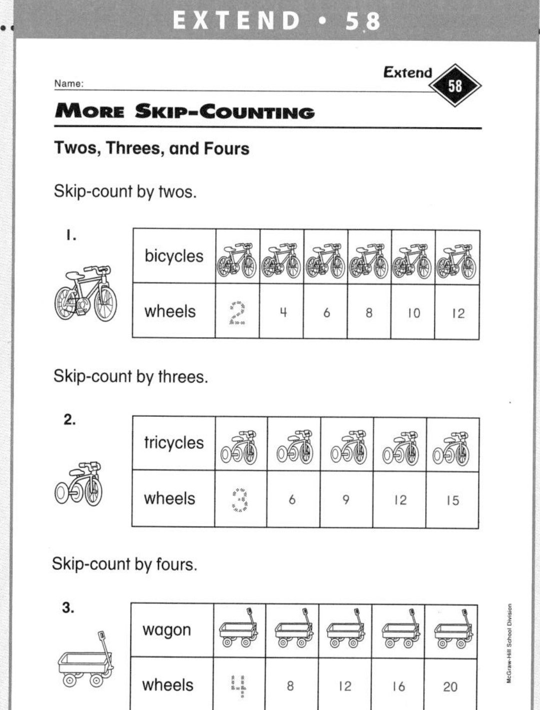

Name: Extend 58

More Skip-Counting

Twos, Threes, and Fours

Skip-count by twos.

1.

bicycles						
wheels	2	4	6	8	10	12

Skip-count by threes.

2.

tricycles					
wheels	3	6	9	12	15

Skip-count by fours.

3.

wagon					
wheels	4	8	12	16	20

LESSON 6.7

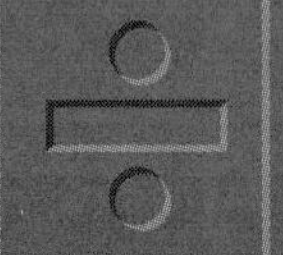

LESSON RESOURCES

Greater and Less

OBJECTIVE Explore comparing numbers to 100.

Day 1 Explore Activity: Greater and Less

RESOURCE REMINDER
Math Center Cards 43
Practice 59, Reteach 59, Extend 59

SKILLS TRACE

GRADE K	• Explore comparing numbers to 12. *(Chapter 8)*
GRADE 1	• Explore comparing numbers to 100.
GRADE 2	• Compare numbers to 100. *(Chapter 3)*

WARM-UP

Whole Class **Kinesthetic**

OBJECTIVE Explore comparing numbers to 100.

Materials 20 paint jars of various colors

▶ Place 7 paint jars on the right side of a table. Then place 5 others on the left side of the table. Ask the rest of the class to count the jars and then to discuss which group has more and which group has fewer jars. Ask how they know. *[Possible answers: Count each group and compare the numbers, match one-to-one.]*

▶ Repeat with larger numbers of jars. Also try this activity counting fingers on groups of childrens' hands.

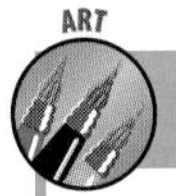

ART

CONNECTION ACTIVITY

Whole Class **Visual/Spatial**

OBJECTIVE Connect comparing numbers to 100 with art.

Resources Literature Big Book: *One Hundred Is a Family*

Materials per child: construction paper, crayons

▶ Read *One Hundred Is a Family.* Turn to the page with "Twenty" and talk about the people climbing on the rocks and those walking in the valley. Ask:

- **Which group is larger?** *[the one climbing on the rocks]*

▶ Have children choose a number to illustrate. When all drawings are finished, publish them in a class book.

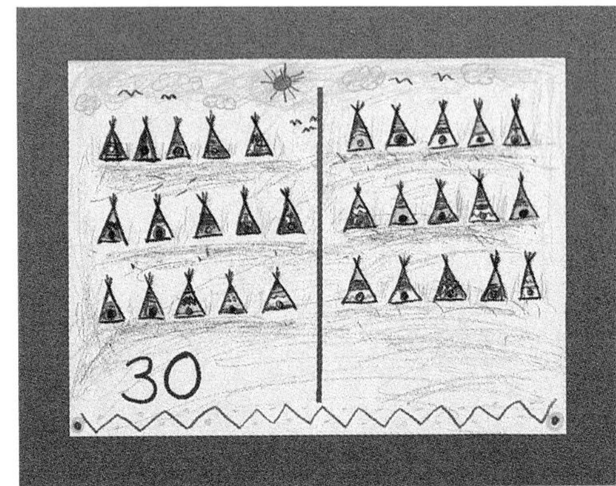

DAILY MATH

PREVIOUS DAY QUICK REVIEW

Skip-count by twos.

1. 26, __, __ *[28, 30]*
2. 10, 12, __ *[14]*
3. 88, __, 92 *[90]*
4. __, 54, __ *[52, 56]*

FAST FACTS

1. 10 – 8 *[2]*
2. 10 – 7 *[3]*
3. 10 – 6 *[4]*
4. 10 – 5 *[5]*

Problem of the Day • 43

Read aloud to children:

Chen has 43 toy cars in his collection. Ming has 37 toy cars in his collection. Who has the greater number of cars? *[Chen—43 > 37]*

TECH LINK

MATH VAN

Tools You may wish to use the Counter tool with this lesson.

MATH FORUM

Idea I have children compare groups of children from different classes. I also have them compare amounts of money using pennies.

Visit our Resource Village at http://www.mhschool.com to see more of the Math Forum.

MATH CENTER

Practice

OBJECTIVE Compare numbers to 100.

Materials per child: number cards, Math Center Recording Sheet (TA 38 optional)

Prepare Make 20 number cards. Use any numbers from 1 to 100 per card without duplicating.

Children will pick two numbers at a time. They compare and record the numbers under headings of LESS and GREATER. *[Answers will vary.]*

PRACTICE ACTIVITY 43 — MATH CENTER, On Your Own

Decision Making • More or Less

YOU NEED: number cards

- Fold a paper.
  Write LESS on one side.
  Write GREATER on the other side.
- Pick two cards.
  Which number is less?
  Write it under LESS.
  Which number is greater?
  Write it under GREATER.
- Play five more times.

LESS	GREATER
14	69

FOLD

Grade Level 1 — McGraw-Hill School Division

Chapter 6, Lesson 7 — Number

NCTM Standards
- ✓ Problem Solving
- Communication
- ✓ Reasoning
- Connections

Problem Solving

OBJECTIVE Compare numbers to 100.

Materials per child: 2 number cubes, Math Center Recording Sheet (TA 38 optional)

Partners will create and compare two 2-digit numbers. They use concepts of place value, greater than, and less than.

PROBLEM-SOLVING ACTIVITY 43 — MATH CENTER, Partners

Game • Roll Them Out

YOU NEED:

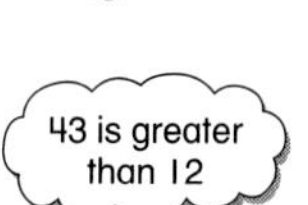

You and your partner do all the steps together.

- Roll two cubes.
  Look at the cubes and write the number.
  Look at your number and your partner's number.
  Which number is greater?
  Which is less?
  Tell your partner:
  "____ is greater than ____."
- Check each other's numbers.

Grade Level 1 — McGraw-Hill School Division

Chapter 6, Lesson 7 — Number

NCTM Standards
- ✓ Problem Solving
- ✓ Communication
- ✓ Reasoning
- Connections

Lesson 6.7

DAY 1

EXPLORE ACTIVITY
Greater and Less

OBJECTIVE Children compare numbers to 100.

Materials per pair: 50 red and 50 blue connecting cubes

1 Motivate — Cooperative Pairs

Materials per pair: 50 red and 50 blue connecting cubes

Draw the following illustrated diagram on the board:

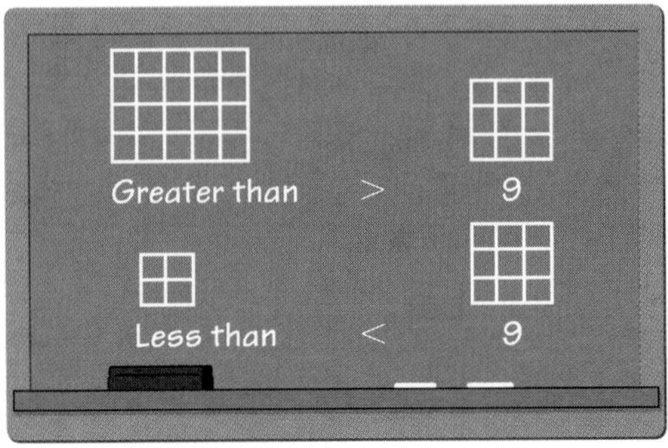

Then place some red cubes and some blue cubes on the table for each pair to count. Have them compare the sets of red and blue cubes. Ask:

- **Which number of cubes is greater than the other?**
- **Which number of cubes is less than the other?**

2 Develop

Page 211

Pairs of children work together to share materials. Each pair does five exercises and each child records on his or her own page. Pairs share their results with the group.

CRITICAL THINKING

After children answer the question on the page, ask:

- **If the number of cubes is the same, who has the greater number of cubes?** *[No one—each has the same number of cubes.]*

Page 212

Try These Assign practice exercises 1–6.

3 Close

Check for Understanding by asking questions about two numbers. Ask:

- **Which number is greater, 43 or 36?** *[43]*
- **How do you know?** *[Possible answers: Count cubes to compare, think of numbers before and after 43 and 36 on a hundred chart.]*

Name ______________________

Working Together

Your group needs 50 and 50 .

Take turns.

- Pick up a handful of .
- Pick up a handful of .
- Complete the chart.

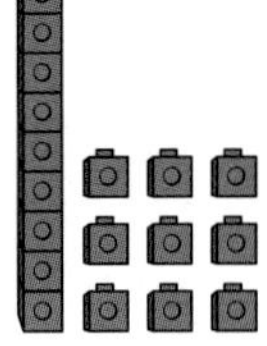

24 **is greater than** 19.

Estimates and numbers may vary. Sample answer is given.

	Estimate which is more. Ring.	Count how many.	Write the greater number.
1	(ringed red cube) / blue cube	32 red, 28 blue	32
2	red / blue	___ red, ___ blue	___
3	red / blue	___ red, ___ blue	___
4	red / blue	___ red, ___ blue	___
5	red / blue	___ red, ___ blue	___

How can you find the number that is less? *When you compare two numbers, the number that isn't greater is less.*

MEETING INDIVIDUAL NEEDS

EARLY FINISHERS

Have several packs of 10 two-digit number cards available for children to pair up and play the "Which Is Greater?" game. Each child turns over one card. The child with the greater number takes both cards.

EXTRA SUPPORT

Provide additional help to children having difficulty understanding the new vocabulary words. Associate the word *greater* with the words *bigger* and *larger;* the word *less* with *smaller* or *fewer.*

ONGOING ASSESSMENT

Observation Checklist Determine if children can compare numbers to 100 by observing their work as they complete page 212.

Follow Up For those children needing more developmental work, assign **Reteach 59.**

Assign **Extend 59** to those children who understand how to compare numbers without using any manipulatives.

Try These!

Use cubes if you want to.

Ring the number that is less.

1 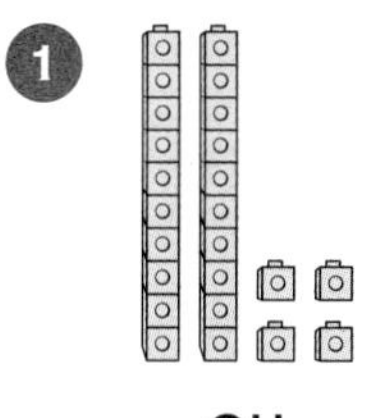 24 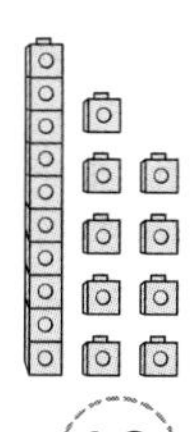 (19)

19 is less than 24.

2	16	(12)	(17)	20	31	(29)
3	27	(24)	(15)	19	(34)	43

Ring the number that is greater.

4 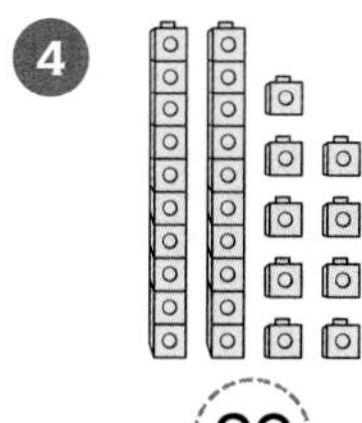 (29) 25

29 is greater than 25.

5	32	(35)	20	(24)	(28)	18
6	17	(22)	(35)	23	29	(31)

Ask your child to tell you if 25 is *less than* or *greater than* 52.

Alternate Teaching Strategy

Materials per pair: 100 pennies, hundred chart (TA 22), bowl

Have pairs of children take a handful of pennies from a bowl. Ask children to guess who might have more. Then have each child count the pennies. Ask who has more.

If partners have trouble deciding, give each child a hundred chart. Have them cover the hundred chart with pennies, and compare rows of tens and the ones to see who has more.

PRACTICE • 59

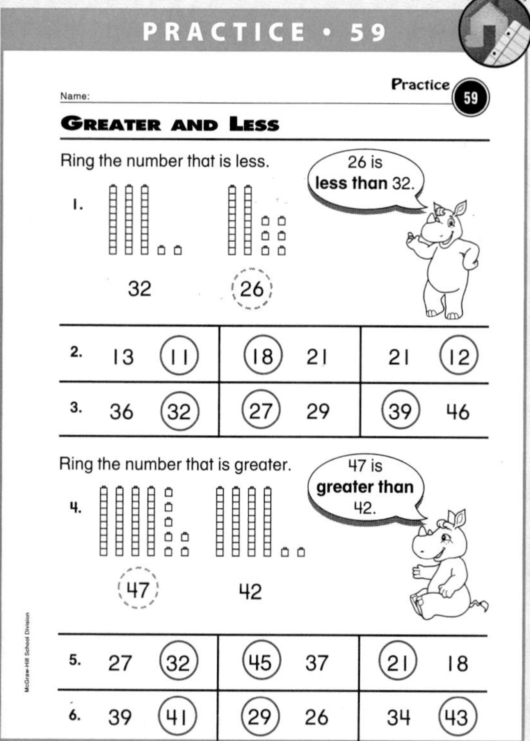

Name: Practice 59

GREATER AND LESS

Ring the number that is less.

26 is less than 32.

1. 32 (26)

2.	13	(11)	(18)	21	21	(12)
3.	36	(32)	(27)	29	(39)	46

Ring the number that is greater.

47 is greater than 42.

4. (47) 42

5.	27	(32)	(45)	37	(21)	18
6.	39	(41)	(29)	26	34	(43)

RETEACH • 59

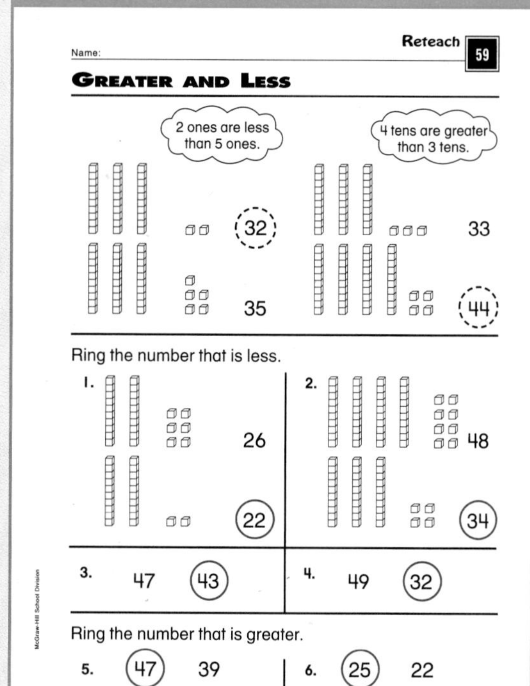

Name: Reteach 59

GREATER AND LESS

2 ones are less than 5 ones.

4 tens are greater than 3 tens.

(32) 35 33 (44)

Ring the number that is less.

1. 26 (22)

2. 48 (34)

3. 47 (43)

4. 49 (32)

Ring the number that is greater.

5. (47) 39

6. (25) 22

EXTEND • 59

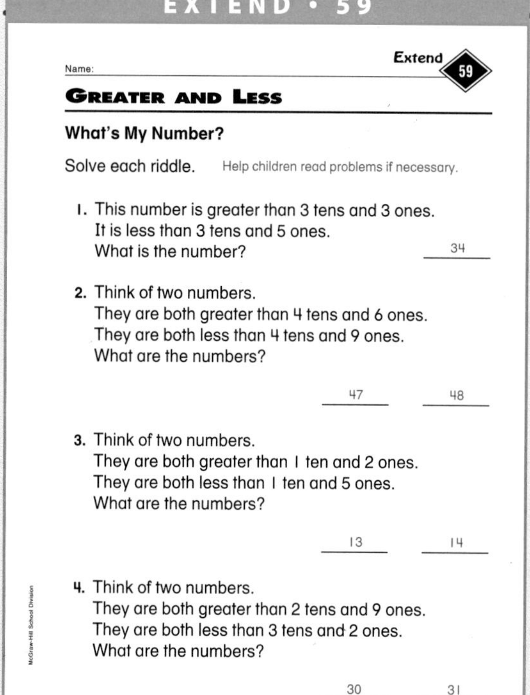

Name: Extend 59

GREATER AND LESS

What's My Number?

Solve each riddle. Help children read problems if necessary.

1. This number is greater than 3 tens and 3 ones. It is less than 3 tens and 5 ones. What is the number? 34

2. Think of two numbers. They are both greater than 4 tens and 6 ones. They are both less than 4 tens and 9 ones. What are the numbers? 47 48

3. Think of two numbers. They are both greater than 1 ten and 2 ones. They are both less than 1 ten and 5 ones. What are the numbers? 13 14

4. Think of two numbers. They are both greater than 2 tens and 9 ones. They are both less than 3 tens and 2 ones. What are the numbers? 30 31

LESSON 6.8

Ordinal Numbers

OBJECTIVE Identify ordinal position.

Day 1 Ordinal Numbers

RESOURCE REMINDER
Math Center Cards 44
Practice 60, Reteach 60, Extend 60

SKILLS TRACE	
GRADE K	• Explore ordinal numbers from first to fifth. *(Chapter 8)*
GRADE 1	• Identify ordinal position.
GRADE 2	• Use ordinal numbers to thirty-first. *(Chapter 5)*

MANIPULATIVE WARM-UP

Whole Class — **Visual/Spatial**

OBJECTIVE Explore identifying ordinal positions first through tenth.

Materials 10 toys, such as dolls, stuffed animals, puppets, cars

▶ Place toys such as a rhino, a doll, a hand puppet, and a dinosaur in a line all facing the same direction. Point out that the dinosaur is first, the hand puppet is second, and so on.

▶ Then ask questions about relative positions.
- **Is the dinosaur first or second?** *[first]*
- **Which toy is fourth?** *[doll]*
- **In which position is the hand puppet?** *[second]*

▶ Repeat the activity using other toys showing positions first through tenth.

CONNECTION ACTIVITY

Whole Class — **Logical/Analytical**

OBJECTIVE Connect ordinal numbers first through tenth with language arts.

Materials 55 sheets of 8 $^1/_2$" x 11" paper, marker, thumb tacks

Prepare Print each letter of the words "first," "second" through "tenth" on separate sheets of paper.

▶ Play the "Ordinal Word" game. Divide the class into two teams. Tack the letters of an ordinal number word facedown on the bulletin board.

▶ Give directions: Say, "I have a mystery ordinal number word on the board. You have to ask questions this way: Is the first letter *s*? Is the fourth letter *t*? If your guess is correct, I turn over the sheet of paper to show the letter. The first team to guess the word is the winner."

DAILY MATH

PREVIOUS DAY QUICK REVIEW

Which is greater?

1. 18, 5 *[18]*
2. 2, 1 *[2]*
3. 99, 66 *[99]*
4. 47, 56 *[56]*

FAST FACTS

1. 9 – 0 *[9]*
2. 9 – 1 *[8]*
3. 9 – 2 *[7]*
4. 9 – 3 *[6]*

Problem of the Day • 44

Read aloud to children:

Four girls were in a race.
Brittany came in third.
Kayla did not finish first or last.
In which place did Kayla finish? *[second]*

TECH LINK

MATH FORUM

Management Tip When my class lines up to go to lunch or recess, I reinforce the use of ordinal numbers by having children arrange themselves in lines of 10 and count off their position in line.

Visit our Resource Village at http://www.mhschool.com to see more of the Math Forum.

MATH CENTER

Practice

OBJECTIVE Identify position using ordinal numbers.

Materials per pair: collection of 10 objects, 10 cards; per child: crayons or markers, Math Center Recording Sheet (TA 38 optional)

Prepare Put collections of 10 things such as a pencil, crayon, counter, and so on in a box. Label cards with ordinal numbers *first* to *tenth*. Children place ordinal number cards in order from left to right. Then they tell each other where to place objects above the ordinal cards.

Problem Solving

OBJECTIVE Identify ordinal position.

Materials per child: Math Center Recording Sheet (TA 38)

Children answer questions about ordinal position. Then children illustrate a problem and identify ordinal positions. *[6 cats; 3 cats. The second cat should be colored red; the ninth cat, yellow.]*

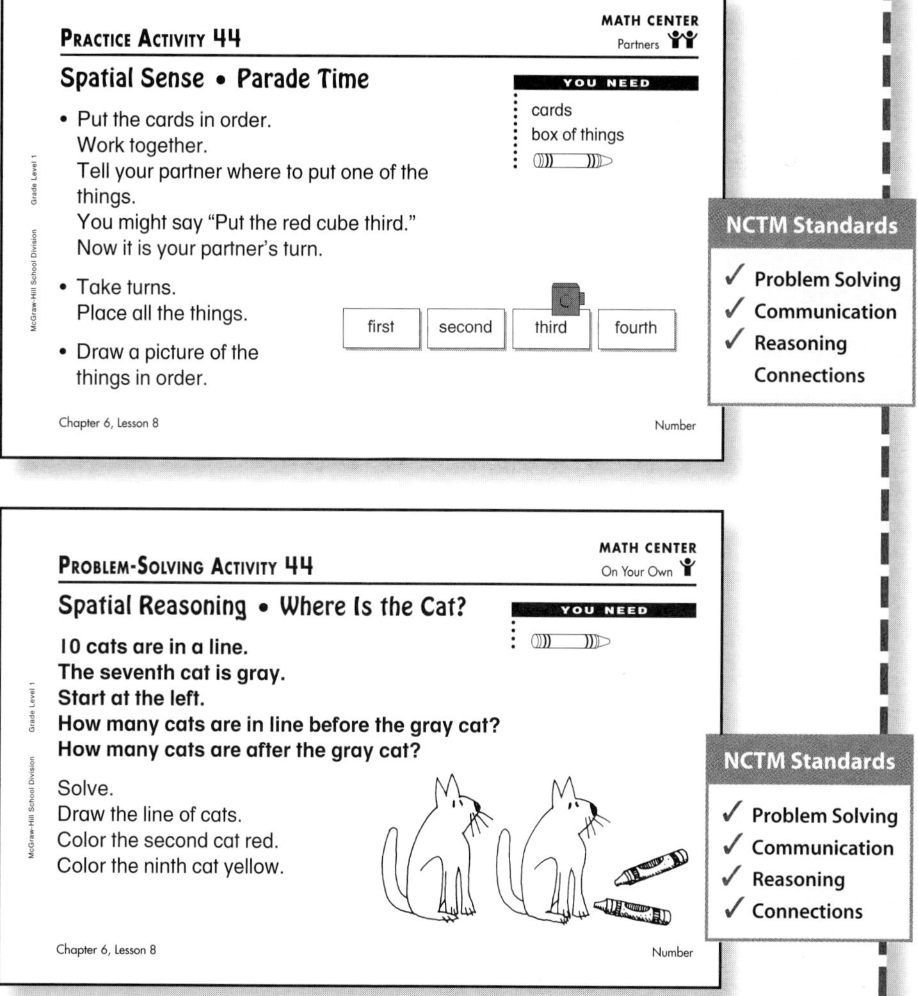

PRACTICE ACTIVITY 44

MATH CENTER
Partners

Spatial Sense • Parade Time

YOU NEED
cards
box of things

- Put the cards in order.
  Work together.
  Tell your partner where to put one of the things.
  You might say "Put the red cube third."
  Now it is your partner's turn.
- Take turns.
  Place all the things.
- Draw a picture of the things in order.

first second third fourth

Grade Level 1
McGraw-Hill School Division

Chapter 6, Lesson 8 — Number

NCTM Standards
- ✓ Problem Solving
- ✓ Communication
- ✓ Reasoning
- Connections

PROBLEM-SOLVING ACTIVITY 44

MATH CENTER
On Your Own

Spatial Reasoning • Where Is the Cat?

YOU NEED

10 cats are in a line.
The seventh cat is gray.
Start at the left.
How many cats are in line before the gray cat?
How many cats are after the gray cat?

Solve.
Draw the line of cats.
Color the second cat red.
Color the ninth cat yellow.

Grade Level 1
McGraw-Hill School Division

Chapter 6, Lesson 8 — Number

NCTM Standards
- ✓ Problem Solving
- ✓ Communication
- ✓ Reasoning
- ✓ Connections

Lesson 6.8

Ordinal Numbers

OBJECTIVE Children identify ordinal positions.

1 Motivate — Whole Class

Call out 5 children's names. Have them march around the classroom. Give each child an ordinal position:

- **Mato will be *first.***
- **Megan will be *second.***
- **Tiffany will be *third.***

Have children in the classroom identify who is *first, second,* and *third.*

Repeat the activity to include up to 10 children, until all children have had a turn and have used the ordinal words *first* through *tenth.*

2 Develop

Page 213

Discuss the picture at the top of the page. Help children count using ordinal numbers in exercises 1 and 2 before they complete them independently.

CRITICAL THINKING

After children answer the Critical Thinking question on the page, ask:

- **What happens to the positions when a line turns around and goes the other way?** *[The last place becomes first, the next to last becomes second, and the first place is last.]*

Page 214

Try These Assign practice exercises 1–3.

Mixed Review Children review addition and subtraction facts from Chapter 5.

3 Close

Check for Understanding by asking questions about the bears in exercise 3 on page 214.

- **Which position is the yellow bear in?** *[fifth]*
- **If this bear is fifth, which bear is sixth?** *[The one that comes after it.]*

Name

Ordinal Numbers

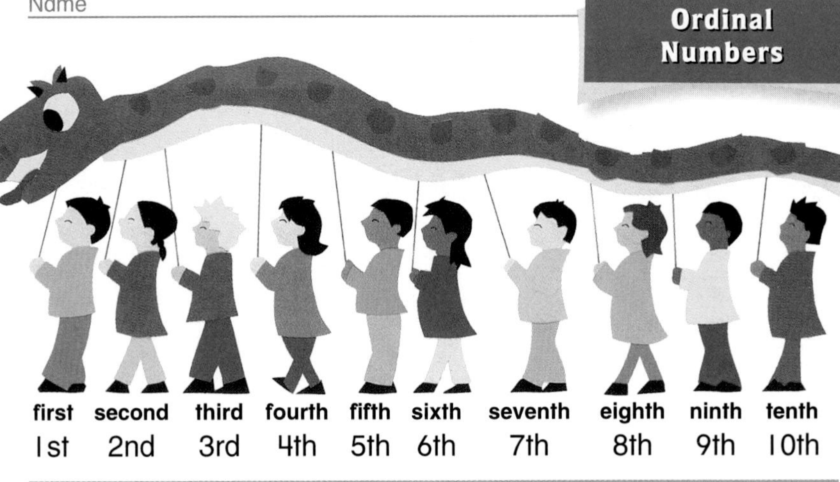

Match.

1

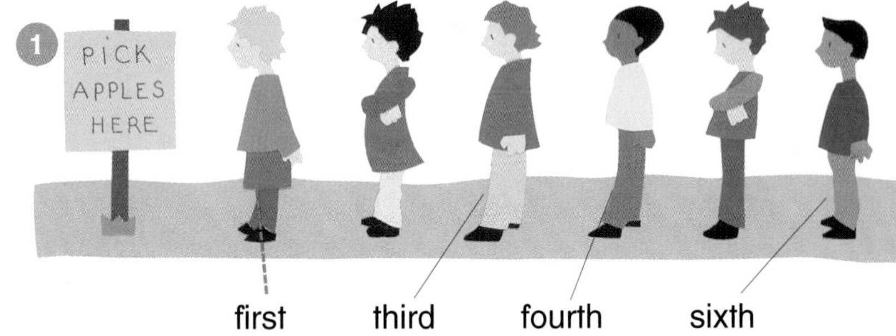

first third fourth sixth

2

second third fifth seventh

How do you know who is first in line? Possible answer: Everyone in line is in back of, or behind, the person who is first.

MEETING INDIVIDUAL NEEDS

EARLY FINISHERS

Children can pair up and play the "Ordinal Word" game found on page 212A.

EXTRA SUPPORT

Provide extra practice using ordinal words when children line up for an activity such as going to recess or to lunch. Have them name their positions in the line.

ONGOING ASSESSMENT

Observation Checklist Determine if children understand ordinal numbers by observing children as they complete the exercises on page 214.

Follow Up For those having trouble identifying positions, do more people line-ups before assigning **Reteach 60.**

For children who identify ordinal positions, assign **Extend 60.**

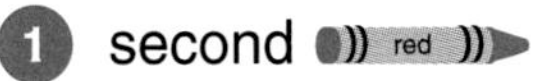

Start at the left. Color.

1 second (red) fourth (yellow) eighth (blue)

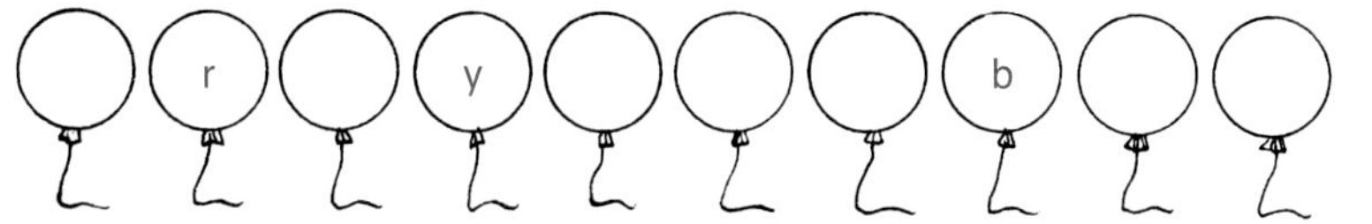

2 third (blue) sixth (red) ninth (yellow)

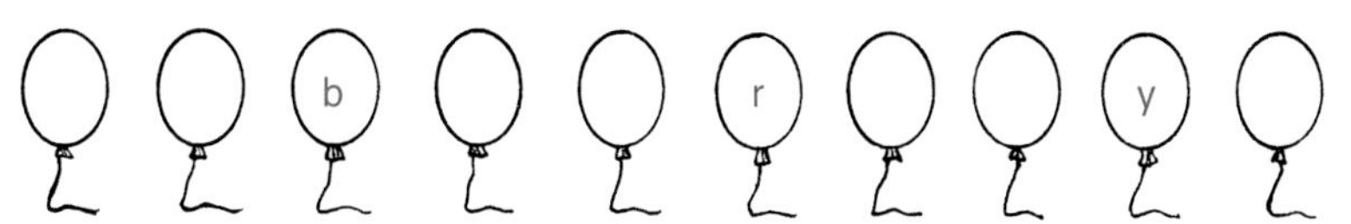

3 fifth (red) seventh (blue) tenth (red)

Mixed Review

Add or subtract.

4

7	4	5	1	4	9
+ 3	+ 2	+ 0	+ 8	+ 4	+ 1
10	6	5	9	8	10

5

10	8	6	7	9	5
− 2	− 4	− 6	− 4	− 1	− 0
8	4	0	3	8	5

Line up some objects. Ask your child which is *first*, *second*, and so on.

Alternate Teaching Strategy

Choose four children to line up facing you. Help them count off as *first, second, third,* and *fourth.*

Play a game of "Mother May I?" by giving directions such as, "Mother says, 'Will the third child take a giant step?' "

Continue the game, adding ordinal numbers through *tenth* until all children have had a turn.

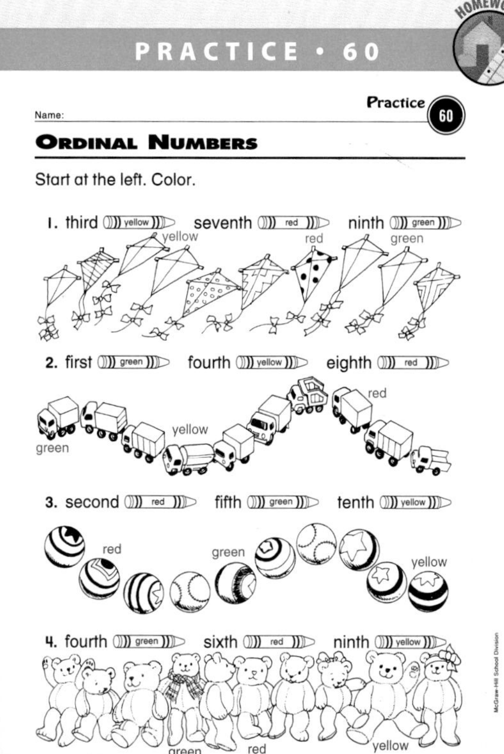

PRACTICE • 60

Homework

Name: Practice 60

Ordinal Numbers

Start at the left. Color.

1. third (yellow) seventh (red) ninth (green)

yellow red green

2. first (green) fourth (yellow) eighth (red)

green yellow red

3. second (red) fifth (green) tenth (yellow)

red green yellow

4. fourth (green) sixth (red) ninth (yellow)

green red yellow

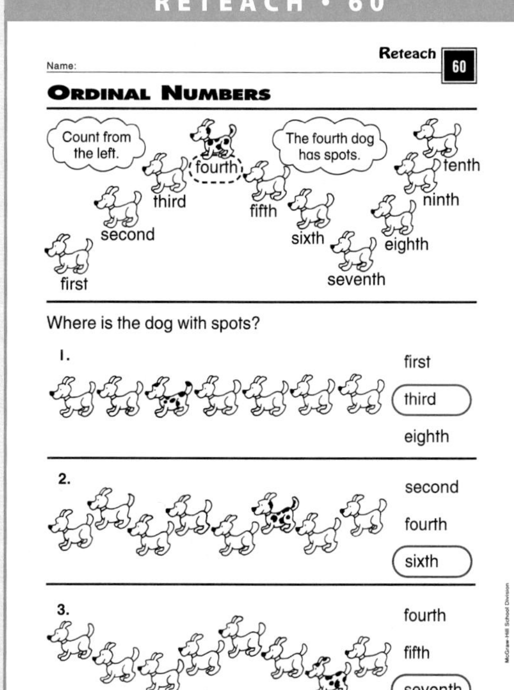

RETEACH • 60

Name: Reteach 60

Ordinal Numbers

Count from the left. The fourth dog has spots.

first second third fourth fifth sixth seventh eighth ninth tenth

Where is the dog with spots?

1. first / third / eighth (third circled)

2. second / fourth / sixth (sixth circled)

3. fourth / fifth / seventh (seventh circled)

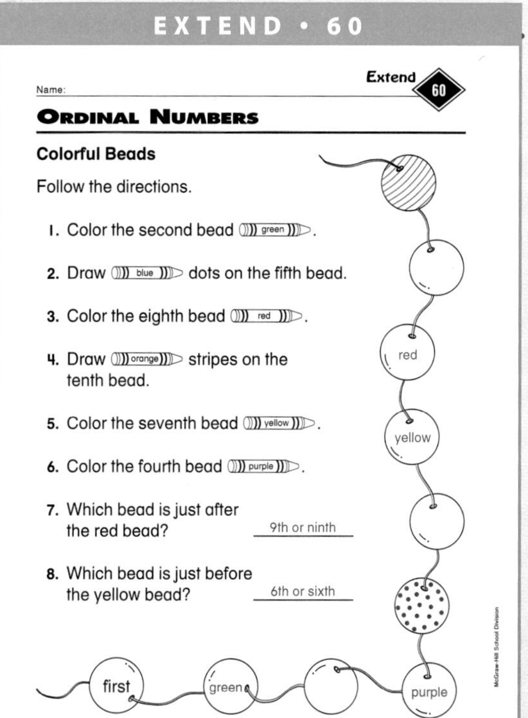

EXTEND • 60

Name: Extend 60

Ordinal Numbers

Colorful Beads

Follow the directions.

1. Color the second bead (green).
2. Draw (blue) dots on the fifth bead.
3. Color the eighth bead (red).
4. Draw (orange) stripes on the tenth bead.
5. Color the seventh bead (yellow).
6. Color the fourth bead (purple).
7. Which bead is just after the red bead? 9th or ninth
8. Which bead is just before the yellow bead? 6th or sixth

first green purple red yellow

Picture Graphs/ Bar Graphs

OBJECTIVE Explore reading and interpreting graphs.

Day 1 Explore Activity: Picture Graphs

Day 2 Explore Activity: Bar Graphs

Teaching With Technology
See alternate computer lesson on pages 218A–218B.

RESOURCE REMINDER
Math Center Cards 45
Practice 61–62, Reteach 61–62, Extend 61–62

SKILLS TRACE

GRADE K	• Explore making and reading a graph. *(Chapter 8)*
GRADE 1	• Explore reading and interpreting picture graphs and bar graphs.
GRADE 2	• Explore reading and interpreting picture graphs and bar graphs. *(Chapter 3)*

LESSON RESOURCES

WARM-UP

Whole Class **Visual/Spatial**

OBJECTIVE Explore making, reading and interpreting a picture graph.

Materials crayons, color markers, color pencils; long sheet of newsprint

▶ Survey children to find out if they prefer crayons, color markers, or color pencils for drawing. Draw a 3-by-10 grid on a sheet of newsprint. Use the drawing tools as labels, and place a number of each on a table.

▶ Each child makes his or her choice and places it on the grid. Ask:
- **Which row has the most? least?**
- **Did more children choose markers or crayons?**
- **How many children chose color pencils?**

CONNECTION ACTIVITY

Whole Class **Social**

OBJECTIVE Connect reading and interpreting a picture graph with physical education.

Materials crayons; horizontal graph form (TA 27)

▶Talk about different sports—such as soccer or baseball—and decide on three of them. Have children survey 10 friends about their favorite sport.

▶ Show children's data with tally marks.

▶ Each child is to make a picture graph of the results and share it with the class. Talk about each graph. Compare the graphs to see if there are any similarities in the information.

Our Favorite Sports

DAILY MATH

PREVIOUS DAY QUICK REVIEW

Rewrite in order.

1. sixth *[fifth]*
2. eighth *[sixth]*
3. fifth *[seventh]*
4. seventh *[eighth]*

FAST FACTS

1. 10 – 7 *[3]*
2. 9 – 6 *[3]*
3. 8 – 5 *[3]*
4. 7 – 4 *[3]*

Problem of the Day • 45

Read aloud to students:

Kyle made a picture graph.
He drew 6 dogs, 8 cats, and 4 fish.
How many more cats were drawn than fish?
[4; 8 – 4 = 4]

TECH LINK

MATH VAN

Activity You may wish to use *Pet Show* to teach this lesson.

MATH FORUM

Idea I have children make a Birthday Picture Graph. We list the 12 months as graph labels, and children place a photo or sketch of themselves on the month of their birthday. It's used to remind us of birthdays throughout the year.

Visit our Resource Village at http://www.mhschool.com to see more of the Math Forum.

MATH CENTER

Practice

OBJECTIVE Construct and interpret a bar graph.

Materials per pair: 1 to 5 of each—connecting cubes, counters, pennies; per child: crayons, Math Center Recording Sheet (TA 38 optional)

Prepare You may wish to draw or copy the graph from the card for children to use.

The children will sort and graph objects by attributes. They will interpret and write about the graph. *[Graphs will vary. Possible answer: I have more counters than pennies.]*

PRACTICE ACTIVITY 45 — MATH CENTER, Partners

Manipulatives • Sort and Graph

YOU NEED

Work with your partner.

- Sort the things into groups.
- Line up the things in each group. Count them.
- Find the cube on the graph. Color one box for each cube you have. Do the same for the counters. Then do the same for the pennies.
- Write three sentences about the graph.

cubes					
counters					
pennies					
0	1	2	3	4	5

McGraw-Hill School Division · Grade Level 1

Chapter 6, Lesson 9 · Graphing

NCTM Standards
- ✓ Problem Solving
- ✓ Communication
- ✓ Reasoning
- Connections

Problem Solving

OBJECTIVE Read and interpret a picture graph.

Materials per child: Math Center Recording Sheet (TA 38 optional), crayons

Children count how many balls, fish, and toy boats are in the pool. They complete a tally and construct a graph to show their results. *[4 balls, 3 boats, 2 fish]*

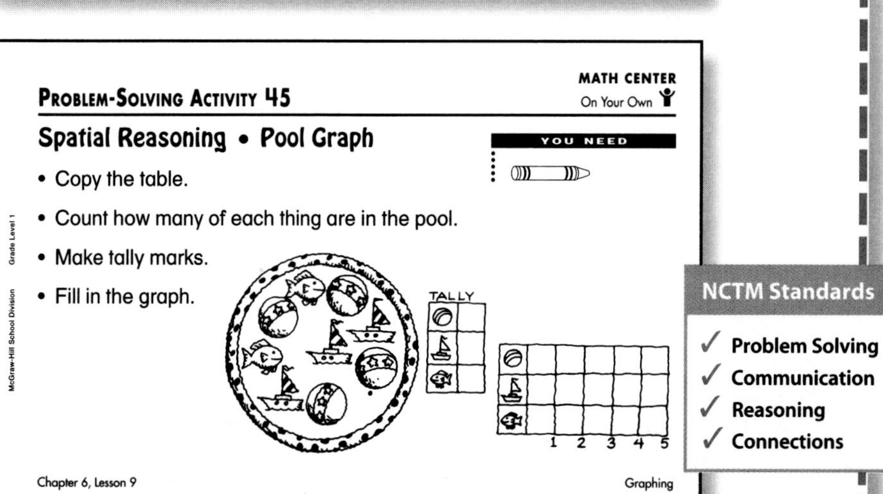

PROBLEM-SOLVING ACTIVITY 45 — MATH CENTER, On Your Own

Spatial Reasoning • Pool Graph

YOU NEED

- Copy the table.
- Count how many of each thing are in the pool.
- Make tally marks.
- Fill in the graph.

TALLY

1 2 3 4 5

McGraw-Hill School Division · Grade Level 1

Chapter 6, Lesson 9 · Graphing

NCTM Standards
- ✓ Problem Solving
- ✓ Communication
- ✓ Reasoning
- ✓ Connections

DAY 1

EXPLORE ACTIVITY

Picture Graphs

OBJECTIVE Children read and interpret a picture graph

Materials per pair: 6 green, 5 orange, and 3 blue pattern blocks

1 Motivate — Whole Class

Resources Jumbo Activity Book, page 12; Stickers, sheet 1 (rhino counters)

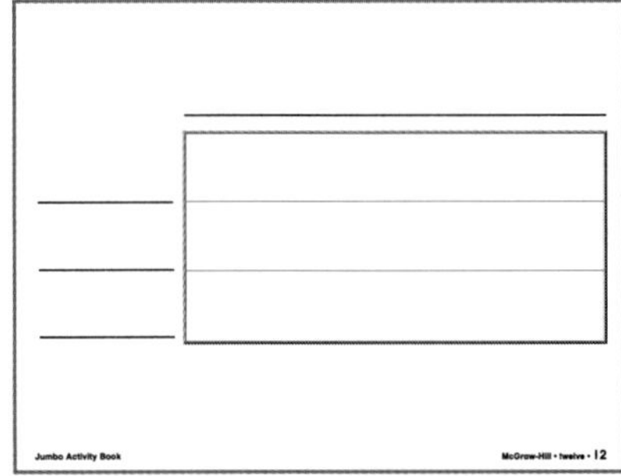

Label the graph *Red, Blue,* and *Yellow* on the left side. Ask children which color of rhino counter is their favorite. Have each child select a rhino sticker and place it on the graph. Tell them this is a *picture graph* because pictures are used instead of tally marks or squares. Ask questions like these:

- **How many children choose red? blue? yellow?**
- **Which color has the most counters? least counters?**
- **Is there a greater number of red counters or yellow counters?**

Have children draw a picture of the rhino graph in their journals and circle their favorite color.

2 Develop

Page 215

Working Together Give partners the pattern blocks. Have them make 3 columns, one for each color. Then remove each block one by one and draw its picture to make a picture graph. Have partners answer the questions on the page and share their results with the rest of the class.

Critical Thinking

After children complete the Explore activity, ask:

- **If one more orange block was added to the graph, which colors would have the most blocks?** *[green; orange]*

Name ______________________

Explore Activity

Picture Graphs

Working Together

You need ▲, ■, and ▰.

Make a **picture graph.**
Draw to show each block.

Start at the bottom.

PATTERN BLOCKS		
△		
△	□	
△	□	
△	□	▱
△	□	▱
△	□	▱
green	orange	blue

Each picture stands for 1 block.

Answers and graph should reflect the number of blocks given to each pair. Samples are shown.

1. Write how many.

   6 ▲

   5 ■

   3 ▰

2. Which is more?

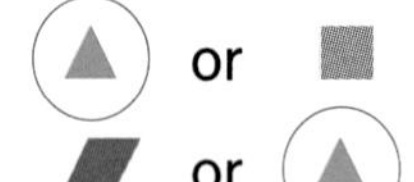

   (▲) or ■

   ▰ or (▲)

3. Which is fewer?

   ■ or (▰)

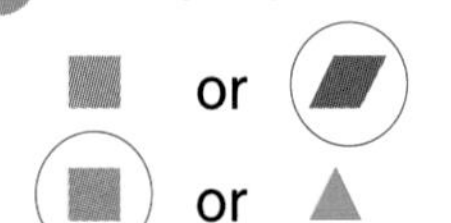

   (■) or ▲

MEETING INDIVIDUAL NEEDS

EARLY FINISHERS

Provide children with centimeter graph paper (TA 26) so they can make bar graphs of the number of letters in their names as compared to the names of their friends or members of their family. Display the graphs.

EXTRA SUPPORT

On Day 2 of this lesson, help children bridge the relationship between picture graphs and bar graphs by looking at both types of graphs side by side for the same information.

ONGOING ASSESSMENT

Interview Determine if children know how to read and interpret picture graphs by asking them to talk about the graph on page 216.

- **Which animal does the school have most of?** *[fish]*

Follow Up Assign **Reteach 61** to children having difficulty.

For those children who complete this lesson successfully, assign **Extend 61.**

Tell a partner what this picture graph shows.

SCHOOL PETS

Hamsters					
Fish					
Rabbits					
Birds					

Each picture stands for 1 pet.

Write how many.

1. 3 hamsters
2. 5 fish
3. 4 rabbits
4. 2 birds

Which is more?

Which is fewer?

Have your child tell you about the picture graph.

Page 216

Try These Assign practice exercises 1–8.

3 Close

Check for Understanding of reading and interpreting picture graphs by asking children different questions about the School Pets graph.

- **Which animal does the school have least of?** *[bird]* **How do you know?** *[There are 2 birds—a number less than the other numbers of pets.]*

Tomorrow children will read and interpret bar graphs.

PRACTICE • 61

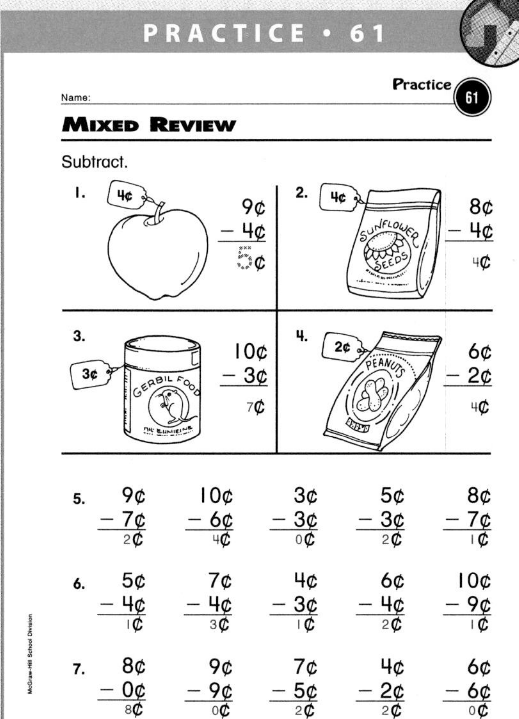

Name: Practice 61

MIXED REVIEW

Subtract.

1. 4¢ — 9¢ − 4¢ = 5¢
2. 4¢ — 8¢ − 4¢ = 4¢
3. 3¢ — 10¢ − 3¢ = 7¢
4. 2¢ — 6¢ − 2¢ = 4¢

5. 9¢ − 7¢ = 2¢ | 10¢ − 6¢ = 4¢ | 3¢ − 3¢ = 0¢ | 5¢ − 3¢ = 2¢ | 8¢ − 7¢ = 1¢
6. 5¢ − 4¢ = 1¢ | 7¢ − 4¢ = 3¢ | 4¢ − 3¢ = 1¢ | 6¢ − 4¢ = 2¢ | 10¢ − 9¢ = 1¢
7. 8¢ − 0¢ = 8¢ | 9¢ − 9¢ = 0¢ | 7¢ − 5¢ = 2¢ | 4¢ − 2¢ = 2¢ | 6¢ − 6¢ = 0¢

RETEACH • 61

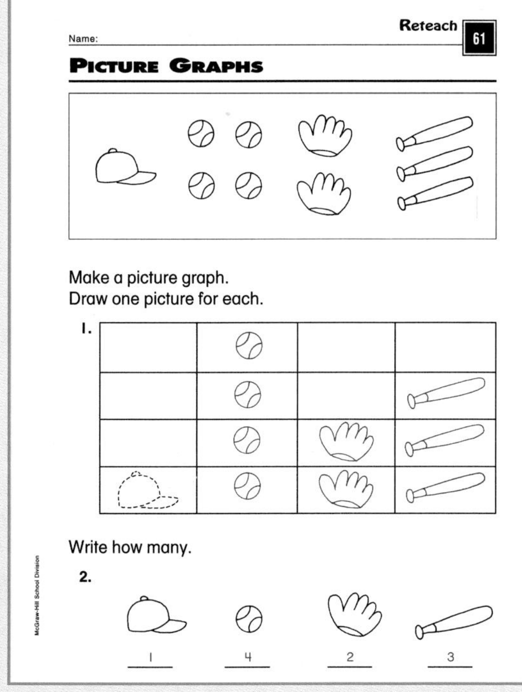

Name: Reteach 61

PICTURE GRAPHS

Make a picture graph.
Draw one picture for each.

1.

Write how many.

2. 1 | 4 | 2 | 3

EXTEND • 61

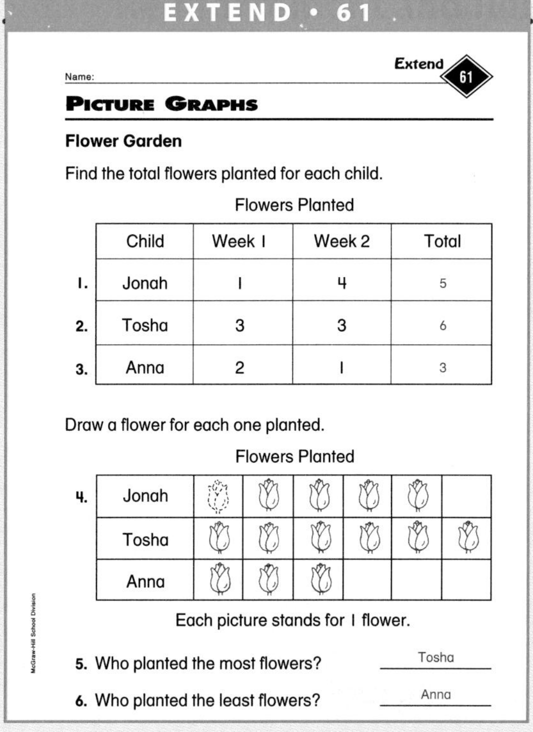

Name: Extend 61

PICTURE GRAPHS

Flower Garden

Find the total flowers planted for each child.

Flowers Planted

	Child	Week 1	Week 2	Total
1.	Jonah	1	4	5
2.	Tosha	3	3	6
3.	Anna	2	1	3

Draw a flower for each one planted.

Flowers Planted

4. Jonah / Tosha / Anna

Each picture stands for 1 flower.

5. Who planted the most flowers? Tosha
6. Who planted the least flowers? Anna

Lesson 6.9

DAY 2

EXPLORE ACTIVITY
Bar Graphs

OBJECTIVE Children read and interpret a bar graph.

Materials per pair: 5 rhino counters, 8 red cubes, 7 blue cubes, 3 two-color counters; 4 different colors of crayons to match the objects

1 Motivate — Whole Class

Resources Jumbo Activity Book, page 13, Stickers, sheets 1 and 3 (rhino counters, square counters)

Make a picture graph on Jumbo Activity Book page 13 with children to show 6 red, 8 blue, and 5 yellow rhino counters. Tell them they are going make a graph of the same information in a different way.

Have children, one by one, replace each animal counter with a corresponding colored square counter. Explain that this is a *bar graph* because the squares next to each other in a row look like a bar. Ask:

- **How are picture graphs and bar graphs the same?** *[They show the same information.]*

2 Develop

Page 217

Working Together Have children place the counters on the grid shown and then color in the squares to make a bar graph. Children answer the questions and then talk about their bar graphs.

Critical Thinking
After children complete the Explore activity, ask:

- **How is a bar graph different from a picture graph?** *[Possible answer: I color squares to make a bar in a bar graph.]*

Page 218

Try These Assign practice exercises 1–5.

Discuss tally marks and how they are used to make a graph.

3 Close

Check for Understanding by asking questions about the bar graph on page 218.

- **What does this graph tell you?** *[Possible answers: How many people voted for each color; the longest bar shows the favorite color.]*

Name ______________________

Explore Activity
Bar Graphs

Working Together

You need , , , and .

Make a **bar graph.**
Color 1 box for each counter.

Answers and graph should reflect the number of counters given to each pair. Samples are shown.

COUNTERS

8
7
6
5
4
3
2
1
0

1. Write how many.
   5 (rhino) 7 (cube)
   8 (cube) 3 (two-color counter)

2. Which is fewer?
   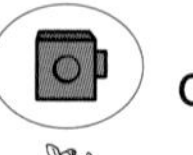 or (cube)
   (rhino) or 
   (cube) or 

3. Which is more?
    or 
   (two-color counter) or (rhino)
   (cube) or (cube)

MEETING INDIVIDUAL NEEDS

INCLUSION

Provide an audiocassette of the questions in this lesson for children who may have difficulty reading them.

STUDENTS ACQUIRING ENGLISH

As you display a picture graph, explain that it is a way to show how to compare numbers of things quickly using pictures instead of words in a word problem.

ONGOING ASSESSMENT

Anecdotal Report Note the progress of each child's ability to read and interpret picture and bar graphs.

- **Can they tell the number of things for each row or column in a graph?**
- **Can they compare any two rows or columns?**
- **Can they tell which category has the most and the least?**

Follow Up Repeat the Motivate activity on page 217 before assigning **Reteach 62.**

Assign **Extend 62** to children who can draw bar graphs.

Tell a partner what the tally marks show.

Use the tally marks to finish the graph.

OUR FAVORITE COLORS

Yellow	////
Blue	𝍸
Red	𝍸 ///

OUR FAVORITE COLORS

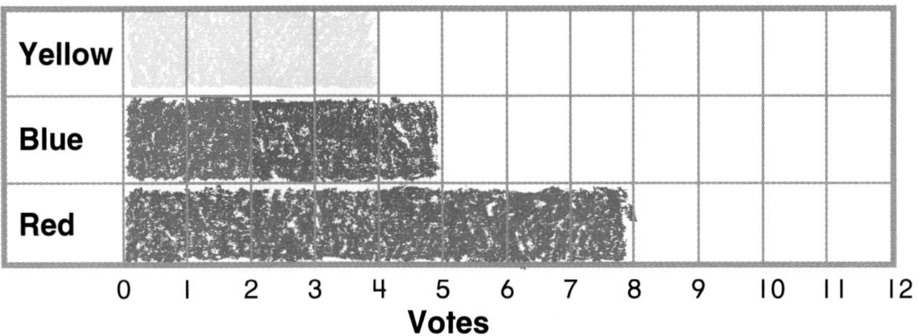

1. How many votes for blue? 5
2. Are there more votes for yellow or blue? blue
   How many more? 1
3. How many votes for red? 8
4. Which color got the most votes? red
   How do you know? Possible answers: I looked for the longest bar, 8 is the greatest number, 8 is more than 4 or 5.
5. Which color would you vote for? Answers may vary.
   Add your vote to the graph.

Ask your child about the graph. Add your vote to the graph.

Alternate Teaching Strategy

Materials per child: 10 rhino counters in three colors, 2 copies of graph form blackline master, crayons or markers to match rhino colors

Prepare Make a blackline master of a 3-by-10 graph form.

Give each child rhino counters and a graph form. Talk about how to find out which color has the most rhinos. Place the rhino counters on the graph. Discuss what this real-life picture graph shows.

Talk about how to show the same information in another kind of graph. Give children the second graph form. Have them work together to make a bar graph, shading a matching color in each square to correspond to each rhino counter.

Put the two graphs side by side. Talk about how they are the same, different, and ways to show information.

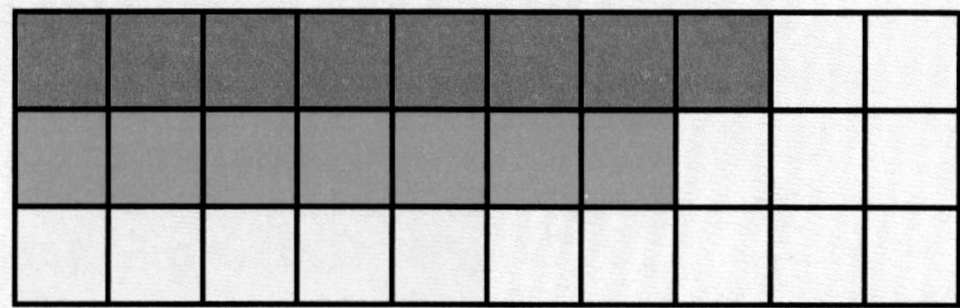

PRACTICE • 62

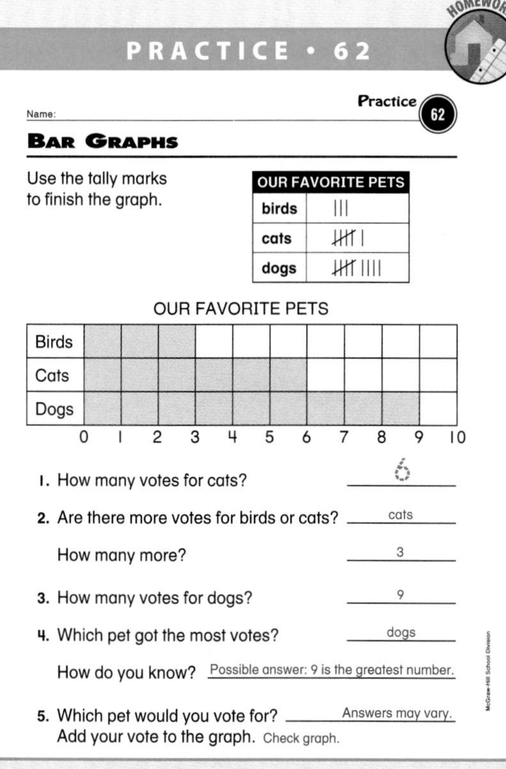

Practice 62

Name:

Bar Graphs

Use the tally marks to finish the graph.

OUR FAVORITE PETS	
birds	///
cats	𝍸 /
dogs	𝍸 ////

OUR FAVORITE PETS

Birds, Cats, Dogs — 0 1 2 3 4 5 6 7 8 9 10

1. How many votes for cats? 6
2. Are there more votes for birds or cats? cats
   How many more? 3
3. How many votes for dogs? 9
4. Which pet got the most votes? dogs
   How do you know? Possible answer: 9 is the greatest number.
5. Which pet would you vote for? Answers may vary.
   Add your vote to the graph. Check graph.

RETEACH • 62

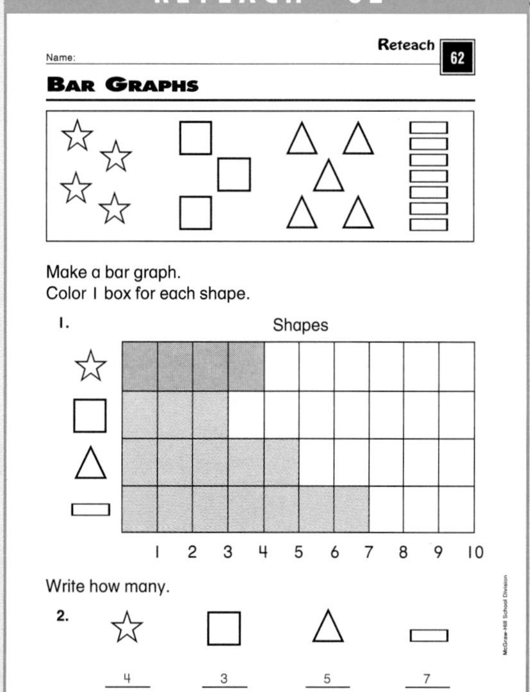

Reteach 62

Name:

Bar Graphs

Make a bar graph.
Color 1 box for each shape.

1. Shapes

1 2 3 4 5 6 7 8 9 10

Write how many.

2. ☆ 4 □ 3 △ 5 ▭ 7

EXTEND • 62

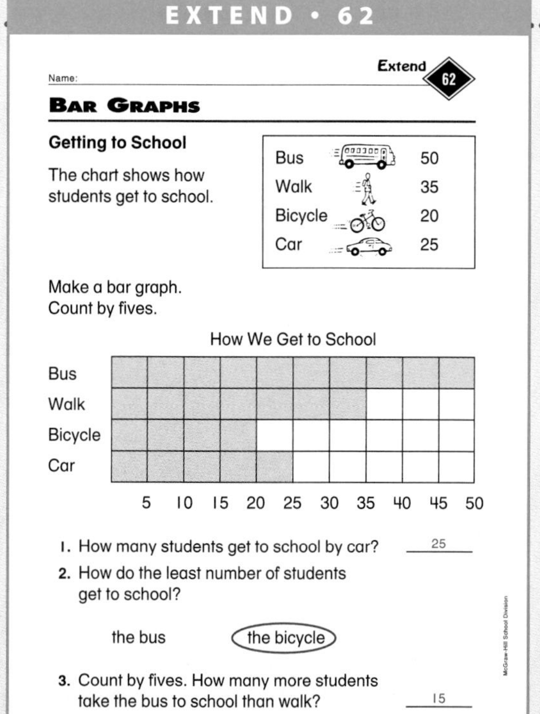

Extend 62

Name:

Bar Graphs

Getting to School

The chart shows how students get to school.

Bus	50
Walk	35
Bicycle	20
Car	25

Make a bar graph.
Count by fives.

How We Get to School

Bus, Walk, Bicycle, Car — 5 10 15 20 25 30 35 40 45 50

1. How many students get to school by car? 25
2. How do the least number of students get to school?
   the bus (the bicycle)
3. Count by fives. How many more students take the bus to school than walk? 15

Teaching With Technology

Picture Graphs/Bar Graphs

AT A GLANCE

OBJECTIVE Children create and interpret picture graphs.

Resource Math Van Activity: *Pet Show*

SET UP

Launch the ***Math Van*** program. Click the right arrow to locate Activity 6, *Pet Show*. After listening to the activity's description, click *Start*.

USING THE MATH VAN ACTIVITY

1 Getting Started Allow children to explore the Graph tool. You may want to explain that the dial in the lower left corner of the screen switches the graph between a horizontal and vertical format.

2 Practice and Apply Children complete a Picture Graph showing the number of different kinds of animals present at a neighborhood pet show. Children stamp the specified number of animals into the appropriate rows to create the graph.

3 Close Have children show the pictures of their graphs and discuss them with you, each other, or the class.

Extend Children create a Bar Graph using the data provided in the *Pet Show* activity. They can explore both vertical and horizontal bar graphs.

TIPS FOR TOOLS

Remind children that they can always get help by clicking the Half Pint character (in the upper right corner of the screen). After activating Half Pint, children can use the cursor to point to things that they want to hear explained.

SCREEN 1

Children listen to the *Pet Show* problem, which asks them to create a Picture Graph of the animals at a pet show.

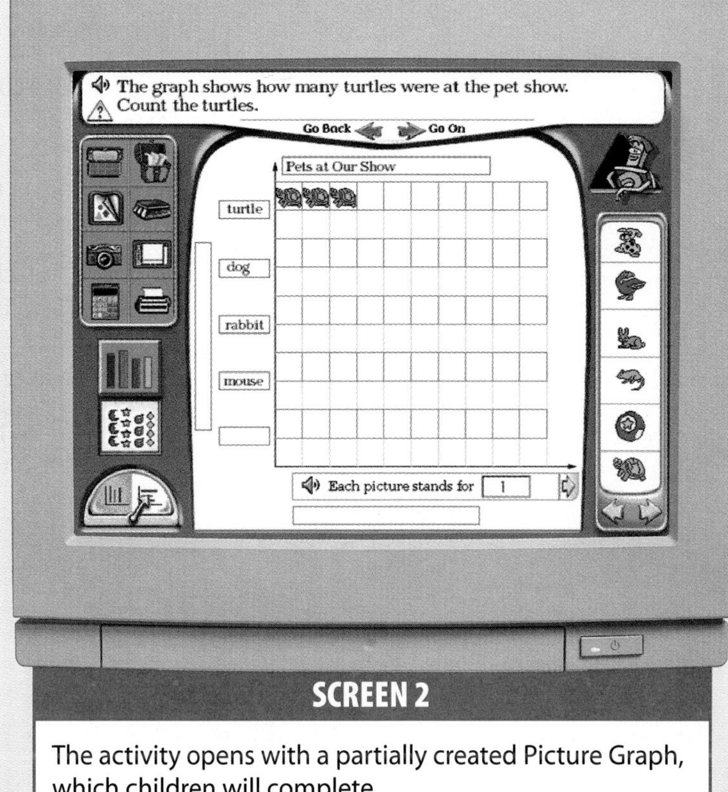

SCREEN 2

The activity opens with a partially created Picture Graph, which children will complete.

SCREEN 3

Using the data provided, children stamp animal counters into the appropriate rows to complete the graph.

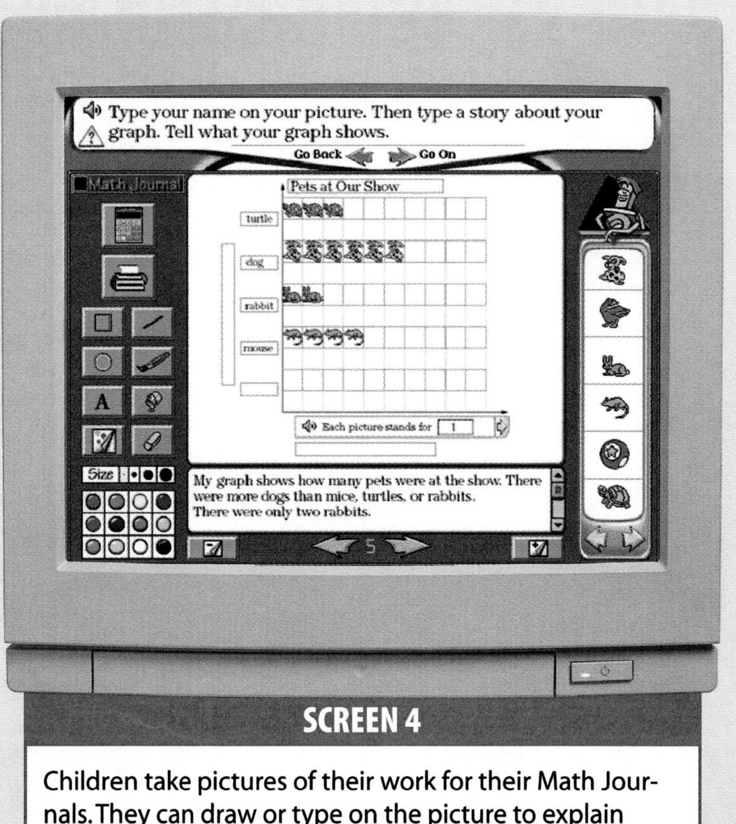

SCREEN 4

Children take pictures of their work for their Math Journals. They can draw or type on the picture to explain what they did.

LESSON 6.10

LESSON RESOURCES

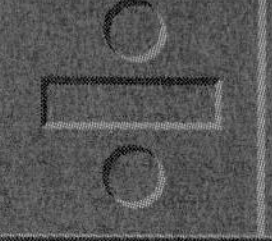

Problem Solvers at Work: Use a Graph

OBJECTIVE Write and solve problems by using information from a graph.

Day 1 Problem Solvers at Work: Use a Graph

RESOURCE REMINDER
Math Center Cards 46
Practice 63, Reteach 63, Extend 63

SKILLS TRACE

GRADE K	• Use information from a graph to solve problems. *(Chapter 8)*
GRADE 1	• Formulate and solve problems using information from a graph.
GRADE 2	• Formulate and solve problems using information from a graph. *(Chapter 3)*

WARM-UP

Whole Class — **Kinesthetic**

OBJECTIVE Explore using a graph to solve problems.

Materials masking tape

Prepare Make a very large 3-by-10 graphing grid on the floor with masking tape.

▶ Tell children they are going to make a real-life picture graph using their shoes. Talk about the different types of shoes. Decide on three types of shoes. Then help children classify the shoes they are wearing so they can place one of them on the graph.

▶ Ask questions about the shoes on the graph. Repeat the activity using another common object.

CONNECTION ACTIVITY

SCIENCE

Whole Class — **Visual/Spatial**

OBJECTIVE Connect using a graph with solving problems in science.

Materials 3" x 3" self-stick notes, marker

Prepare Draw a graph form like the one below on the chalkboard.

▶ Keep track of the weather for one week. Draw or put a self-stick note of a symbol (Sunny or Cloudy) for that day's weather on the grid in the appropriate row. Display the graph and have children explain what the symbols show. Ask:

- **Were more days cloudy or sunny?**

▶ Encourage children to make up questions for each other to answer about the graph.

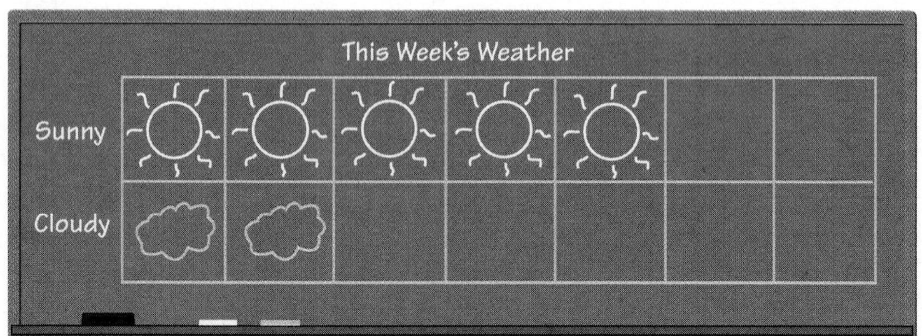

DAILY MATH

PREVIOUS DAY QUICK REVIEW

Tell how many of each color.

Yellow	[3]
Blue	[7]
Red	[6]

FAST FACTS

1. 10 – 9 *[1]*
2. 9 – 8 *[1]*
3. 7 – 7 *[0]*
4. 8 – 6 *[2]*

Problem of the Day • 46

Read aloud to children:

On a picture graph, there are as many apples as oranges.
There are more bananas shown than apples.
Are there more oranges than bananas? *[No.]*

TECH LINK

MATH VAN

Tools You may wish to use the Table and Graph tool with this lesson.

MATH FORUM

Idea I arrange for children to get to know the adults in the school community (teachers, librarians, and so on) by having partners interview them about a favorite thing. Then children display their tally and graph results.

Visit our Resource Village at http://www.mhschool.com to see more of the Math Forum.

MATH CENTER

Practice

OBJECTIVE Construct and interpret graphs.

Materials per child: Math Center Recording Sheet (TA 38 optional), ruler, crayons

Prepare List names of the children on the chalkboard. Next to each name write *bus, car,* or *walk* based on information from the children.

Children will graph how 12 friends get to school. They will interpret and write about the graph. *[Check children's graphs.]*

PRACTICE ACTIVITY 46 — MATH CENTER, On Your Own

Using Data • How We Get to School

YOU NEED: ruler

- Write the names of 12 friends.
- Ask how each friend comes to school—walk, by bus, by car.
- Write how next to each name.
- Make a graph. Show how many come to school in each way.
- Write three things the graph shows.

How My Friends Get to School

0 1 2 3 4 5 6 7 8 9 10

Grade Level 1 — McGraw-Hill School Division

Chapter 6, Lesson 10 — Graphing

NCTM Standards

- Problem Solving
- ✓ Communication
- ✓ Reasoning
- ✓ Connections

Problem Solving

OBJECTIVE Conduct a survey and display results in a graph.

Materials per child: Math Center Recording Sheet (TA 38 optional), crayons

Prepare Provide copies of the graph for children's use.

Children interview 5 children and color the graph to show their responses. Then partners trade graphs and answer questions. Partners check the answers to the information shown on their graphs.

PROBLEM-SOLVING ACTIVITY 46 — MATH CENTER, Partners

Using Data • What I Like to Do

YOU NEED

- Each partner talks to five friends. Ask "What do you like to do? Do you like to play ball? Do you like to ride a bike or skate?"
- Copy the graph. Color the graph.
- Trade graphs with your partner. What do most friends like to do? Write your answers.

What I Like to Do

1 2 3 4 5

Grade Level 1 — McGraw-Hill School Division

Chapter 6, Lesson 10 — Graphing

NCTM Standards

- ✓ Problem Solving
- ✓ Communication
- Reasoning
- Connections

Lesson 6.10

Problem Solvers at Work: Use a Graph

OBJECTIVE Children use information from a graph to solve problems.

1 Motivate — Whole Class

Materials colored chalk

Prepare Draw 1 horizontal 2-by-5 grid on the chalkboard as follows:

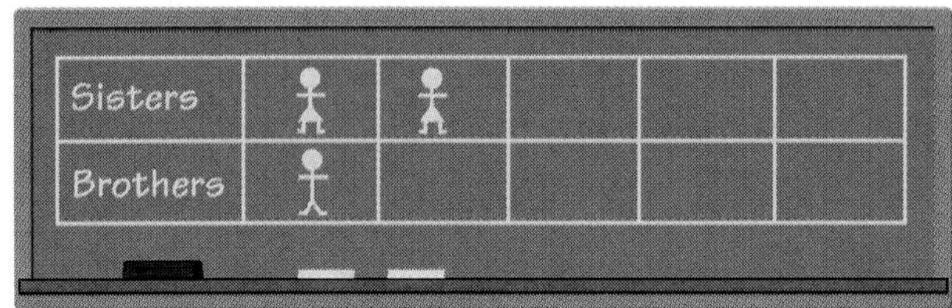

Talk about the number of brothers and sisters in each child's family. Then have volunteers draw stick figures on the chalkboard grid to show 0–5 sisters. Ask:

- **How many sisters does the family have?** *[2]*
- **How do you know?** *[I counted the number of stick figures in the row.]*

Repeat, recording the number of brothers. Talk about other family members such as grandparents, uncles, aunts, and extended family.

2 Develop

Page 219

Talk about the graph.

- **Is it a picture graph or a bar graph?** *[picture graph]*
- **How do you know?** *[Pictures are used instead of colored boxes.]*

Critical Thinking
Before children answer the question on the page, ask:

- **How can you figure out how many relatives Nicole counted to make this graph?** *[Count all the pictures on the graph for a total.]*

Page 220

Try These Assign practice problems 1–4. Encourage children to read their problems.

3 Close

Check for Understanding by asking:

- **How does a graph help you solve problems?** *[Possible answer: I can see the information on the graph.]*

Name ____________

Read
Plan
Solve
Look Back

Use a Graph

Nicole made a graph about some of her family.

1. Does Nicole have more aunts or uncles? aunts
   How many more? 2

2. What does Nicole have the most of? cousins
   How many does she have? 9

3. How many aunts and uncles does Nicole have in all? 8

4. Write a question about Nicole's graph.
   Possible question: How many aunts does Nicole have? 5

How many relatives did Nicole count? 17

MEETING INDIVIDUAL NEEDS

EARLY FINISHERS

Have pairs of children each make a graph of relatives of their choice and ask each other questions about the graphs.

EXTRA SUPPORT

Have children place objects of different colors or shapes in each different row to help them count and compare.

ONGOING ASSESSMENT

Interview Determine if children can solve problems using a graph by asking:

- **How does a picture graph help you answer questions?** *[Possible answer: I can see the answers.]*

Follow Up Do the questions orally with children still having difficulty. Then assign **Reteach 63.**

Assign **Extend 63** to children who are able to read and interpret graphs.

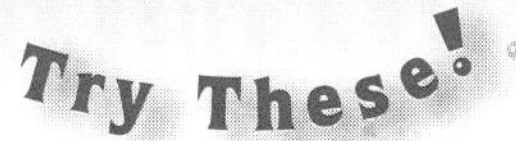

Fred asked his family how many books they read. Then he made a graph.

BOOKS WE READ IN JANUARY

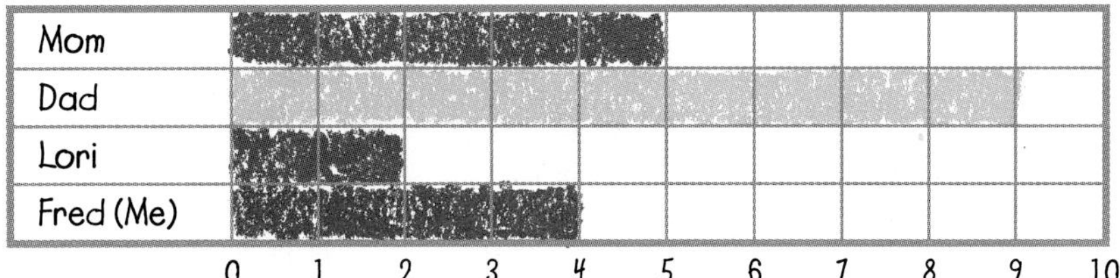

1. How many books did Lori and Fred read in all? 6 books
2. Did they read more books than their mom? Yes.

   How many more? 1 more

Write and Share

Tearna wrote this problem.

Who read more books than Mom?

Tearna Powell
Elephant's Fork School
Suffolk, Virginia

3. Solve Tearna's problem. Dad

How did you solve Tearna's problem?

4. Write a problem. Have a partner solve it. Problems and solutions may vary.

Ask your child about the problem he or she wrote.

Alternate Teaching Strategy

Resources Jumbo Activity Book, page 12; Stickers, sheet 1 (rhinos)

Display Jumbo Activity Book page 12 with 4 yellow, 8 red, and 3 rhino stickers. Ask questions like these:

- **How many rhinos are red?** *[8]* **yellow?** *[4]* **blue?** *[3]*
- **What do you think the graph tells you?** *[Answers may vary.]*
- **How can you figure out how many more red rhinos there are than blue rhinos?** *[Possible answers: I can compare them one-to-one, I can subtract.]*

Encourage children to ask questions about the graph for their classmates to answer.

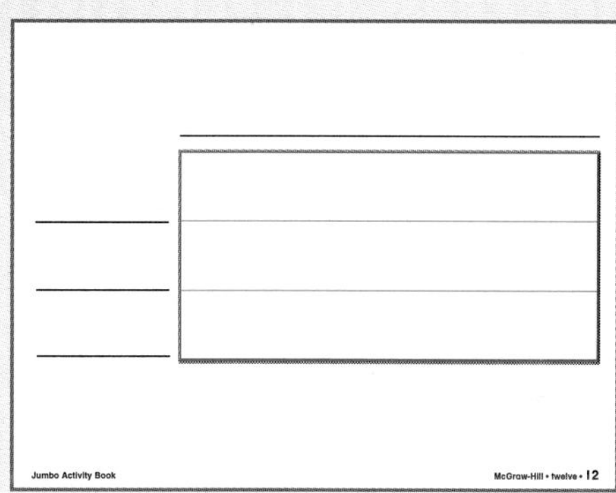

PRACTICE • 63

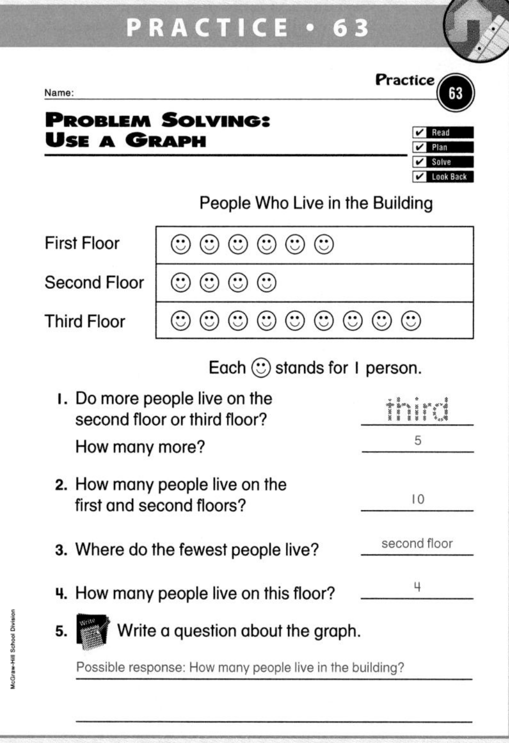

Name:
Practice 63

PROBLEM SOLVING: USE A GRAPH

Read / Plan / Solve / Look Back

People Who Live in the Building

First Floor	☺ ☺ ☺ ☺ ☺ ☺
Second Floor	☺ ☺ ☺ ☺
Third Floor	☺ ☺ ☺ ☺ ☺ ☺ ☺ ☺ ☺

Each ☺ stands for 1 person.

1. Do more people live on the second floor or third floor? third
   How many more? 5
2. How many people live on the first and second floors? 10
3. Where do the fewest people live? second floor
4. How many people live on this floor? 4
5. Write a question about the graph.
   Possible response: How many people live in the building?

McGraw-Hill School Division

RETEACH • 63

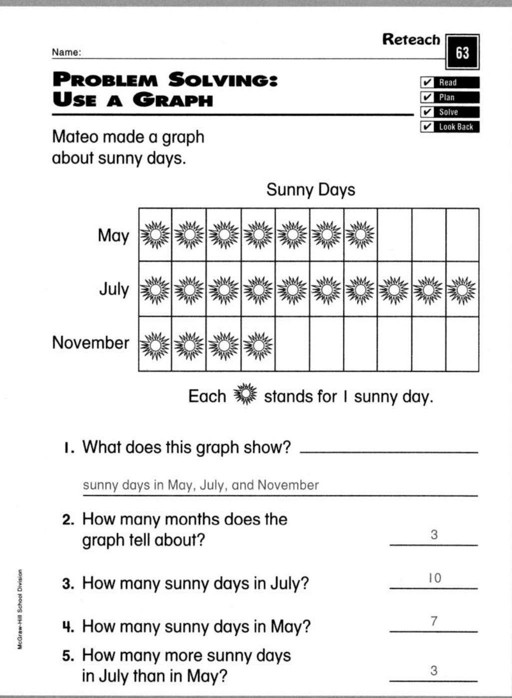

Name:
Reteach 63

PROBLEM SOLVING: USE A GRAPH

Read / Plan / Solve / Look Back

Mateo made a graph about sunny days.

Sunny Days

May	☼ ☼ ☼ ☼ ☼ ☼ ☼
July	☼ ☼ ☼ ☼ ☼ ☼ ☼ ☼ ☼ ☼
November	☼ ☼ ☼ ☼

Each ☼ stands for 1 sunny day.

1. What does this graph show? sunny days in May, July, and November
2. How many months does the graph tell about? 3
3. How many sunny days in July? 10
4. How many sunny days in May? 7
5. How many more sunny days in July than in May? 3

McGraw-Hill School Division

EXTEND • 63

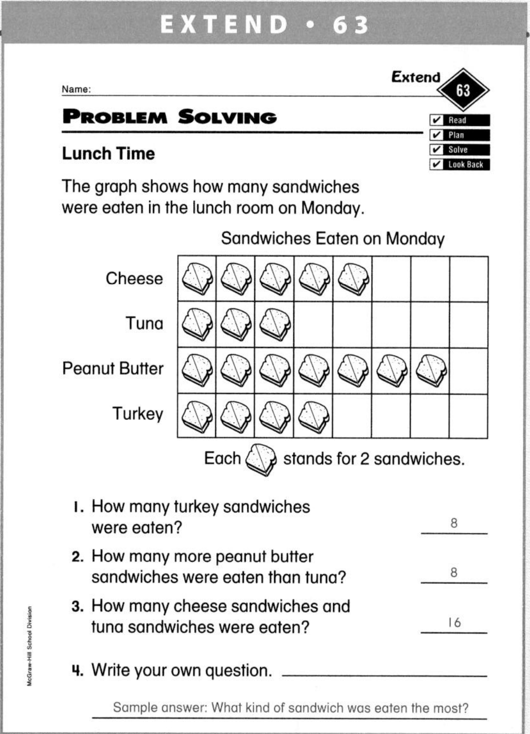

Name:
Extend 63

PROBLEM SOLVING

Read / Plan / Solve / Look Back

Lunch Time

The graph shows how many sandwiches were eaten in the lunch room on Monday.

Sandwiches Eaten on Monday

Cheese	🥪 🥪 🥪 🥪 🥪
Tuna	🥪 🥪 🥪
Peanut Butter	🥪 🥪 🥪 🥪 🥪 🥪 🥪
Turkey	🥪 🥪 🥪 🥪

Each 🥪 stands for 2 sandwiches.

1. How many turkey sandwiches were eaten? 8
2. How many more peanut butter sandwiches were eaten than tuna? 8
3. How many cheese sandwiches and tuna sandwiches were eaten? 16
4. Write your own question.
   Sample answer: What kind of sandwich was eaten the most?

McGraw-Hill School Division

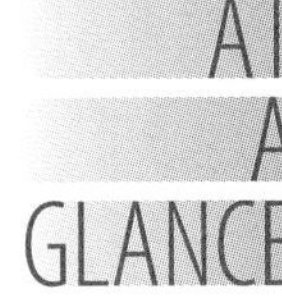

PURPOSE Review and assess the concepts, skills, and strategies that children have learned in this chapter.

Chapter Objectives

6A Read, write, and represent numbers, to 100
6B Compare and order numbers, to 100
6C Read and interpret graphs
6D Count by ones, twos, fives, or tens
6E Identify ordinal position
6F Solve problems, including those that involve numbers to 100, graphs, and estimation

Using the Chapter Review

The **Chapter Review** can be used as review, practice, or chapter test.

What Do You Think? This feature gives children an opportunity for self-assessment. Assure children that there are no right or wrong answers. The emphasis is on what they think and how they justify their answers.

Name

Chapter Review

Write the number.

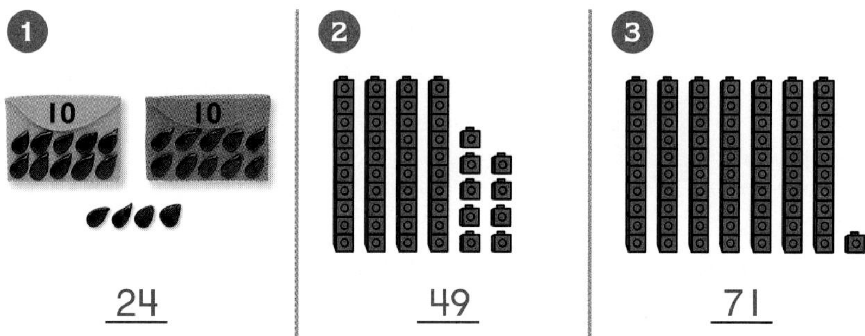

1. 24
2. 49
3. 71

Ring the number that is greater.

4. 78 (85)
5. (21) 12
6. (31) 29

Ring the number that is less.

7. (13) 31
8. 87 (79)
9. (15) 25

Write the numbers in order.

10. 22, 23, 24, 25, 26, 27, 28
11. 47, 48, 49, 50, 51, 52, 53

Estimate to solve.

12. About how many?

about 10 (about 20)

13. About how many?

(about 20) about 50

Reinforcement and Remediation

CHAPTER OBJECTIVES	REVIEW ITEMS	STUDENT BOOK PAGES		TEACHER'S EDITION PAGES		TEACHER RESOURCES
		Lesson	Midchapter Review	Activities	Alternate Teaching Strategy	Reteach
6A	1–3	185–192, 195–198	199	184A, 188A, 194A	188,192, 198	48–51 53–54
6B	4–11	203–206, 211–212		202A, 210A	206, 212	55–56 59
6C	18–20	215–218		214A	218	61–62
6D	14–16	207–210		206A	210	57–58
6E	17	213–214		212A	214	60
6F	12–13, 18–20	193–194, 219–220	199	192A, 218A	194, 220	52, 63

Skip-count.

14 2, 4, 6, 8, 10, 12

15 5, 10, 15, 20, 25, 30

16 10, 20, 30, 40, 50, 60

17 Match.

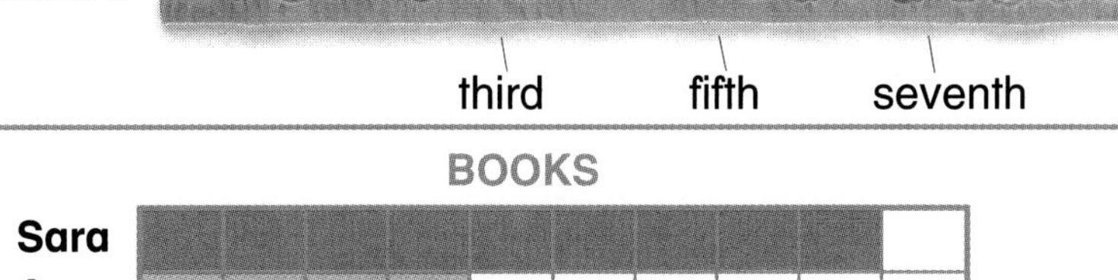

third fifth seventh

BOOKS

	0–1	1–2	2–3	3–4	4–5	5–6	6–7	7–8	8–9	9–10
Sara	■	■	■	■	■	■	■	■	■	
Anne	■	■	■	■						
Larry	■	■	■	■	■	■	■			

0 1 2 3 4 5 6 7 8 9 10

18 Who read the fewest books? Anne

19 How many books did Larry read? 7

20 Who read the most books? Sara

What Do You Think?

How do you like to count?
✔ Check one.

☐ By ones ☐ By tens ☐ By fives ☐ By twos

Why? This self-assessment should not be graded. All explanations are acceptable.

Show what you know about 100.

CHAPTER TEST

AT A GLANCE

PURPOSE Assess the concepts, skills, and strategies that children have learned in this chapter.

Chapter Objectives

6A Read, write, and represent numbers, to 100
6B Compare and order numbers, to 100
6C Read and interpret graphs
6D Count by ones, twos, fives, or tens
6E Identify ordinal position
6F Solve problems, including those that involve numbers to 100, graphs, and estimation

Using the Chapter Test

The **Chapter Test** can be used as a practice test, a chapter test, or as an additional review. The **Performance Assessment** on Student Book page 224 provides an alternate means of assessing children's understanding of numbers to 100, ordinal numbers, and graphs.

Assessment Resources

Test Masters

The Testing Program Blackline Masters provide three forms of the **Chapter Test.** Form C uses a free-response format. Forms A and B use a multiple-choice format.

Teacher's Assessment Resources

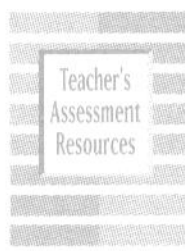

Teacher's Assessment Resources provides resources for alternate assessment. It includes guidelines for Building a Portfolio, pages 6–9 and the Holistic Scoring Guide, pages 29–32.

Name ______

Chapter Test

1 Write the number.

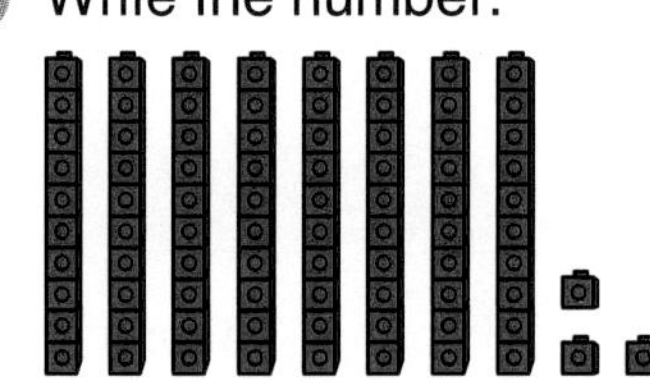

83

2 Ring the number that is greater.

(58) 39

3 Write the numbers in order.

68, 69, 70, 71, 72, 73, 74

Skip-count.

4 2, 4, 6, 8, 10, 12, 14, 16

5 5, 10, 15, 20, 25, 30, 35

6 10, 20, 30, 40, 50, 60, 70

7 Match.

second fourth eighth

8 How many cousins does Lani have? 5

9 Who has the fewest cousins? Maria

COUSINS

Maria, Gene, Lani

0 1 2 3 4 5 6 7 8 9 10

Estimate to solve.

10 About how many fish?

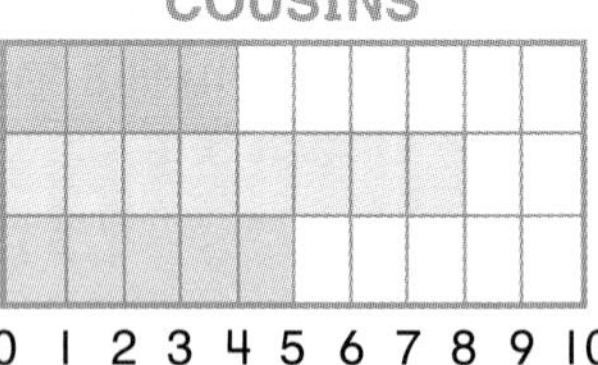

(about 30) about 50

Test Correlation

CHAPTER OBJECTIVES	TEST ITEMS	STUDENT BOOK PAGES
6A	1	185–192, 195–199
6B	2, 3	203–206, 211–212
6C	8–9	215–218
6D	4–6	207–210
6E	7	213–214
6F	10	193–194, 219–220

Performance Assessment

What Did You Learn?

You need 30, 30, and 30.

Take a big handful of each color.

Count how many of each color.
Write the number. Answers may vary.

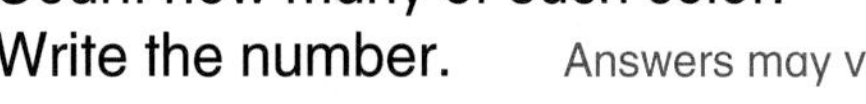

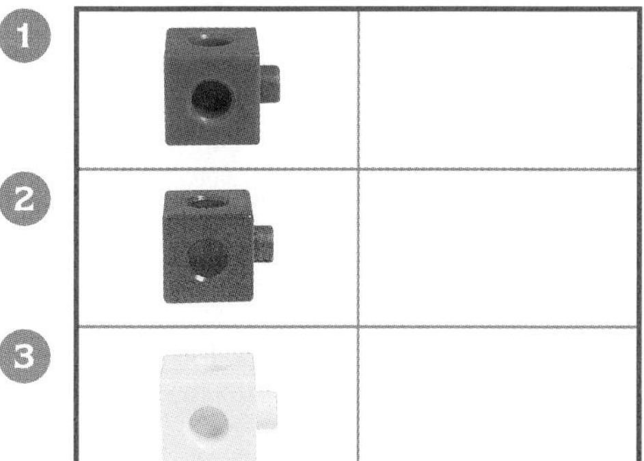

1		
2		
3		

4. Do you have more or ? Answers may vary. ______

5. Do you have fewer or ? Answers may vary. ______

6. About how many do you have in all? Answers may vary.

   Estimate. ______ Count how many. ______

You may want to put this page in your portfolio.

REVIEWING A PORTFOLIO

Have children review their portfolios. Consider including the following items:

- Finished work on a project, page 182F.
- Selected math journal entries, pages 188, 199, and 222.
- Products from investigations, pages 201–202.
- Children's self-selected "best piece" drawn from the work completed during the chapter. Have them attach a note explaining why they chose that piece.
- Any work that you or individual children wish to keep for future reference.

You may wish to take this opportunity to conduct conferences with children.

The Portfolio Analysis Form can help you in the reporting of children's progress. See Teacher's Assessment Resources, page 33.

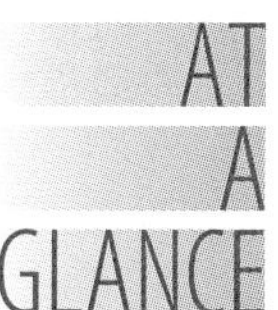

AT A GLANCE

PURPOSE Review and assess the concepts, skills, and strategies that children have learned in this chapter.

Materials per child: 30 blue, 30 red, and 30 yellow connecting cubes

Using the Performance Assessment

Explain to children what they are to do. Assign problems 1–6. Make sure children understand the problems. Give each child 30 blue, 30 red, and 30 yellow connecting cubes. Observe children as they work.

Evaluating Student Work

As you read children's papers, look for the following:

- *Can the child count the number of each color of connecting cubes?*
- *Can the child compare numbers?*
- *Can the child make a reasonable estimate of the total number of connecting cubes?*
- *Can the child count to find the total number of connecting cubes?*

You may wish to use the Holistic Scoring Guide and annotated samples of children's work to assess this task. See pages 29–32 and 37–61 in Teacher's Assessment Resources.

Follow-Up Interviews

Meet with children individually or in small groups to reflect on the Performance Assessment task. You can use the following questions to gain insight into children's thinking and evaluate their level of understanding:

- **Did you count by ones, twos, fives, or tens to find the number of each color? Tell me why you chose that method.**
- **How did you figure out whether there are more blue or more red cubes?**
- **How did you figure out whether there are fewer yellow or fewer blue cubes?**
- **How did you estimate the number of cubes in all?**
- **Did you count by ones, twos, fives, or tens to find the number of cubes in all? Tell me why you chose that method.**

AT A GLANCE

OBJECTIVE Children use a calculator for skip counting 2-digit numbers.

Materials per child: calculator

Using the Math Connection

Talk about the calculator. Have children find the on/clear key (ON/C), numbers keys (0 to 9), and the add (+), subtract (−), and equals (=) keys on the calculator. Use the calculator to solve some basic facts with children.

Work through the example at the top of the page with children to demonstrate how to press the correct calculator key and write the cost of the necklace in the answer blank.

Assign exercises 1–4. Observe children as they press the keys and record their answers. Be sure they press the calculator keys the correct amount of times to compute the cost of the necklaces.

Developing Technology Skills The exercises on this page help children become more proficient using the calculator to find numerical answers to computational problems.

Extending the Activity You can vary the cost and amount of beads to further challenge the class. Children can draw pictures of the new necklaces making sure to draw the correct number of beads and write the cost of the necklace beneath it.

TECH LINK

MATH VAN

Tools You may wish to use the Calculator tool with this lesson.

Math Connection
Calculator

Name ______

Skip-Count

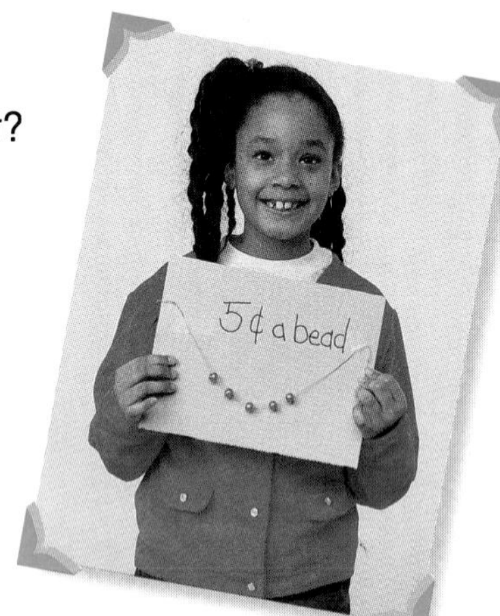

How much does the necklace cost?

You can skip-count by fives to find out.

Press [ON/C] [+] [5].

How many beads? 5

Press [=] 5 times.

The necklace costs 25 ¢.

Talk: Which keys would you press if each bead cost 10¢? [ON/C] [+] [1] [0] [=] [=] [=] [=] [=]

Find the cost of each necklace.

1. 10¢ a bead

7 beads 70 ¢

2. 5¢ a bead

9 beads 45 ¢

3. 2¢ a bead

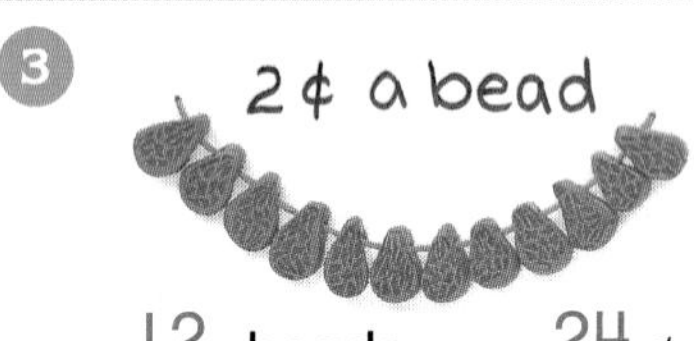

12 beads 24 ¢

4. 6¢ a bead

10 beads 60 ¢

Technology Connection
Computer

Use a Graph

Are there more toy vans or police cars? How do you know?
Possible answer: Police cars; 22 has 2 tens and 19 has 1 ten.

1 Which number of vehicles is the least? 18

2 Which number is the greatest? 22

Vehicles

Vehicles	
Vans	19
Police Cars	22
Trucks	18
Race cars	20
Sports Cars	21

At the Computer

3 Put the numbers in the table in order.
18, 19, 20, 21, 22

4 Link the table to a bar graph. What do you see?
The bars look like steps.

5 Change the numbers in the table. What happens to the graph?
Answers may vary.

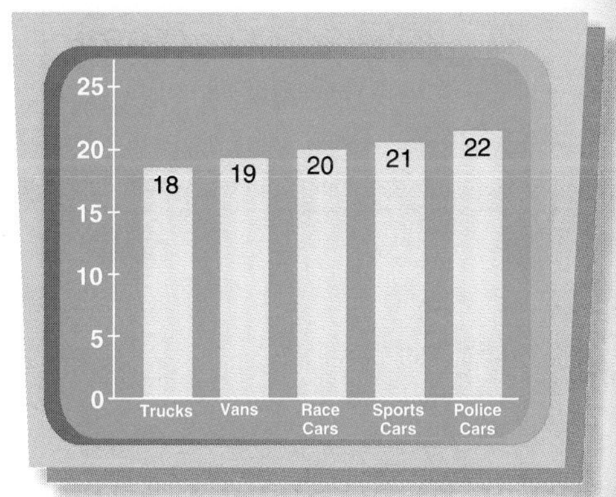

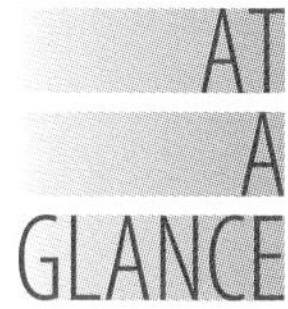

AT A GLANCE

OBJECTIVE Use a graphing program to display and interpret data.

Resources spreadsheet and graphing programs, or Math Van Tools.

Using the Technology Connection

Have children look a the table to compare the numbers of each type of vehicle. Have them tell which is the least number and which is the greatest. If you are using a spreadsheet program, you will need to prepare the columns and rows ahead of time. Have children enter and order the data. Then transfer the data to a bar graph and answer the questions.

If computers and software are not available, allow children to use paper and pencils to make their tables and graphs.

Extending the Activity Have children collect and enter data about the vehicles that pass in front of the school in a given amount of time.

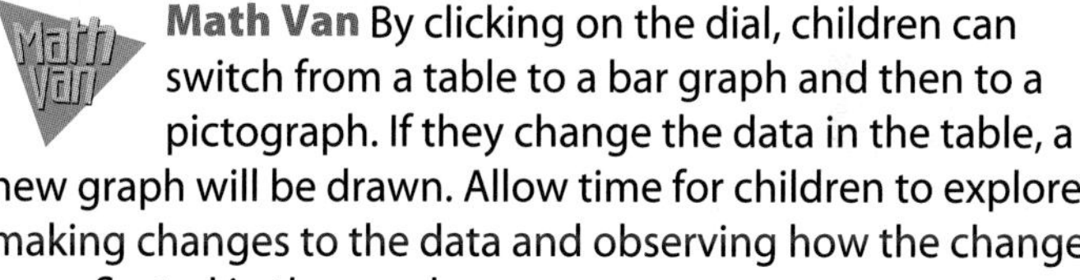

Math Van By clicking on the dial, children can switch from a table to a bar graph and then to a pictograph. If they change the data in the table, a new graph will be drawn. Allow time for children to explore making changes to the data and observing how the changes are reflected in the graph.

PURPOSE Review and maintain the concepts, skills, and strategies that children have already learned.

Using the Cumulative Review

The **Cumulative Review** is presented in a multiple-choice format to provide practice in taking a standardized test.

Assessment Resources

TEST MASTERS

There are multiple-choice Cumulative Tests and a Year-End Test that provide additional opportunities for students to practice taking standardized tests.

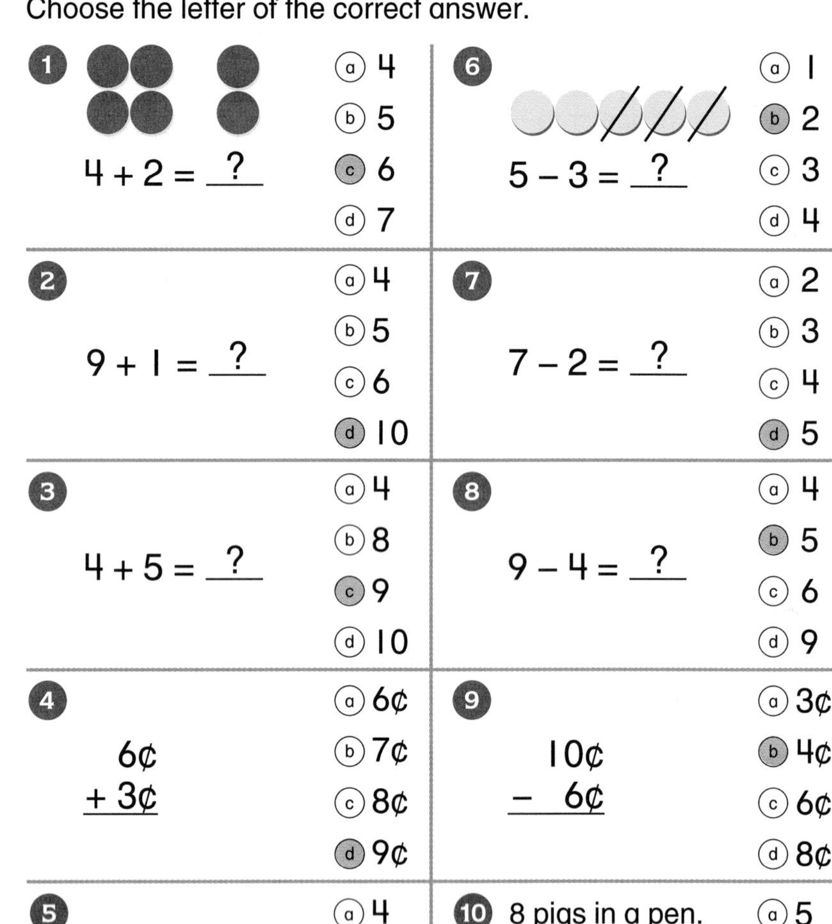

Name

Cumulative Review

Choose the letter of the correct answer.

1. $4 + 2 = \underline{?}$ — (a) 4 (b) 5 (c) 6 (d) 7
2. $9 + 1 = \underline{?}$ — (a) 4 (b) 5 (c) 6 (d) 10
3. $4 + 5 = \underline{?}$ — (a) 4 (b) 8 (c) 9 (d) 10
4. 6¢ + 3¢ — (a) 6¢ (b) 7¢ (c) 8¢ (d) 9¢
5. 3 + 7 — (a) 4 (b) 7 (c) 9 (d) 10
6. $5 - 3 = \underline{?}$ — (a) 1 (b) 2 (c) 3 (d) 4
7. $7 - 2 = \underline{?}$ — (a) 2 (b) 3 (c) 4 (d) 5
8. $9 - 4 = \underline{?}$ — (a) 4 (b) 5 (c) 6 (d) 9
9. 10¢ − 6¢ — (a) 3¢ (b) 4¢ (c) 6¢ (d) 8¢
10. 8 pigs in a pen. 2 pigs get away. How many pigs are left? — (a) 5 (b) 6 (c) 7 (d) 8

CHAPTER 6 *Cumulative Review* two hundred twenty-seven • 227

Cumulative Review Correlation

REVIEW ITEMS	TEXT PAGES	REVIEW ITEMS	TEXT PAGES
1	81–82	11	185–186
2	93–96	12	193–194
3	91–92	13	209–210
4	153–154	14	211–212
5	147–150	15	173–174
6	115–116	16	191–192
7	127–130	17	205–206
8	125–126	18	207–208
9	167–168	19	211–212
10	171–172	20	217–218

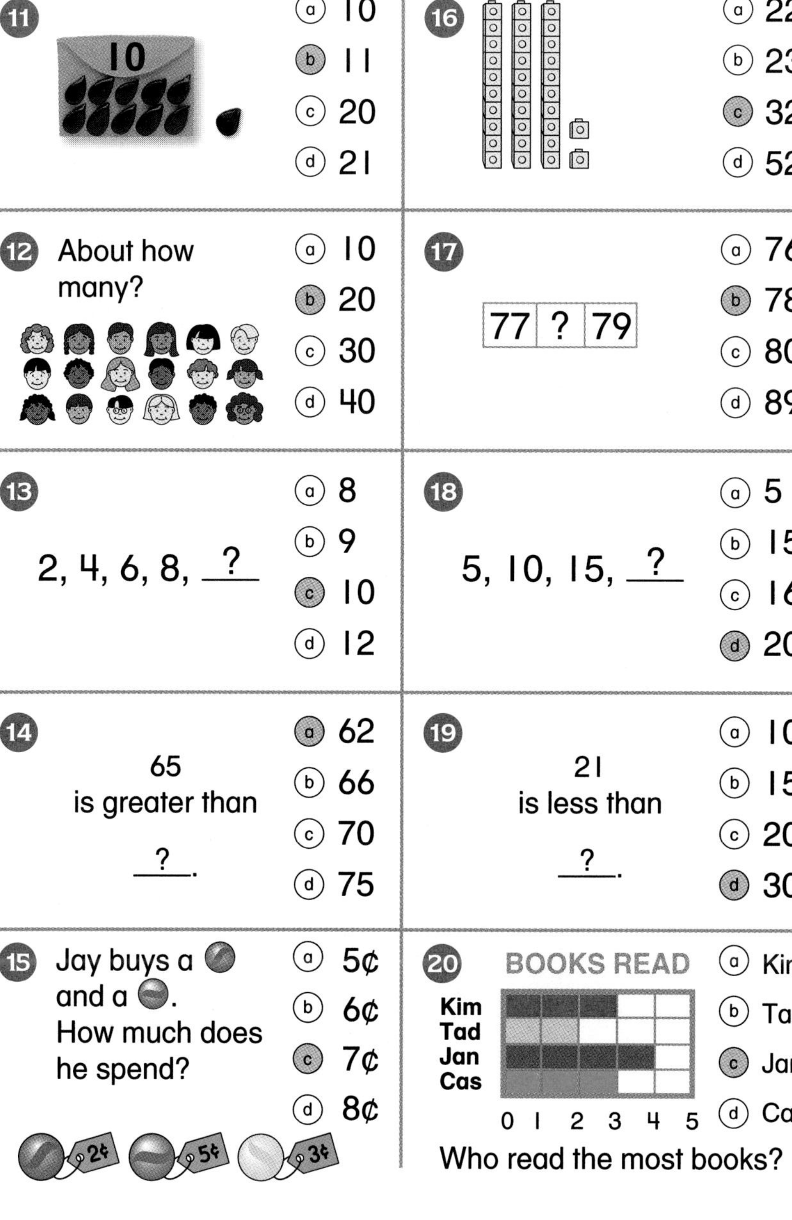

11

10

ⓐ 10
ⓑ 11 (marked)
ⓒ 20
ⓓ 21

16

ⓐ 22
ⓑ 23
ⓒ 32 (marked)
ⓓ 52

12 About how many?

ⓐ 10
ⓑ 20 (marked)
ⓒ 30
ⓓ 40

17

77	?	79

ⓐ 76
ⓑ 78 (marked)
ⓒ 80
ⓓ 89

13

2, 4, 6, 8, ?

ⓐ 8
ⓑ 9
ⓒ 10 (marked)
ⓓ 12

18

5, 10, 15, ?

ⓐ 5
ⓑ 15
ⓒ 16
ⓓ 20 (marked)

14

65 is greater than ?.

ⓐ 62 (marked)
ⓑ 66
ⓒ 70
ⓓ 75

19

21 is less than ?.

ⓐ 10
ⓑ 15
ⓒ 20
ⓓ 30 (marked)

15 Jay buys a [marble] and a [marble]. How much does he spend?

ⓐ 5¢
ⓑ 6¢
ⓒ 7¢ (marked)
ⓓ 8¢

20

Who read the most books?

ⓐ Kim
ⓑ Tad
ⓒ Jan (marked)
ⓓ Cas

Family Activities

PURPOSE Give family members an opportunity to help children maintain concepts and skills learned in the chapter.

Using the Wrap-Up

Page 229

Tell children that this side of the page will help them show their parents what they have been learning in this chapter. Encourage children to practice in class before tryng it at home.

Name ____________________

Every Penny Counts

MATERIALS 100 pennies, paper and pencil

DIRECTIONS Take turns. Find different ways to group 100 pennies in order to make it easy to count them. Keep a record of the ways you group.

How many ways did you group pennies? Which grouping made counting the easiest?

As you engage in this activity with your child, let your child make the grouping decisions. He or she will probably make groups, or stacks, of 2, 5, or 10. You may also choose to make groups of 20 or 25. Then discuss and have your child answer the two questions.

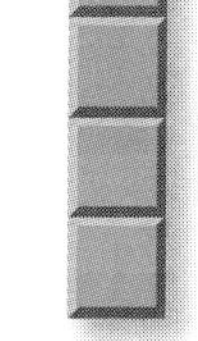

Picture Glossary

add

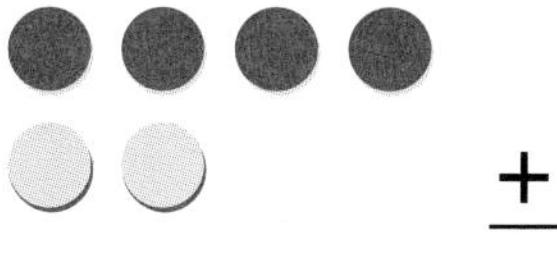

$$\begin{array}{r} 4 \\ +\,2 \\ \hline 6 \end{array}$$

addition sentence

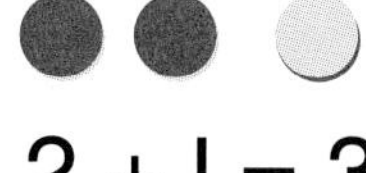

$2 + 1 = 3$

after 43 44

↑ just after 43

before 42 43

↑ just before 43

between

42 43 44

↑ between 42 and 44

calendar

September

Sun.	Mon.	Tues.	Wed.	Thurs.	Fri.	Sat.
					1	2
3	4	5	6	7	8	9
10	11	12	13	14	15	16
17	18	19	20	21	22	23
24	25	26	27	28	29	30

centimeter

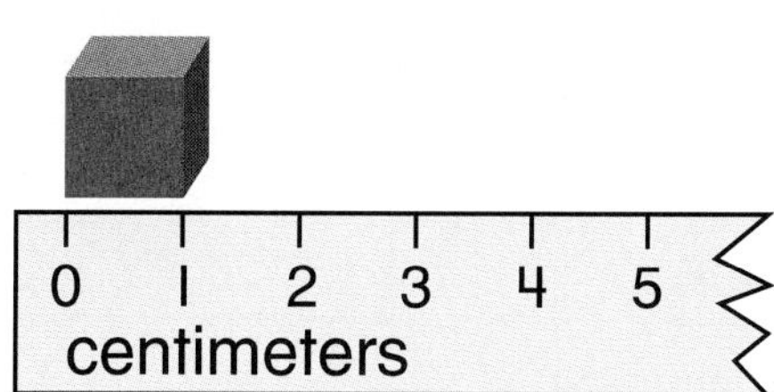

circle

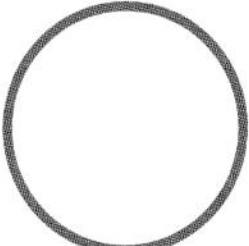

cone

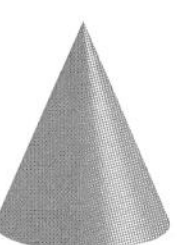

count back

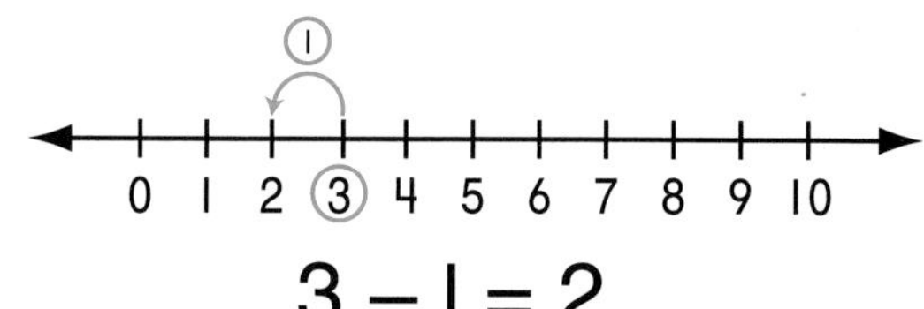

$3 - 1 = 2$

count on

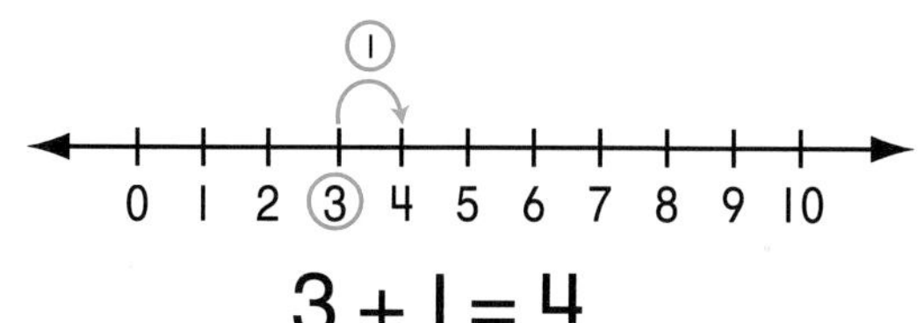

$3 + 1 = 4$

cube

cup

cylinder

difference

$7 - 6 = 1$ ← difference

dime

10¢

double

$$\begin{array}{r} 1 \\ +1 \\ \hline 2 \end{array} \qquad \begin{array}{r} 2 \\ +2 \\ \hline 4 \end{array} \qquad \begin{array}{r} 2 \\ -1 \\ \hline 1 \end{array} \qquad \begin{array}{r} 4 \\ -2 \\ \hline 2 \end{array}$$

equal parts

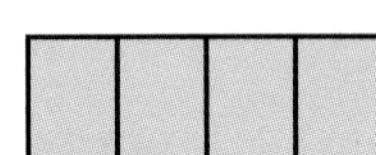

estimate

about 10

fact family

5 + 3 = 8　　8 − 3 = 5
3 + 5 = 8　　8 − 5 = 3

foot

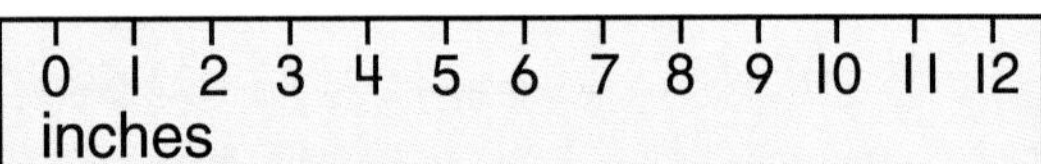

12 inches equal 1 foot.

fourths

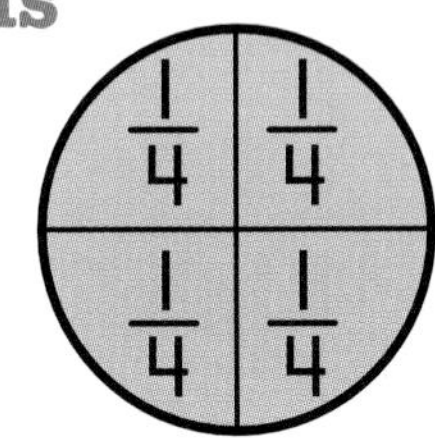

4 equal parts

fraction

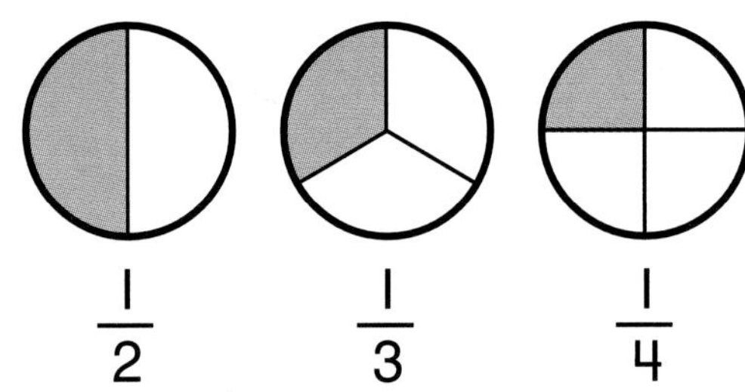

graph

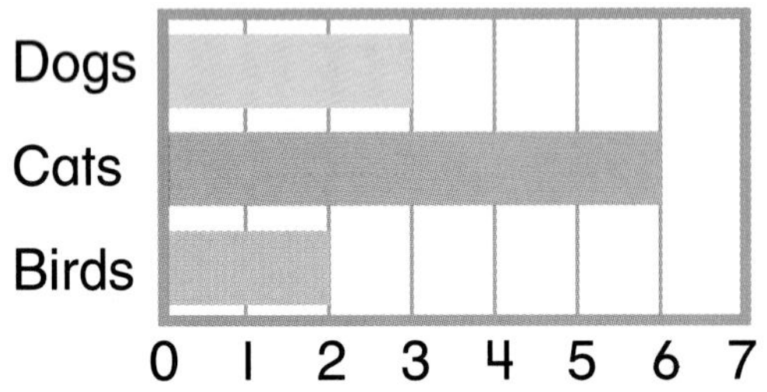

halves

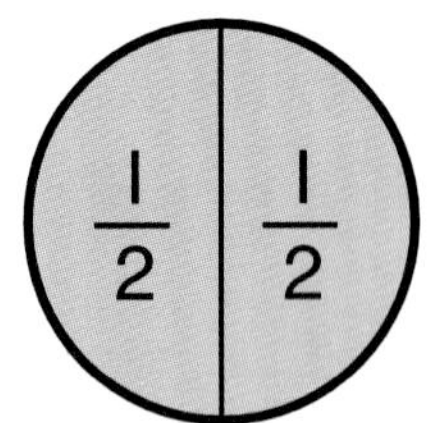

2 equal parts

hour hand

inch

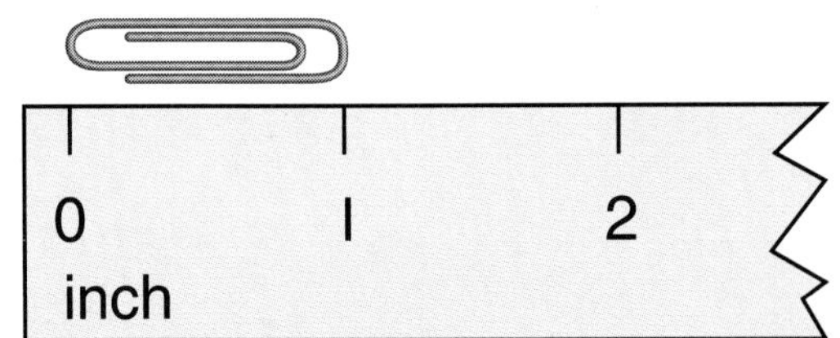

is greater than

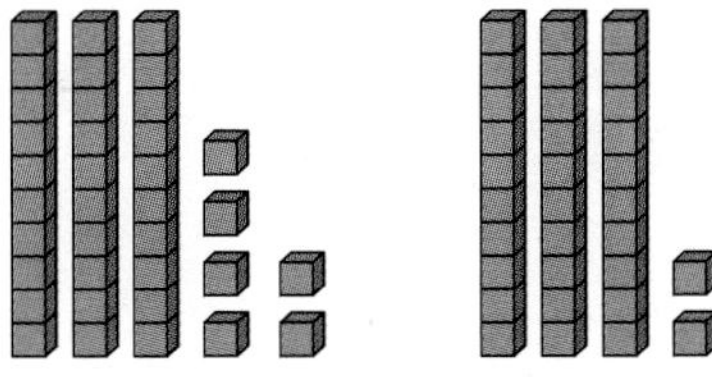

36 > 32

↑ is greater than

is less than

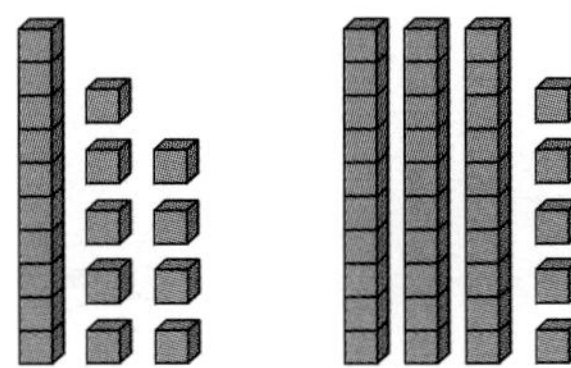

19 < 35

↑ is less than

mental math

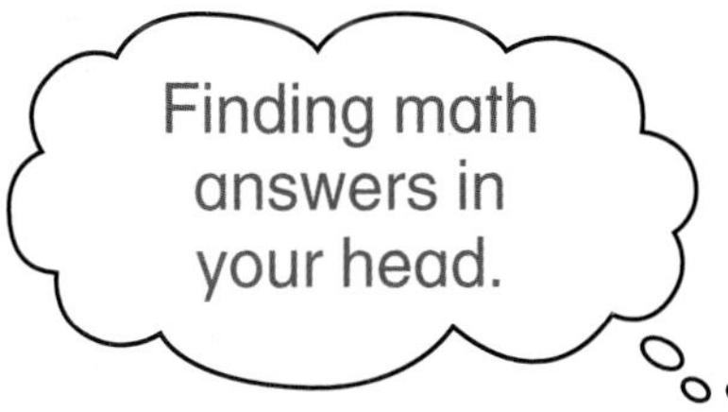

minute hand

nickel

5¢

number line

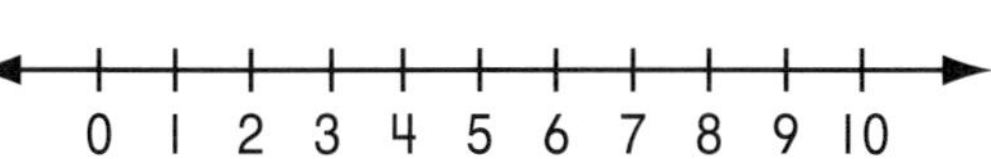

one half

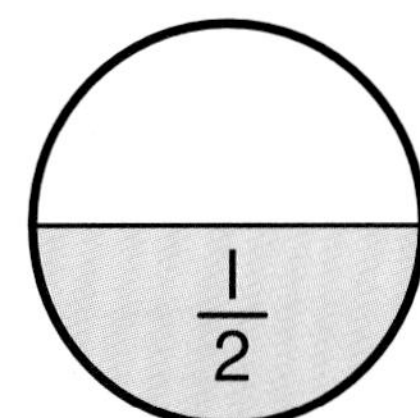

ones

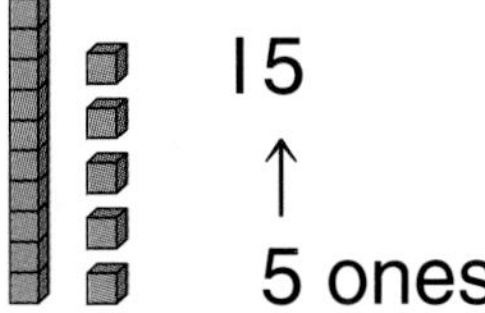

order

0, 1, 2, 3, 4, 5, 6, 7, 8, 9, 10

These numbers are in order.

part-part-total

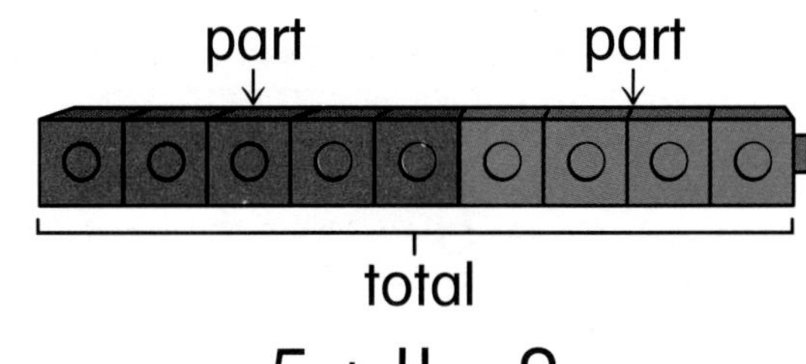

5 + 4 = 9

pattern

penny

1¢

pound

quarter

25¢

rectangle

rectangular prism

related facts

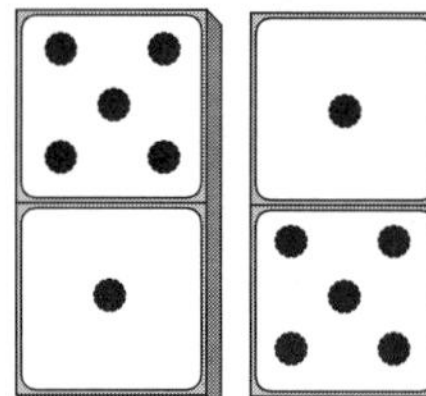

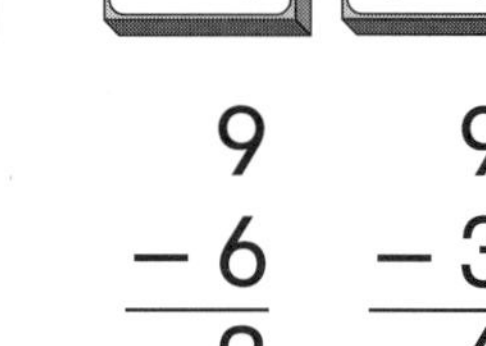

$$\begin{array}{r} 5 \\ +\ 1 \\ \hline 6 \end{array} \quad \begin{array}{r} 1 \\ +\ 5 \\ \hline 6 \end{array} \quad \begin{array}{r} 9 \\ -\ 6 \\ \hline 3 \end{array} \quad \begin{array}{r} 9 \\ -\ 3 \\ \hline 6 \end{array}$$

skip-count

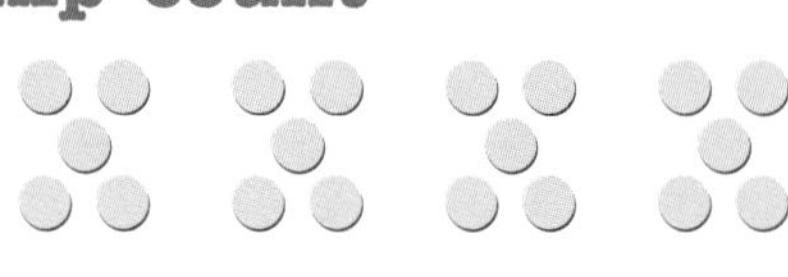

5 10 15 20

sphere

square

subtract

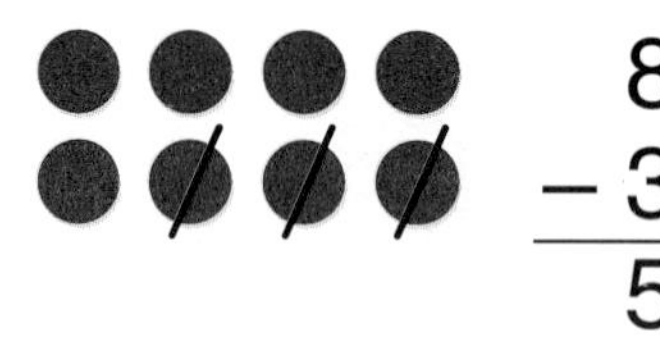

$$\begin{array}{r} 8 \\ -\ 3 \\ \hline 5 \end{array}$$

subtraction sentence

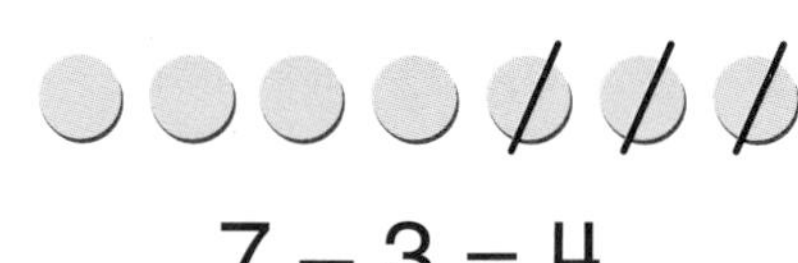

$7 - 3 = 4$

sum

$4 + 5 = 9 \leftarrow$ sum

tens

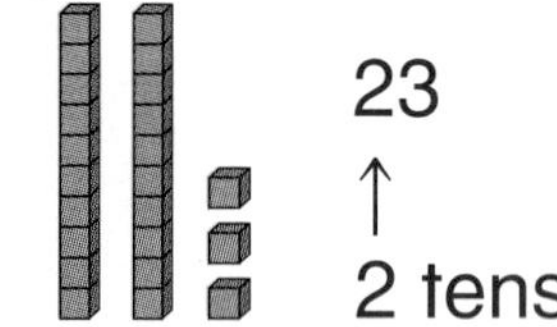

23
↑
2 tens

thirds

3 equal parts

triangle

K–8 Scope and Sequence for McGraw-Hill Mathematics

NUMERATION AND NUMBER THEORY	K	1	2	3	4	5	6	Glencoe * 6	Glencoe * 7	Glencoe * 8
Count	■	■	■	■	■					
Skip-count		■	■	■	■					
Ordinal numbers	■	■	■	■	■					
Place value										
whole numbers		■	■	■	■	■	■	■	■	■
decimals				■	■	■	■	■	■	■
Compare and order										
whole numbers	■	■	■	■	■	■	■	■	■	■
decimals					■	■	■	■	■	■
fractions and mixed numbers			■	■	■	■	■	■	■	■
integers							■	■	■	■
rationals										■
irrationals										■
Round										
whole numbers			■	■	■	■	■	■	■	■
decimals					■	■	■	■	■	■
fractions and mixed numbers				■	■	■	■	■	■	■
Exponents						■	■	■	■	■
Scientific notation									■	■
Square roots									■	■
Factors and multiples				■	■	■	■	■	■	■
Common factors/greatest common factor (GCF)					■	■	■	■	■	■
Common multiples/least common multiple (LCM)					■	■	■	■	■	■
Divisibility rules					■	■	■	■	■	■
Even and odd numbers			■	■	■					
Prime and composite numbers					■	■	■	■	■	■
Prime factorization							■	■	■	■

* *Mathematics: Applications and Connections Courses 1–3 ©1998*

GRADE 1

NUMERATION AND NUMBER THEORY

Count
- one-to-one correspondence, 5-10, 19-20, 269-270, 281-282, 285, 289-290
- understand/count numbers to 10: 5-24, 35-36
  - 1 and 2: 5-6, 7-8, 35-36
  - 3 and 4: 5-6, 7-10, 35-36
  - 5 and zero: 5-6, 9-10, 13-14, 35-36
  - 6 and 7: 19-22, 35-36
  - 8 and 9: 19-22, 23-24, 35-36
  - 10: 5-24, 35-36
  - 1 to 10: 23-24, 35-36
  - to 19: 185-188, 221-222
  - to 39: 185-192, 221-222
  - to 59: 189-192, 195-198, 221-222
  - to 79: 189-192, 195-198, 221-222
  - to 100: 195-198
- write numbers
  - 1 and 2: 7-8, 17-18, 35-36
  - 3 and 4: 7-10, 17-18, 35-36
  - 5 and zero: 9-10, 13-14, 17-18, 35-36
  - 6 and 7: 21-22, 35-36
  - 8 and 9: 21-24, 35-36
  - 10: 23-24, 35-36
  - to 19: 185-188, 221-222
  - to 39: 185-192, 221-222
  - to 59: 189-192, 195-198, 221-222
  - to 79: 195-198, 221-222
  - to 100: 195-198, 203-204, 221-222
- number words to ten, 7-10, 13-14, 21-22, 23-24
- missing numbers, 29, 150, 186

Skip-count
- by 10s, 207-208, 221-222, 227-228, 267-270, 413-416
- by 2s, 209-210, 221-222
- by 5s, 207-208, 221-222, 227-228, 265-266

Ordinal numbers, 213-214, 221-222
- to tenth, 213-214, 221-222

Place value
- whole numbers
  - tens and ones, 187-188, 191-192, 197-199, 200, 207-208, 221-222, 267-270, 417-420, 433-434, 446

Compare and order
- whole numbers, 29-30, 35-36, 203-206, 211-212, 411-414, 427-430
  - same, more, and fewer, 5-6, 19-20, 187-188
  - greater and less, 211-212, 411, 427
  - 0 to 5: 29-30, 35-36
  - 0 to 10: 29-30, 35-36
  - 1 to 100: 203-206, 211-212, 221-222

WHOLE NUMBER COMPUTATION	K	1	2	3	4	5	6	Glencoe* 6	Glencoe* 7	Glencoe* 8
Addition										
Meaning of addition	■	■	■	■	■					
Properties		■	■	■	■	■	■			
Basic facts	■	■	■	■	■					
Fact families		■	■	■	■					
Missing addends		■	■	■	■	■	■			
Add 2-digit numbers		■	■	■	■	■	■			
Add 3-digit numbers			■	■	■	■	■			
Add greater numbers				■	■	■	■			
Add money amounts		■	■	■	■	■	■			
Mental math strategies		■	■	■	■	■	■			
Estimate sums		■	■	■	■	■	■	■	■	■
Write/solve number sentences	■	■	■	■	■	■	■			
Solve equations						■	■	■	■	■
Subtraction										
Meaning of subtraction	■	■	■	■	■					
Properties		■	■	■	■	■				
Basic facts	■	■	■	■	■					
Fact families		■	■	■	■					
Subtract 2-digit numbers		■	■	■	■	■	■			
Subtract 3-digit numbers			■	■	■	■	■			
Subtract greater numbers				■	■	■	■			
Subtract money amounts		■	■	■	■	■	■			
Mental math strategies		■	■	■	■	■	■			
Estimate differences		■	■	■	■	■	■	■	■	■
Write/solve number sentences	■	■	■	■	■	■	■			
Solve equations						■	■	■	■	■

Chart continued on page T3

GRADE 1
WHOLE NUMBER COMPUTATION
Addition

Meaning of addition, 79-87
- readiness, 79-87
- names for numbers, 45-70
- count on to add, 93-98, 101-102, 105, 411-412, 415-416, 423
- sentences, 81-87, 101-102, 144, 419-420
- vertical, 147-148, 151-152, 155, 170, 175-176

Properties
- order, 149-150
- zero, 91-92

Basic facts,
- to 5: 145-156, 169-170, 175-176
- to 10: 145-156, 169-170, 175-176, 413-414
- to 11: 335-345, 357-366, 367-368, 417-420
- to 12: 335-345, 357-366, 367-368, 417-420
- to 13: 335-345, 357-366, 367-368, 417-420
- to 14: 335-345, 357-366, 367-368, 417-420
- to 15: 335-345, 357-366, 367-368, 417-420
- to 16, 17, and 18: 334-345, 357-366, 367-368, 417-420
- add with doubles, 335-338, 367-368
- add three numbers, 343-344, 367-368

Fact families, 363-364, 367-368
Missing addends, 139, 150, 336, 412,
Add 2-digit numbers, 417-420, 423, 441-442
Add money amounts, 91-92, 153-155, 175-176
Mental math strategies, 411-412
Estimate sums, 421-422, 441, 448
Write/solve number sentences, 81-87, 101-102, 144, 419-420

Subtraction

Meaning of subtraction, 113-121
- readiness, 113-121
- count back to subtract, 127-130, 221-222, 427-428, 431-432
- sentences, 115-121, 135-136, 138, 144
- vertical, 161-166, 170, 175-176

Properties,
- zero, 125-126, 135-136

Basic facts,
- to 5: 159-172, 175-176
- to 10: 159-172, 175-176
- to 11: 347-366, 367-368
- to 12: 347-366, 367-368
- to 13: 347-366, 367-368
- to 14: 347-366, 367-368
- to 15: 347-366, 367-368
- to 16, 17, and 18: 347-366, 367-368

Fact families, 363-364, 367-368
Subtract 2-digit numbers, 433-438, 441-442
Subtract money amounts, 125-126, 141, 167-170, 175-176
Mental math strategies, 427-428
Estimate differences, 427
Write/solve number sentences, 115-121, 135-136, 138, 144

* *Mathematics: Applications and Connections Courses 1–3 ©1998*

Chart continued from page T2

WHOLE NUMBER COMPUTATION	K	1	2	3	4	5	6	Glencoe * 6	Glencoe * 7	Glencoe * 8
Multiplication										
Meaning of multiplication		■	■	■	■	■				
Properties				■	■	■	■			
Basic facts			■	■	■	■				
Fact families				■	■	■				
Missing factors				■	■	■	■			
Multiply three factors				■	■	■	■			
Multiply powers of 10					■	■	■	■	■	■
Multiply by 1-digit multiplier				■	■	■	■			
Multiply by 2-digit multiplier					■	■	■			
Multiply money amounts				■	■	■	■			
Mental math strategies				■	■	■	■			
Estimate products				■	■	■	■	■	■	■
Write/solve number sentences			■	■	■	■	■			
Solve equations						■	■	■	■	■
Division										
Meaning of division		■	■	■	■	■				
Properties				■	■	■	■			
Basic facts			■	■	■	■				
Fact families				■	■	■				
Divide powers of 10					■	■	■			
Divide by 1-digit divisor				■	■	■	■			
Divide by 2-digit divisor					■	■	■			
Zeros in quotient					■	■	■			
Divide money amounts				■	■	■	■			
Mental math strategies				■	■	■	■			
Estimate quotients				■	■	■	■	■	■	■
Write/solve number sentences			■	■	■	■	■			
Solve equations						■	■	■	■	■

GRADE 1
WHOLE NUMBER COMPUTATION
Multiplication
Meaning of multiplication, 225, 357-358

Division
Meaning of division, 253-254

* *Mathematics: Applications and Connections Courses 1–3 ©1998*

FRACTIONS AND MIXED NUMBERS	K	1	2	3	4	5	6	Glencoe* 6	Glencoe* 7	Glencoe* 8
Concepts										
Meaning of fractions	■	■	■	■	■	■	■	■	■	■
Equivalent fractions				■	■	■	■	■	■	■
Simplest form					■	■	■	■	■	■
Least common denominator (LCD)					■	■	■	■	■	■
Compare and order			■	■	■	■	■	■	■	■
Round				■	■	■	■	■	■	■
Mixed numbers				■	■	■	■	■	■	■
relate improper fractions					■	■	■	■	■	■
Find fraction of a number						■	■	■	■	■
Reciprocals							■	■	■	■
Computation										
Add fractions										
like denominators					■	■	■	■	■	■
unlike denominators					■	■	■	■	■	■
Add mixed numbers					■	■	■	■	■	■
Estimate sums					■	■	■	■	■	■
Subtract fractions										
like denominators					■	■	■	■	■	■
unlike denominators					■	■	■	■	■	■
Subtract mixed numbers					■	■	■	■	■	■
Estimate differences					■	■	■	■	■	■
Multiply fractions						■	■	■	■	■
Multiply mixed numbers							■	■	■	■
Estimate products						■	■	■	■	■
Divide fractions						■	■	■	■	■
Divide mixed numbers							■	■	■	■
Estimate quotients						■	■	■	■	■
Relate fractions and decimals					■	■	■	■	■	■
Relate fractions and percents						■	■	■	■	■
Write and solve number sentences					■	■	■			
Solve equations							■	■	■	■

GRADE 1
FRACTIONS AND MIXED NUMBERS
Concepts

Meaning of fractions, 247-252
- halves, 247-248, 255-256
- fourths, 249-250, 255-256
- thirds, 251-252, 255-256
- parts of a set, 252
- parts of a whole, 247-256, 255-256

* *Mathematics: Applications and Connections Courses 1–3* ©1998

DECIMALS	K	1	2	3	4	5	6	Glencoe* 6	Glencoe* 7	Glencoe* 8
Concepts										
Place value				■	■	■	■	■	■	■
Equivalent decimals						■	■	■	■	■
Compare and order					■	■	■	■	■	■
Round					■	■	■	■	■	■
Relate decimals and fractions				■	■	■	■	■	■	■
Relate decimals, fractions, and percents						■	■	■	■	■
Terminating and repeating decimals						■	■	■	■	■
Scientific notation									■	■
Computation										
Add decimals				■	■	■	■	■	■	■
Subtract decimals				■	■	■	■	■	■	■
Estimate sums and differences					■	■	■	■	■	■
Multiply by whole number						■	■	■	■	■
Multiply by decimal						■	■	■	■	■
Estimate products						■	■	■	■	■
Divide by whole number						■	■	■	■	■
Divide by decimal							■	■	■	■
Zeros in quotient and dividend						■	■	■	■	■
Estimate quotients						■	■	■	■	■
Mental math strategies					■	■	■			
Write/solve number sentences				■	■	■	■			
Solve equations					■	■	■	■	■	■

GEOMETRY	K	1	2	3	4	5	6	Glencoe* 6	Glencoe* 7	Glencoe* 8
Patterns	■	■	■	■	■	■	■			
Points, lines, line segments, rays, angles				■	■	■	■	■	■	■
Classify angles				■	■	■	■	■	■	■
Measure and estimate angles						■	■	■	■	■
Identify 3-dimensional shapes	■	■	■	■	■	■	■	■	■	■
Identify 2-dimensional shapes	■	■	■	■	■	■	■	■	■	■
Classify polygons				■	■	■	■	■	■	■
Classify triangles					■	■	■	■	■	■
Classify quadrilaterals					■	■	■	■	■	■
Similarity					■	■	■	■	■	■
Congruence		■	■	■	■	■	■	■	■	■
Symmetry		■	■	■	■	■	■	■	■	■
Circles					■	■	■	■	■	■
Use geometric formulas						■	■	■	■	■
Constructions							■	■	■	■
Tessellations				■	■	■	■		■	■
Transformations				■	■	■	■	■	■	■
Coordinate geometry				■	■	■	■	■	■	■
Spatial reasoning	■	■	■	■	■	■	■	■	■	■
Relationships in a right triangle									■	■
Pythagorean theorem									■	■
Tangent, sine, cosine, ratios										■

GRADE 1
GEOMETRY

Patterns
- spatial relationships
  - positional and directional terms on a computer, 74, 260
- classification
  - same object, 74, 232, 235-238
  - same color, 33-34, 232-234, 241, 255-256
  - same shape, 232-234, 241
- copy a pattern, 27-28, 33-34
- continue a pattern, 33-34, 84, 128, 168, 179, 185-186, 189-190, 268, 345, 436
- make a pattern, 27-28, 33-34, 74

Identify 3-dimensional shapes, 233-236, 255-256
Identify 2-dimensional shapes, 235-238, 255-256
Congruence, 245-246, 255-256
Symmetry, 245-246, 255-256
Spatial reasoning, 86, 234, 236, 246

* *Mathematics: Applications and Connections Courses 1–3* ©1998

MEASUREMENT, TIME, MONEY	K	1	2	3	4	5	6	Glencoe * 6	Glencoe * 7	Glencoe * 8
Measurement										
Estimate and measure length										
nonstandard units										
metric/customary units										
Estimate and measure capacity										
nonstandard units										
metric/customary units										
Estimate and measure mass/weight										
nonstandard units										
metric/customary units										
Convert units										
Compute with denominate numbers										
Temperature										
Perimeter										
Circumference										
Area										
Surface area										
Volume										
Angle measure										
Precision										
Indirect measurement										
Measurement sense										
Time										
Read a calendar										
Estimate and tell time										
Find elapsed time										
Convert units										
Money										
Find values of coins and bills										
Make change										
Compare and order										
Round										
Estimate and compute with money amounts										

GRADE 1

MEASUREMENT, TIME, MONEY

Measurement

Estimate and measure length
- nonstandard units, 377-380, 389
  - compare: tallest, longest, 376, 377-382
  - compare: measurement tools, 374-402
  - arbitrary units, 377-380, 389
- metric/customary units, 381-386, 387, 389, 401-402, 406, 407
  - centimeter, decimeter, 385-386, 399-400, 401-402, 430
  - lengths of paths, 406
  - inch, foot, 381-384, 391, 399-400, 401-402, 406

Estimate and measure capacity
- nonstandard units, 396
  - compare: holds more, less, 395-396, 407
- metric/customary units, 395-396, 399-400, 401-402
  - cup, pint, quart, 395-396, 399-400, 401-402

Estimate and measure mass/weight
- nonstandard units, 393-394
- metric/customary units, 391-392, 401-402
  - pound, 393-394, 399-400, 401-402, 430

Temperature, 397-398, 401-402

Perimeter, 387-388

Measurement sense, 391-392, 399-400

Time

Read a calendar, 317-320, 323-324

Estimate and tell time, 299-304, 307-311, 313-314, 321-324
- concept of time, 299-300
  - sequential order, 326
- hour, 301-304, 311, 323-324
- half hour, 307-310, 311, 323-324

Find elapsed time, 304

Money

Find values of coins and bills, 264-270, 277-285, 289-290
- penny, 31-32, 91, 125-126, 141, 153-154, 167-168, 227-229, 264-270, 277-285, 289-290
- nickel, 265-270, 279-285, 289-290
- dime, 267-268, 279-285, 289-290
- quarter, 279-285, 289-290, 295
- money words, 264-268, 270, 279-280, 284-286, 293, 295

Compare and order, 281-284, 289-290

Estimate and compute with money amounts, 91-92, 125-126, 141, 153-155, 167-168, 175-176, 421-422
- add/subtract, 91-92, 125-126, 141, 153-154, 167-168, 175-176

* *Mathematics: Applications and Connections Courses 1–3 ©1998*

■ = shaded cell

PROBLEM SOLVING	K	1	2	3	4	5	6	Glencoe * 6	Glencoe * 7	Glencoe * 8
Use the problem-solving process	■	■	■	■	■	■	■	■	■	■
Use/find a pattern	■	■	■	■	■	■	■	■	■	■
Use/make a table		■	■	■	■	■	■	■	■	■
Use/draw a picture/diagram	■	■	■	■	■	■	■	■	■	■
Use logical reasoning	■	■	■	■	■	■	■	■	■	■
Interpret data	■	■	■	■	■	■	■	■	■	■
Guess, test, and revise	■	■	■	■	■	■	■	■	■	■
Use/make a model	■	■	■	■	■	■	■	■	■	■
Make an organized list	■	■	■	■	■	■	■	■	■	■
Use estimation		■	■	■	■	■	■	■	■	■
Choose a strategy		■	■	■	■	■	■	■	■	■
Write a number sentence		■	■	■	■	■	■			
Check for reasonable answers		■	■	■	■	■	■	■	■	■
Choose the operation	■	■	■	■	■	■	■	■	■	■
Act it out	■	■	■	■						
Choose the method		■	■	■	■	■	■	■	■	■
Work backward			■	■	■	■	■	■	■	■
Solve multistep problems			■	■	■	■	■	■	■	■
Identify extra information			■	■	■	■	■	■	■	■
Solve a similar/simpler problem			■	■	■	■	■	■	■	■
Identify missing information				■	■	■	■	■	■	■
Use alternate solution methods				■	■	■	■			
Interpret the quotient and remainder				■	■	■	■			
Conduct an experiment					■	■	■	■	■	■
Use a fraction vs. use a decimal						■	■	■	■	■
Write an equation							■	■	■	■
Use a formula							■	■	■	■
Eliminate possibilities								■	■	■
Use the Pythagorean theorem									■	■
Factor polynomials										■

GRADE 1
PROBLEM SOLVING

Use the problem-solving process, 27-28, 33-34, 51-52, 67-68, 85-86, 99-100, 119-120, 133-134, 171-172, 173-174, 193-194, 219-220, 239-240, 253-254, 273-274, 287-288, 315-316, 321-322, 359-360, 365-366, 387-388, 399-400, 421-422, 439-440
Use/find a pattern, 27-28, 33-34
Use/make a table, 287-288
Use/draw a picture/diagram, 173-174, 253-254, 387-388
Use logical reasoning, 64, 284
Interpret data, 219-220, 287-288
Guess, test, and revise, 273-274, 286, 290
Use/make a model, 239-240
Make an organized list, 315-316
Use estimation, 193-194, 321-322, 421-422
Choose a strategy, 365-366
Write a number sentence, 85-86, 119-120
Check for reasonable answers, 399-400
Choose the operation, 171-172, 359-360
Act it out, 51-52
Choose the method, 439-440

MATHEMATICAL REASONING	K	1	2	3	4	5	6	Glencoe * 6	Glencoe * 7	Glencoe * 8
Decision making		■	■	■	■	■	■	■	■	■
Critical thinking	■	■	■	■	■	■	■	■	■	■

GRADE 1
MATHEMATICAL REASONING

Decision making, 18, 56, 90, 124, 158, 202, 244, 278, 314, 358, 392, 426
Critical thinking, 45, 47, 49, 51, 57, 59, 61, 63, 79, 83, 91, 93, 113, 125, 127, 133, 147, 149, 153, 161, 163, 167, 189, 191, 193, 197, 203, 209, 211, 213, 219, 233, 235, 237, 245, 247, 249, 265, 267, 279, 287, 299, 301, 309, 317, 335, 337, 339, 341, 343, 349, 351, 363, 377, 381, 383, 395, 397, 411, 413, 417, 427, 429, 433

* *Mathematics: Applications and Connections Courses 1–3* ©1998

ESTIMATION	K	1	2	3	4	5	6	Glencoe * 6	Glencoe * 7	Glencoe * 8
Strategies										
Rounding			■	■	■	■	■	■	■	■
Front-end				■	■	■	■	■	■	■
Compatible numbers					■	■	■	■	■	■
Clustering						■	■	■	■	■
Numbers/Operations										
Whole numbers	■	■	■	■	■	■	■			
sums and differences		■	■	■	■	■	■	■	■	■
products and quotients				■	■	■	■	■	■	■
Money			■	■	■	■	■			
sums and differences			■	■	■	■	■	■	■	■
products and quotients				■	■	■	■	■	■	■
Decimals				■	■	■	■			
sums and differences					■	■	■	■	■	■
products and quotients						■	■	■	■	■
Fractions/mixed numbers				■	■	■	■			
sums and differences					■	■	■	■	■	■
products and quotients						■	■	■	■	■
Percent							■	■	■	■
Measurement										
Length, capacity, mass/weight	■	■	■	■	■	■	■	■	■	■
Time		■	■	■	■	■	■			
Temperature			■	■	■	■	■			
Perimeter, area, volume			■	■	■	■	■	■	■	■
Angle measure						■	■	■		
Problem Solving										
Check for reasonableness		■	■	■	■	■	■	■	■	■
Estimation vs. exact answers				■	■	■	■			
Over- and under-estimating						■	■			

GRADE 1
ESTIMATION
Numbers/Operations
Whole numbers, 193-194, 321-322
sums and differences, 421-422, 441, 448

Measurement
Length, capacity, mass/weight, 201-202, 379-386, 389, 393-396, 407
Time, 321-322

Problem Solving
Check for reasonableness, 193-194, 399-400

TECHNOLOGY	K	1	2	3	4	5	6	Glencoe * 6	Glencoe * 7	Glencoe * 8
Calculator										
Patterns	■	■	■	■	■	■	■			
Computation	■	■	■	■	■	■	■	■	■	■
Choose a calculation method		■	■	■	■	■	■	■	■	■
Order of operations						■	■	■	■	■
Fractions and decimals					■	■	■	■	■	■
Special keys		■	■	■	■	■	■	■	■	■
Computer										
Spreadsheets			■	■	■	■	■	■	■	■
Patterns	■	■	■	■	■	■	■			
Simulations				■	■	■	■	■	■	■
Functions				■	■	■	■	■	■	■
Graphs	■	■	■	■	■	■	■	■	■	■

GRADE 1
TECHNOLOGY
Calculator
Patterns, 225, 436
Computation, 128, 168, 204, 210, 268, 358, 371, 436, 445
addition, 204, 210, 268, 358, 371, 436
subtraction, 358, 371,445
Choose a calculation method, 225, 387, 436, 445
Special keys, 210, 225, 371, 445

Computer
Patterns, 74
Graphs, 226, 328

* *Mathematics: Applications and Connections Courses 1–3 ©1998*

MENTAL MATH	K	1	2	3	4	5	6	Glencoe * 6	Glencoe * 7	Glencoe * 8
Basic Addition/Subtraction Fact Strategies										
Use patterns		■	■	■	■					
Count on		■	■	■	■					
Count back		■	■	■	■					
Use doubles		■	■	■	■					
Use doubles plus 1		■	■	■	■					
Make 10		■	■	■	■					
Skip count		■	■	■	■					
Add/subtract 9		■	■	■	■					
Use related facts		■	■	■	■					
Use fact families		■	■	■	■					
Use properties		■	■	■	■					
Basic Multiplication/Division Fact Strategies										
Use patterns			■	■	■	■				
Break apart numbers				■	■	■				
Use square numbers				■	■	■				
Use related facts				■	■	■				
Use fact families				■	■	■				
Use properties				■	■	■				
Computation Strategies										
Use patterns		■	■	■	■	■	■	■	■	■
Count on/count back		■	■	■	■					
Add/subtract multiples of powers of 10		■	■	■	■	■	■			
Multiply/divide multiples of powers of 10				■	■	■	■	■	■	■
Multiply/divide by multiples of powers of 10					■	■	■	■	■	■
Use properties				■	■	■	■	■	■	■
Work left to right				■	■	■	■			
Break apart numbers				■	■	■	■			
Use compensation					■	■	■	■	■	■
Use divisibility rules					■	■	■	■	■	■
Use equivalence among fractions, decimals, percents						■	■	■	■	■

GRADE 1
MENTAL MATH
Basic Addition/Subtraction Fact Strategies

Use patterns, 84, 128, 168, 179, 207-210, 225, 345, 436
Count on, 93-98, 101-102, 105, 203-204, 411-425
Count back, 29-30, 127-132, 427-428, 431-432
Use doubles, 335-338, 341-342, 351-352, 363-364, 367-368
Use doubles plus 1, 337-338, 367-368
Make 10, 339-344, 367-368
Skip count, 207-210, 221-222, 227-228, 265-266, 280, 413-416
Add/subtract 9, 339-340, 347-348
Use related facts, 149-150, 163-166, 349-352
Use fact families, 363-364, 367-368
Use properties, 91-92, 125-126, 135-136, 149-150

Computation Strategies

Use patterns, 84, 128, 168, 179, 345, 436
Count on/count back, 93-98, 101-102, 105, 127-130, 411-412, 423, 427-428, 431-432, 441-442
Add/subtract multiples of powers of 10, 413-416, 423, 431-432, 441-442

PATTERNS, RELATIONSHIPS, FUNCTIONS	K	1	2	3	4	5	6	Glencoe * 6	Glencoe * 7	Glencoe * 8
Patterns										
Number patterns										
repeating patterns	■	■	■	■	■	■	■	■	■	■
growing patterns			■	■	■	■	■	■	■	■
computation patterns		■	■	■	■	■	■	■	■	■
skip-counting patterns		■	■	■	■			■	■	■
place-value patterns				■	■	■	■			
even and odd number patterns			■	■	■					
use a calculator/computer	■	■	■	■	■	■	■			
Number sequences							■	■	■	■
Geometric/spatial patterns	■	■	■	■	■	■	■	■	■	■
Statistical patterns				■	■	■	■			

Chart continued on page T10

GRADE 1
PATTERNS, RELATIONSHIPS, FUNCTIONS
Patterns

Number patterns
- repeating patterns, 185-186, 189-190, 436
- computation patterns, 84, 128, 168, 179, 268, 345, 436
- skip-counting patterns, 207-210, 225, 414
- use a calculator/computer, 74, 84, 128, 168, 204, 210, 225, 371, 436, 446

Geometric/spatial patterns, 74, 232-234, 241, 255-256

* *Mathematics: Applications and Connections Courses 1–3 ©1998*

Chart continued from page T9

PATTERNS, RELATIONSHIPS, FUNCTIONS	K	1	2	3	4	5	6	Glencoe* 6	Glencoe* 7	Glencoe* 8
Relationships										
Sorting and classifying										
Number relationships										
inequalities										
factors, multiples										
divisibility rules										
Geometric relationships										
shapes										
perimeter, area, volume										
circumference, surface area										
graphing ordered pairs										
Functions										
Meaning										
Function tables										
Geometric functions										

GRADE 1
PATTERNS, RELATIONSHIPS, FUNCTIONS
Relationships

Sorting and classifying, 232, 233, 237

Number relationships

inequalities, 211-212, 221-222, 226, 411, 427, 449

Geometric relationships

shapes, 232-241, 255-256

Functions

Meaning, 179

Function tables, 179

RATIO, PROPORTION, PERCENT	K	1	2	3	4	5	6	Glencoe* 6	Glencoe* 7	Glencoe* 8
Ratio										
Meaning										
Equal ratios										
Rate										
Tangent, sine, & cosine ratios										
Proportion										
Meaning										
Solve proportions										
Scale drawings										
Similar figures										
Scale up or down										
Indirect measurement										
Percent										
Meaning										
Relate fractions and percents										
Relate decimals and percents										
Percents greater than 100% and less than 1%										
Percent of a number										
Percent one number is of another										
Find number when percent of it is known										
Estimate percents										
Mental math										
Percent applications										
circle graphs										
simple/compound interest										
discount/sale price										
Dilations										

* *Mathematics: Applications and Connections* Courses 1–3 ©1998

Glencoe *

ALGEBRA	K	1	2	3	4	5	6	Glencoe* 6	Glencoe* 7	Glencoe* 8
Expressions, Equations, Inequalities										
Patterns, relationships, functions	■	■	■	■	■	■	■	■	■	■
Inverse operations		■	■	■	■	■	■	■	■	■
Properties		■	■	■	■	■	■	■	■	■
Use order of operations						■	■	■	■	■
Write/solve number sentences	■	■	■	■	■	■	■			
Evaluate algebraic expressions					■	■	■	■	■	■
Inequalities		■	■	■	■	■	■	■	■	■
Solve 1-step equations						■	■	■	■	■
with integer solutions									■	■
with two variables									■	■
Solve 2-step equations							■	■	■	■
Use formulas						■	■	■	■	■
Positive/Negative Numbers										
Integers										
meaning of							■	■	■	■
absolute value									■	■
properties							■	■	■	■
compare and order							■	■	■	■
add and subtract							■	■	■	■
multiply and divide								■	■	■
Rational numbers										
identify and simplify rational numbers										■
rational numbers as decimals										■
compare and order rational numbers										■
solve equations with rational number solutions										■
Negative exponents									■	■
Square roots									■	■
Irrational numbers										■
Coordinate Graphing										
Locate points on a number line		■	■	■	■	■	■	■	■	■
Graph coordinates in first quadrant		■	■	■	■	■	■	■	■	■
Graph coordinates in four quadrants							■	■	■	■
Graph functions							■	■	■	■
Graph equations							■	■	■	■
Transformations on a coordinate plane								■	■	■
Quadratic functions										■
To solve systems of equations										■
Slope										■
Polynomials										
Represent and simplify polynomials										■
Add, subtract and multiply polynomials										■
Factor polynomials										■
Multiply binomials										■

GRADE 1
ALGEBRA
Expressions, Equations, Inequalities

Patterns, relationships, functions, *See* Patterns, Relationships, Functions
Inverse operations, 139, 150, 336, 364, 412
Properties, 91-92, 125-126
Write/solve number sentences, 81-87, 101-102, 115-121, 135-136, 138, 144, 419-420
Inequalities, 211-212, 221-222, 411, 427, 449

Coordinate Graphing

Locate points on a number line, 405
Graph coordinates in first quadrant, 405

* *Mathematics: Applications and Connections Courses 1–3 ©1998*

SCOPE AND SEQUENCE

								Glencoe *		
STATISTICS AND GRAPHING	K	1	2	3	4	5	6	6	7	8
Gather and Collect Data										
Collect data	■	■	■	■	■	■	■	■	■	■
Conduct a survey	■	■	■	■	■	■	■	■	■	■
Tally		■	■	■	■	■	■	■	■	■
Conduct an experiment or simulation			■	■	■	■	■	■	■	■
Use sampling						■	■	■	■	■
Organize and Represent Data										
Sort and order data	■	■	■	■	■	■	■	■	■	■
Make a list	■	■	■	■	■	■	■	■	■	■
Make a table/graph/schedule	■	■	■	■	■	■	■	■	■	■
Frequency tables			■	■	■	■	■	■	■	■
Venn diagrams				■	■	■	■	■	■	■
Tree diagrams					■	■	■	■	■	■
Concrete graphs	■	■	■	■	■					
Pictographs	■	■	■	■	■	■	■	■	■	■
Line plots			■	■	■	■	■		■	■
Bar graphs	■	■	■	■	■	■	■	■	■	■
Double bar graphs						■	■	■	■	■
Line graphs					■	■	■	■	■	■
Double line graphs							■	■	■	■
Circle graphs					■	■	■	■	■	■
Stem-and-leaf plots					■	■	■		■	■
Histograms							■			■
Computer generated displays	■	■	■	■	■	■	■	■	■	■
Use a database/spreadsheet				■	■	■	■	■	■	■
Analyze Data and Draw Conclusions										
Read and interpret data	■	■	■	■	■	■	■	■	■	■
Make predictions and generalizations	■	■	■	■	■	■	■	■	■	■
Identify and describe trends					■	■	■	■	■	■
Find mode, range, mean and median				■	■	■	■	■	■	■
Quartiles										■
Misleading statistics						■	■	■	■	■

GRADE 1
STATISTICS AND GRAPHING
Gather and Collect Data

Collect data, 55-56, 123-124, 157-158, 201-202, 220, 277-278, 287-288, 313-314, 327, 357-358, 370, 372, 425-426

Conduct a survey, 55-56, 124, 157-158

Tally, 39, 44, 217-218, 327

Organize and Represent Data

Sort and order data, 123-124

Make a list, 315-316

Make a table/graph/schedule, 73, 105, 179, 157-158, 217-220, 226, 287-288, 313-314, 329-330, 358, 370, 372

Concrete graphs, 377-378

Pictographs, 327-328

Bar graphs, 217-218, 328-330, 372

Computer generated displays, 226, 328

Analyze Data and Draw Conclusions

Read and interpret data, 55-56, 123-124, 157-158, 201-202, 219-220, 287-288, 313-314, 370, 372, 425-426

Make predictions and generalizations, 18, 56, 90, 124, 158, 202, 244, 278, 314, 358, 392, 426

								Glencoe *		
PROBABILITY	K	1	2	3	4	5	6	6	7	8
Meaning		■	■	■	■	■	■	■	■	■
Conduct an experiment/simulation			■	■	■	■	■	■	■	■
Simple events			■	■	■	■	■	■	■	■
Independent events					■	■	■	■	■	■
Dependent events									■	■
Theoretical/experimental probability					■	■	■	■	■	■
Record outcomes				■	■	■	■	■	■	■
Predict outcomes	■	■	■	■	■	■	■	■	■	■
Tree diagrams					■	■	■	■	■	■
Sample space						■	■	■	■	■
Combinations	■	■	■	■	■	■	■	■	■	■
Counting principle							■	■	■	■
Permutations							■		■	■

GRADE 1
PROBABILITY

Meaning, 259

Predict outcomes, 18, 56, 90, 124, 158, 202, 244, 278, 314, 358, 392, 426

Combinations, 89-90, 315-316

* *Mathematics: Applications and Connections Courses 1–3 ©1998*

Perspectives on Meeting Individual Needs

Learning Styles

Students have many different styles of learning mathematics. Three of the most common learning styles are based on different modalities. A kinesthetic learning style entails learning from hands-on and whole-body activities; a visual learning style relies on observations, drawing, and reading; and an auditory or oral learning style uses listening and discussing. Some children are very flexible in their learning styles; that is, they can switch among learning styles, depending on the nature of the problem. Other children may be less flexible; for example, they may simply learn better by modeling problems (kinesthetic) and not understand how a sketch (visual) can help to solve a problem. To accommodate children's different learning styles, you should be flexible in how you present problems to children and in allowing children to explain or show how they figured out a problem's answer.

Howard Gardner, in his book *Multiple Intelligences: The Theory in Practice,* lists the seven types of intelligence that every student brings to the learning process:

- Logical-mathematical intelligence is shown in a sensitivity to and ability to understand logical or mathematical patterns, and in the ability to handle long or complex forms of reasoning;
- Linguistic intelligence manifests itself in sensitivity to the nuances of language;
- Musical intelligence is the ability to appreciate and to reproduce rhythmic sounds and pitch;
- Spatial intelligence involves the perception of the visual and spatial world;
- Kinesthetic intelligence is the control of one's own body movements and the skillful handling of objects;
- Interpersonal intelligence is the capacity to recognize and respond to the moods, temperaments, motivations, and needs of other people;
- Intrapersonal intelligence involves the ability to understand and respond to one's own needs, desires, strengths, and weaknesses.

Everyone has aspects of all seven intelligences, but individuals will vary in how strongly each intelligence has been developed and in how flexibly they can access and apply the different intelligences in the context of particular types of problems.

As you plan each lesson, it may help you to consider how well different students will perform. Choose two or three students in your class and ask yourself how the lesson you are preparing for tomorrow will work for them. Does one student prefer to model and another to listen closely? If so, how will you accommodate these different styles? Will this lesson work well in a small group, or will it need to be individually paced? Are there places where the students you are thinking about might have difficulty understanding? What contingency plans are available? How might the lesson proceed if a student gave an answer that could turn into a teachable moment? Think about different children for each lesson. This exercise will help you to focus on students' individual learning styles.

MEETING INDIVIDUAL NEEDS

Students Acquiring English

Never underestimate what students acquiring English can do. For example, do not automatically assume that they cannot solve word problems; try them and see. And don't isolate a student acquiring English when using small groups: include at least one bilingual student who speaks that child's native language (who can work with and translate for the student acquiring English) and English-speaking students (who can model how to use English when working on mathematics).

- If a problem seems a little difficult, try to simplify the English. Use active voice, present tense, short sentences.
- If a student has trouble providing a solution, encourage the use of the native language.
- If someone else in the class speaks the native language, ask that child to translate for the rest of the class. Ask the second child if the first child's solution seems reasonable.
- When speaking to the class, be sure to enunciate carefully. (This does not mean to speak louder since, when you speak louder, your face may become contorted, and students acquiring English may think you are angry.)
- Avoid asking rhetorical questions, since students may take them literally.
- Be strategic in the questions that you ask students. The easiest questions to understand are those that call for simple yes-or-no answers.
- When asking a series of yes-or-no questions, be sure to vary the pattern so that the correct answers are not either all yes or all no. After yes-or-no questions, students should also be exposed to some multiple-choice questions.
- Finally, students can understand questions that ask who, what, when, where, how, and why. If a student does not understand a particular kind of question, try to simplify it by using one at an easier level.

Gifted and Talented

Gifted and talented students often come up with interesting angles and insights into the mathematical nature of the problems they solve. To help gifted students develop their reasoning skills, try to pose problems that challenge at all levels of understanding and achievement, and that encourage a diversity of approaches to solution.

- Note each child's particular talents and try to connect those talents to specific curricular areas as well as to real-life applications.
- Find local or national contests that involve literary and artistic creativity, and encourage students to exercise their abilities by submitting entries.
- Seek out local businesses that might welcome student-created banners or displays in their windows.
- Encourage preparation of a class magazine or newspaper, and engage interested students forming the editorial and production staff.
- Suggest the formation of a book club or circulating library, with students sharing and reviewing their favorite books and stories.
- Introduce interested students to the stock market, then encourage them to choose stocks and track their progress over a period of time.
- Moderate panel discussions of historical figures, with students researching and then "becoming" real personages whose lives or ideas they find interesting or inspirational.

The most important objective of tailoring instruction to gifted and talented students is to support and encourage their talents in any way possible. Specific strategies should be adjusted on a regular basis to reflect the students' changing needs and interests.

MEETING INDIVIDUAL NEEDS

Inclusion

Children of various abilities will do their best work in an atmosphere in which they feel valued and in which they are made aware that you expect them to think and learn on an equal footing with their classmates. For some children, showing that you value them and have high expectations of them may mean starting each day by listening to their cares and concerns. You can also help them increase their participation by warning them in advance that you will be calling on them and by giving them extra response time. You may initially accept children's one-word answers and then, as the year progresses, encourage students to use phrases, full sentences, and eventually, more fully elaborated explanations. Be sure to communicate to the entire class that everyone is expected to work hard, to value all their classmates as individuals with varying strengths and abilities, and to help one another.

There are many different kinds of special needs students, so it is important to understand the specific nature of each child's needs and to customize your teaching approach accordingly.

- All children, but especially those with special needs, require consistent and well-understood classroom routines.
- Presenting all information both aurally and visually will benefit students with special needs.
- Everyone should know how roles and responsibilities are distributed when doing small-group work.
- Group roles and responsibilities should be posted, and children should be referred to them as the need arises.
- All students should know what criteria are used for assessing whether mathematics work needs to be redone, is acceptable, or excels.

Gender Fair Classrooms

It is important to be aware of messages that girls receive, in school and out of school, about their mathematical abilities and whether mathematics will be important to them as they grow older. Girls often receive the message that they will not need mathematics when they grow up, or that it is okay not to make an effort in mathematics. If such messages come from well-meaning family members, you may need to discuss with the student's family how such messages can discourage their children and hurt their performance in school.

In the classroom, boys sometimes monopolize the teacher's attention by calling out answers or by behaving in inappropriate ways. Also, questions that emphasize critical thinking are sometimes directed at boys more than at girls. You should evaluate your management routines early in the year to be sure that girls are given at least as many meaningful opportunities to participate in class discussions as boys.

Cooperating to Teach

Most elementary schools employ teachers who specialize in teaching students acquiring English, students with special needs, and gifted students. By working together with these teachers, you should be able to provide your students with a more coherent mathematics program. For instance, you might share lesson plans with specialty teachers and ask them for suggestions on how to adapt lessons for specific students in your class. You might also ask specialist teachers to preteach some mathematics concepts so that their students are prepared when they encounter the ideas in your class. Specialists might also help you to better assess your students' understanding of the mathematics that you are teaching. In all cases, the important thing to focus on is: What are my students comprehending? How can I be sure that every one of them has a meaningful and fair chance at learning this material?

Six Perspectives on Cooperative Learning

1 A Way to Teach Academic Content

Learning collaboratively in small groups is an effective instructional method for learning math. In Grade One, motivation to learn comes in part from the building of classroom community. Providing children with opportunities to talk about and act upon mathematical ideas is combined with practicing cooperative skills such as taking turns, listening, and checking for agreement.

2 An Approach to Learning

Cooperative approaches build on basic research about how the brain learns: by developing concepts through relevant discussion, by testing ideas against those of others, and through gaining support and help from others. Activities are built into Grade One where children think on their own, communicate ideas with a variety of partners, help each other, and learn cooperative skills such as restating, coming to agreement, and reflecting.

3 A Community of Learners

A learning community may include teachers collaborating with teachers to improve instruction, or administrators, teachers, students, and parents collaborating to foster relevant and consistent student learning. In Grade One, this can be children collaborating with parents to learn math used in the home, or bringing parents to school to participate in family math events.

4 Diversity as an Asset

Cooperative groups capitalize on the heterogeneity of the modern classroom by bringing together children with different learning strategies and strengths. First Graders are encouraged to value diversity in the group as providing unique perspectives. Children bring their personal experiences and interests to bear on math topics.

5 A Foundation for Success

Most businesses and industries rely heavily on teamwork. Through learning with partners and consulting and comparing with other pairs, Grade One students begin to build the kinds of work relationships and cooperative skills that will serve them later in almost any field of endeavor.

6 Cooperation Is Content That Is Learned in Stages

The goals for children at this grade level fall into three stages. To help you achieve these goals, the following strategies have been built into the program:

1. Developing cooperation by getting acquainted with classmates in community-building activities that also teach mathematical content
   - Community Circle Strategy: taking turns contributing ideas or answers
   - Line-Ups Strategy: learning and practicing problem solving kinesthetically
   - Think-Check-Step Strategy: checking information with classmates and coming to consensus
2. Teaching collaboration through work with several partners
   - Partners Practice Strategy: working side by side; talking about math activities; comparing outcomes
   - Partners Compare Strategy: working alone; then systematically comparing outcomes or methods
   - Partners Think and Share Strategy: considering a question; turning to a partner to discuss it; finally sharing it with the class
   - Partners Check Strategy: checking each other's thinking, problem-solving methods, or strategies
   - Partners Coach Strategy: coaching one another on ways to consider math concepts and problems
   - Partners Experiment Strategy: experimenting and discovering together
   - Partners Brainstorm Strategy: generating ideas by combining and expanding individual lists
3. Beginning to develop teamwork by having two pairs (two sets of partners) meet
   - Pairs Compare Strategy: working individually; comparing with a partner; joining another pair to compare strategies, methods, or answers
   - Pairs Consult Strategy: working with a partner to solve a problem together; coming to an agreement; joining another pair to share problem-solving methods or outcomes; going back to the original partner to review the work

Books for the Teacher

Apelman, Maja, and Julie King. *Exploring Everyday Math: Ideas for Students, Teachers, and Parents.* Portsmouth, NH: Heinemann, 1993.

Artzt, Alice F., and Claire M. Newman. *How to Use Cooperative Learning in the Mathematics Class.* Reston, VA: National Council of Teachers of Mathematics, 1990.

Baratta-Lorton, Mary. *Mathematics Their Way.* Menlo Park, CA: Addison-Wesley, 1976.

_____. *Workjobs II—Number Activities for Early Childhood.* Menlo Park, CA: Addison-Wesley, 1979.

Beyer, Barry K. *Practical Strategies for the Teaching of Thinking.* Boston: Allyn and Bacon, 1987.

Bishop, Alan J. *Mathematical Enculturation.* Dordrecht, The Netherlands: Kluwer Academic Publishers, 1988.

Borasi, Raffaella. *Learning Mathematics Through Inquiry.* Portsmouth, NH: Heinemann, 1992.

Brisby, Linda-Sue, et al. *Measurement: A "Hands On" Approach to Teaching.* Solvang, CA: Hands On, Inc., 1988.

_____. *Patterns and Functions: A "Hands On" Approach to Teaching.* Solvang, CA: Hands On, Inc., 1990.

Burns, Marilyn. *About Teaching Mathematics: A K–8 Resource.* Portsmouth, NH: Heinemann, 1992.

Cooney, Thomas J., ed. *Teaching and Learning Mathematics in the 1990s. (1990 Yearbook)* Reston, VA: National Council of Teachers of Mathematics, 1990.

Copeland, Richard W. *How Children Learn Mathematics: Teaching Implications of Piaget's Research.* New York: Macmillan, 1984.

Corwin, Rebecca B., et al. *Talking Mathematics: Supporting Children's Voices.* Portsmouth, NH: Heinemann, 1995.

Cuevas, Gilbert, and Mark Driscoll, eds. *Reaching All Students with Mathematics.* Reston, VA: National Council of Teachers of Mathematics, 1993.

Del Grande, John, et al. *Geometry and Spatial Sense: Addenda Series, Grades K–6.* Reston, VA: National Council of Teachers of Mathematics, 1993.

Eves, Howard W. *Return to Mathematical Circles.* Florence, KY: PWS Publishers/Kent Publishing Co., 1988.

Farrell, Margaret A., ed. *Imaginative Ideas for the Teacher of Mathematics.* Reston, VA: National Council of Teachers of Mathematics, 1988.

Forseth, Sonia D. *Creative Math-Art Activities for the Primary Grades.* Englewood Cliffs, NJ: Prentice-Hall, 1984.

Gardner, Howard. *Multiple Intelligences: The Theory in Practice.* New York: HarperCollins Publishers, 1993.

Graph Paper Masters. Palo Alto, CA: Dale Seymour Publications, 1989.

Holmes, Emma E. *Children Learning Mathematics: A Cognitive Approach to Teaching.* Englewood Cliffs, NJ: Prentice-Hall, 1985.

House, Peggy A., ed. *Connecting Mathematics Across the Curriculum. (1995 Yearbook)* Reston, VA: National Council of Teachers of Mathematics, 1995.

Lilburn, Pat, and Pam Rawson. *Let's Talk Math: Encouraging Children to Explore Ideas.* Portsmouth, NH: Heinemann, 1994.

Lindquist, Mary M., et al. *Making Sense of Data: Addenda Series, Grades K–6.* Reston, VA: National Council of Teachers of Mathematics, 1992.

Marks, John L., and A.A. Hiatt. *Teaching Elementary School Mathematics for Understanding.* New York: McGraw-Hill, 1985.

Mills, Heidi, et al. *Mathematics in the Making: Authoring Ideas in the Primary Classroom.* Portsmouth, NH: Heinemann, 1996.

Musser, Gary L., and William F. Burger. *Mathematics for Elementary Teachers: A Contemporary Approach,* 2nd ed. New York: Macmillan, 1991.

Neyland, Jim, ed. *Mathematics Education: A Handbook for Teachers, Volume 1.* Reston, VA: National Council of Teachers of Mathematics, 1994

O'Daffer, Phares G., ed. *Problem Solving: Tips for Teachers.* Reston, VA: National Council of Teachers of Mathematics, 1988.

Payne, Joseph N., ed. *Mathematics for the Young Child.* Reston, VA: National Council of Teachers of Mathematics, 1990.

Phillips, Jan. *Math Solutions: Whole Numbers and Money.* Syracuse, NY: New Readers Press, 1995.

Piaget, Jean. *The Child's Conception of Number.* New York: W.W. Norton, 1965.

Reys, Robert, Marilyn N. Suydam, and Mary N. Lindquist. *Helping Children Learn Mathematics.* Englewood Cliffs, NJ: Prentice-Hall, 1984.

Rowan, Thomas, and Barbara Bourne. *Thinking Like Mathematicians: Putting the K–4 NCTM Standards into Practice.* Portsmouth, NH: Heinemann, 1994.

Shasha, Dennis. *The Puzzling Adventures of Dr. Ecco.* New York: W.H. Freeman and Co., 1988.

Slavin, R., et al., eds. *Learning to Cooperate, Cooperating to Learn.* New York: Plenum Press, 1985.

Thiessen, Diane, and Margaret Matthias, eds. *The Wonderful World of Mathematics: A Critically Annotated List of Children's Books in Mathematics.* Reston, VA: National Council of Teachers of Mathematics, 1992.

Webb, Norman L., ed. *Assessment in the Mathematics Classroom. (1993 Yearbook)* Reston, VA: National Council of Teachers of Mathematics, 1993.

Wilson, Jeni, and Lynda Cutting. *It's Time: Celebrating Maths with Projects.* Portsmouth, NH: Heinemann, 1993.

Worth, Joan, ed. *Preparing Elementary School Mathematics Teachers: Readings from the Arithmetic Teacher.* Reston, VA: National Council of Teachers of Mathematics, 1988.

Zaslavsky, Claudia. *Multicultural Math: Hands-On Math Activities from Around the World.* New York: Scholastic Inc., 1994.

Recommended Periodicals

Cooperative Learning. Santa Cruz, CA: International Association for the Study of Cooperation in Education (IASCE).

Instructor. New York: Instructor Publications, Inc.

Teaching Children Mathematics. Reston, VA: National Council of Teachers of Mathematics.

Technology & Learning. Dayton, OH: Peter Li, Inc.

Books for the Student

Allen, Robert. *1-2-3: A First Counting Book.* New York: Putnam, 1981.

Anno, Mitsumasa. *Anno's Counting Book.* New York: Thomas Crowell/Harper & Row, 1977.

INDEX

D

E

INDEX

M

N

O

ACKNOWLEDGMENTS

COVER PHOTOGRAPHY Jade Albert for MMSD.

PHOTOGRAPHY All photographs are by the McGraw-Hill School Division (MMSD), David Mager for MMSD, Ken Lax for MMSD and Scott Harvey for MMSD except as noted below.

Chapter 1 3: Brent Peterson/The Stock Market; 17: Brent Peterson/The Stock Market; 34: Denver Public Library; 40: b.r. Eric Wheater; **Chapter 2** 43: Tom McCarthy/The Stock Market; 44: t. Lawrence Migdale/Stock Boston, Inc.; 50: b.l. Brooklyn Museum of Art; 55: t. Tony Arruza/The Image Works; 66: Nancy Simmerman/Tony Stone Images; 73: t. Bruce Plotkin/Liaison International; **Chapter 3** 77: John Stuart/The Image Bank; 89: t. Tom Tracey/The Stock Market; 97: Jeff Greenberg/Photo Researchers; **Chapter 4** 123: Porter Gifford/Gamma Liaison; 138: t.r. George Kleiman/Photo Researchers; **Chapter 5** 153: t.r.i. Doug David for MMSD; 154: Doug David for MMSD; 158: Amanda Merullo/Stock Boston; 169: Stephanie Hollyman/Liaison International; 178: Russkinne/Comstock; **Chapter 6** 183 : Kevin Kolczynski for MMSD; 193: t. Tony Stone Images/Charles Thatcher; 193: b. Charlie Westerman/Liaison International; 200: D. Young-Wolff/PhotoEdit; 206: Maxwell Mackenzie/Uniphoto; **Chapter 7** 231: HMS Images/The Image Bank; 235: Monica Stevenson for MMSD; 235: b.i. Monica Stevenson for MMSD; 243: t.r. Chris Luneski/Image Cascade. 244: Don Smetzer/Tony Stone Images; 250: b.r. Superstock, Inc.; **Chapter 8** 270: Doug David for MMSD; 274: Tom Tracy/The Stock Market; 280: t.l.i. Doug David for MMSD; 294: b.r. Doug David for MMSD; **Chapter 9** 297: Uniphoto; 301: t. Index Stock; 302: b.r. Frank Moscati/The Stock Market; 302: t.l. Richard Hutchings/PhotoEdit; 302: t.r. Steve Dunwell/The Image Bank; 302: b.l. David Young-Wolff/Tony Stone Images; 302: m.l. Comstock; 302: m.r. Bob Daemmrich/Uniphoto; 308: t.l. Tom McCarthy/PhotoEdit; 308: t.r. Daemmrich/The Image Works; 308: m.l. Myrleen Ferguson MR/PhotoEdit; 308: m.r. Jim Pickerell/The Image Works; 308: b.l. Tony Freeman/PhotoEdit; 308: b.r. David Young Wolff/Tony Stone Images; 321: b.r. Vivian Holbrooke/The Stock Market; 322: t.r. Brad Martin/The Image Bank; **Chapter 10** 333: Stephen Dalton/Photo Researchers; 334: t. Peter Beck/The Stock Market; 334: b. Lawrence Migdale; 341: David Forbert/Superstock, Inc.; 345: Kelvin Altken/Peter Arnold, Inc.; 357: t. Darryl Torckler/Tony Stone Images; 357: b. Kevin & Cat Sweeney/Tony Stone Images; 364: Terry Vine/Tony Stone Images; **Chapter 11** 375: Henley & Savage/The Stock Market; 391: t. Michael L. Peck & Dolores R. Fernandez; 404: Rich Frishman/Tony Stone Images; **Chapter 12** 409 : Robert E. Daemmrich/Tony Stone Images; 415: Superstock, Inc.; 425 : Richard Gross/The Stock Market; 426: Joe Sohm/Chromosohm/Photo Researchers; 437: t.r. David Young-Wolff/PhotoEdit.

ILLUSTRATION Winky Adam; 213, 216, 248, 250 • Jo Lynn Alcorn: 383, 386 • Bill Basso; 85, 86, 119, 120 • Shirley Beckes; 23, 24 • Menny Borovski; 27, 28, 36, 37, 89, 115, 117, 123, 124, 132, 234, 235, 236, 238, 239, 245, 246, 250, 252, 256, 257, 296, 298, 301, 302, 317, 318, 319, 320, 324, 325 • Ken Bowser; 83, 84, 302, 312, 337 • Lizi Boyd: 219, 277, 294, 388, 389, 402, 403 • Hal Brooks; 91, 92 • Roger Chandler: 345, 346, 353, 368 • Genevieve Claire: 356, 363, 364, 397, 398 • Margaret Cusack; 184, 188, 232 • Nancy Davis: 270, 276 • Betsy Day: 206, 214, 223 • Daniel Del Valle; 106, 109, 133, 134, 243, 314, 327 • Denise & Fernando: 180 • Eldon Doty: 178, 181 • Gloria Elliott: 142, 145, 146, 159, 160, 169 • Arthur Friedman; 326 • Doreen Gay-Kassel; 7, 9 , 156, 165, 335, 336, 338, 341, 357, 376, 380, 382 • Michael Grejniec; 112, 113, 114, 137, 148, 157, 174, 175, 176, 177, 189, 190 • Shari Halpern: 149, 151, 162, 163, 194, 203, 204, 205, 221 • Tom Leonard: 358 • Franklin Hammond; 88 • Oki Han: 164 • Eileen Hine: 165 • Rita Lascaro; 144, 199, 228, 291, 292, 390, 396, 303, 304 • Jim Maltese; 47, 48, 53, 72 • Claude Martinot; 5, 6, 19, 20, 410, 422, 430, 433, 437, 439, 444• Hatley Mason; 121, 135, 136, 138, 234, 241 • Bonnie Matthews; 242 • Daphne McCormack; 131 • Hima Pamoedjo; 33, 39, 54, 73, 79, 80, 130 • Brenda Pepper; 87, 93, 94, 101, 102, 103, 127, 128, 129, 139 • Lisa Pomerantz; 15, 35, 38, 350, 351, 354, 406 • Mary Power; 62, 64, 315, 316, 324, 325, 359, 365, 370, 371 • Ellen Rixford; 31, 32 • Audrey Schorr; 45, 46, 95 • Fred Schrier; 259 • Jackie Snider: 171, 172, 265, 267, 289 • Terri Starrett; 16 • Matt Straub; 21, 22, 39, 97, 98, 273, 274, 275, 281, 287, 288, 412, 414, 416, 418, 436, 445 • Peggy Tagel; 2, 3, 42, 43, 182, 183, 230, 231, 262, 263, 296, 297, 305, 306, 332, 333, 374, 375, 408, 409 • Mike Takagi; 13 • Don Tate; 44, 55, 67, 68, 70, 71, 107, 108, 239, 240, 241, 434, 448 • Terry Taylor: 195, 196, 199, 200, 207, 209, 221, 222, 225, 228, 417, 423, 435 • George Ulrich; 299, 300, 311, 330 • Sally Jo Vitsky; 4, 81, 122, 285, 286, 290, 419, 420, 424 • Matt Wawiorka; 11, 25, 41 • Nina Wallace: 404, 405.

All photographs are by the McGraw-Hill School Division (MMSD), David Mager for MMSD, Scott Harvey for MMSD, Bonnie West for MMSD, Monica Stevenson for MMSD, and Doug David for MMSD.

All props and illustrations are by the McGraw-Hill School Division (MMSD), Jeff Hernandez for MMSD, Raymond Hernandez for MMSD, Carmen Pujols for MMSD, Marina Brolin for MMSD, William Touchet for MMSD, Daniel DelValle for MMSD, and Deirdre Kennedy for MMSD.